P,   7. dkevitch

MW00423531

WELL PERFORMANCE

WELL PERFORMANCE
SECOND EDITION

MICHAEL GOLAN

CURTIS H. WHITSON

University of Trondheim

The Norwegian Institute of Technology — NTH

PRENTICE HALL, Englewood Cliffs, New Jersey 07632

Library of Congress Cataloging-in-Publication Data

Golan, Michael
    Well performance / Michael Golan, Curtis H. Whitson.
        p.   cm.
    Includes bibliographical references.
    ISBN 0-13-946609-6
    1. Oil fields--Production methods. 2. Oil reservoir engineering.
I. Whitson, Curtis H.   . II. Title.
TN870.G63 1991
622'.3382--dc20   90-7086
                                                            CIP

Editorial/production supervision: **Karen Bernhaut**
Cover design: **Ben Santora**
Manufacturing buyer: **Kelly Behr**

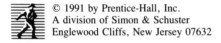 © 1991 by Prentice-Hall, Inc.
A division of Simon & Schuster
Englewood Cliffs, New Jersey 07632

All rights reserved. No part of this book may be
reproduced, in any form or by any means,
without permission in writing from the publisher.

Printed in the United States of America

10 9 8 7 6 5 4 3 2 1

ISBN   0-13-946609-6

Prentice-Hall International (UK) Limited, *London*
Prentice-Hall of Australia Pty. Limited, *Sydney*
Prentice-Hall Canada Inc., *Toronto*
Prentice-Hall Hispanoamericana, S.A., *Mexico*
Prentice-Hall of India Private Limited, *New Delhi*
Prentice-Hall of Japan, Inc., *Tokyo*
Simon & Schuster Asia Pte. Ltd., *Singapore*
Editora Prentice-Hall do Brasil, Ltda., *Rio de Janeiro*

CONTENTS

PREFACE

This book has evolved from course notes prepared for production engineering courses taught at the Norwegian Institute of Technology (NTH) in Trondheim and for industry courses dealing specifically with the performance of high-capacity oil and gas wells. Although the purpose of the book is to aid in the teaching of well performance, it should be useful as a reference book for engineers already performing some elements of well performance.

We recognize that the topic of well performance is not complete without a basic understanding of well test analysis, production geology and log interpretation, equipment design, and multiphase flow in pipes—subjects we have only discussed in passing. However, the aspects of well performance that *are* covered in detail in this book do constitute, in our opinion, the fundamentals of well performance as required by petroleum engineers.

Numerous examples are included in the text. For the most part, each new concept is accompanied by at least one example. Whenever possible, we have chosen examples from published *field* data. In fact, obtaining published data for examples was one of our most difficult tasks. It seems that most examples cited in the recent literature (last 10 to 20 years) either give incomplete data or are "generated" by a computer. Many of our examples are from confidential sources and we have adapted the use of fictitous well names and geographic locations.

As most practicing engineers can verify, field data *never* seem to fit textbook theory. This has been a challenge since most of our examples are from actual wells. The inconsistencies in application of theory to field data has given us the opportunity to present a critical view and better understanding of the limitations of theory used in well performance engineering.

Production rates from oil and gas wells around the world vary by several orders of magnitude. One author grew up in the oil fields of Oklahoma where a "good" oil well produces 10 to 100 barrels per day, and a gas discovery coming in at more than a million cubic feet per day makes the daily newspapers. The other author started his career in the oil fields of the Middle East, where production ranges from several hundred to several thousand barrels per day, and gas is usually flared. The authors first met some eight years ago and have since worked mostly with oil and gas production in offshore Norway. Here, a good oil well produces no less than 10,000 barrels per day and a strong gas well will never produce to capacity because of equipment limitations. In this book we have tried to consider a wide range of well capacities based on our experience with small- and large-capacity oil and gas wells.

We have chosen to use conventional oilfield units such as barrels per day, feet, and millidarcy. The choice is made reluctantly since the switch to SI units appears imminent. However, there are two good reasons for using the more conservative oilfield set of units in a textbook. First, we the authors are most familiar with oilfield units and there is less chance for errors in equations, figures, and examples than had the more unfamiliar SI system been chosen. Second, the industry still uses oilfield units. For students "brought up" with the SI system through high school, it is important that they learn the oilfield system to properly function in an industry that applies both systems simultaneously. Also, most petroleum engineering literature prior to 1980 uses oilfield units, and to readily access this literature it is necessary to have worked with oilfield units.

Since the early 1920s many engineers have contributed to our understanding of well performance. Pioneering work by Millikan, Muskat, Poettmann, Gilbert, Vogel, and Fetkovich (among others) have paved the way for modern well performance analysis. Others, since then, have synthesized, organized, and presented the concepts of well performance in course notes, textbooks, and lectures.

Two persons, Mike J. Fetkovich and Marshall B. Standing, have been particularly influential on how and what we chose to present in this text. Mr. Fetkovich has founded, in our opinion, two classic concepts in the application of standard engineering to well performance. First, he draws the analogy between oil and gas wells in his 1973 paper on multirate testing of oil wells. There he shows that the standard backpressure gas equation is equally applicable to oil wells because (1) multiphase flow in oil wells is analogous to the effect of pressure-dependent properties in gas wells and (2) high-velocity or non-Darcy flow typically associated with gas production is also prevalent in oil wells. The second major contribution of Fetkovich was application of the constant-pressure solution for interpreting and forecasting rate decline. Numerous developments of the type-curve approach to decline-curve analysis have come subsequent to Fetkovich's original publication on the subject. We have tried to digest the large amount of material presented by Fetkovich and others and to present it in a manner readily understood by engineers not familiar with transient test theory.

Dr. Standing taught production and reservoir engineering courses at NTH from 1974 to 1975, following a long industrial career with Standard Oil of California. Dr. Standing is perhaps best known for his contributions in phase behavior of oil and gas systems. However, at NTH he demonstrated a comprehensive knowledge of reservoir and production engineering disciplines. Dr. Standing's ability to convey difficult concepts in simple written form has been appreciated by many hundreds of his students. While at NTH, Dr. Standing wrote a series of lecture notes (unfortunately never published) including a Data Book, three traditional reservoir engineering manuals, diverse production notes, a classic volume on relative permeability, and several "how to write" guides. Most of these were modified and improved during his almost ten-year position at Stanford University (1975 to 1983). We have chosen to use many of the ideas in these notes as the starting point for discussions in the present text. Coupled with his broad range of interests and experience, Dr. Standing's contribution as a teacher will not be surpassed for many years to come.

We would like to thank Dr. Augusto L. Podio from the University of Texas for his critical review of chapters one and two. We have adopted most of his numerous comments and suggestions. We also would like to thank Mr. David M. Deering from Tenneco Oil for his assistance in preparing the artwork, and Mr. Roy Davis for drafting the figures.

Phillips Petroleum Company Norway and Tenneco Oil Exploration and Development have provided necessary financial support towards the completion of our work. A special thanks to the engineers within these and other companies who also have contributed through their discussions and critique of the text.

Finally, we want to thank family, friends, and colleagues who have provided us with needed support and understanding, even when our work has required selfish dedication during weekends and holidays.

Michael Golan and Curtis H. Whitson
Trondheim, Norway

WELL PERFORMANCE

1   CONCEPTS IN WELL PERFORMANCE ENGINEERING

This chapter describes the basic principles used to analyze well performance problems. A simple oil or gas production system is described, followed by a brief discussion of the major mechanical elements and the general arrangement of the system. Also included is the overall strategy for solving problems involving production rates and flow conditions in oil and gas wells. The chapter introduces the basic concepts used to solve production problems, including

1. phase behavior of reservoir and surface fluids
2. reservoir inflow performance relation (IPR)
3. gradient curves and tubing performance
4. wellhead performance
5. choke performance
6. flowline performance

Finally, this chapter shows how to use these concepts to predict natural flow conditions and artificial lift requirements.

1.1   **INTRODUCTION TO PRODUCTION SYSTEMS.** A production system is essentially a system that transports reservoir fluid to the surface and separates it into oil, gas, and water. The oil and gas streams are treated if necessary and prepared for sale or transport from the field. Any water produced is also treated and prepared for disposal or reinjection into the reservoir. The basic mechanical elements of a production system are

1. wells
2. flowlines
3. production manifold
4. separators and process equipment
5. metering intruments
6. storage vessels

Figure 1.1 illustrates a simple production system with three naturally flowing oil wells and two separators in parallel.

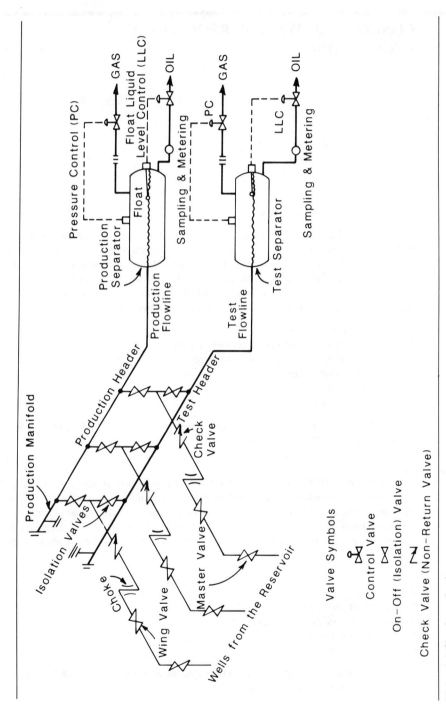

Figure 1.1 Simple production system.

EXAMPLE 1.1 DESIGN OF A PRODUCTION MANIFOLD

Illustrate the arrangement of the isolation valves in a production manifold that collects the production from five wells and directs it to a test separator and two production separators installed in parallel.

SOLUTION

An effective manifold should divert the production of any well to any of the three separators. This can be achieved by constructing a manifold with three headers, each connected through a flowline to one separator. The flow from any well is selectively diverted to any separator by three isolation (on/off) valves arranged in the pattern illustrated in figure E1.1

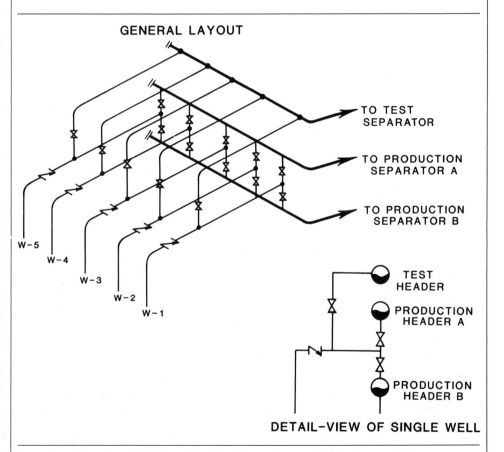

GENERAL LAYOUT

TO TEST
SEPARATOR

TO PRODUCTION
SEPARATOR A

TO PRODUCTION
SEPARATOR B

W-5

W-4

W-3

W-2

W-1

TEST
HEADER

PRODUCTION
HEADER A

PRODUCTION
HEADER B

DETAIL-VIEW OF SINGLE WELL

Figure E1.1 General layout of a five-well production manifold connected to three parallel separators.

Production from the three wells in figure 1.1 passes through the flowlines to the production manifold. By a suitable valving arrangement in the manifold, it is possible to divert the flow to either of the two illustrated separators. In the separators the produced fluid is split into liquid and gas streams, which are metered and transferred to further treatment or sales. The manifold valves isolate production from any individual well, directing flow into one of the two collecting pipes, called headers (or collectors). For this simple production system, one separator serves for continuous handling of the production (production separator) while the second is used for routine testing of individual wells (test separator). The header pipe connected to the production separator is called a production header, and the second header pipe connected to the test separator is called a test header. The production of each well can be directed through the production header and onto the production separator, or it can be diverted through the test header and to the test separator. Check valves are installed between the well and the manifold. Such valves prevent backflow through the manifold from high- to low-pressure wells. The design of a multiwell production system should always allow flow from any well to any separator, unless the additional costs do not justify the additional flexibility.

Parallel separators, as arranged in example 1.1, allow continuous separation of flow using two smaller production separators instead of one large one. Also, such an arrangement allows separate treatment of a group of wells, as might be needed for wells with high water/oil ratios (WOR), requiring water removal or emulsion treatment.

For a closer look at the elements of a simple production system, figure 1.2 shows a naturally flowing oil well. The principal elements of the well that are relevant to production engineering include (1) the production casing or liner, (2) the tubing string, (3) the production packer, (4) the wellhead and tubing hanger, and (5) the christmas tree.

The production casing is perforated along the hydrocarbon-bearing formation to allow reservoir fluid to enter the well and flow upward through the production tubing. The annular space between the casing and the tubing is sealed at the lower part of the well with a production packer, which isolates the tubing from the tubing–casing annulus. The tubing can be anchored at the packer, or it can move freely in reaction to tubing length changes caused by temperature and pressure variation. In either case, a seal is kept between the tubing and the annulus at the packer. The tubing string may also include accessories such as a seating nipple, safety valve, circulation sleeve, and blast joints.

The tubing string is suspended from a tubing hanger installed at the wellhead. The tubing hanger also provides a sealing between the top of the tubing and the top of the tubing–casing annulus. A series of isolation valves is installed above the tubing hanger, combining to form the christmas tree assembly (often written *x-mas tree*). The x-mas tree may be a single block type, where all the valves are machined in a single steel block, or it may consist of several valves flanged (joined) together. The simple x-mas tree illustrated in figure 1.2 consists of a single master valve at the lower end and a flow tee at the upper end, which splits the flow into three directions. The horizontal outlets lead to wing valves. The swab valve is found at the top of the

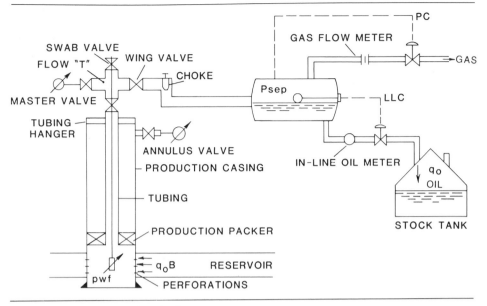

Figure 1.2 Simple single-well production system.

tree. Usually, only one side outlet connects to a wing valve, and the other is blocked off by a blind flange or plug. The master and wing valves are used to open and shut in flow as desired. An additional valve illustrated in figure 1.2 is the annulus access valve. In wells producing by artificial lift, the annulus and the annulus access valve are used to either vent or inject gas.

During regular production, the fluid flows through the master valve and the wing valve to the flowline. The other wing valve is usually closed and blanked, and the swab valve is normally closed. High-pressure gas wells may require a series of two master valves and two wing valves (one on each side outlet), to contend with high surface pressures and greater safety requirements. A choke valve is mounted downstream from the wing valve and upstream from the connection to the flowline. The choke valve regulates the rate of flow and reduces the wellhead pressure to the lower flowline pressure (downstream). In satellite wells of offshore platforms, the choke is often mounted at the inlet to the manifold rather than on the x-mas tree, thereby providing easy access to control, inspect, or maintain the choke valves.

Isolation (on/off) valves on the x-mas tree and manifold are not provided for regulating flow rate, because erosion may cause damage and premature valve failure. In high-rate wells, it is good practice to shut off the well by gradually closing the adjustable choke valve and then, when flow ceases, closing the wing and master valves. It is important to realize that the choke is the only valve designed to regulate flow rate from a well.

The well illustrated in figure 1.2 is flowing during a routine production test, and bottomhole pressure is measured and recorded with a wireline-retrievable downhole gauge. At the same time, liquid rate is measured at the surface in the stock tank after solution gas has been separated from the oil. Gas from the separator is measured by a flowmeter installed in the gas line, and volumetric rates are reported at standard conditions of pressure and temperature (e.g., 14.7 psia and 60°F). The separator is regulated by two controls: the liquid level controller (LLC) and the separator pressure controller (PC). Liquid level in the separator is regulated by a control valve on the liquid outlet. The valve is regulated by a controller connected to a float that monitors the liquid level in the separator, compares it with a preset level, and activates the valve to increase its opening when the liquid level is too high or decrease it when the level drops. Separator pressure is controlled by a backpressure valve in the gas line. The valve is activated by a pressure regulator, which decreases the valve opening when the separator pressure drops below a preset value or increases it when the pressure exceeds this value.

In a simple production system, oil from the separator may flow to a stock tank where it is stored at atmospheric conditions. The gas flows directly to the gas-gathering pipeline. In such cases the oil is gauged in the stock tank and gas is metered on-line. Where an on-line oil meter is used to measure separator oil rate, the meter should be installed upstream from the LLC valve to minimize the amount of free gas present in the oil meter. Oil meters are not accurate in the presence of free gas. Oil leaving the separator is gas saturated, and any drop in pressure will result in gas coming out of solution. Therefore, metering should be made as close to the outlet of the separator as possible.

The production system described so far is relatively simple but in principle is representative of most onshore and smaller offshore fields. The layout is significantly more complicated when more wells, separators, and other process equipment are required to produce the field. The basic elements indicated in figures 1.1 and 1.2 still preserve their tasks in a more complex production system, and an understanding of the basic principles behind these elements plays a central role in designing production systems. Figure 1.3 illustrates a subsea production manifold controlling production from four templates and three satellite wells. The manifold is situated on the seabed, whereas separators and process facilities are located on the deck of a floating vessel. Surface equipment is connected to the manifold by means of flexible flowlines and production risers.

In addition to the conventional production control tasks, the illustrated manifold provides possibilities to inject gas through a gas-injection header to gas-lift wells. For that purpose, an additional injection line connects the annulus of each well with the manifold. The system designer chose to locate chokes on the manifold upstream from the production header. An additional choke, located upstream from the test separator, allows regulation of production rate during a test. The design in figure 1.3 provides the possibility for

1. normal production with natural flow and continual monitoring of annulus pressure;
2. testing a single well while producing the other wells;
3. gas lifting the template wells only;
4. converting satellite wells to water injectors while producing template wells under natural flow;

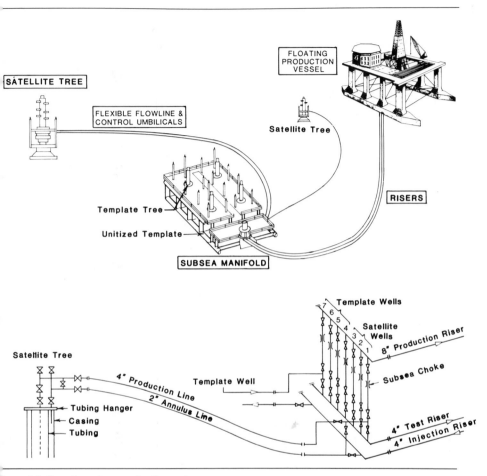

igure 1.3 Complex subsea production system.

5. producing all wells when one 4-in. line to a satellite well is damaged;
6. producing the entire field while divers service a subsea choke at the manifold.

The reader is encouraged to identify the flow path in figure 1.3 during each of the situations listed here.

Having discussed the mechanical arrangement of a production system, we can investigate the flow characteristics of the system. The reservoir provides the source of fluid and energy to move it to the surface. Flow from the reservoir into and up the wellbore, through surface equipment, and finally to a storage vessel or pipeline, is accompanied by a series of pressure drops. Figure 1.4 illustrates a hypothetical pressure traverse for a single well producing at a constant flow rate. Pressure at the outer boundary of the reservoir is the starting point for the pressure traverse, which ends at transfer line pressure or at atmospheric pressure in the stock tank.

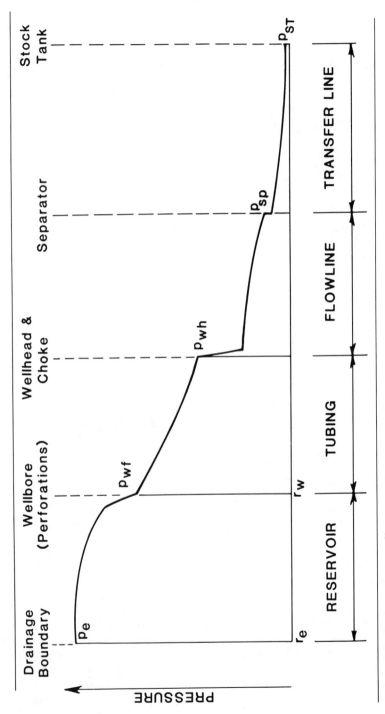

Figure 1.4 Production pressure profile.

A higher flow rate will result in larger pressure gradients through the system. Larger pressure gradients, on the other hand, result in increased production rate. The dependence of rate on pressure drop is the essence of most production engineering problems. It is usually considered in two ways.

1. The rate–pressure relationship is considered at a specific point along the flow path, that is, at the wellbore or at the wellhead.
2. The pressure traverse along the flow path is considered at a constant flow rate, that is, pressure distribution around the wellbore or along the tubing.

More generally, engineering analysis of well performance is essentially an investigation of the pressure–rate relationship in three cases:

1. steady state production
2. gradual long-term changes due to reservoir depletion
3. short-term transient behavior following a sudden change in flow conditions

Before proceeding, it is important to recognize the special nature of production calculations and the limitations on accuracy one can expect. Design calculations almost always use incomplete and often inaccurate data. Also, flow phenomena of reservoir and surface fluids are complex and do not lend themselves to simple mathematical description. Consequently, the best we can often attempt is a qualitative analysis giving insight into the cause-and-effect nature of the production system. Campbell and Farrar (1972) express the special nature of petroleum production by noting that "we can only react to the environment, never control it."

The requirement for solving many production-related engineering problems is a fast, simple calculation procedure that approximates the complex phenomena related to producing reservoir fluids. This is perhaps most important when the end result of our analysis is the prediction of a production profile for economic analysis of a new field, or perhaps the determination of the economic impact of alternative well completions and stimulation methods.

Certainly there is no substitute for practical experience supported by good intuition. Often, however, basing decisions on intelligent judgment instead of engineering analysis may lead to costly errors. Consider, for example, the three completion options shown in figure 1.5. Try to deduce which of the three will result in the most cost-effective and practical solution. Any attempt to quickly think through the solution to this problem will probably be in vain. There is no trivial solution. Rather, the solution depends on the specific criteria one uses (economic or mechanical), on available data, and on the engineering tools available. By the end of this chapter you should develop the ability to solve this problem using your own criteria for comparison.

When is well performance engineering necessary? Practically, it is needed any time you have to predict production rates or want to decide on mechanical details of the well or surface system. You also need it to assess the effect of changes in the system on production rate. In early feasibility studies, production forecasts are used to study the commerciality of a field, to plan strategy for field development, and so forth. Once commerciality is declared, the design of production installations and equipment specifications becomes the primary reason for engineering well

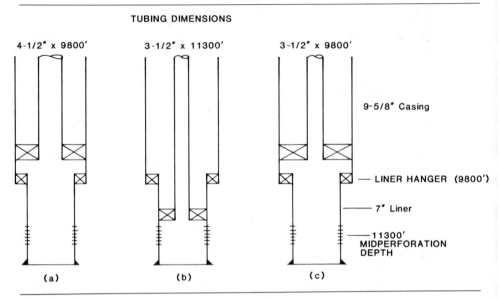

Figure 1.5 Alternative well completion designs.

performance. Finally, when the field is under development it is important to determine the need and type of stimulation and/or artificial lift system required by individual wells. Interpreting production data and diagnosing reservoir, mechanical, or other well problems are also tasks of well performance engineering.

The rest of this chapter explains the basic calculating techniques used in well performance engineering and introduces the basic phenomena that govern the steady-state production of a well. The first aspects to be introduced are the phase behavior and volumetric changes of reservoir fluid as it flows along the production system.

1.2   PHASE BEHAVIOR OF RESERVOIR AND SURFACE FLUIDS. Oil flowing from the reservoir drainage boundary to a wellbore, up the production tubing, and through the surface and process equipment eventually reaches a saturated state. Thereafter, gas comes out of solution as pressure drops along the flow path, forming a two-phase gas/oil system. Depending on the properties of the oil and the pressure and temperature at the drainage boundary, the point where oil reaches its saturated state may lie anywhere along the flow path toward the stock tank or transport line. The gas liberated and separated during the flow process may be collected in a pipeline, vented to the atmosphere, processed to extract natural gas liquids, burned as fuel for field operations, reinjected into the producing reservoir, stored in an underground storage system, or perhaps some combination of the preceding. Final liberation of gas from the oil takes place in a stock tank or storage vessel.

The amount of gas dissolved in oil at reservoir conditions is dependent on the overall composition of the fluid. The amount of gas remaining in solution at any other condition depends on the prevailing pressure and temperature. The amount and rate of gas liberation therefore depend on the pressure and temperature profile along the flow path. As gas evolves, the oil shrinks (decreases in volume) until it stabilizes in the stock tank at standard conditions of pressure and temperature. The ratio of the volume of oil at reservoir conditions, V_R, to the volume of oil resulting in the stock tank, V_{STO}, is called the *formation volume factor (FVF)*.

In review, the total change in local gas and oil volumes along the flow path results from a combination of:

1. expansion of free gas
2. shrinkage of saturated oil
3. mass transfer between oil and gas phases (gas liberation)

To facilitate calculation of the pressure drop in pipe, it is useful to define volumetric fractions occupied by the liquid and gas phases at a given cross section. These are expressed as

$$E_L = A_L/(A_L + A_g) \tag{1.1}$$

and

$$E_g = 1 - E_L = A_g/(A_L + A_g), \tag{1.2}$$

where A_L is the cross-sectional area occupied by liquid (oil and water), A_g is the cross-sectional area occupied by gas, E_L is the fraction of the total area occupied by liquid, and E_g is the fraction of the total area occupied by gas. The term E_L is often referred to as *liquid holdup*. It has several uses in pipe flow calculations, one of the more important ones being the estimation of flow regime.

Two schematic views of a pipe cross section are shown in figure 1.6. Two phases, oil and gas, are moving through the pipe, but the distribution of phases is different in each figure. Figure 1.6(a) shows a view where the one phase (liquid) is found as drops or slugs entrained in the other phase (gas). At lower gas/ratios the inverse might be found, with gas entrained in the liquid as bubbles or slugs. Figure 1.6(b) shows the two phases segregated. This distribution is indicative of horizontal or downhill flow at low velocities. Several other distinct flow regimes—patterns of gas/liquid distribution—have been observed experimentally.

In either case, segregated or entrained two-phase flow, the quantities of liquid and gas volume fraction (i.e., no-slip holdup), E_L and E_g, are useful quantities for pipeflow calculations. Physically, the meaning of *no-slip holdup* is that if a flowing, two-phase mixture was trapped between two fast-closing valves along a short segment of pipe, the volume fractions of the liquid and gas would equal the area fractions, A_L and A_g, respectively. Volume fraction for a short pipe segment can be expressed in terms of volumetric flow rates for each phase entering and leaving the

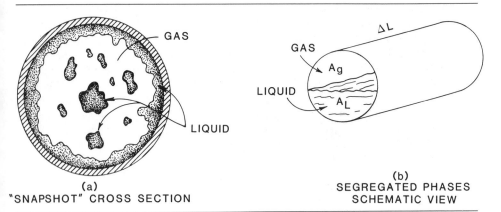

(b)
SEGREGATED PHASES
SCHEMATIC VIEW

(a)
"SNAPSHOT" CROSS SECTION

Figure 1.6 Cross-sectional view of two-phase flow in pipe.

segment. Assuming both phases move through the pipe with similar velocities (no-slip assumption), the no-slip E_L can be defined as

$$E_L = q_L(p, T)/[q_L(p, T) + q_g(p, T)],\qquad(1.3)$$

where $q(p, T)$ indicates that the volumetric flow rate corresponds to the pressure p and temperature T at the cross section being studied. The no-slip E_g is merely expressed as $1 - E_L$.

Another parameter important to two-phase flow calculations is the apparent density of mixtures. It can be approximated using the no-slip assumption, where apparent mixture density is defined as the total mass produced (gas, oil, and water) divided by the total volume of all three phases. Total mass is a constant, and only the proportions of gas and liquid change with pressure and temperature. Therefore, using the no-slip holdup E_L and E_g, together with phase densities ρ_L and ρ_g, the mixture density ρ_m is expressed as

$$\rho_m = \rho_L E_L + \rho_g(1 - E_L).\qquad(1.4)$$

This value is used to calculate pressure drop due to gravity in vertical or inclined pipe, and in some correlations it is used to define the Reynold's number ($R_e = \rho v d/\mu$), which is related to pressure loss due to friction.

To calculate densities and no-slip holdup it is necessary to determine the volumes of liquid and gas at the prevailing pressure and temperature at the cross section being studied. Pressure, volume, and temperature (PVT) correlations are usually used in volumetric calculations, although more complicated equations of state may be required for gas condensate fluids. The pressure–temperature (p–T) diagram is a very useful tool for describing the phase behavior of oil and gas mixtures as they flow in a production system. Figure 1.7 shows a typical p–T diagram for a petroleum mixture found as an undersaturated oil at initial reservoir conditions.

A p–T diagram outlines the regions where a mixture behaves as a single phase

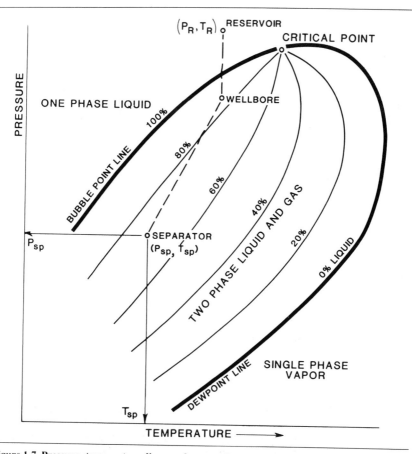

Figure 1.7 Pressure–temperature diagram for an undersaturated reservoir oil.

and where it separates into two phases, gas and oil. The *bubble-point* curve defines the conditions when a mixture acts as a liquid and, if pressure is reduced, gas is liberated to form a two-phase system. The *dewpoint* curve defines the conditions when a mixture acts as a gas and, if pressure changes, liquid is condensed to form a two-phase system. The point joining the bubble-point and dewpoint curves is the *critical point*, and it represents a unique thermodynamic condition. A mixture at pressure and temperature lying outside the two-phase envelope is considered in an undersaturated state.

The dewpoint curve is usually divided into two regions, the *retrograde* and *normal* segments. A drop in pressure from the *retrograde* dewpoint curve results in liquid condensation, whereas an increase in pressure from the *normal* dewpoint curve results in liquid condensation. The point joining the two dewpoint segments is found at the highest temperature at which the mixture can exist as two phases (cricondentherm).

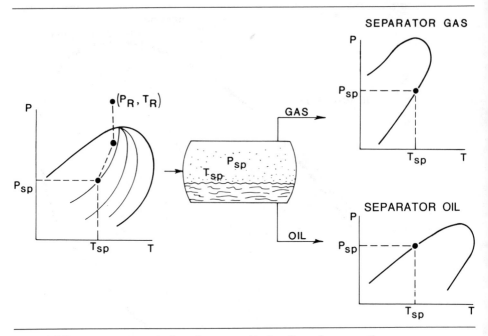

Figure 1.8 Pressure–temperature phase diagram used to describe surface separation.

On the phase diagram in figure 1.7 we follow the path corresponding to flow from the reservoir drainage boundary to the wellbore (an isothermal process), through the production tubing and choke, and finally to the separator. In the separator the gas and oil separate into different flowstreams, each constituting a new mixture with a different composition and phase diagram. The gas starts at a point on the dewpoint curve of its $p-T$ diagram, and the oil starts at a point on the bubble-point of its $p-T$ diagram. The separation process is shown in terms of the resulting gas and oil $p-T$ diagrams in figure 1.8. Note that much of the gas leaving the separator may have been previously liberated along the flow path from the reservoir to the separator.

Gas liberation, gas expansion, and oil shrinkage along the production tubing can be treated as a series of successive incremental states where saturated oil and gas coexist in equilibrium. This model is shown in figure 1.9. At (a) the single-phase oil enters the wellbore; (b) marks the first evolution of gas, at the mixture's bubble point; and both (c) and (d) show the traverse into the two-phase region. Note that the gas and oil $p-T$ diagrams describing equilibrium phases at points (c) and (d) are not the same. This means that the composition of equilibrium gas and oil phases changes continuously in the two-phase region, even though the mixture $p-T$ diagram is unchanged. In review, as the two-phase region is entered and gas is liberated, oil and gas phases change in volume and composition but they are always

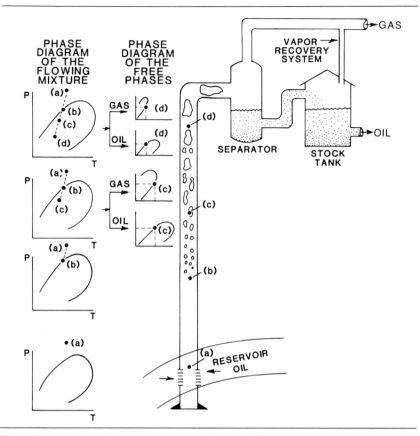

Figure 1.9 Changes in phase behavior in the production tubing.

in a saturated state (the gas at its dewpoint and the oil at its bubble point).

Sophisticated PVT models such as *equations of state* can describe the complicated phase behavior just described, but for production calculations we rely on approximate correlations and some simplifications. The minimum data required to predict PVT behavior are surface properties of the gas and stock tank oil produced and an estimate of the temperature profile along the path of flow. Oil and gas gravities and gas/oil ratio (GOR) are the primary surface properties needed to use PVT correlations. Gravities are defined differently for gas and oil. Gas gravity is the ratio of gas density to air density, both at standard conditions, and oil gravity is the ratio of oil density to distilled water density, also at standard conditions. Gravity is dimensionless, but it is associated with a reference density defined at standard conditions, usually 14.7 psia and 60°F.

Typically, PVT correlations have been developed using oilfield units. Appendix C discusses the method of conversion from oilfield to SI units. Oilfield units used in PVT correlations are API gravity, γ_{API}, given in degrees API (°API); total gas

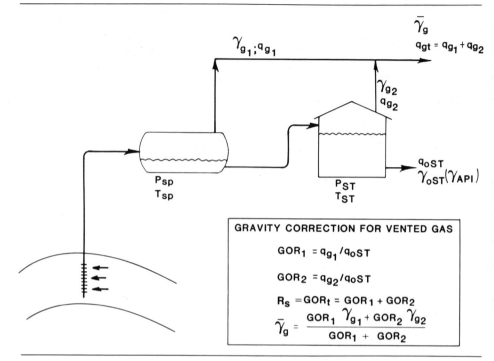

Figure 1.10 Definitions of surface properties reported from production data.

gravity, $\bar{\gamma}_g$; initial solution gas/oil ratio, R_s, given in standard cubic feet per stock-tank barrel (scf/STB); and reservoir temperature, in °F. Figure 1.10 shows a schematic diagram of the typical definitions used for reporting surface properties from production data.

The relation of API gravity to oil gravity, γ_o, is

$$\gamma_{API} = 141.5/\gamma_o - 131.5 \tag{1.5}$$

$$\gamma_o = 141.5/(131.5 + \gamma_{API}), \tag{1.6}$$

where we recall that γ_o is defined at standard conditions of 14.7 psia and 60°F. To calculate stock-tank oil density, ρ_{STO}, it is necessary to use the density of distilled water at standard conditions, equal to about 62.37 lbm/ft³, giving

$$\rho_{STO} = 62.37\gamma_o, \tag{1.7}$$

also in lbm/ft³.

Solution gas/oil ratio, R_s, is the total volume of gas collected from all stages of separation, divided by the volume of stock-tank oil. The magnitude of the solution gas/oil ratio depends on the number of separators and conditions used to process the reservoir fluid. A basic assumption in this case is that the mixture entering the wellbore is a single-phase liquid, thereby ensuring that (1) none of the initial solution gas has been trapped in the reservoir, and (2) none of the produced gas is free gas in the reservoir.

By definition, gas gravity is the ratio of gas density to air density, both reported at standard conditions. Equally correct, gas gravity is the ratio of gas molecular weight to the molecular weight of air (28.97). Total gas gravity, $\bar{\gamma}_g$, is the molar average of gas gravities from each stage of separation. Gas gravity should be measured at each stage of separation, along with the gas/oil ratio for each stage. Average gas gravity can be shown to equal the GOR-weighted average of gases from all stages of separation. Gas density is merely the ratio of mass to volume, and for a gas it can be written

$$\rho_g = 28.97\gamma_g p/ZRT, \tag{1.8}$$

where 28.97 is the molecular weight of air and $28.97\gamma_g$ represents the molecular weight of gas. Density has the unit lbm/ft^3, if pressure is given in psia ($lbf/in.^2$), temperature in °R (°R = °F + 460), and the gas constant R is 10.73 ($lbf\,ft/mol°R$). The compressibility factor Z is dimensionless. At standard conditions,

$p = 14.7\,psia$,
$T = 520°R$ (60°F),
$Z = 1.000$,
$R = 10.73$,

and gas density in lbm/ft^3 is expressed as

$$\rho_{gsc} = 0.0763\gamma_g. \tag{1.9}$$

Example 1.2 illustrates the preparation of surface production data for use with standard PVT correlations. The PVT properties of most interest to well performance calculations are volume factors, solution gas/oil ratio, and bubble-point pressure. A brief description of each is given in the following:

GAS VOLUME FACTOR, B_g, having a unit of ft^3/scf, is the volume in cubic feet (ft^3) that one standard cubic foot (scf) will occupy at a specific state of pressure and temperature (p, T).

OIL VOLUME FACTOR, B_o, is the volume in barrels (bbl) occupied by one stock-tank barrel (STB) oil and its associated solution gas when recombined to a single-phase liquid at a specific state (p, T), having a unit of bbl/STB.

WATER VOLUME FACTOR, B_w, is the volume in bbl occupied by one STB water and possibly some solution gas when recombined to a single-phase liquid at a specific state (p, T) having a unit of bbl/STBW.

SOLUTION GAS/OIL RATIO, R_s, having a unit of scf/STB, is the volume of gas in standard cubic feet that will dissolve (go into solution) in one stock-tank barrel of oil at a given (p, T).

EXAMPLE 1.2 PREPARING SURFACE PRODUCTION DATA TO USE WITH
STANDARD PVT CORRELATIONS

Production data from the Hobart No. 1, a discovery wildcat in the Anadarko basin,
was recorded during a three-day testing period consisting of the following
sequence:

1. short initial flow period..................................... 15 minutes
2. short shut-in period.. 1 hour
3. main flow period .... 12 hours
4. main shut-in period.. 60 hours

Oil production during the main flow period was stable at a rate between 250 and
275 bbl/D at separator conditions, or an average of 265 bbl/D with 5% variation.
Measurements made during the main flow period are:

1. bottomhole flowing pressure and temperature, recorded by a downhole tool
   assembly consisting of tandem pressure and temperature gauges run on a
   wireline
2. wellhead pressure and temperature—pressure was measured with a dead-
   weight tester and temperature with a standard thermometer
3. separator pressure and temperature (gauges)
4. separator gas flow rate, measured with an orifice gas meter
5. separator gas gravity, measured using a portable gas gravity meter
6. separator oil flow rate, measured with a positive displacement meter
   downstream from the separator—conditions at the meter are maintained as
   close to separator pressure and temperature as possible
7. oil shrinkage between the flowmeter and stock-tank conditions (14.7 psia and
   60°F), measured on a sample of separator oil and analyzed by a PVT laboratory
8. stock-tank oil gravity from the separator oil sample tested for shrinkage
9. gas gravity of the gas liberated from the separator oil sample tested for
   shrinkage
10. gas/oil ratio of the separator oil sample tested for shrinkage
11. water/oil ratio, measured by taking a sample of wellstream fluid, freeing the
    gas in solution, and centrifuging the remaining water/oil mixture—liquid
    effluent from the separator was also sampled and analyzed, following the same
    procedure

The results of surface measurements were:

wellbore flowing pressure, end of test .... 2800 psia
bottomhole temperature .... 160 °F
wellhead flowing pressure, end of test .... 800 psia
wellhead flowing temperature, end of test .... 120 °F
separator gas flow rate .... 96 Mscf/D
separator liquid flow rate................................. 265 bbl/D

EXAMPLE 1.2 continued

separator/stock-tank oil volume factor	1.15 bbl/STB
separator pressure	200 psia
separator temperature	90 °F
separator oil gas/oil ratio	30 scf/STB
separator gas gravity	0.69 (air = 1)
stock-tank vapor (gas) gravity	0.89 (air = 1)
stock-tank oil gravity	28 °API
	0.863 (water = 1)
stock-tank water/oil ratio	0.07

Tasks
1. Calculate the stock-tank oil rate.
2. Calculate the total gas/oil ratio and average gas gravity.

SOLUTION

1. The stock-tank oil rate q_o can be calculated from the separator liquid rate q_{Lsp}, the separator/stock-tank oil volume factor B_{osp}, and the stock-tank water/oil ratio F_{wo}:

$$q_o = q_{Lsp}/[B_{osp} + F_{wo}]$$

$$= 265/[1.15 + 0.07]$$

$$= 217 \, STB/D.$$

This equation is easily derived by noting that

$$q_{Lsp} = q_o B_{osp} + q_o F_{wo} B_{wsp},$$

$$F_{wo} = q_w/q_o,$$

and assuming $B_{wsp} = 1.0$. Note that the subscript *sp* in this example refers to separator conditions.
2. Total gas/oil ratio is $R = q_g/q_o$, where q_g and q_o are total gas and stock-tank oil rates. Total gas rate is not measured directly. Instead, gas rate from the separator q_{gsp} and gas/oil ratio of the separator oil $R_{s,sp}$ are measured. The expression for R, then, is

$$R = q_{gsp}/q_o + R_{s,sp}$$

$$= 96000/217 + 30$$

$$= 442 + 30$$

$$= 472 \, scf/STB.$$

EXAMPLE 1.2 continued

Average gas gravity is the gas/oil ratio weighted average,

$\gamma_g = [442(0.69) + 30(0.89)]/(442 + 30)$

$= 0.703$

These PVT quantities are used to determine oil, liquid (oil plus water), and gas rates at points along the flow path between the reservoir and the surface, defined by conditions (p, T). That is, given rates at standard conditions q_o, q_w, q_g, we can find the rates at any set of conditions (p, T). First, however, note that surface rates of gas and water are usually expressed as ratios, relative to one stock-tank barrel of oil (i.e., $R = q_g/q_o$ and $F_{wo} = q_w/q_o$). The ratio R is the total or produced gas/oil ratio and should not be confused with R_s, which is the solution gas/oil ratio. R is not related to a set of conditions (p, T) as is R_s. Sometimes we make use of the gas/liquid ratio $F_{gL} = q_g/(q_o + q_w)$.

The oil flow rate at conditions (p, T) where q_o is the stock-tank oil rate is merely

$$q_o(p, T) = q_o B_o(p, T), \tag{1.10}$$

where q_o has a unit of STB/D, $B_o(p, T)$ has a unit of bbl/STB, and the resulting unit of $q_o(p, T)$ is bbl/D. It should be noted that a barrel (bbl) and a stock-tank barrel (STB) both represent the same volumetric quantity (e.g., 5.615 ft^3), but the use of bbl indicates that the conditions (p, T) are different from those at stock-tank conditions (14.7 psia, 60°F), STB.

Total liquid rate (oil plus water) at conditions (p, T) is given by

$$q_L(p, T) = q_o[B_o(p, T) + B_w(p, T)F_{wo}], \tag{1.11}$$

where B_o and B_w have units of bbl/STB, F_{wo} has a unit of STBW/STB, q_o has a unit of STB/D, and the resulting q_L has a unit of bbl/D. Note the use of the abbreviations STB for stock-tank barrel *oil* and STBW for stock-tank barrel *water*, since it is assumed that STB indicates an oil quantity.

The rate of *free gas* at conditions (p, T) is given by

$$q_g(p, T) = q_o[R - R_s(p, T)]B_g(p, T), \tag{1.12}$$

where R and R_s have units of scf/STB, B_g has a unit of ft^3/scf, q_o has a unit of STB/D, and the resulting q_g has a unit of ft^3/D. The use of ft^3 indicates that the gas volume is at conditions different from standard conditions, scf.

The volume fraction of liquid along a short segment of pipe, E_L (no-slip liquid holdup), is the ratio of liquid volumetric flow rate to gas plus liquid rate at conditions (p, T). Because different units are used for gas and liquid rates (ft^3/D and bbl/D), it is necessary to introduce the conversion factor 5.615 ft^3/bbl, resulting in the following expression for E_L:

$$E_L = \frac{5.615B_o}{(R - R_s)B_g + 5.615(B_o + B_w F_{wo})}. \tag{1.13}$$

In most flow calculations it is acceptable to approximate the water formation volume factor, B_w, with unity ($B_w = 1$). If production is water-free, then $F_{wo} = 0$ and the no-slip holdup relation is simplified.

Gas volume factor, B_g, is easily expressed in terms of pressure p, temperature T, and the gas compressibility factor Z. For standard conditions ($p_s = 14.7$ psia and $T_s = 520°R$)

$$B_g = (p_s/T_s) TZ/p = 0.02827 TZ/p,$$ (1.14)

where T has a unit of $°R$, p has a unit of psia, Z has no unit, and the unit of B_g is ft^3/scf.

The compressibility factor, Z can be determined in a stepwise fashion, starting with the estimation of pseudocritical pressure p_{pcm} and pseudocritical temperature T_{pcm} of the gas mixture. By definition, the pseudocritical properties are the mole-average of critical properties for individual components making up the mixture (e.g., methane, ethane, and others, including heptanes-plus). An approximate value for pseudocritical properties can be calculated from average gas gravity, γ_g, using a correlation developed by Standing (1981).

California "Dry Gas" Correlation:

$$p_{pcm} = 677 + 15.0\gamma_g - 37.5\gamma_g^2,$$ (1.15)

$$T_{pcm} = 168 + 325\gamma_g - 12.5\gamma_g^2.$$ (1.16)

Average "Gas-Condensate" Correlation:

$$p_{pcm} = 706 - 51.7\gamma_g - 11.1\gamma_g^2,$$ (1.17)

$$T_{pcm} = 187 + 330\gamma_g - 71.5\gamma_g^2.$$ (1.18)

Having determined pseudocriticals of the mixture, the next step is to calculate pseudoreduced properties, defined as $p_{pr} = p/p_{pcm}$ and $T_{pr} = T/T_{pcm}$. A generalized (corresponding state) correlation is then used to calculate Z. The Standing–Katz Z-factor correlation (1942) is a graphical correlation generally accepted as the industry standard. Best-fit equations for the Standing–Katz chart have been published by several authors, and the one suggested here [see Standing (1981)] is an equation given by Beggs and Brill (1973):

$$Z = A + (1 - A)/e^B + Cp_{pr}^D,$$ (1.19)

where

$$A = 1.39(T_{pr} - 0.92)^{0.5} - 0.36T_{pr} - 0.101,$$
$$B = (0.62 - 0.23T_{pr})p_{pr} + \left[\frac{0.066}{(T_{pr} - 0.86)} - 0.037\right]p_{pr}^2 + \frac{0.32}{10^{9(T_{pr} - 1)}}p_{pr}^6,$$
$$C = (0.132 - 0.32\log T_{pr}),$$
$$D = 10^{(0.3106 - 0.49T_{pr} + 0.1824T_{pr}^2)}.$$

The oil volume factor B_o and solution gas/oil ratio R_s are best determined by laboratory experiments performed on reservoir fluid samples. Two limitations of experimental PVT data are cost and that measurements are only made at reservoir temperature. Generalized PVT correlations can also be used to estimate B_o and R_s when lacking better information. Standing's correlations (1942, 1981) are given here, but it should be noted that there are several alternative correlations available for specific oil types from different areas of the world.

The procedure suggested for using the generalized PVT correlations is as follows.

1. Record stock-tank oil gravity γ_o and its equivalent API gravity γ_{API}, average gas gravity γ_g, and producing gas/oil ratio R.

2. Calculate bubble-point pressure at the temperature being considered. This will determine whether the pressure being considered is above or below the bubble point, and therefore whether the oil is saturated or undersaturated. Standing's bubble-point correlation (1981) is

$$P_b = 18.2(W - 1.4),$$ (1.20)

where

$$W = (R_s/\gamma_g)^{0.83}10^{(0.00091\,T - 0.0125\gamma_{API})}.$$ (1.21)

3. If the pressure p being considered is less than p_b, then calculate the amount of gas in solution, R_s:

$$R_s = \gamma_g(1.4 + p/18.2)^{1.205}10^{(0.0151\gamma_{API} - 0.0011\,T)}.$$ (1.22)

If the pressure p being considered is greater than p_b, then $R_s = R$. That is, the solution gas/oil ratio equals the producing gas/oil ratio, and undersaturated oil compressibility c_o must be calculated. The Vazquez (1977) correlation for c_o is

$$c_o = 10^{-5}[-1433.0 + 5.0R_s + 17.2T - 1180.0\gamma_g + 12.61\gamma_{API}]/p.$$ (1.23)

4. Calculate the oil formation volume factor B_o. If the oil is *saturated* (i.e., $R > R_s$ or $R = R_s$), then calculate B_o using Standing's correlation:

$$B_{ob} = 0.9759 + 12 \times 10^{-5}Y^{1.2},$$ (1.24)

where

$$Y = 1.25T + R_s(\gamma_g/\gamma_o)^{1/2}.$$ (1.25)

If the oil is *undersaturated* ($R < R_s$), then calculate B_o using

$$B_o = B_{ob}\exp[c_o(p_b - p)],$$ (1.26)

where B_{ob} is the oil volume factor at the bubble-point pressure, calculated from the Standing correlation (eq. [1.24]) using $R_s = R$.

Some useful relations for density of oil, water, liquid, and mixtures are given to help solve problems in the following chapters.

$$\rho_o = [62.4\gamma_{STO} + 0.0136\gamma_g R_s]/B_o, \tag{1.27}$$

$$\rho_w = 62.4\gamma_w/B_w, \tag{1.28}$$

$$\rho_L = [62.4(\gamma_{STO} + \gamma_w F_{wo}) + 0.0136\gamma_g R]/(B_o + B_w F_{wo}), \tag{1.29}$$

$$\rho_m = [62.4(\gamma_{STO} + \gamma_w F_{wo}) + 0.0136\gamma_g R]/ \\ [B_o + B_w F_{wo} + (R - R_s)B_g/5.615], \tag{1.30}$$

where ρ has a unit of lbm/ft^3, γ_g is for air $= 1$, γ_{STO} and γ_w are for distilled water $= 1$, F_{wo} has a unit of STBW/STB), R and R_s have units of scf/STB, B_g has a unit of ft^3/scf, and both B_o and B_w have units of bbl/STB.

In equations (1.21)–(1.25), temperature T is given in °F, pressure in psia, gas/oil ratio in scf/STB, and other terms are in oilfield units. Example 1.3 illustrates the use of the standard PVT correlations given previously. Example 1.4 shows the use of PVT properties to calculate no-slip liquid holdup (liquid volume fraction) E_L and apparent two-phase density. To complete the discussion of PVT property application, example 1.5 is given to illustrate how the meter factor for high-pressure liquid metering equipment can be estimated. The meter factor is actually nothing more than a shrinkage factor indicating the change in oil volume from the metering station (usually downstream from the separator) to the stock tank. It is easily shown that the shrinkage equals the reciprocal of the oil volume factor. A word of caution: do not confuse the calibration coefficient for a specific meter (provided by the manufacturing company) with the oil shrinkage factor. Both corrections must be applied to the flowmeter readings.

In conclusion, we emphasize the importance of understanding and applying PVT data to well performance calculations. The simple correlations in this section have been presented to help estimate the more important PVT properties, including volume factors and solution gas/oil ratio.

EXAMPLE 1.3 ESTIMATING PVT PROPERTIES

Use the Standing PVT correlations to answer the following questions about the Hobart No. 1 initial well test.

1. Determine if the fluid entering the wellbore is a two-phase oil/water mixture or a three-phase gas/oil/water mixture.
2. Calculate the liquid flow rate at the wellbore flowing pressure of 2800 psia.
3. Calculate the mixture density of the fluid entering the wellbore.

SOLUTION

1. To determine if the mixture flowing into the wellbore is all liquid it is necessary to estimate the bubble-point pressure of the oil. If bubble-point pressure is less

EXAMPLE 1.3 continued

than the flowing wellbore pressure (2800 psia), then the oil is undersaturated and the mixture is oil/water. Using equations (1.20) and (1.21), bubble-point pressure is

$$W = (472/0.703)^{0.83}\{10^{[0.00091(160) - 0.0125(28)]}\} = 138.7$$

and

$$p_b = 18.2(138.7 - 1.4)$$

$$= 2498\,\text{psia},$$

which indicates undersaturated oil and an oil/water mixture.

2. To calculate the liquid flow rate at the wellbore flowing pressure of 2800 psia, it is necessary to estimate the oil formation volume factor (FVF). We will assume the water FVF is equal to unity. Standing's correlation (eq. [1.24]) is used to calculate the bubble-point oil FVF, B_{ob}, at 2498 psia:

$$Y = 1.25(160) + 472(0.703/0.863)^{0.5} = 626$$

and

$$B_{ob} = 0.9759 + 12 \times 10^{-5}(626)^{1.2}$$

$$= 1.248\,\text{bbl/STB}.$$

Undersaturated oil compressibility c_o is estimated from equation (1.23):

$$c_o = 10^{-5}[-1433.0 + 5.0(472) + 17.2(160) - 1180.0(0.703) + 12.61(28)]/2498.0$$

$$= 12.8 \times 10^{-6}\,1/\text{psi}.$$

Equation (1.26) is used to calculate the undersaturated oil FVF, B_o:

$$B_o = 1.248\exp[12.8 \times 10^{-6}(2498 - 2800)]$$

$$= 1.243\,\text{bbl/STB}.$$

The oil rate at the wellbore is

$$q_o B_o = (217\,\text{STB/D})(1.243\,\text{bbl/STB})$$

$$= 270.0\,\text{bbl/D},$$

and the water rate

$$q_w B_w = (q_o F_{wo})B_w$$

EXAMPLE 1.3 continued

$$= (217)(0.07)(1.00)$$

$$= 15.2\,\text{bbl/D},$$

giving a total liquid rate at the wellbore of

$$q_t(p_{wf}) = 270.0 + 15.2$$

$$= 285.2\,\text{bbl/D}.$$

3. Mixture density is for a two-phase water/oil fluid. Water density is assumed equal to $64.0\,\text{lbm/ft}^3$, or an equivalent specific gravity of 1.026, and water FVF is assumed equal to unity. Oil density is calculated from equation (1.27):

$$\rho_o = [62.4(0.863) + 0.0136(0.703)(472)]/1.243$$

$$= 46.9\,\text{lbm/ft}^3.$$

The mixture density lies between oil and water densities. Since $\rho_m = \rho_L$, mixture density is given by equation (1.29):

$$\rho_m = \{0.0136(0.703)(472) + 62.4[0.863 + 1.026(0.07)]\}/ \\ \{[1.243 + 1.0(0.07)]\}$$

$$= 352.5/7.372$$

$$= 47.8\,\text{lbm/ft}^3.$$

EXAMPLE 1.4 PREPARING DATA FOR TWO-PHASE FLOW COMPUTATIONS

Calculate the following, given the wellhead flowing conditions in example 1.2 for the Hobart No. 1 well:

1. wellhead oil rate
2. wellhead liquid rate
3. wellhead gas rate
4. liquid volume fraction (no-slip holdup) at the wellhead
5. average mixture density at the wellhead

SOLUTION

1. To calculate oil rate at the wellhead conditions (800 psia and 120°F), it is first necessary to estimate oil formation volume factor, B_{owh}. Using Standing's correlation, the bubble-point pressure at 120°F is estimated.

EXAMPLE 1.4 continued

$$W = (427/0.703)^{083} \times 10^{[0.00091(120) - 0.0125(28)]} = 127.5,$$

$$p_b(120°F) = 18.2(127.5 - 1.4)$$

$$= 2295 \text{ psia},$$

which indicates that the oil is saturated at 800 psia and a substantial amount of gas has been liberated. The gas remaining in solution is estimated from equation (1.22):

$$R_s = 0.703(1.4 + 800/18.2)^{1.205} \times 10^{[0.0151(28) - 0.0011(120)]}$$

$$= 136 \text{ scf/STB}.$$

Free gas is merely the initial solution gas (472 scf/STB) less the remaining gas in solution, or $472 - 136 = 336$ scf/STB. The FVF of the saturated oil, B_o, is estimated from equations (1.24) and (1.25):

$$Y = 1.25(120) + 136(0.703/0.863)^{0.5} = 272.7$$

and

$$B_o = 0.9759 + 12 \times 10^{-5}(272.7)^{1.2}$$

$$= 1.076 \text{ bbl/STB}.$$

Then oil rate at wellhead conditions is

$$q_o B_o = 217(1.076)$$

$$= 233.5 \text{ bbl/D}.$$

2. Water rate at wellhead conditions, assuming water FVF of 1.0, equals stock-tank water rate, which is merely 7% of the oil rate, or

$$q_w B_w = F_{wo} q_o$$

$$= 0.07(217)$$

$$= 15.2 \text{ bbl/D}.$$

Thus the total liquid rate is

$$q_L = q_o B_o + q_w B_w = 233.5 + 15.2 = 248.7 \text{ bbl/D}.$$

3. Gas rate at the wellhead is calculated from the liberated gas/oil ratio, $R - R_s$, oil rate q_o, and gas FVF at wellhead conditions. Gas FVF is given by equation

EXAMPLE 1.4 continued

(1.14), but requires an estimate of the gas compressibility factor Z. Using a gas gravity of 0.703, the estimated pseudocritical properties are given by the condensate correlations, equations (1.17) and (1.18):

$p_{pcm} = 664.2\,\text{psia}$,

$T_{pcm} = 383.6°\text{R}$,

resulting in pseudoreduced properties at 800 psia and 120°F,

$p_{pr} = 800/664.2 = 1.204$,

$T_{pr} = (120 + 460)/383.6 = 1.512$.

Substituting p_{pr} and T_{pr} in eq. (1.19) gives

$Z = 0.887$,

and the gas FVF is calculated from equation (1.14):

$B_g = 0.02827(120 + 460)(0.887)/800$

$ = 0.0182\,\text{ft}^3/\text{scf}$.

The gas rate at wellhead conditions, then, is

$q_g B_g = q_o(R - R_s) B_g$

$ = 217(472 - 136)(0.0182)$

$ = 1327\,\text{ft}^3/\text{D}$

$ = 236.3\,\text{bbl/D}$.

4. The liquid volume fraction (no-slip holdup) is given by equation (1.3), which requires total liquid and gas rates at specified conditions of pressure and temperature (800 psia and 120°F). Total liquid rate at the wellhead is 233.5 (oil) plus 15.2 (water), or 248.7 bbl/D. Gas rate at the wellhead is 236.3 bbl/D. Then liquid volume fraction is

$E_L = 248.7/(248.7 + 236.3)$

$ = 0.513$

$ = 51.3\%$.

5. The average mixture density is given by equation (1.30):

EXAMPLE 1.4 continued

$$\rho_m = \{0.0136(0.703)(472) + 62.4[0.863 + 1.026(0.07)]\}/$$
$$[1.243 + 1.0(0.07) + (472 - 136)0.0182/5.615]$$

$$= 352.5/13.49$$

$$= 26.1 \, \text{lbm/ft}^3.$$

EXAMPLE 1.5 CALCULATING THE METER FACTOR FOR HIGH-PRESSURE LIQUID METERING EQUIPMENT

The oil handling system of the Hobart No. 1 consists of a primary separator at 350 psia and 90°F followed by continuous transfer and metering into an oil pipeline. Because of title problems and offset pooling orders, the development of the Hobart field will be postponed as much as two years. This means that only the Hobart No. 1 will produce during this period.

A capacitance probe will be installed to monitor water cut (BS & W) and divert the wellstream to holding tanks in the event that water fraction exceeds 0.5%. Sales are based on a stock-tank barrel price, and the meter rates at separator conditions must be converted accordingly. Suggest a method for computing the oil rate in STB/D, based on liquid meter readings.

SOLUTION

The solution to the present problem is similar to the solution given in part 1 of example 1.2. The stock-tank oil rate q_o is

$$q_o = q_{Lsp}/[B_{osp} + F_{wo}].$$

It is necessary to determine B_{osp} and to meter liquid separator rate and water/oil ratio continuously. Instead of water/oil ratio, however, the capacitance probe measures water cut, f_w, at the prevailing conditions in the metering device. The definition of f_w is

$$f_w = q_w B_w/(q_w B_w + q_o B_o).$$

Assuming $B_w = 1$, it is easily shown that the relation of f_w to F_{wo} is

$$F_{wo} = B_o/(1/f_w - 1),$$

which, when substituted into the relation for oil rate q_o, is

$$q_o = q_{Lsp}(1 - f_w)/B_{osp}.$$

The Standing correlations can be used to estimate B_{osp}. First, the bubble point at 90°F is estimated with equations (1.20) and (1.21):

29

EXAMPLE 1.5 continued

$$W = (472/0.703)^{0.83}[10^{0.00091(90)-0.0125(28)}] = 119.8$$

$$p_b(90°F) = 18.2(119.8 - 1.4)$$

$$= 2155\,\text{psia},$$

which confirms that the oil is saturated at separator conditions of 350 psia and 90°F. The gas remaining in solution after separation is estimated from equation (1.22):

$$R_s = 0.703(1.4 + 350/18.2)^{1.205} \times 10^{[0.0151(28)-0.0011(90)]} = 56.8\,\text{scf/STB}$$

Saturated oil FVF is estimated from equation (1.24):

$$Y = 1.25(90) + 56.8(0.89/0.863)^{0.5} = 170$$

and

$$B_{osp} = 0.9759 + 12 \times 10^{-5}(170)^{1.2} = 1.033\,\text{bbl/STB}.$$

Thus, liquid volumes measured at the meters should be multiplied by $(1 - f_w)$ and divided by 1.033 to obtain the stock-tank oil volumes.

Note that equation (1.21) can be applied only for saturated oil. This condition should be checked before using R_s calculated by this equation.

If the calculated R_s is greater than the surface gas/oil ratio, then the oil is undersaturated at the considered pressure and temperature. The R_s of an undersaturated oil is then equal to producing GOR.

1.3 **RESERVOIR INFLOW PERFORMANCE.** Development of the bottomhole pressure gauge in the late 1920s led to the practice of testing wells by simultaneous measurement of surface production rate and bottomhole pressure. The obvious reason for testing a well is to determine what the production rate will be if a certain backpressure is exerted at the wellhead. Since the early days of testing wells, most efforts have concentrated on the formulation of simple equations expressing the relation between surface rate q and bottomhole flowing pressure p_{wf}, over the practical range of production conditions. The expression *inflow performance relation* (IPR) customarily is used to define the relation between surface oil rate and wellbore flowing pressure. Another expression, *backpressure curve*, is commonly used by engineers dealing with the performance of gas wells. *Bottomhole flowing pressure*, P_{wf}, used in the IPR and backpressure equations, is usually expressed at the depth of mid perforations. In this book the term bottomhole flowing pressure is used interchangeably with the term *wellbore flowing pressure*.

Perhaps the simplest and most widely used IPR equation is the *straight-line* IPR, which states that rate is directly proportional to pressure drawdown in the reservoir. The constant of proportionality is called the *productivity index, J*, defined

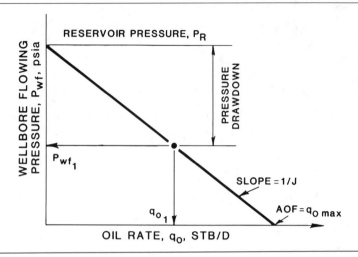

Figure 1.11 Straight-line IPR.

as the ratio of rate to pressure drop in the reservoir. Nowadays, the straight-line IPR is only used for undersaturated oils, so we can write the equation as

$$q_o = J(p_R - p_{wf}),$$ (1.31)

where p_R is the average pressure in the volume of the reservoir being drained by the well. It is not uncommon to use initial reservoir pressure, p_i, or pressure at the external boundary of the drainage area, p_e, instead of P_R, the difference is inevitably small and can be neglected.

Figure 1.11 shows a plot of the straight-line IPR. Several important features of the straight-line IPR can be seen in figure 1.11:

1. By convention, the dependent variable rate defines the x axis and the independent variable, wellbore flowing pressure, defines the y axis.
2. When wellbore flowing pressure equals average reservoir pressure (sometimes referred to as static pressure), rate is zero and no flow enters the wellbore due to the absence of any pressure drawdown.
3. Maximum rate of flow, q_{max}, or *absolute open flow*, AOF, corresponds to wellbore flowing pressure equal to zero. Although in practice this may not be a condition at which the well can produce, it is a useful definition and has widespread usage in the petroleum industry, particularly for comparing the performance or potential of different wells in the same field.
4. The slope of the straight line equals the reciprocal of the productivity index (slope = $1/J$).

Example 1.6 illustrates the construction and use of the straight-line IPR.

EXAMPLE 1.6 STRAIGHT-LINE IPR CALCULATION

The Lamar No. 1 was tested for eight hours at a rate of about 38 STB/D. Wellbore flowing pressure was calculated to be 585 psia, based on acoustic liquid level measurements. After shutting the well in for 24 hours, the bottomhole pressure reached a static value of 1125 psia, also based on acoustic level readings. The rod pump used on this well is considered undersized, and a larger pump can be expected to reduce wellbore flowing pressure to a level near 350 psia (just above the bubble-point pressure). Calculate the following:

1. productivity index J
2. absolute open flow based on a constant productivity index
3. oil rate for a wellbore flowing pressure of 350 psia
4. wellbore flowing pressure required to produce 60 STB/D

Draw the IPR curve on Cartesian coordinate paper, indicating the calculated quantities.

SOLUTION

1. The productivity index J is calculated from equation (1.32), giving

    $J = 38/(1125 - 585)$

    $= 0.0704\,\text{STB/D/psi.}$

2. Absolute open flow is merely $q_{o\max} = Jp_R$, or

    $q_{o\max} = 0.0704(1125)$

    $= 79.2\,\text{STB/D.}$

3. The rate that can be expected from a flowing wellbore pressure of 350 psia is

    $q_o = 0.0704(1125 - 350)$

    $= 54.6\,\text{STB/D.}$

4. The wellbore flowing pressure providing a rate of 60 STB/D is

    $p_{wf} = 1125 - 60/0.0704$

    $= 273\,\text{psia.}$

    Figure E1.6 is a plot of the IPR curve. It also indicates the calculated quantities.

EXAMPLE 1.6 continued

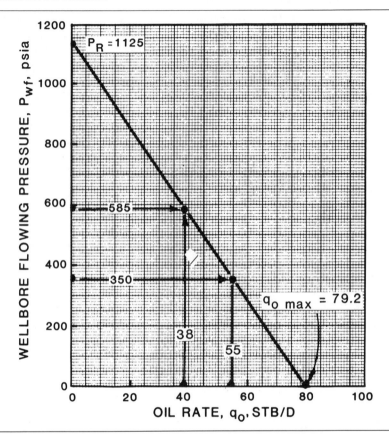

Figure E1.6 The IPR curve of the Lamar No. 1 oil well.

The straight-line IPR can be derived using Darcy's law and certain simplifying assumptions about rock and fluid properties. Field observation shows conclusively that, for undersaturated oil wells (and water wells), equation (1.31) applies with the accuracy needed for well performance calculations. The productivity index as a concept is very useful for describing the relative potential of a well. It combines all rock and fluid properties, as well as geometrical considerations, into a single constant, thus making it unnecessary to consider these properties individually. A constant productivity index states that the ratio of rate to pressure drop is always the same for varying rates:

$$J = \frac{q_{o1}}{p_R - p_{wf1}} = \frac{q_{o2}}{p_R - p_{wf2}} = \cdots = \frac{q_o}{p_R - p_{wf}}. \tag{1.32}$$

Units of J are STB/D/psi if the rate is given in STB/D and pressure in psia.

It is important to realize that the concept of stable inflow performance, and constant productivity in particular, assumes the condition of *pseudosteady state* (pss). Simply stated, pss represents the condition when the entire drainage volume of a well contributes to production. A certain time is usually required to reach the condition of pseudosteady state. However, in high-permeability formations, pss is reached almost instantaneously. Figure 1.12A shows well behavior during a multirate test in a reservoir with high permeability.

In low-permeability formations the pss condition may not be reached for years. The time before reaching pss conditions is often referred to as *infinite-acting* flow, indicating that the well responds as if it were in an infinite reservoir. Figure 1.12B shows the response of pressure during a multirate test for a well producing from a lower-permeability formation (compare with fig. 1.12A). The duration of infinite-acting flow may last years in some tight oil and gas wells, in which case the concept of stabilized IPR loses its practical application.

A limitation on the straight-line IPR is the assumption that oil is undersaturated, that is, only slightly compressible. Obviously, this condition does not apply to gases or saturated oil wells (which evolve considerable amounts of gas), both of which are highly compressible. The effect of compressible gas and two-phase flow on IPR was observed in the 1920s and 1930s during field testing. Instead of linear rate increase with pressure drawdown, it was observed that larger-than-linear pressure drops were required to increase the rate. The rate pressure relation shows curvature pronounced at higher rates. In terms of productivity index, J decreases with increasing drawdown. Figure 1.13 illustrates the continuous variation in J with drawdown. Note that J is not represented by the tangent to the rate pressure curve, but is defined as $J = q_o/(p_R - p_{wf})$.

Several equations have been suggested to represent the nonlinear IPR resulting from gas and two-phase flow. The observations of Bureau of Mines engineers resulted in the simple but accurate relation

$$q = C(p_R^2 - p_{wf}^2)^n \qquad (1.33)$$

for both gas and saturated oil wells. The exponent n ranges in value from 0.5 to 1.0. A plot of rate versus $p_R^2 - p_{wf}^2$ (written Δp^2 in shorthand) on log–log paper results in a straight line with slope $1/n$. Note that q is defined along the x axis and Δp^2 along the y axis (by convention), as shown in figure 1.14. Equation (1.33), often referred to as the *backpressure equation*, generally has been accepted for gas wells. It has yet to receive widespread use for oil wells, even though Fetkovich (1973) reconfirmed its general application to oil wells. Example 1.7 shows the use of equation (1.33) for describing the inflow performance of a gas well.

An IPR equation traditionally used to describe oilwell performance in saturated oil reservoirs is the Vogel (1968) equation

$$q_o/q_{o\max} = 1 - 0.2(p_{wf}/p_R) - 0.8(p_{wf}/p_R)^2, \qquad (1.34)$$

where $q_{o\max}$ is the maximum oil rate (AOF) when wellbore flowing pressure, p_{wf}, equals zero. Vogel's equation is a best-fit approximation of numerous simulated well performance calculations. Figure 1.15 shows a Cartesian plot of equation (1.34). No field verification is given by Vogel, although his equation is very simple to use, as illustrated in example 1.8.

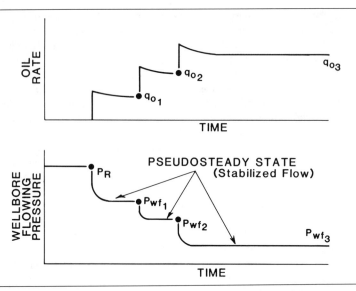

Figure 1.12a Rapid pseudosteady-state response of a well tested with a multirate sequence.

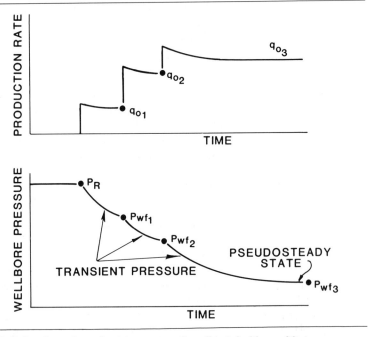

Figure 1.12b Delayed pseudosteady-state response of a well tested with a multirate sequence.

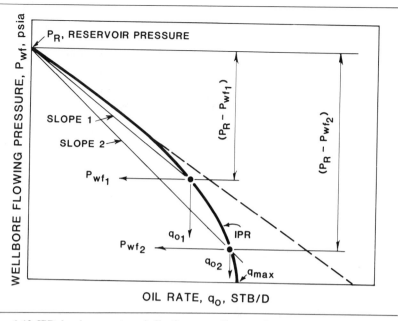

Figure 1.13 IPR showing curvature, indicating gas and/or two-phase flow.

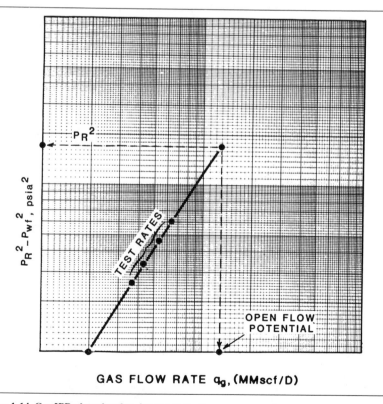

Figure 1.14 Gas IPR plotted on log–log paper (backpressure curve).

EXAMPLE 1.7 MULTIRATE GASWELL TEST TO DETERMINE INFLOW
PERFORMANCE

The Elk City No. 3 produced gas from the Red Fork formation at rates varying
from 1.0 to 5.5 MMscf/D during a four-point multirate isochronal test. Table E1.7
gives results of that test.

Tasks
1. Calculate the backpressure slope n by plotting rate versus the change in pressure
   squared (q_g vs. Δp^2) on log–log paper.
2. Determine the IPR constant C in equation (1.33) from the log–log plot, and
   then calculate the absolute open flow (i.e., calculated maximum rate).

SOLUTION
1. The log–log plot of rate versus change in pressure squared is shown in figure
   E1.7. The slope of the curve is about 1.61, which gives a value for n of 0.62
   ($=1/1.61$). The slope of a line on log–log paper is measured most easily with a
   ruler. Choose two points on the curve, measure the vertical and horizontal
   distance in, say, centimeters, Δy and Δx, then take the ratio of Δy to Δx
2. Having calculated the value of n, the constant C is easily found by choosing an
   arbitrary point from the straight line (it does not necessarily need to be one of
   the measured points). Substitute the rate and difference in pressure squared into
   equation (1.33) and then calculate C directly:

$$C = q/(p_R^2 - p_{wf}^2)^n$$

$$= 2.0(10^6)/[8(10^5)]^{0.62}$$

$$= 438 \, \text{scf/D/psi}^{1.24},$$

which gives

$$q_g = 438(p_R^2 - p_{wf}^2)^{0.62},$$

or in dimensionless form (see eq. [1.35]),

$$q_g/q_{g\text{max}} = [1 - (p_{wf}/p_R)^2]^{0.62},$$

where $q_{g\text{max}} = Cp_R^{2n} = 438(3355)^{1.24} = 10.3 \, \text{MMscf/D}$.

EXAMPLE 1.7 continued

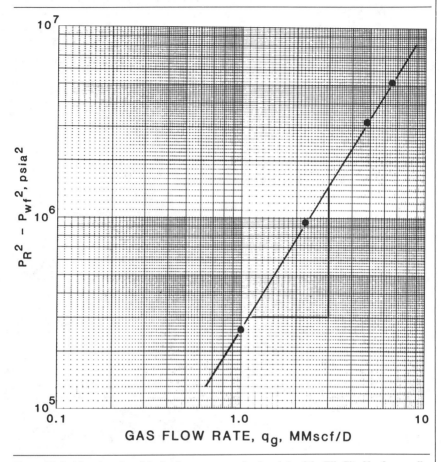

Figure E1.7 A log–log plot of the back pressure production data of the Elk City No. 3 gas well.

Table E1.7 Multirate Data for the Elk City No. 3 Well

Point	p_{wf} (psia)	$p_R^2 - p_{wf}^2$ (psi^2)	q_g (MMscf/D)
S.I.	3355	0.000	0.000
1	3314	0.273×10^6	1.012
2	3208	0.965×10^6	2.248
3	2992	2.304×10^6	3.832
4	2651	4.228×10^6	5.480

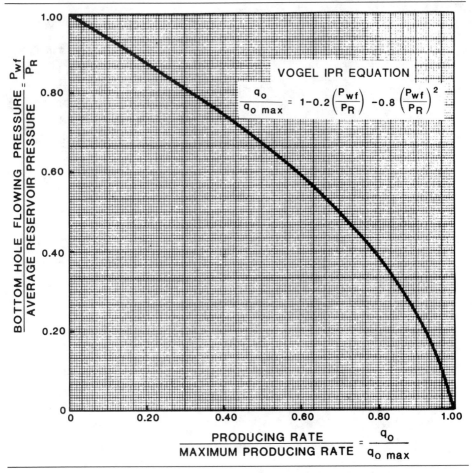

Figure 1.15 Vogel IPR for saturated oil wells. Reprinted by permission of the SPE-AIME from Vogel 1968, fig. 5, p. 243. © 1968 SPE-AIME.

EXAMPLE 1.8 USE OF VOGEL'S IPR EQUATION

A discovery well, the Haskell No. 3, was tested in the Viola Sand at a rate of 200 STB/D with a bottomhole flowing pressure of 3220 psia. Bubble-point pressure was calculated with a correlation using surface data measured when the well was producing at a low rate. The estimated bubble point of 3980 psia indicates that the well is draining saturated oil, since initial reservoir pressure was measured at 4000 psia. Plot the IPR using the Vogel equation.

SOLUTION

First, calculate the maximum oil rate, $q_{o\max}$, by substituting the test data into the Vogel equation:

$$q_{o\max} = 200/[1 - 0.2(3220/4000) - 0.8(3220/4000)^2]$$

$$= 625 \, \text{STB/D}.$$

Now calculate several rates at specified drawdowns to have enough points to plot the IPR. Table E1.8 gives a few calculated values for this example. Figure E1.8 shows the plot of the IPR using only the preceding points.

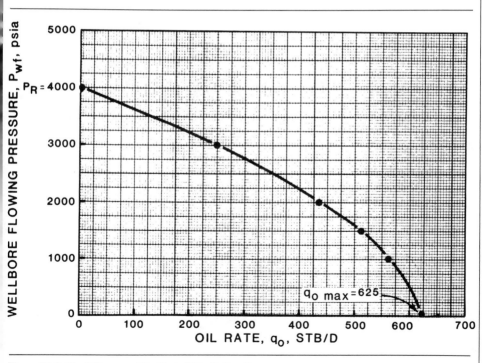

Figure E1.8 The IPR curve of the Haskell No. 8 oil well.

EXAMPLE 1.8 continued

Table E1.8 Inflow Performance Data for the Haskell No. 3 Well

p_{wf} (psia)	q_o (STB/D)
4000	0
3000	250
2000	437
1500	508
1000	562

Perhaps Vogel's principal contribution was the idea of normalizing the IPR equation and including the AOF (q_{omax}) as the primary constant to be determined. In fact, if equation (1.33) had been written in the same form as equation (1.34) in the late 1920s when it was suggested, then it would be obvious that Vogel's equation is substantiated by field observations. We consider the normalized form of equation (1.33)

$$q_o/q_{omax} = [1 - (p_{wf}/p_R)^2]^n. \tag{1.35}$$

as a better alternative than Vogel's equation for saturated oil wells because it is simpler and it considers the effect of high-velocity (non-Darcy, turbulent) flow through the inclusion of exponent n.

It is easily shown that equations (1.34) (Vogel) and (1.35) are nearly identical if $n = 1$, as was first noted by Fetkovich (1973). For $n = 1$, equation (1.35) becomes

$$q_o/q_{omax} = 1 - (p_{wf}/p_R)^2. \tag{1.36}$$

This equation is only slightly different from Vogel's, somewhat more conservative but simpler and easier to use. Most of all, it is based on field observations. In this book we will consider equation (1.36) as the basic working IPR equation for saturated oil wells. If multirate data are available, then equation (1.35) is preferred, since it includes the effect of high-velocity (turbulent) flow, a factor important for high-rate wells. A logarithmic plot of q_o versus Δp^2 (just as for gas multirate tests) will result in a straight line with a slope of $1/n$. Example 1.9 illustrates the analysis of a multirate oilwell test, using the general IPR equation for saturated oil wells (eq. [1.35]).

EXAMPLE 1.9 MULTIRATE TEST ANALYSIS OF A SATURATED OIL WELL

In 1931 a paper by Millikan and Sidewell gave multirate test data for a well producing from the Hunton Lime in the Carry City field in Oklahoma. These data are given in table E1.9a.

EXAMPLE 1.9   continued

Tasks

1. Calculate the productivity index J, based on the lowest four rates. What is the extrapolated maximum oil rate, based on the straight-line IPR assumption?
2. Plot the data on Cartesian coordinate paper. Use only point 10 (1260 STB/D, 1267 psia) to determine q_{omax} with the Vogel equation (eq. [1.34]). Plot and tabulate the calculated rates corresponding to the the bottomhole flowing pressure given in table E1.9a.
3. Repeat step 2 using the normalized backpressure equation (1.35) with $n = 1$ instead of the Vogel equation.
4. Plot the data on log–log paper to establish if equation (1.33) is valid. What are the constants C and n for this well?
5. Repeat step 2 using equation (1.35), with $n = 0.7$ instead of the Vogel equation. The value $n = 0.7$ is taken from the log–log plot in step 4. What is the calculated AOF?

SOLUTION

1. The values of J for each of the four lowest rates (235, 565, 610, and 720 STB/D) are 5.59, 5.48, 4.92, and 5.54 STB/D/psi. An average value is 5.4 STB/D/psi, resulting in a calculated maximum oil rate of 5.4 × 1600, or 8608 STB/D. Note that the measured rate at the lowest flowing pressure of 166 psia is only 2435 STB/D, which is much lower than predicted by the straight-line IPR (7715 STB/D).
2. Figure E1.9a is a Cartesian plot of the mulitrate data from table E1.9a. Using the Vogel equation and point 10, the calculated q_{omax} is 3706 STB/D. Table E1.9b lists the calculated rates and compares them with measured values given in table E1.9a. Figure E.19c plots the calculated IPR and compares it with the measured IPR.
3. Using point 10 and equation (1.35) with $n = 1$ results in a maximum oil rate, q_{omax} of 3379 STB/D, which is slightly lower than predicted by the Vogel equation. Table E1.9b compares the calculated rates with measured rates at the flowing pressures given in table E1.9a.
4. Figure E1.9b is a log–log plot of the multirate data. The constants in equation (1.33) obtained from the plot are $C = 0.08$ and $n = 0.7$.
5. Using equation (1.35) with $n = 0.7$ results in a maximum oil rate q_{omax} of 2513 STB/D, which is lower than predicted by either the Vogel equation or equation (1.35) with $n = 1$. Table E1.9b compares the calculated rates ($n = 0.7$) with measured rates at the flowing pressures given in table E1.9a. The calculated IPR is compared with the true IPR in Figure E1.9c.

   From this example we find that the Vogel equation and pressure-squared equation with $n = 1$ are not adequate to describe observed rate–pressure data. The pressure-squared equation with $n < 1$ gives an excellent fit of well test data for the Carry City well, substantiating numerous observations made by Fetkovich (1973) for high-rate oil wells.

EXAMPLE 1.9 continued

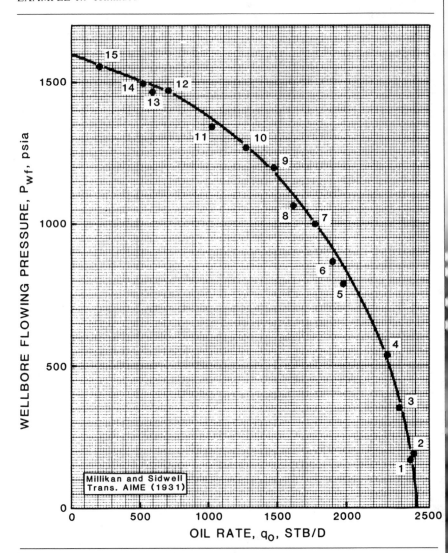

Figure E1.9a Production data recorded in an oil well in the Carry City field, Oklahoma. After Millikan and Sidewell 1931 by permission of Amerada Hess.

EXAMPLE 1.9 continued

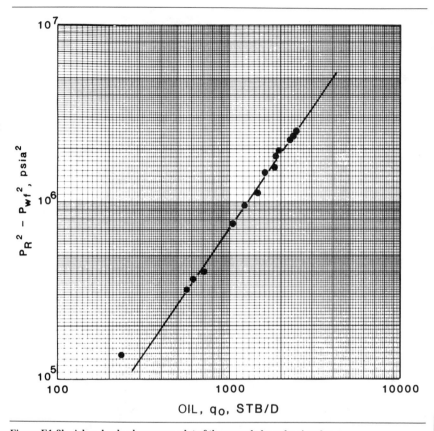

Figure E1.9b A log–log backpressure plot of the recorded production data.

Table E1.9a Multirate Data for a Carry City Well

Point	p_{wf} (psia)	q_o (STB/D)	Point	p_{wf} (psia)	q_o (STB/D)
1	166	2435	9	1194	1470
2	183	2460	10	1267	1260
3	351	2352	11	1342	1045
4	534	2260	12	1470	720
5	787	1965	13	1476	610
6	867	1895	14	1497	565
7	996	1765	15	1558	235
8	1066	1625	16	1600	0

Note: The actual rate sequence is different than indicated here. See Millikan and Sidwell (1930) for a discussion of the actual test sequence.

EXAMPLE 1.9 continued

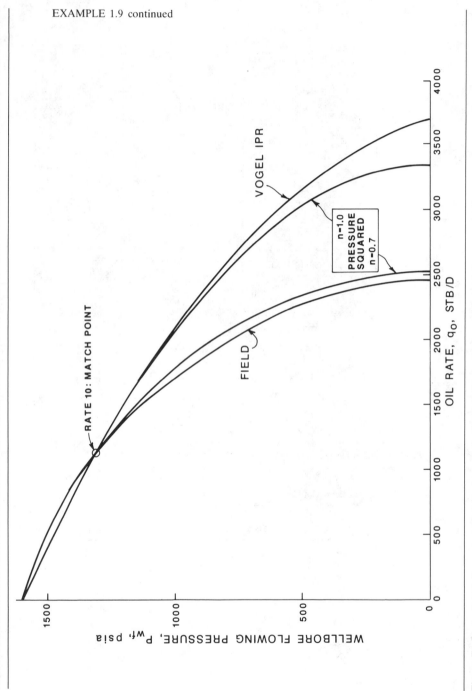

Figure E1.9c A plot of the measured data compared with Vogel's equation and the backpressure equation.

EXAMPLE 1.9 continued

Table E1.9b Calculated IPR Results for the Carry City Well

		q_o(STB/D)			
Point	p_{wf} (psia)	Field	Vogel	Pressure-Squared (Equation 1.35) ($n = 1.0$)	($n = 0.7$)
1	166	2435	3597	3343	2494
2	183	2460	3582	3335	2490
3	351	2353	3401	3216	2428
4	534	2260	3128	3003	2314
5	787	1965	2624	2561	2070
6	867	1895	2434	2387	1970
7	996	1765	2096	2070	1783
8	1066	1625	1896	1879	1667
9	1194	1470	1501	1497	1422
10	1267	1260	1260	1260	1260
11	1342	1045	999	1002	1073
12	1470	720	522	527	684
13	1476	610	499	503	663
14	1497	565	417	421	585
15	1558	235	173	175	316
16	1600	0	0	0	0

Note: Rate No. 10 was used to fit the Vogel and pressure-squared ($n = 1$) equations. The pressure-squared equation with $n = 0.7$ was fit using the complete test sequence and a backpressure plot.

Many oil wells produce from reservoirs with pressure above the bubble-point pressure but with wellbore flowing pressure below the bubble point. The IPR for such wells is illustrated in figure 1.16, showing a straight line at flowing pressures above the bubble point and curvature below. Considering only the straight-line region above the bubble point, for $p_b \leq p_{wf} \leq p_R$, the IPR equation is

$$q_o = J(p_R - p_{wf}).$$ (1.37)

If flowing pressures are below the bubble point, then the following IPR equation can be used:

$$q_o = J(p_R - p_b) + \left(\frac{J}{2p_b}\right)(p_b^2 - p_{wf}^2),$$ (1.38)

where J is the productivity index indicated by production when flowing pressure p_{wf} is above the bubble-point pressure p_b, given by equation (1.37). Example 1.10 illustrates the use of equations (1.37) and (1.38).

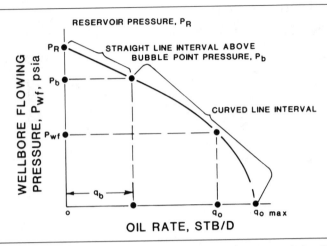

RESERVOIR PRESSURE, P_R

STRAIGHT LINE INTERVAL ABOVE
BUBBLE POINT PRESSURE, P_b

CURVED LINE INTERVAL

WELLBORE FLOWING PRESSURE, P_{wf}, psia

OIL RATE, STB/D

Figure 1.16 IPR of an undersaturated oil well producing at flowing pressure below the bubble point.

EXAMPLE 1.10 IPR CALCULATION FOR AN UNDERSATURATED OIL WELL PRODUCING AT FLOWING PRESSURES BELOW THE BUBBLE POINT

The Ardmore No. 5 well produced from an interval in the Oil Creek Sand at a rate of 108 STB/D with a bottomhole flowing pressure of 1980 psia. Surface samples were collected and sent to a PVT laboratory, which determined the bubble-point pressure of the recombined reservoir fluid to be 1825 psia at a temperature of 195°F. An initial reservoir pressure of 3620 psia was recorded during the 48-hour buildup following the flow test.

Tasks
1. Determine the undersaturated productivity index J that is valid if flowing bottomhole pressure is greater than the bubble point.
2. Calculate the oil rate if bottomhole flowing pressure is held at the bubble point to avoid gas blockage in the near-wellbore region.
3. Using equation (1.38), calculate the maximum oil rate that can be expected from the well.
4. Calculate and plot the IPR for the entire range of wellbore flowing pressures, both above and below the bubble point.

SOLUTION

1. The productivity index J is simply $108/(3620 - 1980)$, or $J = 0.066$ STB/D/psi. If wellbore flowing pressure had been below the bubble point, then equation (1.38) should be solved for J instead of using the definition of productivity index.

47

EXAMPLE 1.10 continued

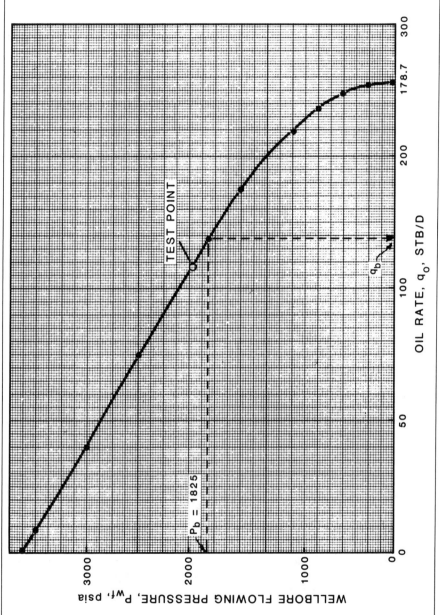

Figure E1.10 The IPR curve of the Ardmore No. 5 oil well.

EXAMPLE 1.10 continued

Table E1.10 Calculated IPR for the Ardmore No. 5 Well

p_{wf} (psia)	q_o (STB/D)	p_{wf} (psia)	q_o (STB/D)
3620	0.0	1500	138.1
3500	7.9	1000	160.7
3000	40.9	750	168.6
2500	73.9	500	174.3
2000	106.9	250	177.7
1825	118.5	0	178.7

2. The oil rate that can be expected if bottomhole flowing pressure equals the bubble-point pressure is

$$q_{ob} = 0.066(3620 - 1825)$$

$$= 118.5 \, \text{STB/D}.$$

3. The maximum oil rate q_{omax} expected from the well is not $J_{p_R} = 239 \, \text{STB/D}$, which is calculated by extrapolating the linear IPR to $p_{wf} = 0$. Rather, it is found by solving equation (1.38) when $p_{wf} = 0$:

$$q_{omax} = 0.066(3620 - 1825) + (0.066/2/1825)(1825)^2$$

$$= 118.5 + 60.2$$

$$= 178.7 \, \text{STB/D}.$$

4. Figure E1.10 shows the IPR plotted from the equation

$$q_o = 0.066(3620 - p_{wf}) \text{ for } p_{wf} > p_b = 1825 \, \text{psia},$$

$$q_o = 118.5 + 1.81(10^{-5})(1825^2 - p_{wf}^2) \text{ for } p_{wf} < p_b,$$

with several points as tabulated in table E1.10:

In summary, we have introduced basic aspects of inflow performance for gas and oil wells. Simple expressions for rate-pressure relationships were presented. The expressions were developed empirically from field observations for several types of production conditions. Theoretical background for inflow performance calculations is presented in chapter 2. The transient behavior of wells is discussed in chapter 4.

1.4   TUBING PERFORMANCE AND GRADIENT CURVES. The pressure drop required to lift a fluid through the production tubing at a given flow rate is one of the main factors determining the deliverability of a well. If therefore appears in most well performance calculations. First, we fix either the wellhead or bottomhole flowing pressure given the rates of oil, gas, and water. The pressure drop along the production tubing can be calculated by charts or correlations, and the resulting flowing pressure at the other end of the tubing can be determined. For example, if wellhead pressure is specified, then a *gradient curve* can be used to determine the wellbore flowing pressure at several different oil rates. The resulting relation between bottomhole flowing pressure and oil rate is called *tubing performance relation (TPR)*, and it is valid only for the specified wellhead pressure.

The pressure drop in tubing due to flow of homogeneous (single-phase) fluid can be calculated by conventional pipe flow equations. Gas and highly undersaturated oil wells come under this category. Just a small quantity of free gas mixed with oil and/or water creates considerably more complicated flow conditions which can be described only approximately by including empirical corrections to the conventional pipe flow equations. The tubing performance relationship of wells producing multiphase mixtures is therefore difficult to estimate with any accuracy.

For dry gas wells there are several methods for calculating pressure loss in vertical or inclined pipe. A simple and accurate equation for vertical flow of gas (Katz et al. 1959, p.306), which can be solved directly (i.e., without integration or trial and error), is

$$q_g = 200,000 \left[\frac{sD^5(p_{in}^2 - e^s p_{wh}^2)}{\gamma_g TZHf_M(e^s - 1)} \right]^{0.5}, \tag{1.39}$$

where

q_g = gas flow rate, scf/D,
Z = average gas compressibility factor,
T = average temperature, °R,
f_M = Moody friction factor,
γ_g = gas gravity, air = 1,
D = tubing diameter, in.,
p_{in} = flowing tubing intake pressure, psia,
p_{wh} = flowing wellhead pressure, psia,
H = vertical depth, ft,
s = $0.0375\gamma_g H/TZ$.

Average temperature is simply the arithmetic average between the temperatures at the wellhead and intake to the tubing (usually reservoir temperature). The average compressibility factor is evaluated at the average temperature and the arithmetic average between the flowing wellhead and intake pressures.

A valid assumption for most gas wells is that flow is turbulent, resulting in an expression for f_M that depends only on the relative roughness of the pipe:

$$f_M = \{2\log[3.71/(\varepsilon/D)]\}^{-2}, \tag{1.40}$$

where ε is the absolute pipe roughness and $\varepsilon = 0.0006$ in. for most commercial pipe. Equation (1.40) is the best-fit equation for the fully turbulent region of the Moody diagram and is sufficiently accurate for most engineering calculations.

The simplest application of equation (1.39) is for calculating a table of rate versus flowing intake pressure, given a fixed wellhead flowing pressure and pipe size. Example 1.11 illustrates the use of equations (1.39) and (1.40), assuming a fixed wellhead pressure. Higher wellhead pressures would result in tubing performance curves that shift upward and to the left, while lower wellhead pressures would shift the TPR down and to the right.

EXAMPLE 1.11 TUBING PERFORMANCE RELATION FOR A GAS WELL

The Elk City No. 3 well is to be produced into a high-pressure, gas-gathering line requiring a minimum wellhead pressure of about 800 psia. Available tubing has a 2⅞-in. nominal diameter (about a 2.5-in. inner diameter). Other relevant data for the well include:

vertical length of tubing	7250 ft
depth to midperforations	7310 ft
gas gravity	0.75 (air = 1)
average tubing temperature	120 °F
average gas Z-factor	0.78
pipe roughness	0.0006 in.

Use equation (1.39) to calculate the tubing performance relation of this well (up to the rate of 24 MMscf/D).

SOLUTION

The first step in calculating the approximate tubing performance relation is to determine s in equation (1.39):

$$s = 0.0375(0.75)(7300)/(120 + 460)(0.78)$$

$$= 0.454.$$

The Moody friction factor is estimated from equation (1.40):

$$f_M = \{2\log[3.71/(0.0006/2.5)]\}^{-2}$$

$$= 0.0142.$$

The approximate tubing performance relation then becomes

$$q_g = 9368(p_{in}^2 - 1.0 \times 10^6)^{0.5}.$$

A few values of intake flowing pressure are chosen, and table E1.11 gives the calculated flow rates corresponding to each pressure. Figure E1.11 is a plot of the rate pressure data in table E1.11.

EXAMPLE 1.11 continued

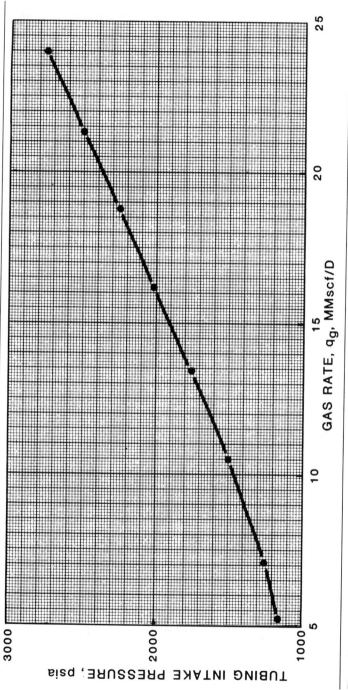

Figure E1.11 The tubing performance of the Elk City No. 3 gas well.

EXAMPLE 1.11 continued

Table E1.11 Calculated Tubing Performance Relation for the Elk City No. 3 Well

p_{in} (psia)	$p_R{}^2 - p_{in}{}^2$ (psi^2)	q_g (MMscf/D)	p_{in} (psia)	$p_R{}^2 - p_{in}{}^2$ (psi^2)	q_g (MMscf/D)
1150	9.9×10^6	5.32	2000	7.3×10^6	16.23
1250	9.7×10^6	7.03	2250	6.2×10^6	18.88
1500	9.0×10^6	10.47	2500	5.0×10^6	21.46
1750	8.2×10^6	13.45	2750	3.7×10^6	24.00

The approximate TPR equation (1.39) can be used only for dry gas. If water or condensate is produced as an entrained liquid phase (GOR greater than about 7000 scf/STB), then gas velocity must generally exceed 18 to 20 ft/s if equation (1.39) is to be used. At lower velocities it has been observed that liquid accumulates, thereby increasing pressure loss considerably above that calculated from equation (1.39). If velocity decreases to 10 to 12 ft/s, then the well will probably die. The reason for this is that equation (1.39) cannot be applied to gas condensate wells or water-producing gas wells with a gas/liquid ratio less than about 7000 scf/STB; gradient curves or multiphase correlations must be used instead.

Let us examine the pressure elements constituting the total pressure at the bottom of the tubing:

1. backpressure exerted at the surface from the choke and wellhead assembly (wellhead pressure)
2. hydrostatic pressure due to gravity and the elevation change between the wellhead and the intake to the tubing
3. friction losses, which include irreversible pressure losses due to viscous drag and slippage

Figure 1.17 illustrates the three components of pressure in a TPR curve for a single-phase liquid, a dry gas, and a two-phase gas/oil mixture. Additional pressure loss due to acceleration of an expanding fluid is usually insignificant when compared with the other losses and therefore neglected in most design calculations.

In the case of single-phase liquid (e.g., undersaturated oil or water), density is assumed constant and the hydrostatic pressure gradient (pressure loss per unit length) is a constant. Friction loss, on the other hand, is rate-dependent, characterized by two flow regimes—laminar and turbulent—separated by a transition zone. The rate dependence of friction-related pressure loss differs with the flow regime. At low rates the flow is laminar and the pressure gradient changes linearly with rate or flow velocity. At high rates the flow is turbulent and the pressure gradient increases more than linearly with increasing flow rate.

In gas wells, there is interdependence between flow rate, flow velocity, density and pressure. In general, increasing gas rate results in increasing total pressure loss as computed by equation (1.39).

In multiphase mixtures, friction-related and hydrostatic-pressure losses vary with rate in a much more complicated manner than for gas. Increasing rate may change

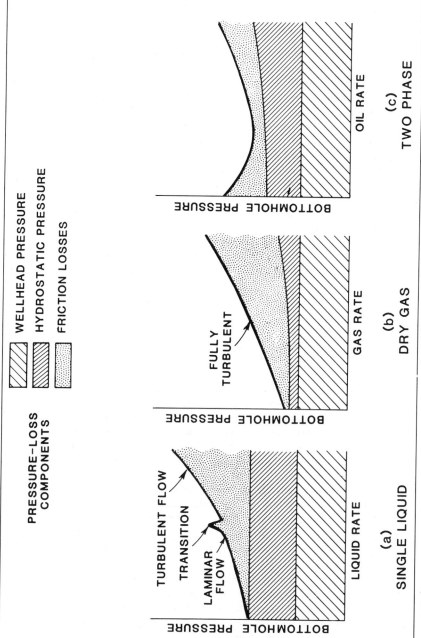

Figure 1.17 Components of pressure loss in tubing.

the governing pressure loss mechanism from predominantly gravitational to predominantly friction. The result of this shift is a change of trend in the TPR curve.

For a given flow rate, wellhead pressure, and tubing size, there is a particular pressure distribution along the tubing, starting its traverse at the wellhead pressure and increasing downward toward the intake to the tubing. The pressure–depth profile is called a *pressure traverse*, as shown in figure 1.18. Once again, we consider single-phase liquid flow, gas flow, and multiphase gas/oil flow separately.

In single-phase liquid, both gravitational and friction pressure gradients are constant along the tubing and therefore the pressure traverse is linear with depth. In gas, it is very nearly linear even though the friction and hydrostatic pressure gradients vary significantly with depth.

In multiphase mixtures there is general trend of increasing pressure gradient with depth. Unfortunately, we do not have analytical equations or simple procedures for calculating the pressure traverse of multiphase mixtures. Rather, there are numerous correlations based on field and experimental observations, which take the form of either generalized pressure versus distance curves, called gradient curves (e.g., Gilbert [1954]), or empirical pipe flow equations. A severe drawback of the correlations based on experimental data is that application to producing wells is limited to the conditions of rate, geometry, gas/oil ratio, and fluid properties used in the experimental study.

Multiphase pipeflow correlations can be classified into three broad categories:

1. gradient curves
2. homogeneous mixture correlations
3. flow regime correlations

Historically, the development of these engineering tools began with homogeneous mixture correlations, followed by the development of gradient curves based on field data, and finally the use of more sophisticated correlations based on the flow regime concept. Brown (1967), and a recent API handbook (1984) give excellent reviews of the history of multiphase pipe flow correlations. Although none of the existing correlations are accurate for all engineering purposes, it is generally believed that the list above indicates an increasing order of reliability. The list also indicates an increasing order of complexity, and therefore limited accessibility (small computing machines are needed for flow regime correlations, where programmable calculators are sufficient for homogeneous mixture correlations).

Gradient curves have the salient feature of being graphical, and thus are independent of the need for any computing device. Recently developed gradient curves are based on the flow regime correlations, and not on field data as originally proposed by Gilbert. Published gradient curves based on field data are generally limited to small and medium oil rates, but they generally cover wide ranges of gas/liquid ratios, these two parameters being the most important in gradient curve application. We have selected only a few gradient curves, to illustrate their use in solving well performance problems. They are taken from the original work by Gilbert (1954), who developed his correlations using light (25 to 45°API) crudes produced mainly from California fields, representing tubing sizes of 1.66, 1.90,

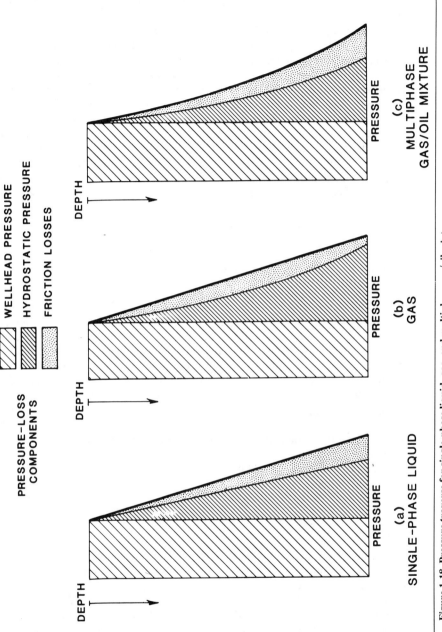

Figure 1.18 Pressure traverse for single-phase liquid, gas, and multiphase gas/oil mixture.

2.875, and 3.50 in. for oil flow rates from 50 to 600 STB/D and gas/liquid ratios of 0 and up. We include in Appendix A only the curves for 2.875-in. and 3.50-in. tubings.

Gilbert noted that the main parameters in vertical multiphase pipe flow are pipe diameter, oil rate, and gas/liquid ratio. Other parameters that might have an effect on pressure gradient include liquid surface tension, viscosity, densities (oil, gas, and water gravities), flowing temperature, gas/liquid solubility, and water cut. Gilbert also noted that his gradient curves would not apply if an emulsion formed in the tubing. It should be noted that pipe diameters usually reported on gradient curves are given in nominal size, representing the *outer* diameter and not the actual flow path (inner) diameter. Depending on the tubing specifications, the difference between nominal (outer) diameter and actual (inner) diameter varies according to the tubing weight, expressed in pounds per foot (lb/ft). Heavy tubing has a smaller inner diameter than light tubing. The difference in inner diameters for different weights is at most 7 to 8 percent. Example 1.12 illustrates the use of gradient curves.

EXAMPLE 1.12 HOW TO USE GRADIENT CURVES

The Okemah No. 1 produces from the Wapanuka formation at a depth of about 5000 ft. The oil is relatively heavy and contains little solution gas, thereby requiring gas lift to produce. Available tubing and gas-lift equipment from another lease can be used to test the success of artificial lift without investing in new equipment. The tubing is 3.5-in. nominal diameter. Preliminary calculations indicate that 1000 scf/STB gas can be injected at an economical cost. Added to the 200 scf/STB solution gas, this gives a total of 1200 scf/STB total GOR. Consider production at an oil rate of 200 STB/D. Assume that the gas is injected at the bottom of the tubing (the tubing shoe).

1. Determine the required tubing intake pressure if the wellhead is fixed at 500 psia.
2. Determine the available wellhead pressure when tubing intake pressure (located near the wellbore) is 2000 psia.

SOLUTION

First locate the gradient curve in Appendix A that corresponds to 3.5-in. nominal tubing diameter and an oil rate of 200 STB/D. Figure E1.12 is a reproduction of the gradient curve (fig. A-8).

1. Find 500 psia along the x axis at the top of the gradient curve. Place a straightedge vertically along the 500-psia grid. Move down until the GLR = 1200 scf/STB curve is found, and label this point A.
   Place the straightedge horizontally along the grid intersecting point A. This

57

EXAMPLE 1.12 continued

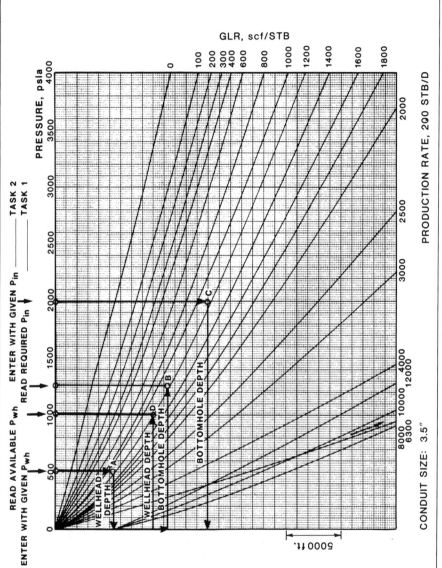

Figure E1.12 The use of a gradient curve to determine flowing bottomhole pressure and flowing wellhead pressure in an oil well. After Gilbert 1954 by permission of API.

EXAMPLE 1.12 continued

depth represents zero datum. Now add 5000 ft to the zero datum by moving downward. You may want to position the straightedge horizontally at this depth, which represents the intake to the tubing.

Locate the GLR = 1200 scf/STB curve that intersects the horizontal line representing the iⁿtake depth. Label this point B and move upward to the x-axis scale that gives the pressure at the tubing intake, 1250 psia.

2. Enter the x axis at 2000 psia, representing the tubing intake pressure. Move down vertically until the GLR = 1200 scf/STB curve is found. Label this point C.

Move upward a distance of 5000 ft and place the straightedge horizontally along the grid. Move horizontally to the left until the GLR = 1200 scf/STB curve is located and mark the intersection point D.

Move vertically upward to the x axis to read the pressure corresponding to the wellhead (5000 ft above the tubing intake), 1000 psia.

Four points about the use of gradient curves should be noted:

1. The vertical axis represents distance traveled vertically from a given point where the pressure is known. From a given point with known pressure it is possible to determine the pressure at any other point by moving along the gradient curve for a distance corresponding to the distance between the two points. Alternatively, if the pressure at the second point is known, it is possible to determine which distance corresponds to the pressure difference between the two points by moving along the gradient curve an interval corresponding to the pressure change between the two points.

2. The gradient dp/dH decreases with increasing gas/liquid ratio (GLR) until a minimum gradient is reached. Thereafter the trend reverses and dp/dH increases with increasing gas/liquid ratio. The physical reason for this is a change in the predominant pressure loss mechanism caused by an increasing gas/liquid ratio.

3. For convenience, the high-GLR gradient curves are shifted down on the depth scale to avoid intersection with lower-GLR curves.

4. If production is water-free, then gas/liquid ratio, GLR equals gas/oil ratio, GOR. Examples in the text generally assume water-free production, but if water/oil ratio, WOR, is reported, then the relation between GLR and GOR is GLR = GOR/(1 + WOR), or $F_{gL} = R/(1 + F_{wo})$, where F_{gL} is gas/liquid ratio (GLR), F_{wo} is water/oil ratio (WOR), and R is gas/oil ratio (GOR).

Figure 1.19 shows how to use a set of gradient curves to construct the tubing performance of an oil well producing through tubing with a given diameter and length at a specific gas/liquid ratio and wellhead pressure. The wellhead pressure is specified as a constant. Selecting a gradient curve with the specified GLR, we find the point where pressure equals wellhead pressure. Zero depth corresponds to this point. Moving down vertically a distance equal to the tubing length and then horizontally until the same GLR curve is reached, the bottomhole pressure is read on the x-axis scale. This pressure is the intake flowing pressure for the rate corresponding to the gradient curves chosen. Similarly, intake pressure is

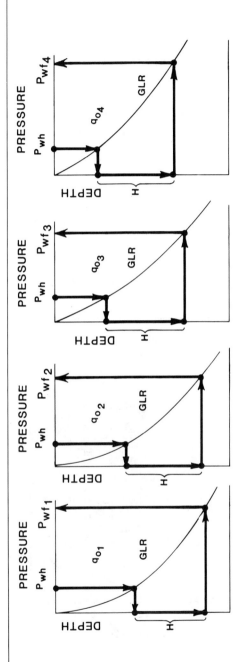

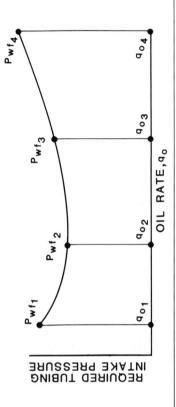

Figure 1.19 Construction of the tubing performance relation (TPR) using gradient curves.

determined for several other rates. The rate–intake pressure points are then plotted to form the tubing performance curve. Example 1.13 illustrates the procedure for using gradient curves.

EXAMPLE 1.13 CONSTRUCTING THE TUBING PERFORMANCE CURVE FOR AN OIL WELL

The Davis No. 3 produces from the Bromide Sand at a depth of 8000 ft. Solution gas/oil ratio is 600 scf/STB. Use of 3.5-in. nominal tubing is suggested by the production engineer, who claims there will be a need for gas life after only one to two years of production. Construct the present tubing performance curve, assuming a wellhead pressure of 200 psia.

SOLUTION

The 3.5-in. gradient curves are found in Appendix A. The procedure given for part 1 of example 1.12 should be followed for each flow rate and a constant wellhead pressure of 200 psia. The depth from wellhead to tubing intake is 8000 ft and approximately equals the total vertical depth of the Bromide formation. Results are given in table E1.13. These data are plotted in figure E1.13. Note the curvature and minimum at a rate of about 350 STB/D and an intake pressure of 1600 psia.

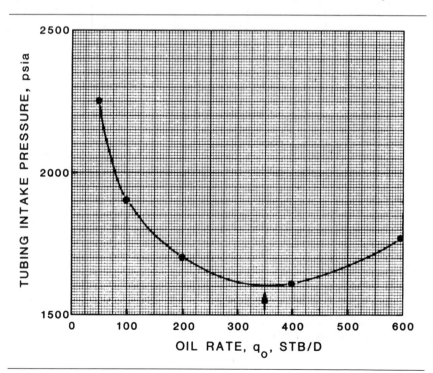

Figure E1.13   Tubing performance curve of the Davis No. 3 oil well.

EXAMPLE 1.13 continued

Table E1.13 Tubing Performance Data for the Davis No. 3 with Constant Wellhead Pressure of 200 psia

q_o (STB/D)	p_{in} (psia)
50	2250
100	1900
200	1700
400	1610
600	1760

Using a sheet of tracing paper can speed up the reading of data from the gradient curves and thus simplify the process of constructing TPRs. Referring to example 1.13, two horizontal lines representing zero depth and 8000 ft depth will be drawn on the tracing paper at a distance corresponding to 8000 ft on the depth scale of the gradient curves. The tracing paper will then be overlaid on the first gradient curve (i.e. 50 STB/D). Subsequently, the paper will be shifted with the two drawn depth lines kept parallel to the pressure axis of the gradient curve until the upper line intersects the well-head pressure point on the 600 scf/STB GLR line. At this position, the point of intersection obtained between the 8000 ft line (on the tracing paper) and the 600 GLR curve is the sought tubing input pressure. In a similar manner, the same tracing paper can be repeatedly overlaid on the 100, 200, 400, and 600 STB/D gradient curves to read the respective tubing inlet pressure and produce table E1.13.

When shifting the paper, it is important to ensure that the depth lines on the overlaid tracing paper are kept parallel to the depth lines of the gradient curve. Further speed-up can be achieved by adding two vertical lines, zero pressure and wellhead pressure (200 psia in example 1.13), to the tracing paper. Then, the matching of the zero depth line to the wellhead pressure point on the 600 scf/STB gradient curve is done by simply moving the tracing paper vertically, with the zero pressure line overlaying the depth-axis, until the zero-depth line intersects the gradient line. Note that the use of tracing paper for speed up of depth readings is possible only if all the gradient curves are of the same scale.

The TPR is valid only for a specific set of well data. Changing wellhead pressure, gas/liquid ratio, or tubing dimensions will change the tubing performance curve and will require construction of a new curve.

1.5   **NATURAL FLOW.** Based on only a few pieces of data, it is possible to calculate and plot both inflow and tubing performance relations. For the typical case when the tubing shoe (inlet) reaches the perforation depth, wellbore flowing pressure and tubing intake pressure are considered at the same depth. When at a specific rate these two pressures are equal, the flow system is in equilibrium and flow is stable.

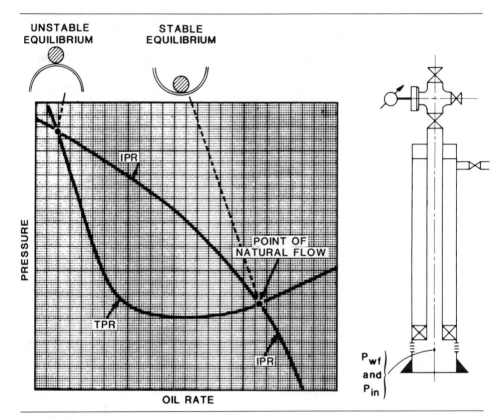

Figure 1.20 Natural flow condition.

The intersection of the IPR and TPR curves determines the rate of stable flow that can be expected from the particular well. At the wellbore (i.e., at perforation depth) the available pressure—wellbore flowing pressure—determined by the IPR equals the required pressure—tubing intake pressure—determined by the TPR. The equilibrium rate and pressure constitute what is called the *natural flow point*. The equilibrium rate is called the *natural flow rate*. Figure 1.20 illustrates the condition of natural flow, with a Cartesian plot of IPR and TPR curves.

If inflow and tubing performance relations had simple algebraic expressions, then the point of natural flow could be determined analytically, or perhaps by trial and error. Generally, graphical determination of natural flow is necessary because IPR and TPR may not have simple algebraic expressions. Also, graphical solution of natural flow is simple, and it illustrates the effect of differing conditions of flow such as depletion, changing GLR, and wellhead pressure.

As indicated in figure 1.20, there may be two points of intersection for multiphase mixtures. One represents a stable flow condition and the other an unstable one. The stable point of natural flow is to the right. By analogy it represents a ball locked in a concave circular container (having upward curvature). If the ball (i.e., rate) is pushed either to the left or right, then it will always return to its original point of equilibrium. The unstable point of natural flow is to the left. Once again by analogy, it represents a ball located on top of a convex surface (having downward curvature). If the ball is pushed to the right or left then it will continue its descent until a stable, upward-curving (or flat) surface is reached. Mathematically, the stable point of natural flow exists when the two performance relations intersect with slopes (i.e., derivatives) of opposite sign. If the two curves have slopes of similar sign at the point of intersection, then only a small change in rate will cause the system to change its state of equilibrium, either killing the well or moving it toward the stable point of natural flow. Graphical determination of stable natural flow is illustrated by examples 1.14 and 1.15.

Natural flow rate and pressure usually change with reservoir depletion, depending on the variation in IPR and TPR resulting from changes in reservoir pressure and flow characteristics. Usually the change of natural flow is toward a lower rate if all well parameters remain unchanged. To offset the natural decline in rate, it is possible to change equipment or operating criteria to maintain the desired rate of production. Lowering the wellhead pressure by choke manipulation or lowering of separator pressure is perhaps the simplest and most common of the adjustments made by the operator. Introducing artificial lift or treating wells by stimulation are both more complicated and costly alternatives for maintaining a desired rate of production. The effect of changing well conditions is considered in detail below.

CHANGING WELLHEAD PRESSURE. Decreasing wellhead pressure by increasing choke opening will usually shift the TPR curve downward to a lower intake pressure, consequently increasing the rate of natural flow (fig. 1.21). If the wellhead pressure is reduced to atmospheric condition, then the well will produce at its maximum flow rate.

Increasing the wellhead pressure by reducing the choke opening will shift the TPR curve upward, resulting in a decrease in rate. If the wellhead pressure is increased beyond a certain point, then the well will stop producing because the required pressure exceeds the available pressure. Figure 1.21 shows the effect of changes in wellhead pressure on natural flow.

CHANGING GAS/LIQUID RATIO. The effect of a changing gas/liquid ratio is not as straightforward as for the case of changing wellhead pressure. It has different effects on the two components of pressure loss in tubing—friction and hydrostatic. Increasing GLR lightens the mixture density and therefore reduces the pressure loss due to hydrostatic forces. Larger quantities of gas will, however, usually result in larger pressure losses due to friction. The composite effect of gas on total pressure loss in tubing is illustrated in figure 1.22. An increase in gas/liquid ratio tends to shift the TPR upward and to the right. The result is an increase in natural flow rate. The trend continues up to a certain gas/liquid ratio, where the trend is then reversed. Injecting gas from the surface to the lower sections of the tubing is a conventional artificial lift method called gas lift. Chapter 5 will show that it only pays to increase GLR to a certain point, because at higher GLRs, the incremental

EXAMPLE 1.14 DETERMINING NATURAL FLOW FOR AN OIL WELL

The Davis No. 3 well discussed in example 1.13 has been tested at a rate of 202 STB/D during a three-day period. Stabilized wellbore flowing pressure measured 3248 psia. The Davis No. 1 and 2 wells were previously tested with a multirate sequence, which indicated the exponent in the IPR equation (eq. [1.33] and eq. [1.35]) ranges from 0.77 to 0.81. A value of 0.8 is assumed to apply to the Davis No. 3 well. Average reservoir pressure p_R is 4000 psia. The resulting IPR equation, then, is

$$q_o = 480[1 - (p_{wf}/p_R)^2]^{0.8}$$

or

$$q_o = 0.000828[p_R^2 - p_{wf}^2]^{0.8}$$

Determine the rate of natural flow, assuming the tubing performance calculations in example 1.13 apply (i.e., $p_{wh} = 200$ psia, GLR = 600 scf/STB, and 8000 ft of tubing having a 3.5-in. nominal diameter).

SOLUTION

Figure E1.14 shows a plot of the tubing and inflow performance curves on Cartesian paper. The intersection indicates a natural flow of about 415 STB/D at a flowing bottomhole pressure near 1600 psia.

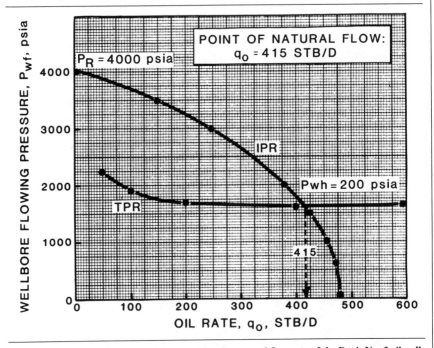

Figure E1.14 A graphical solution to determine the natural flow rate of the Davis No. 3 oil well.

EXAMPLE 1.15 DETERMINING NATURAL FLOW FOR A GAS WELL

Solve the following problems for the Elk City No. 3 well discussed in examples 1.7 and 1.11.

1. Plot gas rate versus the difference of average reservoir pressure squared and intake flowing pressure squared on the same log–log plot as was made in example 1.7. Determine the point of natural flow for this well.
2. Plot the gas IPR and the tubing performance curves on Cartesian coordinates. Once again determine the point of natural flow.
3. Discuss the advantages of a log–log plot of the well performance curves over a Cartesian plot.

SOLUTION

1. Figure E1.15a shows the IPR and tubing performance curves plotted on log–log paper, indicating a natural flow rate of about 9.0 MMscf/D. The straight-line IPR is a reproduction of figure E1.7. The tubing performance curve expressed as $p_R^2 - p_{in}^2$ is plotted using the data in table E1.11.
2. Figure 1.15b shows the IPR and tubing performance curves plotted on Cartesian coordinates, indicating a natural flow of about 9.2 MMscf/D at a flowing pressure of 1400 psia.
3. The main advantage of the log–log deliverability plot of a gas well over a Cartesian plot is that the same log–log curve applies at all points during the life of the well (assuming stabilized flow exists). On a Cartesian scale the IPR appears as a family of curves, one curve for each stage of depletion. The disadvantage of the logarithmic plot is that the tubing performance curve plotted as $\log (p_R^2 - p_{in}^2)$ versus $\log q$ changes as p_R declines with depletion.

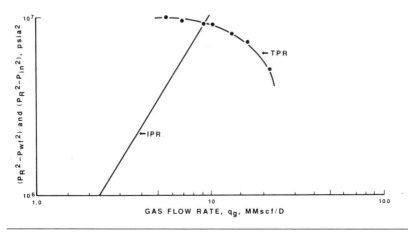

Figure E1.15a A log–log plot of the backpressure equation and the tubing performance of the Elk City No. 3 gas well.

EXAMPLE 1.15 continued

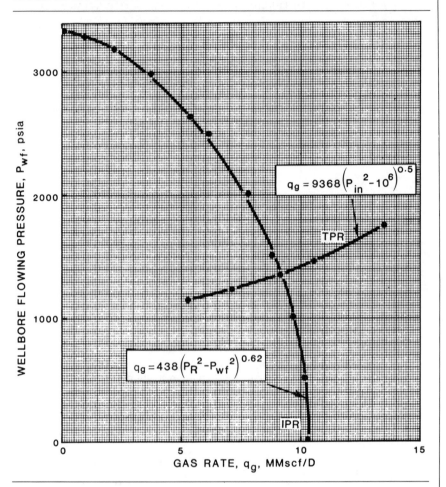

Figure E1.15b A Cartesian plot of the IPR and the tubing performance to determine the natural flow rate in the Elk City No. 3 gas well.

oil produced does not offset the additional costs of increasing the injected gas. Setting aside economic considerations for the moment, it can be shown that the rate of natural flow decreases with additional injection of gas (i.e., at increasing GLRs) once a critical gas/liquid ratio has been reached.

CHANGING TUBING DIAMETER. The effect of tubing diameter on natural flow is similar to the effect of gas/liquid ratio. Increasing diameter increases the rate of

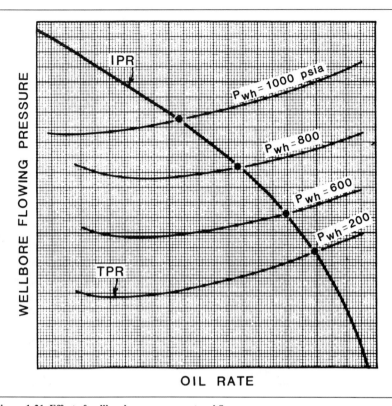

Figure 1.21 Effect of wellhead pressure on natural flow.

natural flow until a critical diameter is reached. For higher diameters the rate will decrease. This is due to change of dominance in pressure loss from friction to gravity, and to holdup forces that occur with increasing pipe diameter. Figure 1.23 indicates the general effect of tubing diameter on natural flow. Natural flow is the primary criterion used to choose tubing size. Other criteria include price, availability, mechanical considerations, and future production characteristics.

CHANGING INFLOW PERFORMANCE. Deteriorating inflow performance is the natural result of reservoir depletion. First, average reservoir pressure decreases in the absence of artificial pressure maintainance or a strong natural water drive. Gas and water injection can be used to arrest the decline in IPR caused by depletion. Additional reductions in inflow performance may result from (1) damage near the wellbore related to drilling and completion operations, (2) reduced drainage area

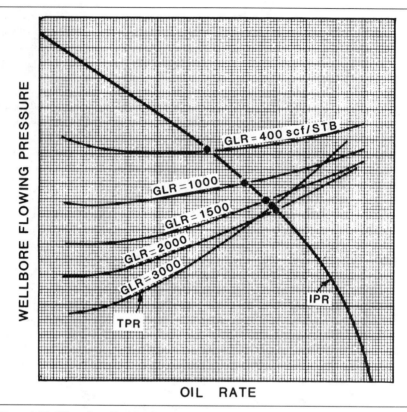

Figure 1.22 Effect of gas/liquid ratio on natural flow.

due to infill drilling, (3) reduced permeability due to two-phase flow, compaction, or fines migration, (4) increased viscosity due to gas liberation from reservoir oil, or (5) transient effects usually associated with low-permeability formations. Figure 1.24 shows the effect of changing IPR on natural flow.

PUMPING WELL. Installing a pump at the bottom of the tubing string creates an artificial lifting capacity and increases the available pressure to flow up the tubing. The effect of a downhole pump is shown in figure 1.25. The pump adds a controlled amount of pressure to the IPR, thereby sustaining flow at higher than the natural rate. Wells producing with a pump may not have the capacity to produce in the absence of artificial lift, as indicated in figure 1.25. Other situations may arise where a pump is installed in a well that is producing by natural flow, but at a rate

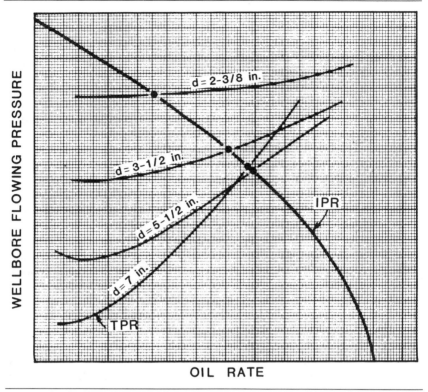

Figure 1.23 Effect of tubing diameter on natural flow.

lower than desired. In either case, we consider the well to be producing by artificial lift. Calculations of flow rates in pumping wells are discussed in chapter 5.

Thus far we have considered wells with tubing intake at or near the perforations, to equate the inflow and tubing intake performance curves. For most flowing wells, the actual difference in elevation between midperforations (representing the datum for wellbore flowing pressure) and the tubing shoe (representing the datum for tubing intake pressure) is only about 30 feet, or the length of one joint of tubing. In other situations, the tubing shoe is substantially above the perforations, and wellbore flowing pressure does not equal tubing intake pressure. Figure E1.16 illustrates a completion configuration where the tubing is about 2000 feet above midperforations.

To correct for the distance between the tubing intake and midperforations,

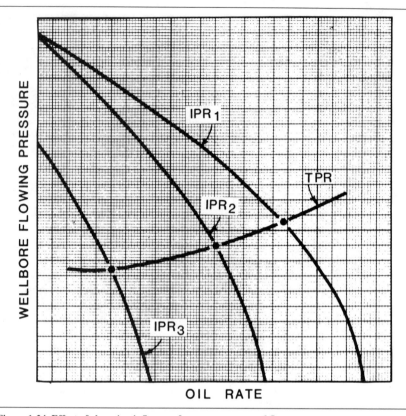

OIL RATE

Figure 1.24 Effect of changing inflow performance on natural flow.

consider the separation interval as an extension of the tubing. An additional pressure drop along the interval is merely added to the pressure drop in the tubing and the composite is used to develop the tubing performance relation. The modified TPR can be combined with the IPR to determine natural flow, just as has been previously described. An expression for approximating pressure drop between the tubing shoe and midperforations is

$$\Delta p = G_f(H_{mp} - H_{ts}),\tag{1.41}$$

where G_f is the flowing pressure gradient in the interval between midperforations and the tubing shoe, H_{mp} is the depth to midperforations, and H_{ts} is the depth to the tubing shoe. The flowing gradient can be measured directly by pressure gauges or pressure gradient gauge (gradiomanometer). If no other information is available, then the hydrostatic gradient can be used. Example 1.16 shows the adjustment of tubing performance for the distance between midperforations and the tubing shoe.

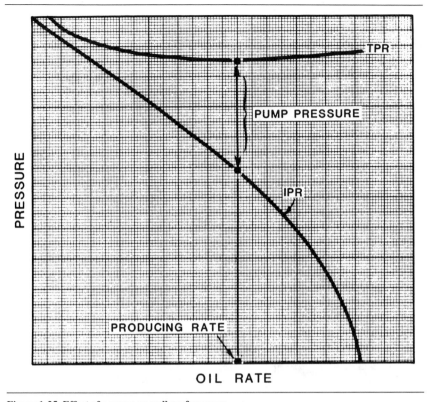

Figure 1.25 Effect of a pump on well performance.

EXAMPLE 1.16 DEPTH ADJUSTMENT TO THE TUBING PERFORMANCE
RELATION

Production from the Davis No. 5 (examples 1.13 and 1.14) suddenly dropped after
five years of production. By running a special tubing gauge tool, it was determined
that the tubing had collapsed at 6537 ft. During a workover job to replace the
tubing, it was discovered that the casing had also collapsed at the same depth. The
collapsed casing interval has been reamed out to full bore and has been milled out
throughout the pay zone. A 5½-in. liner has been set inside the damaged casing
from 6000 to 8000 ft. The well has been completed with 3.5-in. tubing which was
run only to 5950 (see fig. E1.16[a]). A changeover to 2⅞-in. to run the tubing inside
the liner up to the perforations depth was considered too costly and unnecessary.

A test following the workover indicated an average reservoir pressure of
2000 psia and a gas/oil ratio of 2500 scf/STB. In addition, a flowing pressure
gradient in the 5.5-in. liner was measured as $G_f = 0.26$ psi/ft. During the test a rate
of 320 STB/D was recorded, with a stabilized flowing bottomhole pressure of 842

EXAMPLE 1.16 continued

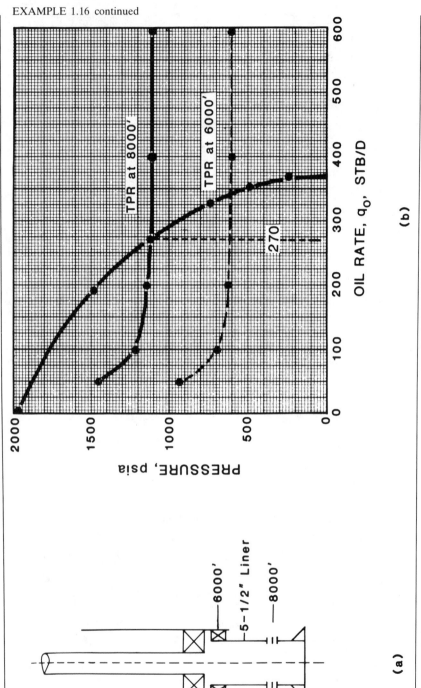

(a)

(b)

Figure E1.16 The arrangement and the performance of the Davis No. 5 oil well with 5½-inch liner installed to recomplete the well after a workover.

EXAMPLE 1.16 continued

psia. Assuming exponent n equals 0.8 in the backpressure equation (see example 1.14), maximum oil rate is

$$q_{o\max} = 320/[1 - (842/2000)^2]^{0.8}$$

$$= 374\,\text{STB/D},$$

which gives the IPR equation:

$$q_o = 374[1 - (p_{wf}/p_R)^2]^{0.8}.$$

It is required to predict the natural flow of the well with 200 psia wellhead pressure.

SOLUTION

For constructing the tubing performance curve, a constant flowing gradient of 0.26 psi/ft is assumed in the 5.5-in. liner from 8000 to 6000 ft.

From 6000 ft to the wellhead, the gradient curves for 3.5-in. tubing and GLR = 2500 scf/STB are used. Wellhead pressure is constant at 200 psia, marking the starting point for the calculation of tubing performance.

For a given oil rate—for example, 50 STB/D—we enter the gradient curve at 200 psia and move down 6000 ft and then horizontally to the GLR curve of 2500 scf/STB. From this point we move vertically to the x axis and read the pressure corresponding to 6000 ft.

Having determined the pressure at the top of the liner, pressure loss between the perforations and 6000 ft is calculated: $\Delta p = 0.26(8000 - 6000) = 520$ psi. This value is added to the intake pressure at 6000 ft calculated using the gradient curve. The resulting pressure is the intake pressure to the liner, that is, the flowing pressure at the wellbore. Table E1.16 lists results of calculations for several rates for which gradient curves are available.

Figure E1.16(b) plots IPR and TPR curves for the Davis No. 5 well. The rate of natural flow is 270 STB/D at a flowing wellbore pressure of 1135 psia.

Table E1.16 Tubing Performance Calculations for the Davis No. 5 Well

	p_{in} at	
q_o (STB/D)	6000 ft (psia)	8000 ft (psia)
50	950	1470
100	710	1230
200	640	1160
400	605	1125
600	600	1120

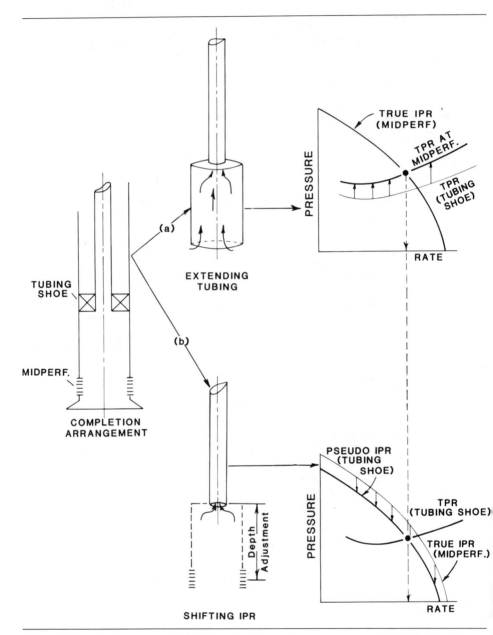

Figure 1.26 Depth adjustment by (a) adjusting the tubing performance curve and (b) shifting the inflow performance curve.

An alternative to adjusting the TPR curve for depth separation is to transfer the IPR up to the level of the tubing shoe. The resulting performance curve will be called the pseudo-IPR (or shifted IPR). We do not recommend this procedure in general, but for special applications such as solving downhole pump problems the pseudo-IPR may prove useful. Figure 1.26 illustrates the difference between pseudo-IPR and adjusted TPR methods.

Another depth correction is necessary in production tests when flowing pressure is measured with a tubing/gauge assembly that does not reach midperforations. This might be the case if the tubing cannot be lowered below a certain point, for example, below a set of cement-squeezed perforations. Here, the pressure gauge must be locked mechanically within the tubing/nipple assembly to withstand drag force due to high flow rates. If this problem arises, then the measured pressures should be corrected to the midperforation depth by use of equation (1.41) and an appropriate estimate of the flowing gradient G_f. (See example 1.17.)

EXAMPLE 1.17 CORRECTING WELL TEST DATA FOR DEPTH TO ESTABLISH THE TRUE IPR

An offshore well, the Sandnes No. 1, produces from the Tor formation (a Cretaceous chalk) at a depth of 10,380 ft. A previous attempt to produce from the Ekofisk formation (Danian in age) at a depth of 9230 ft was unsuccessful, and the perforations were plugged off to avoid water production. By Norwegian law, a packer cannot be set below a set of perforations, even if they have been plugged off. The resulting production tubing configuration appears in figure E1.17, showing the packer set at 9190 ft and the inlet to the tubing at 9205 ft. Midperforations are at 10,380 ft.

A multirate test was run on the Tor formation. No water was produced at the surface, which indicated that the plugged-off perforations in the Ekofisk formation were effective. Casing pressure indicated that the packer was holding and the production system was functioning as designed. The pressure gauge assembly was housed in the seating nipple at a depth of about 9200 ft. Results from the multirate test are given in table E1.17.

Flowing pressures are measured some 1180 ft above the midperforations. To correct these pressures to wellbore pressures, it is necessary to add the pressure loss from midperforation to the tubing inlet. Pressure gradient surveys have been run in 7-in. casing on other wells in this field, indicating that a flowing gradient of about 0.35 psi/ft can be used. The additional pressure to be added to measured flowing pressures is then

$$p_{wf} = p_f(9200\,\text{ft}) + 0.35(1180)$$

$$= p_f(9200\,\text{ft}) + 413.$$

Results are shown in table E1.17.

EXAMPLE 1.17 continued

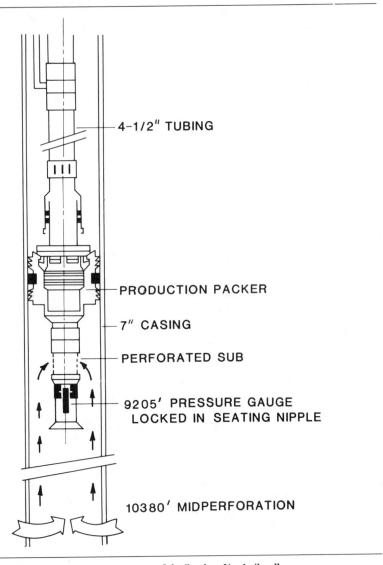

4-1/2" TUBING

PRODUCTION PACKER

7" CASING

PERFORATED SUB

9205' PRESSURE GAUGE
LOCKED IN SEATING NIPPLE

10380' MIDPERFORATION

Figure E1.17 The completion arrangement of the Sandnes No. 1 oil well.

EXAMPLE 1.17 continued

Table E1.17 Multirate Test Results for the Sandnes No. 1 Well

| q_o (STB/D) | Flowing pressure at | |
	Pressure gauge (psia)	Wellbore (psia)
5000	5200	5613
12286	3725	4138
17750	2225	2638

Some flowing wells are produced through a tapered tubing string consisting of two or more pipe sections of varying diameter. To construct the tubing performance relation, it is necessary to calculate pressure drops for each pipe diameter separately, then add them together to form the composite TPR. This is illustrated in example 1.18.

EXAMPLE 1.18 TUBING PERFORMANCE OF A TAPERED, VARYING-DIAMETER TUBING STRING

An alternative completion to the Davis No. 5 is to extend the tubing into the liner by running a 2⅞-in. tubing from 6000 ft to the perforations at 8000 ft as illustrated in figure E1.18. A crossover from the 3.5-in. to 2⅞-in. tubing makes the connection at 6000 ft, and a packer is set above the perforations. Determine the rate of natural flow using this production string configuration and compare it with the results in example 1.16.

SOLUTION

Tabulated in example 1.16 are the intake pressure to 3½-in. tubing at 6000 ft with 200 psia wellhead pressure. These intake pressures are equal to the top pressures at the 2⅞-in. tubing. Entering with these pressures the gradient curves of 2⅞-in. tubing, moving 2000 ft vertically downward, and horizontally back to the curve determine the corresponding tubing intake pressures. For example, at 50 STB/D the pressure calculated at 6000 ft was 950 psia. The 2⅞-in. gradient curve for 50 STB/D is entered at 950 psia. Then move vertically downward until the GLR curve of 2500 scf/STB is found, and label that point. Moving down vertically 2000 ft along the depth scale and then horizontally until the same GLR curve is reached, the pressure of 1250 is read from the x-axis scale. Table E1.18 gives results of calculations for the other oil rates.

Combining the inflow and composite tubing performance curves results in the point of natural flow, as shown in figure E1.18. It indicates a 330 STB/D natural flow rate. In example 1.16 we obtained a natural flow rate of 270 STB/D. Using the present tubing configuration results in a natural flow of 330 STB/D, or an increase of 60 STB/D. It appears from these calculations that the additional string of 2⅞-in.

EXAMPLE 1.18 continued

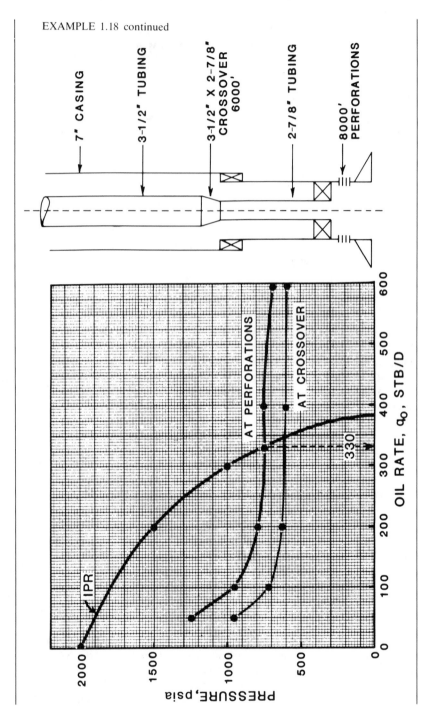

Figure E1.18 An alternative arrangement to recomplete the Davis No. 5 oil well and its corresponding well performance.

EXAMPLE 1.18 continued

tubing is justified economically. Perhaps the only questionable assumption made in this comparison is the flowing pressure gradient of 0.35 psi/ft used in example 1.16. Empirical gradient curves for 7-in. tubing (i.e., casing) are not commonly available, and a multiphase flow correlation is necessary to substantiate the approximation of a constant flowing gradient.

Table E1.18 Composite Tubing Performance Curve for $3\frac{1}{2} \times 2\frac{7}{8}$-in. Production String

q_o (STB/D)	p_{in} at	
	6000 ft $3\frac{1}{2}$-in. (psia)	8000 ft $3\frac{1}{2} \times 2\frac{7}{8}$-in. (psia)
50	950	1250
100	710	950
200	640	800
400	605	750
600	600	680

Additional pressure losses in tubing may result from mechanical constrictions such as safety valves, downhole chokes, nipples, or tubing patches. Special consideration for each type of restriction is necessary, although some or all of these lesser causes for pressure loss can be overlooked. Example 1.19 considers tubing performance of a well producing by gas lift through tapered tubing with several flow restrictions in the pipe.

EXAMPLE 1.19 TUBING PERFORMANCE OF A COMPLEX TUBING CONFIGURATION

The Torsk No. 3 is an offshore well in the Narrow Pass Block 17, Gulf of Mexico. It has been completed with a dry subsea system including a dry chamber for housing the wellhead at atmospheric pressure. Figure E1.19 shows the well configuration. After two years of trouble-free production with continuous gas lift, communication between the tubing and annulus is spotted and the well has to be shut down. An acoustic level detector has been used to locate the approximate depth of the communication, believed to be at 3070 ft.

Replacing the tubing in this particular type of subsea well is impractical and very costly. An alternative would be to mend the tubing by wireline, inserting an isolation sleeve to serve as a patch. The inner diameter of the patch is only 1-in., which is considerably smaller than the 3.5-in. tubing. The restriction caused by the patch will result in additional pressure losses. A test bench was used to estimate the relation between patch-related pressure loss and rate, $\Delta p = 0.001 q_L^2$, where Δp is in psi and q_L is in STB/D.

To develop the composite tubing performance after inserting the patch it is necessary to specify the producing conditions:

EXAMPLE 1.19 continued

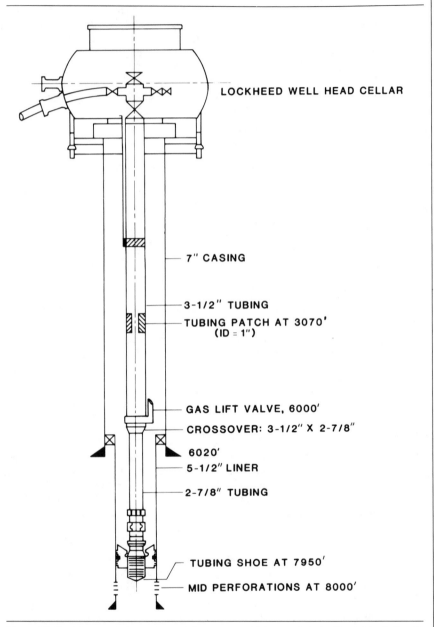

LOCKHEED WELL HEAD CELLAR

7″ CASING

3-1/2″ TUBING

TUBING PATCH AT 3070′
(ID = 1″)

GAS LIFT VALVE, 6000′

CROSSOVER: 3-1/2″ X 2-7/8″

6020′

5-1/2″ LINER

2-7/8″ TUBING

TUBING SHOE AT 7950′

MID PERFORATIONS AT 8000′

Figure E1.19a The completion string and the proposed tubing patch in the Torsk No. 3 oil well.

EXAMPLE 1.19 continued

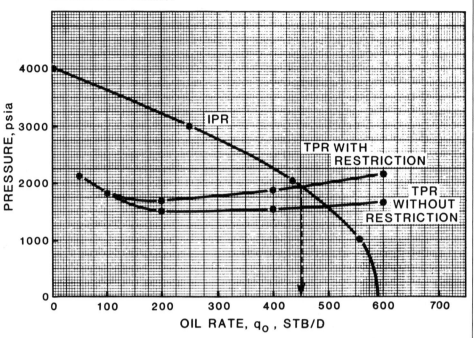

Figure E1.19b The natural flow rate in the Torsk No. 3 oil well with and without the restriction of the tubing patch.

reservoir pressure .... 4000 psia
wellhead pressure .... 500 psia
formation gas/oil ratio .... 600 scf/STB
injection gas/oil ratio .... 1400 scf/STB
gas injection depth .... 6000 ft

Inflow performance has been determined from a single-point test and is expressed in equation form as

$$q_o = 580[1 - (p_{wf}/p_R)^2].$$

SOLUTION

Practically, the tubing configuration can be simplified into four sections by neglecting the short intervals between the gas-lift valve and crossover, and between the tubing shoe and midperforations. In summary, the four sections are

1. wellhead to tubing patch, 0 to 3070 ft
2. restriction at 3070 ft

EXAMPLE 1.19 continued

3. large-diameter (3.5-in.) tubing string, 2930 ft, from 3070 to 6000 ft
4. small-diameter (2.875-in.) tubing string, 2000 ft, from 6000 to 8000 ft

Using appropriate gradient curves and the patch pressure loss equation, we begin at the wellhead, calculate down to the patch, across the patch, and finally down to the midperforations. Table E1.19a gives results of the calculations at five rates for which gradient curves are available in Appendix A. Table E1.19b gives results of the same calculations for the well without a tubing patch (to be used as a reference for quantifying the effect of the patch).

Figure E1.19 plots the inflow performance and composite tubing performance curves on graph paper. The rate of natural flow is 455 STB/D, including the tubing patch restriction. Without the restriction a natural flow rate of 500 STB/D is indicated. The apparent loss of production (45 STB/D) is acceptable, and the final decision to install the isolation valve is a matter of operational and mechanical considerations. Uncertainties in the calculations used to solve this problem include the assumption of a constant injection gas/oil ratio (usually the gas injection rate is specified), and, perhaps more important, the relation used for pressure loss across the tubing patch.

Table E1.19a Composite Tubing Performance with Tubing Patch Restriction

q_o STB/D	p above restriction psia	Δp restriction psi	p below restriction psia	p at 6000 ft psia	p at 8000 ft psia
50	1100	2	1102	1750	2340
100	940	10	950	1400	1900
200	890	40	930	1300	1780
400	880	160	1040	1420	1900
600	900	360	1260	1690	2200

Table E1.19b Composite Tubing Performance without Tubing Patch

q_o STB/D	p_{in} at 6000 ft 3½-in. psia	p_{in} at 8000 ft 3½ × 2⅞-in. psia
50	1540	2120
100	1240	1700
200	1160	1620
400	1160	1600
600	1180	1600

This section has addressed the relationship between the pressure and the flow rate at the bottom of the wellbore. The next section investigates the corresponding relationship at the wellhead.

1.6   WELLHEAD, CHOKE, AND FLOWLINE PERFORMANCE. Controlling production rate is often done by adjusting the choke size, which results in a change in wellhead pressure. Figure 1.21 shows the effect of wellhead pressure on production rate. For each wellhead pressure there is a different tubing performance curve, each intersecting the inflow performance curve at a different point. The general trend observed in figure 1.21 is that flow rate increases as wellhead pressure decreases (resulting from an increasing choke size).

The choke can be manipulated to change flow rate. Determining the effect of choke size on production rate is an important design task. In doing so, however, one should recognize that there usually exists a maximum flowing wellhead pressure above which flow ceases. This is illustrated in figure 1.25. At a critical wellhead pressure the TPR curve is tangent to the IPR, and at higher wellhead pressures the flow ceases altogether.

The points of intersection between TPR and IPR curves in figure 1.21 can be plotted as rate versus wellhead pressure. The resulting curve is referred to as the *wellhead performance relation* (WPR). Figure 1.27 illustrates a WPR curve superimposed on the same graph as IPR and TPR curves. The distance between the TPR curves and the WPR curve represents the pressure loss in the tubing.

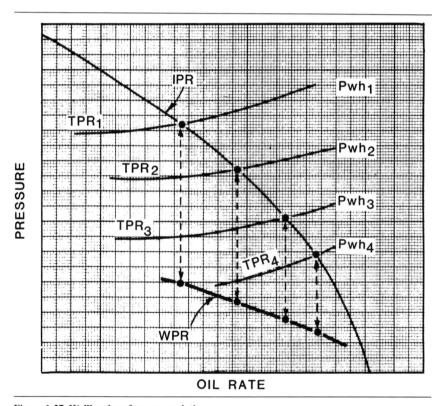

Figure 1.27 Wellhead performance relation.

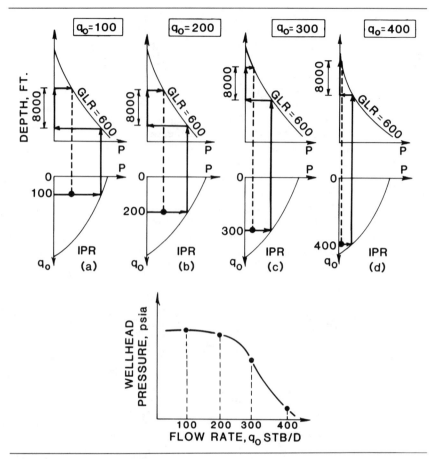

Figure 1.28 A procedure for constructing the wellhead performance curve.

The following procedure can be used to develop the WPR:

1. Calculate and plot the IPR curve.
2. Tabulate the wellbore flowing pressures at rates for which gradient curves are available (e.g., 50, 100, 200, 400, and 600 STB/D).
3. For the specific tubing configuration and the given rate and GLR, enter the gradient curve at the corresponding wellbore flowing pressure.
4. Move vertically upward along the length of the tubing, starting from the wellbore flowing pressure on the gradient curve.
5. Move horizontally to the left until the same GLR curve is found. Read the pressure at this point from the x-axis grid. This pressure represents the wellhead pressure.

The procedure is shown in figure 1.28. For more details of the steps listed previously, see example 1.20.

EXAMPLE 1.20 CONSTRUCTING A WPR CURVE

Alternative production plans for the Davis No. 3 (examples 1.13 and 1.14) require the estimate of natural flow rate at three wellhead flowing pressures: 200, 500, and 800 psia. Perform the necessary calculations *without* determining tubing performance curves for each wellhead pressure.

SOLUTION

Using the IPR equation given in example 1.14, calculate and tabulate the wellbore flowing pressures for rates that correspond to the available gradient curves (50, 100, 200, 400, and 600 STB/D). Rewriting the IPR equation in terms of p_{wf} gives

$$p_{wf} = [p_R^2 - (q_o/0.000828)^{1.25}]^{0.5}.$$

Results are tabulated in columns 1 and 2 of table E1.20.

For a given rate, enter the gradient curve at the wellbore flowing pressure and note the intersection with the GLR of 600 scf/STB. Moving vertically up the length of the tubing (8000 ft) and then horizontally until the same GLR curve is found, read the flowing wellhead pressure from the x axis. This procedure is repeated for each rate and results are tabulated in table E1.20. A plot of wellhead flowing pressure versus rate is given in figure E1.20. Entering wellhead pressures of 200, 500, and 800 psia we read the corresponding flow rates of 415, 325, and 245 STB/D.

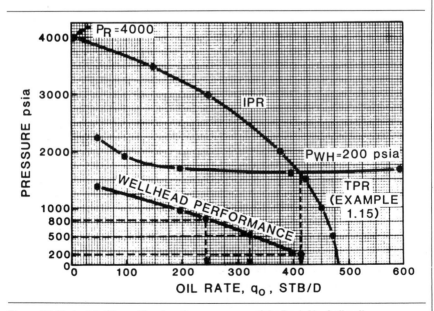

Figure E1.20 A plot of the wellhead performance curve of the Davis No. 3 oil well.

EXAMPLE 1.20 continued

Table E1.20 Rate–Pressure Calculations

q_o (STB/D)	p_{wf} (psia)	p_{wh} (psia)
50	3880	1350
100	3708	1150
200	3263	950
400	1807	250

A sheet of tracing paper overlaid on the gradient curves can speed up the procedure of constructing the WPR. Two parallel lines drawn on the tracing sheet at a distance equal to the length of the tubing allows reading the sought wellhead pressure from the gradient curves.

When the tubing bottom line (e.g. 8000 ft) on the tracing paper intersects the gradient line at the tubing inlet pressure point, the upper depth line (zero depth) intersects the same gradient line at the sought tubing head pressure. The procedure is similar to the one described in section 1.4, where tracing paper is used to construct a TPR. The main difference is that here the depth measurements are taken from the bottom-hole upwards, rather than from the wellhead downwards as done when constructing the TPR.

The WPR is a relation stating that for a given rate of flow there is a certain discharge pressure available at the wellhead. How this pressure is used or dissipated depends on the choke size and downstream choke conditions. Typically, the choke is located directly adjacent to the wellhead assembly. Offshore installations may require that the choke be located a considerable distance from the wellhead, for example, at the inlet to the manifold in a subsea installation. Several types of chokes are available, but they generally fall into one of two categories: positive or fixed choke, and adjustable choke. Each type has its own advantages, and the operator may choose one or the other based on field experience.

The *positive choke* is a replaceable, fixed-dimension orifice threaded into an L-shaped housing. The end connections of the body may be flanged or threaded. The orifice is always made from a hard material, to resist erosion. It may be slightly rounded at the entrance. Total orifice length is usually 6 in., but it may be as short as 2 in. Bore sizes range from 1/8 in. to 2 in. in diameter, and they are usually expressed in 64ths of an inch. For example, an 8/64 choke refers to a choke with an inner diameter bore of 1/8 in. Figure 1.29 shows a sketch of a positive choke.

An adjustable choke allows for gradual changes in the size of the opening. The most common adjustable choke is a needle valve, which is calibrated to read in effective diameter openings (see fig. 1.30). Another type of adjustable choke is the rotary positive choke, illustrated in figure 1.31. This choke employs two circular rotating disks of hardened material, each with a pair of orifices. One disk is fixed in the valve body, while the other disk can rotate through 90 degrees to expose all or part of the orifice flow area.

Choke selection involves mechanical, operational, and economical considerations. This discussion will be limited to selection of a choke to deliver a specific flow

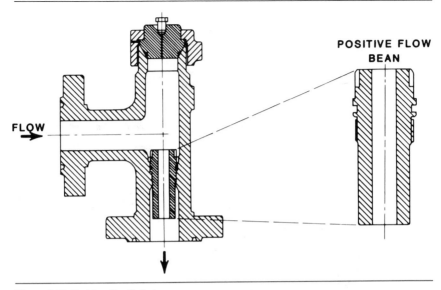

Figure 1.29 Positive (fixed) choke.

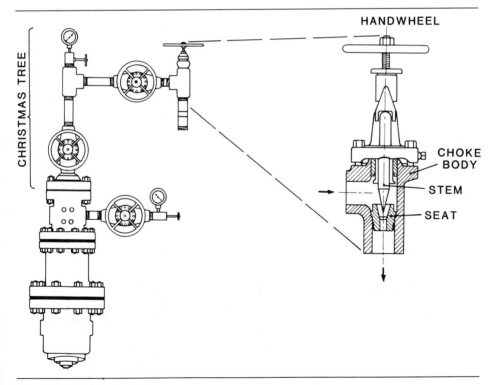

Figure 1.30 Needle valve choke.

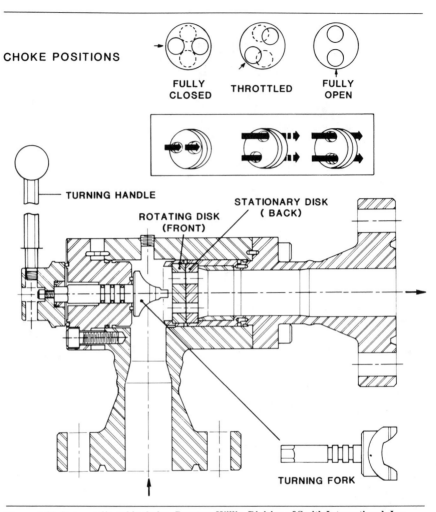

CHOKE POSITIONS

FULLY
CLOSED   THROTTLED   FULLY
OPEN

TURNING HANDLE

ROTATING DISK
(FRONT)

STATIONARY DISK
(BACK)

TURNING FORK

Figure 1.31 Rotary adjustable choke. Courtesy Willis, Division of Smith International, Inc. from "Willis General Catalogue."

rate. Before covering the use of standard choke equations it is worth considering the principle of choke functioning.

The main function of a choke is to dissipate large amounts of potential energy (i.e., pressure losses) over a very short distance. The design of a choke takes advantage of the flow regime resulting from a sudden disturbance in continuous flow through a circular conduit. Figure 1.32 gives a schematic of the normal flow character of fluid passing through a fixed choke. It describes the combined effect of a sudden flow restriction, a small-bore flow tube, and an abrupt enlargement. As the fluid approaches the orifice, it leaves the pipe wall and contracts to form a high-velocity jet. The jet converges to a minimum called the throat or *vena contracta*, and then it expands toward the wall of the choke bore. After leaving the

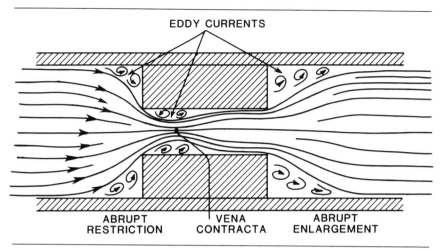

Figure 1.32 Flow regime in a fixed choke.

choke, the stream of fluid expands and returns to a flow geometry similar to what it was before entering the choke. An area of turbulence just beyond the choke exit also contributes to pressure loss. Total irreversible losses are summarized in the following:

1. friction throughout the choke and near-choke areas
2. turbulence near the entrance and exit to the choke
3. slow eddy motions between the contracted jet and the pipe walls
4. abrupt expansion at the exit to the choke

An important observation about the general nature of compressible flow through a choke is that there exists a maximum flow rate, which can flow through the orifice for given upstream conditions. Consider, for instance, the test apparatus shown in figure 1.33. It consists of a large container discharging gas at a constant pressure p_1. Gas flows through the orifice at a rate controlled by a backpressure valve, which maintains a constant downstream pressure p_2. If p_2 is varied and the mass rate $\dot{m}$ is monitored with the downstream flowmeter, then a relation can be developed between $\dot{m}$ and p_2. Figure 1.34 shows the general characteristic of this relationship. At initial conditions the flow control valve is closed, the rate is zero, and $p_2 = p_1$. Maintaining p_1 constant, the control valve is gradually opened. This results in a reduction of p_2 and an increase in flow rate. As p_2 decreases the rate gradually starts to level off until it finally reaches a plateau, which represents the maximum flow rate that can pass through the choke for the given upstream pressure p_1. The ratio $R_c = p_2/p_1$, at the start of the plateau, is called the *critical pressure ratio*. If p_2/p_1 is greater than the critical ratio, then the flow is subcritical. If p_2/p_1 is less than or equal to the critical ratio, then flow is critical.

For gas flow, the critical downstream pressure is reached when the velocity at the *vena contracta* (throat) reaches sonic velocity. Simply stated, a disturbance downstream from the choke must travel at a speed greater than sound to be felt

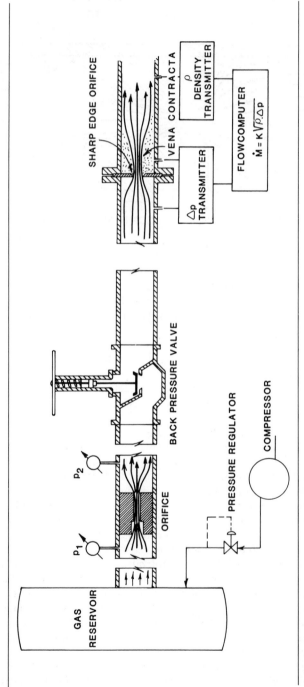

Figure 1.33 Test apparatus for determining choke characteristics.

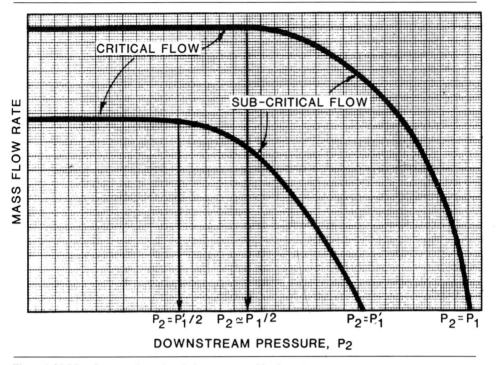

Figure 1.34 Mass flow rate through a choke as governed by downstream pressure.

upstream from the choke. Analytical equations for the critical pressure ratio can be derived using the assumptions of ideal gas, no friction losses, and adiabatic flow. In general, the ratio R_c is about 0.5, and a good rule of thumb is that upstream pressure should be double the downstream pressure for critical flow conditions to exist. As illustrated in figure 1.34, the choke exhibits similar characteristics with other upstream pressures. The only difference is in the value of the critical ratio and the critical flow rate. It was observed that the upstream pressure is directly proportional to the critical flow rate.

Critical pressure ratio and critical flow conditions are observed for all types of compressible flow including gas/liquid mixture flow. Similar phenomena are *not* observed for incompressible liquid flow.

Two-phase gas/liquid mixtures exhibiting critical flow through chokes generally have a critical ratio R_c ranging between 0.5 and 0.6. The exact value is determined experimentally for the particular choke and reservoir fluid. Because most field conditions result in critical two-phase flow, there has been considerable effort to develop a general, rate–pressure relation for critical flow in chokes. Several investigators have proposed specific equations of the same general form:

$$p_1 - D = A q_L F_{gL}{}^B / d_{64}{}^C, \tag{1.42}$$

Table 1.1 Empirical Coefficients for Two-Phase Critical Flow Correlations

Correlation	A	B	C	D
Gilbert	10.00	0.546	1.89	14.7
Ros	17.40	0.500	2.00	0

where p_1 is the upstream pressure (psia), q_L is the liquid flow rate (STB/D), F_{gL} is the gas/liquid ratio (scf/STB), and d_{64} is the choke diameter in 64ths of an inch (e.g., $d_{64} = 32$ indicates a choke diameter of 0.5 in.). Constants A, B, C and D are experimentally determined constants. Table 1.1 lists the values of A, B, C, and D suggested by Gilbert (1954) and Ros (1960).

For a given choke size, the rate–pressure relation plots as a straight line with the intercept near the origin. The resulting line is called the *choke performance curve*, and it is usually plotted on the same graph with the wellhead performance curve. The intersection of the WPR and choke performance curve defines the rate of natural flow for the given choke size. Example 1.21 illustrates the use of the choke performance curve.

EXAMPLE 1.21 NATURAL FLOW DETERMINED BY CHOKE AND WELLHEAD PERFORMANCE RELATIONS

This example will determine the relation of choke size to oil rate for the Davis No. 3 well (examples 1.13, 1.14, and 1.20). Perform the three following tasks:

1. Determine the choke size that will produce the well at a rate of 415 STB/D.
2. Determine the flow rate resulting from a 20/64 choke.
3. Determine the flow rate that will result from a 10/64 choke.

Use the Gilbert choke equation.

SOLUTION

1. In example 1.20 the wellhead flowing pressure corresponding to 415 STB/D was determined to be 200 psia. Substituting in equation (1.42) and solving for diameter,

$$d_{64} = [10(415)(600)^{0.546}/(200 - 14.7)]^{1/1.89}$$

$$= 34.9$$

Practically, the closest standard choke size is 32/64.

EXAMPLE 1.21 continued

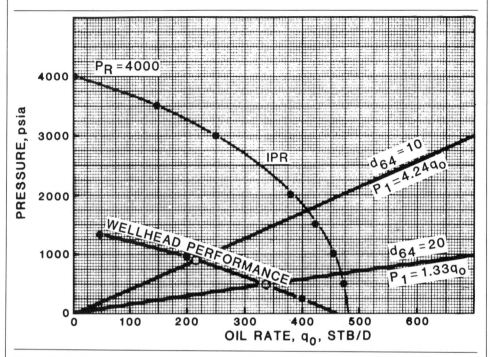

Figure E1.21 Choke performance curve and the graphical procedure to determine flow rates with various choke openings.

2. To predict the flow rate for a 20/64 choke, it is necessary to use the Gilbert equation and plot the choke performance curve on the same plot as the wellhead performance curve. This is shown in figure E1.21. The natural flow rate is 345 STB/D.

3. Repeating the same procedure as in part 2 with a 10/64 choke, figure E1.21 shows that the rate of natural flow is 215 STB/D.

The linear choke performance curve is valid for critical flow of gas/liquid mixtures as long as the pressure ratio p_2/p_1 is less than the critical ratio R_c. Usually, the primary separator is regulated by a backpressure regulator, maintaining a constant separator pressure. To avoid the situation when variations in separator pressure affect well performance upstream from the choke, it is a good rule of thumb to maintain wellhead pressure of at least double the separator pressure (i.e., $R_c \leqq 0.5$). For wellhead pressures below this value, the choke performance has some curvature, as shown in figure 1.35.

Pressure–rate equations for subcritical flow are usually determined experimentally for a particular choke. The general equation form is quadratic and plots as a parabola, as shown in figure 1.36 for gas, liquid, and gas/liquid mixtures.

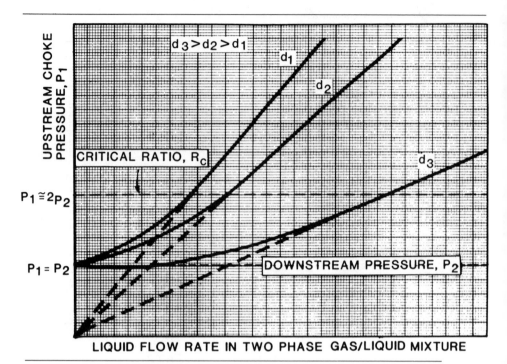

Figure 1.35 Choke performance curve.

Generalized equations for predicting subcritical pressure loss as a function of rate can be found in API 14BM (1978). These equations are accurate for gas and liquid flow but only approximate for gas/liquid mixtures.

Many naturally flowing wells are not controlled by chokes. Others produce with chokes at subcritical conditions. For these cases the flowline backpressure determines the rate of flow. Consider a well not regulated by a choke. If the separator pressure is known and the distance from the wellhead to the separator is substantial, then a flowline performance curve can be calculated to predict the natural rate of flow. This involves calculating the rate–pressure relation at the inlet to the pipeline, assuming a constant separator pressure. Similarly, for gas wells producing directly into a pipeline without first passing through a separator, operating pipeline pressure will determine flowline performance and the natural rate of flow.

Pressure loss calculations for horizontal and inclined pipe are similar to vertical pipe calculations. The simplest flow system is dry gas, which can be accurately described by the Weymouth equation,

$$q_g = 15320E[(p_1{}^2 - p_2{}^2)d^{16/3}/\gamma_g TZL]^{0.5}, \tag{1.43}$$

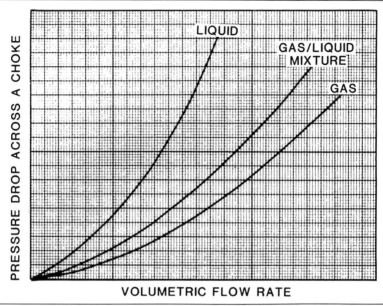

Figure 1.36 Subcritical choke performance curves for gas, liquid, and gas/liquid mixtures.

where

q_g = gas flow rate, scf/D,
d = pipe diameter, in.,
p_1 = inlet pressure, psia,
p_2 = outlet pressure, psia,
L = pipe length, miles
T = average temperature, °R,
Z = average compressibility factor,
γ_g = gas gravity (air = 1),
E = flow efficiency, usually set to 0.9.

In the absence of a choke, wellhead delivery pressure equals the intake pressure to the flowline. By plotting the wellhead performance curve, together with the flowline rate–pressure relation, the rate of natural flow is easily defined as the intersection of the two curves. Example 1.22 illustrates the calculation of natural flow for a gas well producing directly into a gathering pipeline without first being regulated by a choke. The example demonstrates that higher operating pipeline pressure shifts the flowline performance curve up and to the left, resulting in a lower rate of natural flow. Similarly, an increase in flowline length or decreased flowline diameter results in a lower rate.

EXAMPLE 1.22 NATURAL FLOW DETERMINED BY WELLHEAD AND
FLOWLINE PERFORMANCE CALCULATIONS IN THE ABSENCE OF CHOKE
RESTRICTION

The Elk City No. 3 gas well is to be connected to a high-pressure, 8-in. pipeline by a
3-in. schedule 80 flowline covering a distance of about one mile (5280 ft). Normal
operating pressure of the pipeline is 700 psia. Average temperature in the flowline
is estimated to be 80°F, and an average pressure of 900 psia is used for calculating
a Z-factor of 0.8 (gas gravity is reported at 0.75, air = 1). Solve the following
problems.

1. Use the Weymouth equation to calculate the flowline performance curve, giving
   rate versus wellhead pressure. Note that the inside diameter of a 3-in. schedule
   80 flowline is 2.9-in.
2. Determine the natural flow rate if a choke is not installed at the wellhead.
   Although this is an unusual situation for onshore gas wells, the choke on a
   subsea completion may well be at the manifold, located far from the wellhead.
3. What rate of natural flow would be expected if the operating pressure of the
   pipeline was increased to 1000 psia?

SOLUTION

Task 1

Solving equation (1.43) for inlet pressure p_1 when q_g is expressed in MMscf/D gives

$$p_1 = \left[p_2^2 + \left(\frac{q_g \times 10^6}{15{,}320E} \right)^2 \left(\frac{\gamma_g TZL}{d^{16/3}} \right) \right]^{0.5}.$$

Substituting flowline data

$$p_1 = \left[700^2 + \frac{10^{12}(0.75)(460 + 80)(0.8)(1.0)q_g^2}{(15{,}320)^2(0.9)^2(2.9)^{5.33}} \right]^{0.5}$$

gives the flowline performance equation

$$p_1 = [700^2 + 5833.3q_g^2]^{0.5}.$$

Points calculated by the equation are listed as p_1 versus q_g in table E1.22 and
plotted in figure E1.22.

Task 2

Substituting well data from example 1.11 in the vertical flow equation (1.39),

$$q_g = 10^{-6}(200{,}000) \left[\frac{0.454(2.5)^2(p_{in}^2 - e^{0.454}p_{wh}^2)}{0.75(460 + 120)(0.78)(7250)(0.0142)(e^{0.454} - 1)} \right]^{0.5}$$

EXAMPLE 1.22 continued

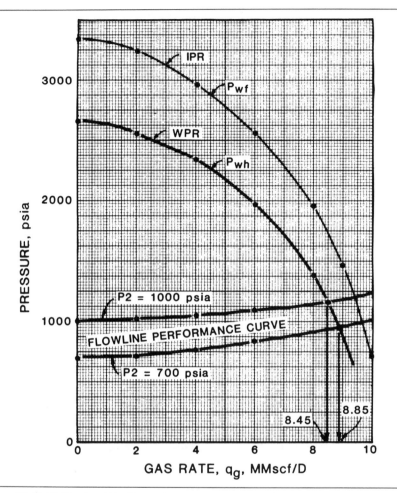

Figure E1.22 Wellhead and flowline performance curve for the Elk City No. 3 gas well.

gives

$$q_g = 10^{-6}(9399)(p_{in}^2 - 1.574 p_{wh}^2)^{0.5}$$

and when solving for p_{wh} gives an expression for wellhead pressure

$$p_{wh} = [0.635 p_{in}^2 - 7190.4 q_g^2]^{0.5}.$$

The tubing intake pressure, p_{in}, in the preceding expression is approximately the flowing bottomhole pressure, p_{wf}, in the IPR equation established in example 1.7,

EXAMPLE 1.22 continued

Table E1.22 Inflow, Wellhead, and Flowline Performance of the Elk City No. 3 Gas Well

q_g MMscf/D	p_{wf} psia	p_{wh} psia	p_1 ($p_2 = 700$) psia	p_1 ($p_2 = 1000$) psia
0.0	3355.0	2673.5	700.0	1000.0
2.0	3232.9	2570.6	716.5	1011.6
4.0	2966.7	2339.6	763.8	1045.6
6.0	2557.4	1973.4	836.7	1100.0
8.0	1939.7	1388.9	929.2	1171.9
9.0	1482.5	930.0	—	—
10.0	723.3	—	1036.0	1258.3

$q_g = 10.3[1 - (p_{wf}/3355)^2]^{0.62}$.

Solving the IPR equation for p_{wf} gives

$$p_{in}^2 \approx p_{wf}^2 = 3355^2[1 - (q_g/10.3)^{1.61}],$$

where q_g is in MMscf/D.

Table E1.22 lists $p_{wf} = p_{in}$ calculated from the IPR equation and also the corresponding wellhead pressure, p_{wh}, calculated from the vertical flow equation. The wellhead performance curve (p_{wh} versus q_g) is plotted in figure E1.22 and it intersects the flowline performance curve at $q = 8.85$ MMscf/D, which is the stabilized natural flow rate of the well.

Task 3
The flowline performance equation for a case of 1000 psia pipeline delivery pressure is

$$p_1 = [1000^2 + 5833.3q_g^2]^{0.5}$$

Table E1.22 tabulates pressure versus rate for this case.

Figure E1.22 includes a plot of flowline performance curve for this case also. The intersection point with the wellhead performance curve indicates 8.45 MMscf/D natural flow rate.

We have chosen to limit our discussion of horizontal and inclined flowline deliverability to dry gas. It should be noted, however, that the method of determining natural flow for multiphase systems, in the absence of choke regulation, is similar to that illustrated by the previous example. The main difference is the need for more complicated horizontal flow models (or gradient curves) to determine the flowline performance curve.

To determine natural flow for a well regulated by a choke at subcritical conditions, it is necessary to add the pressure loss in the choke to the pressure loss in the flowline. The composite pressure loss versus rate relation is plotted with the

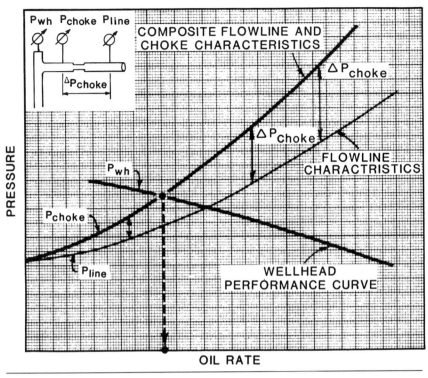

Figure 1.37 Natural flow determined by choke regulation at subcritical conditions.

WPR curve to determine the rate of natural flow. Figure 1.37 illustrates this method.

The importance of flowline performance should be emphasized particularly for offshore subsea installations. The length and configuration of flowlines are important design parameters in the engineering of subsea production systems.

1.7   **EXTENSION OF THE NATURAL FLOW CONCEPT.** Thus far, natural flow conditions were determined and investigated at two particular cross sections, namely the midperforations and the wellhead (see figure 1.38). The natural flow analysis, however, is more general and can be performed at any arbitrary cross section along the flow path in the well. For this purpose it is necessary to define the direction of pressure calculations. The pressure versus flow rate relationship can be calculated in either the *concurrent* (in the flow direction) or *countercurrent* (against the flow direction). In the simple flow tube in figure 1.39a, a concurrent calculation starts at the inlet point that has a known flowing pressure, and the result is the pressure at

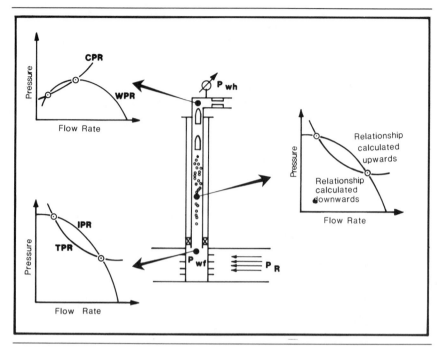

Figure 1.38 Natural flow analysis in wells.

the outlet point. Conversely, a countercurrent calculation starts at the outlet pressure point and calculates the pressure-rate relationship at the inlet point. At any arbitrary cross section, A-A, along the flow path (see figure 1.39b), a pressure calculated concurrently is referred to as *upstream pressure*, and a pressure calculated countercurrently is referred to as *downstream pressure*. In production engineering the upstream pressure is sometimes called *available pressure* and the downstream pressure is called *required pressure*. The cross section being considered is called a *node*, a term borrowed from pipeline network analysis where it refers to an intersection or "joint" of two or more pipe legs.

Complying with two basic principles of fluid mechanics, continuity and the conversion of mass in flow systems, the pressure calculated upstream and downstream at any arbitrary cross section, as well as the upstream and downstream flow rates, should be equal. These two conditions, referred to as flow equilibrium conditions, are sufficient to determine the pressure and rate prevailing at the considered node.

In the particular case of naturally flowing wells, the steady state flow equilibrium is referred to as *natural flow*. In sections 1.5 and 1.6, it is shown that the natural flow conditions are determined graphically as the intersection point of the upstream and downstream pressure-rate functions when plotted on a common graph. This is, in fact, a simultaneous solution of the equilibrium conditions that imply equal flow rate and equal flow pressure upstream and downstream at the considered node.

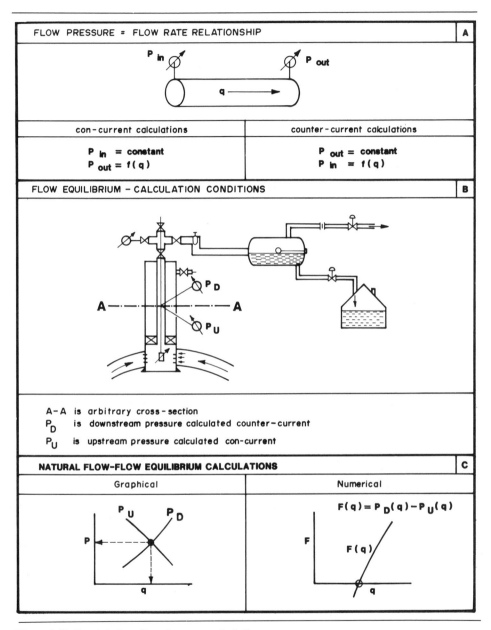

Figure 1.39 Concepts in well performance calculations.

Currently, it is most common to develop or acquire computer programs to calculate pressure-rate relationships in wells. These programs determine the natural flow conditions in a similar way to the described method, but by using numerical techniques. As this book is committed to showing how graphical methods are used to solve most practical problems, computerized solutions will not be discussed here. However, for orientation only, figure 1.39c gives an indication of the numerical approach to determine the natural flow point. The difference between the upstream and downstream pressure functions is defined as a function whose root is sought at the solution point. A root of a function is calculated numerically by an iterative procedure such as the method of Successive Bisection, the Secant method, or the Newton-Raphson method.

Depending on the upstream and downstream relationships, the mathematical solution for natural flow conditions might give two points, one of them representing an unstable equilibrium. Figure 1.40 illustrates a two-point solution, a stable and unstable natural flow point, with their mechanical analog. The stable point is analog to a ball located in a concave circular container (having upward curvature). If the ball (i.e., rate or pressure) is pushed either to the left or right, then it will always return to its original stable state. The unstable point is analog to a ball located on top of a convex surface (having downward curvature). If the ball is pushed to the right or left it will continue its descent spontaneously until a stable state (an upward curving or a flat surface) is reached.

Multiphase flow in the tubing is very erratic with random or cyclic fluctuations of pressure and rate that tend to disturb the flow. If the flow equilibrium is stable, the system will dampen any disruption, and the pressure and rate will converge to the original equilibrium state. But when the flow equilibrium is at the unstable point, even a small disruption will be amplified and the flow conditions will diverge away until they reach a more stable equilibrium.

Figure 1.40 is a schematic illustration of a typical two-solution case which was originally presented and discussed by Gilbert (1954). The natural flow is investigated for wellhead conditions by first solving the CPR and the WPR. Then, the stability or instability of a natural flow state is determined by the relative trends of the WPR and CPR. For the illustrated case, Gilbert states that the left-hand equilibrium point is unstable. As seen from the plot, a small momentary increase of the flow rate above the equilibrium rate provokes a pressure difference, where the required pressure is lower than the available one. This pressure separation drives the system away from the equilibrium point. The right-hand equilibrium point is a stable one. There, a momentary increase of flow rate above the equilibrium increases the required pressure and reduces the available one. This pressure separation dampens the disturbance and drives the system to converge to the original equilibrium level.

Mathematically, an equilibrium point will be stable if the following condition is satisfied:

$$(dp/dq)^{\text{upstream}} < (dp/dq)^{\text{downstream}} \tag{1.44}$$

As suggested by the original publication of Gilbert (1954) the stability analysis is conveniently applied to wellhead conditions. The concept, however, is more general and can be applied to any node along the flow path. To illustrate this, the wellhead conditions in figure 1.40 are supplemented by the corresponding down-hole condi-

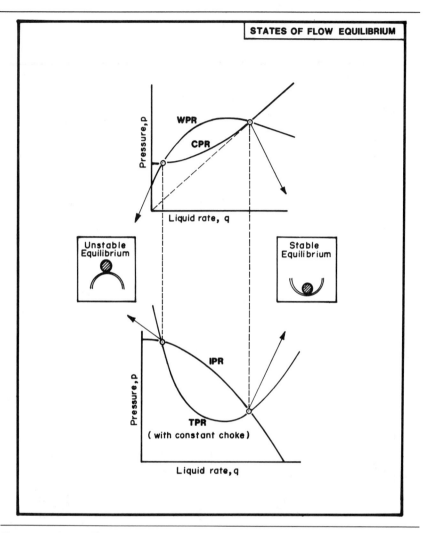

Figure 1.40 States of flow equilibrium.

tions. The same considerations applied by Gilbert for the wellhead node are valid for the bottom hole conditions as well. Note that the illustrated tubing intake pressure curve is different from the customary TPR. While the conventional TPR is constructed for a constant wellhead pressure, the illustrated intake performance curve is constructed for a constant choke size, because it has to match the corresponding wellhead conditions. A constant choke size implies an increase of wellhead pressure with increasing rate. Unfortunately, the first edition of this book (1986) failed to state this observation explicitly. Inquiries from confused readers indicated that they erroneously

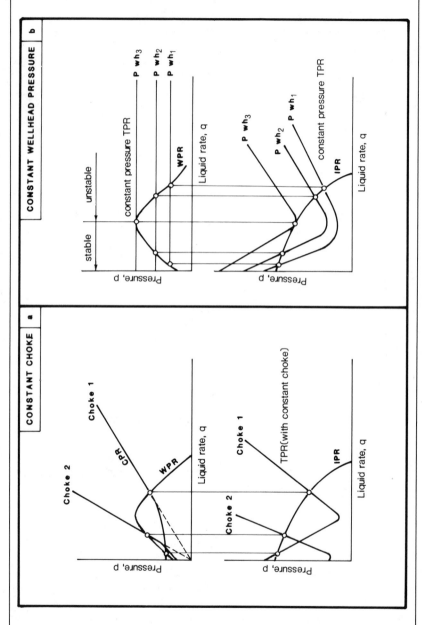

Figure 1.41 Stability analysis with and without choke.

applied a constant wellhead pressure TPR to analyze the stability of wells with fixed chokes. To avoid any further misunderstandings, figure 1.41 displays the fixed choke and the fixed wellhead pressure cases side by side. In the constant pressure case (fig. 1.41b), the tubing intake performance is the customary constant wellhead pressure TPR. Correspondingly, the *Flow-line Performance Relationship*, FPR, is a horizontal line implying constant wellhead pressure.

Note that figure 1.41b exhibits a distinct region of stable flow solutions to the right of the apex of the WPR, while the left side of the apex is always unstable. It is essential to recognize that the stable and unstable domains on both sides of the apex are relevant only to the analysis of the constant wellhead pressure case.

Truly, stability analysis in flowing wells is of limited practical use. It is introduced here primarily to prepare the readers for more realistic stability problems in gas-lift wells to be discussed in Chapter 5. There are, however, known cases where flowing wells producing smoothly at high rates become unstable and die when choked to comply with a lower production allowable. The observed instability in those wells substantiates theoretical stability considerations.

The erratic nature of flow in the well also sets limitations on the validity of conventional well performance analysis. While the analysis assumes smooth flow represented by time-averaged pressure and rate quantities, the actual flow, particularly in the well-bore and the tubing, is often very erratic. When the amplitudes of the fluctuating pressure and rate are large, the conventional analysis becomes meaningless. This is particularly true for wells where the upstream and downstream pressure relation curves approach each other asymptotically without a clear single solution point. There, the separation between the two time averaged performance curves might be smaller than the amplitude of the fluctuations over a wide range of the graph.

1.8   **SUMMARY.** This introductory chapter has addressed the most important aspects for engineering successful well performance. We began by discussing the elements of a production system, starting at the outer boundary of the formation, moving along the flow path, and terminating at the point of shipping to the pipeline. Two important concepts were considered throughout the chapter: the *pressure profile* along the path of flow, and the role of the *pressure gradient* as the primary driving force for moving fluid force. We mentioned several production systems and indicated the overall strategy and engineering methods used to analyze them successfully.

Phase behavior of reservoir and surface fluids is perhaps the most important physical concept used in well performance engineering. Petroleum production involves the flow of gas, oil, water, or some mixture of the three. Description of phase behavior relevant to the physics of fluid flow is often as important as the laws of flow themselves. We adopt the belief that a solid understanding of the most basic relations between pressure, volume, and temperature provides the engineer with fundamental tools that can be applied to any flow problem. Thus we introduced generalized PVT correlations for the calculation of volumetric properties. Instead of merely suggesting PVT correlations, we have tried to show why they are needed and how they can be used to solve practical well performance problems.

The inflow performance relation introduced the problem of reservoir flow toward the wellbore. Only the simplest IPR relations have been suggested, without going into their physical justification. The productivity index was suggested as an important quantity for ranking deliverability. It is also the constant of proportionality between rate and pressure drop for ideal liquids or undersaturated oils. We recommended empirical rate–pressure relations developed in the 1920s for describing the IPR of gas wells and saturated oil wells. The IPR of undersaturated oil wells is the composite of the straight-line IPR and the empirical saturated IPR.

Methods for calculating pressure loss in tubing were described, while specific equations and so-called gradient curves were introduced to quantify pressure losses for gas and gas/liquid mixtures. The main components of pressure loss in vertical conduits are friction, slippage, and hydrostatic forces. The approximate rate–pressure relation given for dry gas considers friction and hydrostatic components only. Gradient curves, which relate pressure to depth in flowing wells, account for all three components of pressure loss. Although gradient curves provide what many consider only a gross approximation, they give insight into the physical conditions of multiphase flow and how the tubing performance changes with geometry, gas/liquid ratio, and rate. We did not consider directly the numerous multiphase flow correlations that take into account flow regime and slippage.

The concept of natural flow was introduced by combining the results of inflow and tubing performance calculations. By specifying either wellhead flowing pressure or flow rate, the natural flow conditions of a well can be determined. Specifically, we considered the effect of wellhead pressure, gas/liquid ratio, tubing diameter, and inflow performance (e.g., depletion) on natural flow. If a well cannot flow on its own, then it is necessary to introduce artifical lift, usually in the form of a pump or gas lift. Special problems relating to the adjustment of depth were considered. In particular: (1) correcting tubing intake pressure so that it corresponds with wellbore flowing pressure, (2) correcting measured flowing pressures to the midperforation datum, and (3) adjusting the IPR to the tubing or pump intake datum to aid in the design of pump requirements.

Wellhead pressure is generally controlled with a choke. The interrelation of the choke opening to wellhead pressure, wellbore flowing pressure, and rate was discussed and shown by example. Wellhead, choke, and flowline performance relations were introduced separately and as a composite tool for solving well performance problems. The function of a choke was discussed in detail, reviewing the physics of flow near a choke and the mechanical design that results in large pressure losses over short distances. The concept of critical flow through a choke was discussed; specifically, the general rate/pressure relation for critical flow of gas/liquid mixtures was given. Flow from the wellhead to the pipeline by means of a flowline can often govern well performance if production does not first pass through a choke, or if subcritical flow through the choke is prevalent. Calculating pressure drop in horizontal pipe is the basis for determining flowline performance. A simple expression has been given for gas flow to illustrate the general effect of flowline performance on production. Multiphase flow in flowlines is a more difficult task and requires methods that are not discussed in this book. In review, the effect of choke and flowline performance on natural flow was considered.

Finally, the natural flow analysis was related to the flow equilibrium concept, a universal fluid mechanics concept. This establishes the basis to analyze, in consequent chapters, more complicated cases such as gas-lift production. Furthermore, while the upstream and downstream pressure-rate relationships are solved to determine the natural flow or the flow equilibrium conditions, their relative trends indicate the stability of the flowing state.

2   RESERVOIR ASPECTS OF
WELL PERFORMANCE

In section 1.3 we established that the inflow performance relation (IPR) describes the effect of the reservoir on well performance. Empirical IPR equations were suggested for gas, undersaturated oil, and saturated gas/oil systems. They were used to illustrate how reservoir inflow is integrated with the composite flow system making up the production unit. This chapter discusses the theoretical considerations for developing inflow relations.

Darcy's law sets the foundation for all calculations of flow in porous media. We begin by using it to develop the IPR equation of an ideal well that produces an ideal liquid by radial flow from an infinite reservoir. The ideal well model and the inflow equation are then adjusted to account for real conditions in oil and gas wells by considering the effects of

1. pressure conditions at the outer boundary of the drainage area
2. pressure dependence of volume factors and viscosity of reservoir fluids; undersaturated oil, saturated oil and gas
3. flow restrictions existing at the entry or near an actual wellbore
4. high-velocity flow near the wellbore exceeding the range of validity for Darcy's law
5. flow reduction due to the presence of a gas in saturated oil reservoirs
6. depletion of the reservoir
7. shape of the outer boundary of the well's drainage area
8. transient production, starting when a well is put on production and stabilizing when outer boundary effects become dominant

The outcome of the model and its adjustments is a set of equations useful for predicting or analyzing the inflow of wells in terms of reservoir properties and well data.

2.1   **FLOW TOWARD THE WELLBORE.** Flow of reservoir fluids toward the wellbore is caused by pressure gradients along the path of flow and/or gravity drainage. By assuming horizontal flow, we can neglect gravity effects on flow. The pressure

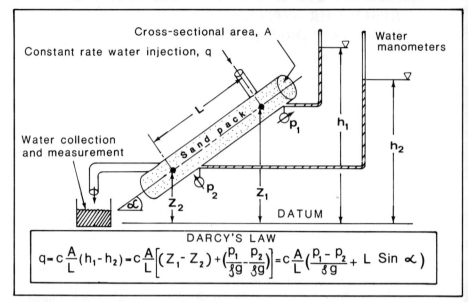

Figure 2.1 Sand-pack apparatus showing the method used by Darcy to develop his flow equation.

profile along the path of flow is characterized by a maximum pressure at the outer boundary and a minimum pressure at the inner boundary, the wellbore. Between these two points the pressure varies as a function of the distance from the wellbore. Pressure drop in the reservoir results from the dissipation of mechanical energy or loss of momentum as fluid flows against the resistance of the porous media. The actual path of flow is a maze of small, irregular channels with a sharply varying cross section. It is impractical to describe flow along the microscopic path by trying to take into account the flow regime (laminar or turbulent), velocity distribution, fluid-to-pore surface contact, and so forth. Instead, Darcy (d'Arcy 1856) chose to quantify the flow of fluid through porous media using a macroscopic model.

Figure 2.1 shows a schematic of the sand-pack apparatus used by Darcy to establish the rate–pressure relation of fluid flow through porous media—that is, Darcy's law. The creation of a pressure differential Δp, across a sand pack of length L results in a constant flow rate q, given by

$$q = cA\,(h_1 - h_2)/L = cA\,[(p_1 - p_2)/\delta g + L \sin \alpha/L \qquad (2.1a)$$

or for horizontal flow

$$q = CA\,\Delta p/L, \qquad (2.1b)$$

where C is a proportionality constant indicating the character of both fluid and porous media. Darcy's approach to quantifying the microscopic flow phenomenon in terms of macroscopic quantities sets the cornerstone for engineering calculations of flow in porous media.

Only in 1934 did Wycoff, Botset, Muskat, and Meres separate the constant

C into its two independent factors—viscosity and permeability—expressing independently the effects of the fluid and the rock. They also were the first to introduce the unit of permeability, the darcy (D), as it is used today. Writing flow velocity v as the ratio of volumetric rate to cross-sectional area perpendicular to flow, $v = q/A$, Darcy's law can be expressed

$$v = \left(\frac{k}{\mu}\right) \frac{(p_2 - p_1)}{L}. \tag{2.2}$$

Permeability k is a measure of the ease by which fluid flows through a particular rock. The unit darcy results from the choice of cgs units by Wycoff et al.:

$$\text{darcy [D]} = \frac{[\text{cm/s}][\text{cp}][\text{cm}]}{[\text{atm}]}. \tag{2.3}$$

Dimensional analysis of the unit darcy shows that permeability has dimensions of length squared (L^2). Appendix C gives the procedure for expressing the darcy in specific units of area:

darcy = $9.869 \times 10^{-9} \, \text{cm}^2$

$\quad = 9.869 \times 10^{-13} \, \text{m}^2 \ (\approx 1 \, \mu\text{m}^2 = 10^{-12} \, \text{m}^2)$

$\quad = 1.530 \times 10^{-9} \, \text{in.}^2$

$\quad = 1.062 \times 10^{-11} \, \text{ft}^2.$

Most reservoir rocks have permeability much less than one darcy. As a result, the oil industry has adopted the millidarcy (md) as its standard unit of permeability. We see that

1 darcy = 1000 millidarcies = 1000 md.

Reservoir rocks that produce oil and gas range in permeability from less than 0.0001 md to more than 10,000 md. Such a wide range, covering about 10 orders of magnitude, necessitates the introduction of an arbitrary classification scale. Our choice is given in table 2.1.

Table 2.1 Classification of Reservoir Type According to Absolute Permeability

Permeability Classification	Millidarcy (md)		Darcy ($\approx \mu\text{m}^2$)	
	Minimum	Maximum	Minimum	Maximum
Very low	0	0.01	0	0.00001
Low	0.01	1	0.00001	0.001
Average	1	100	0.001	0.1
High	100	10,000	0.1	10
Very high	10,000	100,000	10	100

Note that the darcy is nearly equivalent to a micrometer[2], that is, the approximation of 1 darcy = 1 μm^2 can be used for most engineering calculations based on the SI unit system.

Darcy's law is applicable to the great majority of reservoirs producing oil and gas. The proportionality of velocity to pressure drop is a simple relationship, which allows many complicated flow problems to be solved analytically. At high flow velocities, however, Darcy's law breaks down. Observations show that at high flow velocity, pressure drop in porous media increases more than linearly with increasing rate. At low flow velocity, the difference between the actual pressure drop and that calculated by Darcy's law is negligible. But as the velocity increases, the difference becomes significant.

Several models have been suggested to represent high-velocity flow. The most accepted model is the quadratic equation proposed by Forchheimer (1901). In general, the oil industry has adopted the approach of using Darcy's law and correcting the calculated pressure losses by adding a rate-dependent pressure-loss component (see sections 2.4 and 3.5).

Application of Darcy's law to reservoir flow requires definition of the inner and outer reservoir boundaries. Figure 2.2 shows several flow geometries that might be expected when fluid flows toward a wellbore:

1. cylindrical/radial flow (fig. 2.2a)
2. converged flow (fig. 2.2b)
3. linear flow (fig. 2.2c)
4. elliptical flow (fig. 2.2d)
5. pseudoradial flow (fig. 2.2e)
6. spherical flow (fig. 2.2f)
7. hemispherical flow (fig. 2.2g)

Two-dimensional, cylindrical/radial flow geometry is probably the most representative for the majority of producing oil and gas wells. Partial penetration and vertically fractured well geometries are the next most representative. True spherical flow is seldom found in producing wells, although hemispherical flow may be a close approximation for wells penetrating only the very tops of formations. In general, the inner boundary flow geometry is the most important to well performance, because a disproportionate large percentage of the pressure drop occurs near the wellbore.

Despite the effect that nonradial boundaries have on fluid flow, we can generally use the radial/cylindrical model by including correction factors for nonradial flow. The term *skin factor*, discussed in section 2.3, and chapter 3, provides the simplest correction for nonideal flow effects, including the effect of nonradial geometries.

2.2   **STEADY-STATE RADIAL FLOW FOR IDEAL LIQUIDS.** The simplest IPR considered in chapter 1 is the straight-line equation for undersaturated oils (eq. [1.31]), assuming the flowing wellbore pressure remains above the bubble point:

$$q_o = J(p_R - p_{wf}). \tag{1.31}$$

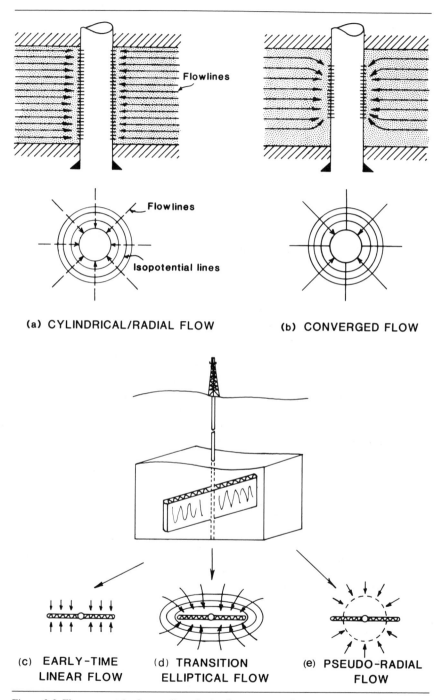

(a) CYLINDRICAL/RADIAL FLOW

(b) CONVERGED FLOW

(c) EARLY-TIME LINEAR FLOW

(d) TRANSITION ELLIPTICAL FLOW

(e) PSEUDO-RADIAL FLOW

Figure 2.2 Flow geometries for a well producing from a reservoir.

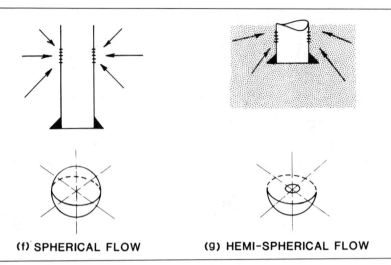

(f) SPHERICAL FLOW   **(g) HEMI-SPHERICAL FLOW**

Figure 2.2 (continued)

Equation (1.31) is based on field observations. It is, in fact, anticipated by Darcy's law. The reservoir properties determining J, the productivity index, will be discussed in this section.

Figure 2.3 illustrates a cylindrical/radial model of an ideal well penetrating a reservoir formation of constant thickness. An ideal well is one that drains a rock with uniform permeability (in all directions), completely penetrated and open to the producing interval through a radial wellbore. Flow is only in the radial direction, and the outer boundary is circular. Darcy's law, written in differential form for flow across a cylindrical envelope of infinitesimal thickness dr at an arbitrary distance r from the center, is

$$v = \frac{qB}{2\pi rh} = \left(\frac{k}{\mu}\right)\frac{dp}{dr}. \tag{2.4}$$

The term qB represents the volumetric flow rate across the area $2\pi rh$ at reservoir conditions where q is the surface volumetric rate and B is the formation volume factor. The expression dp/dr represents the pressure drop across a very thin cylindrical wall. To solve equation (2.4) for pressure drop in terms of constant rate, we must first separate variables (pressure p and radius r) and integrate from the wellbore to an arbitrary radius,:

$$\frac{2\pi kh}{q\mu B}\int_{p_{wf}}^{p} dp = \int_{r_w}^{r} dr/r, \tag{2.5}$$

where

$$\int_{r_w}^{r} dr/r = \ln(r/r_w). \tag{2.6}$$

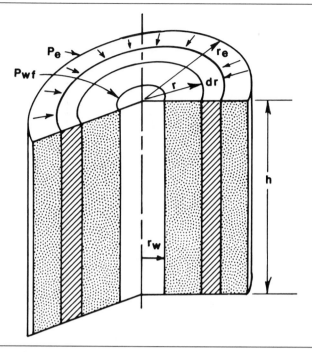

Figure 2.3 A radial flow model.

Solved in terms of pressure, equation (2.5) is written

$$p = p_{wf} + \frac{q\mu B}{2\pi kh}\ln(r/r_w).$$ (2.7)

Equation (2.7) expresses the radial pressure distribution around a well producing at a constant rate from a reservoir with homogeneous, isotropic, and constant rock and fluid properties. Note that pressure is proportional to the logarithm of the radius. Figure 2.4 shows a plot of pressure versus radius and pressure versus $\ln(r)$. Equation (2.7) assumes a set of consistent units. If field units are preferred, then equation (2.7) should be written

$$p = p_{wf} + \frac{141.2 q_o \mu_o B_o}{kh}\ln(r/r_w),$$ (2.8)

where q_o is in units of STB/D, μ_o is in cp, B_o is in bbl/STB, k is in md, h is in ft, p is in psia, and r is in ft. Example 2.1 illustrates that the greatest percentage of pressure drop occurs very near to the wellbore.

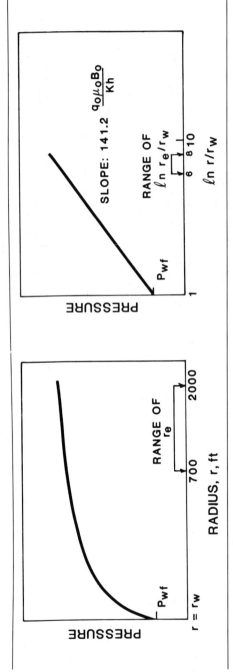

Figure 2.4 Radial steady-state pressure distribution for infinite reservoir.

EXAMPLE 2.1 PRACTICAL IMPLICATIONS OF THE RADIAL PRESSURE
DISTRIBUTION

A prolific oil well, the Willow No. 5, produces from the Lower Granite Wash.
After cleanup following a light acid treatment, the well produced at a stabilized rate
of 1325 STB/D for 22 hours. Downhole pressure gauges run into the well indicate
that the flowing pressure had stabilized at about 1850 psia. The flow period was
followed by a buildup test. Interpretation of buildup data gave a permeability-
thickness product kh of 3640 md-ft. The bit diameter drilled through the Granite
Wash was 8.5 in. giving a wellbore radius $r_w = (8.5/2 \text{ in.})/(12 \text{ in./ft}) = 0.354 \text{ ft}$.
Bottomhole samples were analyzed by a PVT laboratory, which reported bubble-
point pressure of 1610 psia and undersaturated oil FVF ranging from 1.2352 bbl/
STB at 2600 psia to 1.2450 bbl/STB at the bubble point ($B_o = 1.24 \text{ bbl/STB}$ is an
average). Undersaturated oil viscosity of 1.62 cp was measured with a rolling-ball
viscometer.

Calculate the theoretical pressure distribution and list the pressure drop across
1-ft intervals from r_w to 1.354 ft, 4 to 5 ft, 49 to 50 ft, and 499 to 500 ft.

SOLUTION

Substituting well data into equation (2.8), we obtain

$$p = 1850 + \frac{141.2(1325)(1.6)(1.24)}{3640} \ln(r/0.354)$$

$$= 1850 + 102 \ln(r/0.354)$$

$$= 1956.0 + 102 \ln(r).$$

Table E2.1 gives results of the calculations. The pressure loss at an interval directly
adjacent to the wellbore is 6 times greater than at 5 ft, 70 times greater than at 50 ft,
and 700 times greater than at 500 ft.

**Table E2.1 Pressure Distribution Calculation for the Willow
No. 5 Well, Producing at a Rate of 1325 STB/D**

Radius (ft)	Pressure (psia)	Radius interval (ft)	Pressure drop (psia)
0.354	1850.0	0.354–1.354	137.0
1.354	1987.0		
4.0	2097.4	4.0–5.0	22.8
5.0	2120.2		
49.0	2353.0	49.0–50.0	2.0
50.0	2355.0		
499.0	2589.7	499.0–500.0	0.2
500.0	2589.9		

To express the pressure distribution (eq. [2.8]) as an IPR equation, we need to define the outer boundary conditions and solve for rate in terms of pressure drop. Two types of outer-boundary conditions are considered here:

1. Constant-pressure outer boundary, representing the boundary along which reservoir pressure is maintained at its initial value. The constant-pressure boundary condition is usually caused by either water influx from a very large aquifer, or by water or gas injection in offsetting wells, or any combination of the three.
2. No-flow outer boundary, representing a boundary along which no fluid enters the drainage area. Typically, no-flow boundaries result from the pressure of offset producing wells and/or geological barriers such as faults and pinchouts.

After an initial production period with transient well pressure and rate, the outer boundary starts affecting production at the wellbore and flow stabilizes (see section 2.6). When stabilization is reached, the constant-pressure boundary outer condition results in what is usually called steady-state flow. Wells producing under steady-state conditions do not experience depletion, since average reservoir pressure remains constant. Stabilized flow from wells with no-flow boundaries is usually referred to as pseudosteady-state flow. Pseudosteady-state production, by definition, results from depletion, and a major consequence is that average reservoir pressure declines.

Returning to equation (2.8), we first consider the IPR for steady-state flow. In this case, at the outer drainage boundary the pressure p_e remains constant by encroachment of extraneous fluids coming from outside the drainage area. Substituting p_e and r_e for p and r in equation (2.8) results in

$$q_o = \frac{kh(p_e - p_{wf})}{141.2\mu_o B_o \ln(r_e/r_w)}. \tag{2.9}$$

In practice, pressure (p_e) at the outer boundary cannot be measured readily, but p_e does not deviate substantially from initial reservoir pressure if a strong aquifer is present and active (i.e., if permeability is high and field withdrawal rate is limited).

Well test results often report the volumetric average pressure p_R, which is defined by equation (2.116) in section 2.6. Average reservoir pressure is a useful quantity for reservoir material balance calculations. Craft and Hawkins (1959) showed that the volumetric average pressure is located at about 61% of the drainage radius r_e for steady-state flow. That is, substituting $0.61r_e$ in the radial pressure distribution (eq. [2.8]) gives a close approximation to the volumetric average pressure p_R:

$$p(r = 0.61r_e) = p_R$$

$$= p_{wf} + \frac{141.2q_o\mu_o B_o}{kh}\ln(0.61r_e/r_w), \tag{2.10}$$

or in terms of rate,

$$q_o = \frac{kh(p_R - p_{wf})}{141.2\mu_o B_o \ln(0.61 r_e/r_w)}.$$ (2.11)

But, since $\ln(0.61 r_e/r_w) = \ln(r_e/r_w) - 0.5$, we can write

$$q_o = \frac{kh(p_R - p_{wf})}{141.2\mu_o B_o [\ln(r_e/r_w) - 0.5]}.$$ (2.12)

For the case of pseudosteady-state flow, the volumetric average reservoir pressure occurs at about half the distance to the external radius:

$$p(r = 0.472 r_e) = p_R$$

$$= p_{wf} + \frac{141.2 q_o \mu_o B_o}{kh} \ln(0.472 r_e/r_w).$$ (2.13)

In terms of rate,

$$q_o = \frac{kh(p_R - p_{wf})}{141.2\mu_o B_o \ln(0.472 r_e/r_w)}$$ (2.14)

or, since $\ln(0.472) = -0.75$,

$$q_o = \frac{kh(p_R - p_{wf})}{141.2\mu_o B_o [\ln(r_e/r_w) - 0.75]}.$$ (2.15)

Figure 2.5 illustrates graphically the difference between steady-state and pseudosteady-state flow. Practically, whether one uses 0.5 or 0.75 for productivity calculations is not important. The underlying assumptions for steady- and pseudosteady-state flow are, however, quite different, and the resulting differences in reservoir performance are important. Steady-state flow implies that p_R does not change with time, while pseudosteady-state flow is based on the fact that p_R declines as a result of depletion. Most reservoirs exhibit at least partial decline, and the industry standard is to use the pseudosteady-state assumption in productivity calculations (eq. [2.15]).

Equation (2.15) is the equivalent of equation (1.31), the straight-line IPR. This allows us to define the productivity index J in terms of reservoir parameters:

$$q_o = J(p_R - p_{wf}),$$ (1.31)

where

$$J = \frac{kh}{141.2\mu_o B_o [\ln(r_e/r_w) - 0.75]}.$$ (2.16)

Viscosity (μ_o) and formation volume factor (B_o) are pressure-dependent properties. For undersaturated oils the variation in $\mu_o B_o$ is not great, as shown in

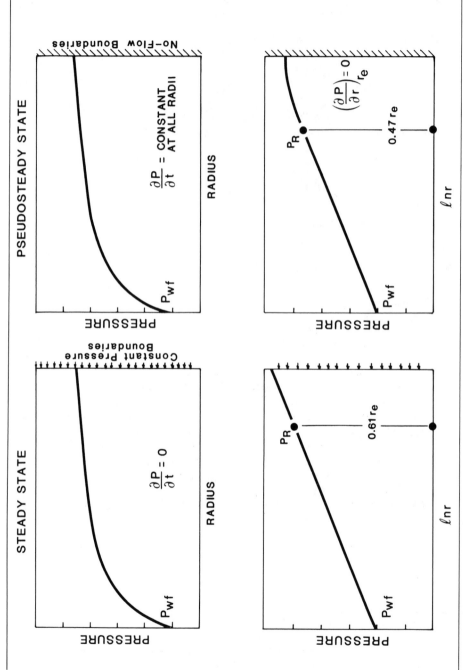

Figure 2.5 Pressure distributions representing steady-state and pseudosteady-state production.

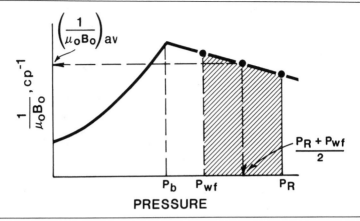

Figure 2.6 Undersaturated oil pressure function.

figure 2.6. Viscosity increases with pressure, while oil formation volume factor (FVF) decreases with pressure. The composite effect is that $1/\mu_o B_o$ decreases almost linearly with pressure. If we want to account for the pressure dependence of viscosity and FVF, then they should be included inside the pressure integral of the radial flow equation (eq. [2.5]):

$$\frac{kh}{141.2q_o}\int_{p_{wf}}^{p_e}\frac{dp}{\mu_o B_o}=\int_{r_w}^{r_e}dr/r$$

$$=\ln(r_e/r_w). \tag{2.17}$$

Solving for oil rate q_o,

$$q_o=\frac{kh}{141.2\ln(r_e/r_w)}\int_{p_{wf}}^{p_e}\frac{dp}{\mu_o B_o}. \tag{2.18}$$

The pressure integral equals the area under the curve when $1/\mu_o B_o$ is plotted versus pressure (shaded area in fig. 2.6). Since $1/\mu_o B_o$ is approximated by a straight line, the area is a trapezoid. Defining $(1/\mu_o B_o)_{av}$ as the value at an average pressure, $p_{av}=(p_e+p_{wf})/2$, then it is easily shown that

$$\int_{p_{wf}}^{p_e}\frac{dp}{\mu_o B_o}=\frac{p_e-p_{wf}}{(\mu_o B_o)_{av}}. \tag{2.19}$$

The resulting inflow equation for pseudosteady-state flow is

$$q_o=\frac{kh(p_R-p_{wf})}{141.2(\mu_o B_o)_{av}[\ln(r_e/r_w)-0.75]}, \tag{2.20}$$

where $(\mu_o B_o)_{av}$ is evaluated at $p_{av} = (p_R + p_{wf})/2$. Example 2.2 calculates the IPR of an oil well, using reservoir rock and fluid properties.

EXAMPLE 2.2 CALCULATING THE IPR OF AN OIL WELL FROM RESERVOIR ROCK AND FLUID PROPERTIES

The Willow No. 5 (example 2.1) produces from the Granite Wash, a typical oil-producing formation spaced on 80-acre units. Initial reservoir pressure of 2608 psia has been measured with bottomhole gauges.

A gas contract to sell the associated gas has been negotiated with a company that has a low-pressure pipeline laid about 80 miles from the new discovery. It will take about six months to complete the connecting pipeline. Meanwhile, the operator has to reduce the amount of gas wasted by flaring. Initial gas/oil ratio is 620 scf/STB. A reservoir study indicates that producing the well below the bubble point at high rates will result in a producing GOR of 750 scf/STB (mainly due to gas saturation buildup and unfavorable gas/oil relative permeability curves).

The maximum gas rate that can be flared is regulated by state law. One limit is an absolute maximum of 1 MMscf/D, and another is 125% of the initial gas/oil ratio (e.g., 775 scf/STB). Since the 1 MMscf/D limit will apply to this well before gasline hookup, calculate the following:

1. The undersaturated productivity index J from reservoir and well data specified here and in example 2.1. Assume 80-acre drainage. Compare this value with J as calculated from the rate/pressure data recorded in the initial flow test reported in example 2.1. Discuss the difference.
2. What rate can be produced by maintaining wellbore flowing pressure at the bubble point? Will the gas rate exceed the 1 MMscf/D limit?
3. When average pressure has dropped to 2000 psia, what rate will result, considering the 1 MMscf/D flaring allowable? Note that the flowing pressure will be below the bubble point (with GOR of 750 scf/STB).

SOLUTION

1. The drainage radius r_e for 80-acre spacing is approximated by equation (2.22),

$$r_e = [80(43560)/\pi]^{0.5}$$

$$= 1053\,\text{ft}.$$

Substituting reservoir and well data in the equation for productivity index (eq. [2.16]), we find

$$J = \frac{3640}{141.2(1.6)(1.24)[\ln(1053/0.354) - 0.75]}$$

$$= 1.793\,\text{STB/D/psi}.$$

Productivity index calculated from the test data is

EXAMPLE 2.2 continued

$J = 1325/(2608 - 1850)$

$= 1.75\,\text{STB/D/psi}$,

which is a reasonable check. It is not certain that the actual area drained during the test was 80 acres. For example, a slightly negative skin (see section 2.3) would balance the effect of a larger drainage area.

The effect of well spacing on the productivity index is easily shown to be small. For example, assuming 20-acre spacing results in a drainage radius of 530 ft, or 50% less than for 80-acre tracts. The productivity index for 20-acre drainage is 1.92 STB/D/psi, or an increase of 10%, corresponding to an additional 17.5 STB/D per 100 psi pressure drawdown.

2. The rate when flowing pressure equals the bubble point is

$q_o = 1.75(2608 - 1610)$

$= 1746\,\text{STB/D}$.

The corresponding gas rate is

$q_g = 1746(620)$

$= 1.08\,\text{MMscf/D}$,

which is very close to the flaring allowable.
3. As depletion progresses, and flowing pressure sinks below the bubble point, the allowable oil rate decreases. When p_R has reached 2000 psia, the oil rate corresponding to the 1 MMscf/D flaring allowable is

$q_o = 1.0 \times 10^6/750$

$= 1333\,\text{STB/D}$.

The corresponding flowing pressure is estimated from the appropriate IPR equation, equation (1.38),

$q_o = J(p_R - p_b) + (J/2p_b)(p_b{}^2 - p_{wf}{}^2)$,

or

$p_{wf} = \{p_b{}^2 - (2p_b/J)[q_o - J(p_R - p_b)]\}^{0.5}$

$= \{1610^2 - 2(1610/1.75)[1333 - 1.75(2000 - 1610)]\}^{0.5}$

$= 1180\,\text{psia}$.

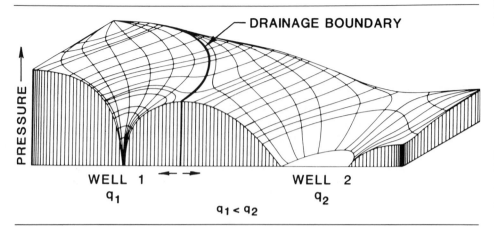

Figure 2.7 Outer drainage boundaries for two wells in a rectangular area. After Matthews and Lefkovitz 1955 by permission of the SPE-AIME.

The outer boundary of a well can be either a geological structural barrier or a hydrodynamic no-flow boundary that has occurred during the simultaneous production of several wells from a common reservoir. The latter type of boundary depends on the flow rate of the wells, since any change in production from one well in the reservoir will change the flow boundaries of all neighboring wells. The hydrodynamic no-flow boundary is an imaginary surface, which divides the reservoir so that fluid on its "right side" may flow only to the well at its right, and fluid on its "left side" may flow only to the well at its left. Figure 2.7 shows a three-dimensional schematic of the pressure distribution around two wells draining a rectangular area.

The rate of Well 2 in figure 2.7 is greater than the rate of Well 1, and the drainage area of is Well 2 proportionally larger than the area of Well 1.

To convey the practical meaning of no-flow drainage boundaries, an attorney reportedly used an interesting analogy to animal anatomy at a Michigan corporation commission hearing. The lawyer's client was trying to convince the commission that his well was not draining neighboring acreage. The lawyer argued that each well in a common source of supply drains in a similar manner to each teat on a cow's milk bag. His client lost the case, but not because of a poor analogy. The corporation commissioner, an earlier Secretary of Agriculture, was not aware that each teat on a cow's bag drains its own separate sac.

A method for approximating drainage area of wells producing from a common reservoir is to assume that the volume drained by a single well is proportional to it's rate of flow. Assuming constant reservoir properties, identical wells, and a uniform producing thickness, the approximate drainage area for a single well, A_w, is

$$A_w = A_R(q_w/q_R), \tag{2.21}$$

where q_w equals well rate, q_R equals total field rate, and A_R equals total field area (equal to pore volume divided by average pay zone porosity thickness).

The equivalent drainage radius r_e corresponding to the well's drainage area is

$$r_e = (A_w/\pi)^{0.5}. \qquad (2.22)$$

Equation (2.21) gives only an approximate value for the drainage area, yet as illustrated in example 2.2, the small error in drainage radius r_e has only a slight effect on the rate equation.

The concept of drainage area is particularly important in the United States, where individuals own the mineral rights associated with producing oil and gas properties. The basic units of area are township, section, acre, and square feet. All areas are square, and they are related as follows:

1 township = 6 sections × 6 sections

= 36 sections,

1 section = 1 mile × 1 mile (1 square mile)

= 640 acres,

1 acre = 43,560 square ft.

Well spacing designates the area per well that can be drilled and produced from a specific formation. Typical spacing for gas wells is one governmental section (640 acres), but with tighter formations the spacing may be as little as 160 acres (quarter spacing). Oil wells are usually spaced on 40-acre tracts, but the range may be from 10 to 160 acres.

Well spacing and density indicate the number of wells that can be drilled into and produced from a specific formation in the spaced area. Usually, the well density is one well per spacing unit. Special requests for increased density can be made after there is sufficient evidence that the wells drilled on the present spacing/density arrangement are not sufficient to drain the spaced area economically. In general, it is preferable to increase well density instead of decreasing spacing when a particular common source of supply (reservoir) is developed and/or producing from one-well density units.

A common governmental regulation used to mediate the effect of excess supply of oil and gas is definition and enforcement of allowables. An allowable defines the percentage of a well's open-flow potential that can be produced. The basic reasoning for regulation by allowables is that the supply of gas or oil should come from as many producers as possible. The result, theoretically, is that all producers have the right to sell their reserves, and at the same time there remains an incentive to search for new sources of oil and gas. Various regulatory authorities define allowables using different criteria, but the general rule is that from 25% to 50% of the calculated open-flow potential can be produced.

Although the preceding discussion has been directed at policies typical in the United States, similar regulations are found throughout the world. The concept of spacing and well density is particular to the United States, but analogous units of area are usually found in other countries.

2.3   **SKIN EFFECT.** The expression for radial pressure distribution of an oil well draining an infinite reservoir was given in section 2.2:

$$p(r) = p_{wf} + \frac{141.2 q_o \mu_o B_o}{kh} \ln(r/r_w). \qquad (2.23)$$

This expression is developed using several simplifying assumptions. It assumes that the reservoir has a uniform thickness, the well penetrates throughout the formation, and the flow is purely radial. In relation to permeability, it assumes that the formation is homogeneous and isotropic over the entire drainage region. It also assumes that the wellbore is clean and uncased. Finally, it assumes that Darcy's law is valid and characterizes the flow over the entire drainage zone.

Using the simplifying assumptions, it is implied in section 2.2 that the equation for pseudosteady-state flow (eq. [2.15]) can be written in terms of *ideal* pressure drop, $p_R - p_{wf}'$,

$$p_R - p_{wf}' = \frac{141.2 q_o \mu_o B_o}{kh} [\ln(r_e/r_w) - 0.75], \qquad (2.24)$$

where p_{wf}' indicates the wellbore flowing pressure for the case of an ideal well producing under the assumptions of the ideal radial model.

Rarely does a real well produce under the conditions of the ideal well model. Typically, the permeability of the formation near the wellbore is altered during the drilling and completion of the well, operations that are performed with well pressure overbalancing the formation pressure. Flux of solids and fluids from the wellbore tends to damage the permeability near the wellbore. The permeability is altered again by cleanup and stimulation treatments meant to remove formation damage or increase the productivity of the well. Other deviations from the ideal well are caused by flow restrictions in the perforations and convergence to the perforated interval, which is often only a fraction of the net pay zone.

The overall result is that the pressure distribution in an actual well differs from the calculation for an ideal well. The difference is larger near the wellbore and diminishes away from the wellbore. Figure 2.8 shows an artist's sketch of how the actual pressure distribution in a real well appears, compared to an ideal well.

The pressure difference between the ideal and actual wellbore flowing pressure, $p_{wf}' - p_{wf}$, represents an additional pressure loss due to formation damage, stimulation of the near-wellbore region, and other flow restrictions at the entry to the well. We usually refer to this additional pressure loss as Δp_s, or pressure loss due to "skin". A dimensionless skin factor s, proportional to Δp_s, is defined as

$$s = \frac{kh}{141.2 q_o \mu_o B_o} \Delta p_s \qquad (2.25)$$

or

$$\Delta p_s = \frac{141.2 q_o \mu_o B_o}{kh} s. \qquad (2.26)$$

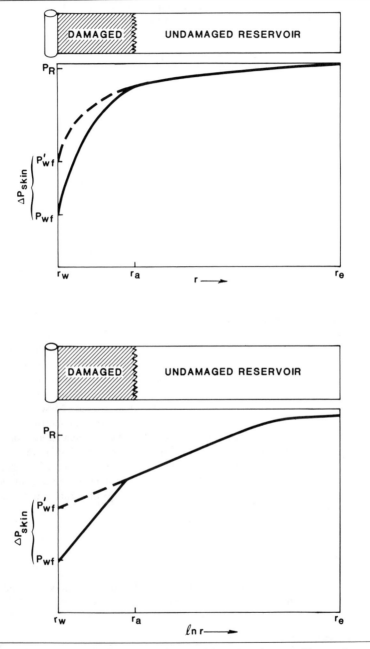

Figure 2.8 Actual pressure distribution of a well with an altered near-wellbore region.

Since $p_{wf}' - p_{wf} = \Delta p_s$, we can combine equations (2.24) and (2.26) to express the actual pressure loss $p_R - p_{wf}$ in terms of skin factor:

$$p_R - p_{wf}' = \frac{141.2q_o\mu_oB_o}{kh}[\ln(r_e/r_w) - 0.75],$$

plus

$$p_{wf}' - p_{wf} = \frac{141.2q_o\mu_oB_o}{kh}s,$$

which gives

$$p_R - p_{wf} = \frac{141.2q_o\mu_oB_o}{kh}[\ln(r_e/r_w) - 0.75 + s]. \qquad (2.27)$$

Rearranging equation (2.27) and solving for rate gives

$$q_o = \frac{kh(p_R - p_{wf})}{141.2\mu_oB_o[\ln(r_e/r_w) - 0.75 + s]}. \qquad (2.28)$$

Skin factor gives an indication of the character of flow near the wellbore, relative to an ideal well. Positive skin indicates damage or restriction to flow, and negative skin indicates stimulation or reduced restriction to flow. The magnitude of a skin factor—for example, +3, −2, or +25—is a relative measure of a nonideal effect on inflow performance of a given well. For example, a +2 skin in one well may result in additional pressure losses making production uneconomical, whereas in another well with a +20 skin the additional pressure losses are unimportant to production. To quantify the actual effect of the skin factor, it is necessary to calculate the constant $(141.2q_o\mu_oB_o/kh)s$ (or an equivalent expression for gas wells), which gives pressure loss due to skin. This pressure loss is then compared with pressure losses elsewhere in the well (reservoir, tubing, flowline, etc.).

It is sometimes more useful to express the effect of damage and stimulation in terms of flow efficiency, E_F, defined as the ratio of actual rate to ideal rate for a given pressure drawdown.

$$E_F = \frac{q_{actual}}{q_{ideal}}. \qquad (2.29)$$

In terms of the actual and ideal wellbore flowing pressures required to produce a given rate, flow efficiency has the form

$$E_F = \frac{p_R - p_{wf}'}{p_R - p_{wf}}. \qquad (2.30)$$

In terms of skin, it is easily shown that flow efficiency is expressed as

$$E_F = \frac{\ln(r_e/r_w) - 0.75}{\ln(r_e/r_w) - 0.75 + s}. \tag{2.31}$$

For most wells the term $\ln(r_e/r_w)$ ranges from 6.5 to 8.5. Using an average of $\ln(r_e/r_w) - 0.75 = 7.0$, we can write an approximate expression for flow efficiency in terms of skin:

$$E_F = \frac{7}{7 + s}, \tag{2.32}$$

which can be used as a rule of thumb.

Service companies often report nonideal conditions in terms of a damage ratio R_d, which is nothing more than the reciprocal of flow efficiency:

$$R_d = 1/E_F. \tag{2.33}$$

Another expression used to quantify nonideal flow conditions is the apparent wellbore radius r_{wa},

$$r_{wa} = r_w e^{-s}, \tag{2.34}$$

which, when substituted for wellbore radius, r_w, in equation (2.28) gives

$$q_o = \frac{kh(p_R - p_{wf})}{141.2 \mu_o B_o [\ln(r_e/r_{wa}) - 0.75]}. \tag{2.35}$$

Figure 2.9 illustrates the concept of apparent wellbore radius. A damaged well is indicated by an apparent wellbore radius *less* than the actual wellbore radius. A stimulated well is identified by an apparent wellbore radius greater than the actual value and sometimes approaching the drainage radius r_e. Table 2.2 reviews the character of damaged, stimulated, and "ideal" wells expressed in terms of skin, flow efficiency, damage ratio, and apparent wellbore radius.

Skin factor, or in shorter form, *skin*, is certainly the most familiar expression used by engineers to quantify nonideal flow conditions. It can be calculated with accuracy from reliable well test data. Otherwise, in the absence of test data it may be estimated from general correlations discussed in more detail in chapter 3. Example 2.3 illustrates a typical use of skin factor to determine the effect of nonideal flow on inflow performance.

Table 2.2 Characteristics of Damaged, Stimulated, and Unaltered (Ideal) Wells

Status of well	Quantifiable Effect of Nonideal Flow				
	Δp_s	s	E_F	R_D	r_{wa}
Damaged	$\Delta p_s > 0$	$s > 0$	$E_F < 1$	$R_D > 1$	$r_{wa} < r_w$
Unaltered	$\Delta p_s = 0$	$s = 0$	$E_F = 1$	$R_D = 1$	$r_{wa} = r_w$
Stimulated	$\Delta p_s < 0$	$s < 0$	$E_F > 1$	$R_D < 1$	$r_{wa} > r_w$

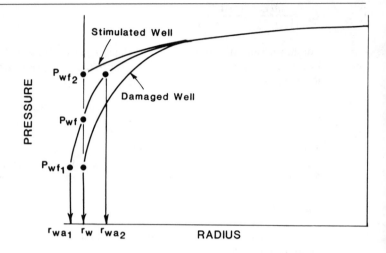

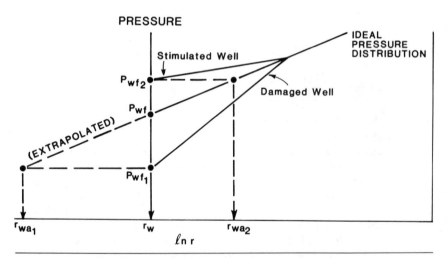

Figure 2.9 Illustration of the apparent wellbore radius concept.

EXAMPLE 2.3 USE OF SKIN FACTOR TO CORRECT FOR NONIDEAL FLOW

A satellite discovery, the Vik No. 1, lies adjacent to the Sandnes field. It produces light-gravity oil from a Cretaceous chalk formation. Data obtained from production testing, logging, and core evaluation are given in table E2.3. The test before acid treatment indicated a skin of +18.5, and after acid treatment this value was reduced to −4.2.

Calculate before and after acid treatment flow efficiency E_F, apparent wellbore radius r_{wa}, damage ratio R_d, and pressure loss due to skin Δp_s. The drainage per well is not known, and development plans have not indicated a proposed spacing.

EXAMPLE 2.3 continued

SOLUTION

Flow efficiency is approximated from skin using equation (2.32). Assuming $\ln(r_e/r_w) - 0.75 = 7$,

$E_F(\text{pre-acid}) = 7/[7 + 18.5]$

$\qquad\qquad = 0.27$

$\qquad\qquad = 27\%,$

$E_F(\text{post-acid}) = 7/[7 - 4.2]$

$\qquad\qquad = 2.5$

$\qquad\qquad = 250\%.$

Apparent wellbore radius is calculated from skin using equation (2.34):

$r_{wa}(\text{pre-acid}) = 0.29 \exp(-18.5)$

$\qquad\qquad = 2.68 \times 10^{-9} \, \text{ft},$

$r_{wa}(\text{post-acid}) = 0.29 \exp(+4.3)$

$\qquad\qquad = 21.4 \, \text{ft}.$

The damage ratio is merely the inverse of flow efficiency: pre-acid $R_d = 3.7$, and post-acid $R_d = 0.4$.

The pressure drop due to skin is calculated from equation (2.26):

$$\Delta p_s(\text{pre-acid}) = \frac{141.2(q_o)(0.31)(1.5)}{24(80)}(18.5)$$

$\qquad\qquad = 0.0342(18.5)q_o$

$\qquad\qquad = 0.633q_o,$

$\Delta p_s(\text{post-acid}) = 0.0342(-4.3)q_o$

$\qquad\qquad = -0.147q_o.$

For rates of 500, 1000, and 5000 STB/D the pre-acid $\Delta p_s = 316$, 633, and 3165 psi, and post-acid $\Delta p_s = -74$, -147, and -735 psi. The meaning of the negative Δp is that the pressure drawdown required in the stimulated well is less than that calculated for the ideal well.

EXAMPLE 2.3 continued

Table E2.3 Reservoir and Well Data for the Vik No. 1

Initial reservoir pressure	7055 psia
Initial oil FVF	1.5 bbl/STB
Total pay thickness	80 ft
Average permeability	24 md
Initial oil viscosity	0.31 cp
Bubble-point pressure	4800 psia
Wellbore radius (7-in. casing)	0.29 ft
Skin factor before acid treatment	+18.5
Skin factor after-acid treatment	−4.2

This section has discussed only the effect of steady-state or constant skin on the pressure drawdown and production rate. A rate-dependent skin is discussed in the following section. The physical aspects of the skin phenomenon are addressed in chapter 3.

2.4   RATE–PRESSURE RELATION FOR GAS WELLS. Rawlins and Schellhardt (1936), engineers from the U.S. Bureau of Mines, developed the classic backpressure equation relating gas rate to flowing pressure:

$$q_g = C(p_R^2 - p_{wf}^2)^n. \tag{1.33}$$

The equation was developed after interpreting several hundred multirate gas well tests. A linear trend was observed on a log–log plot of rate versus delta pressure-squared, $p_R^2 - p_{wf}^2$. At the time equation (1.33) was initially suggested, it was not obvious why pressure-squared, instead of pressure, should be used. Nor was it obvious why the exponent n was limited to a value between 0.5 and 1.0. Also absent from the early pioneers' work was an expression for C in terms of reservoir rock and fluid properties (when $n < 1.0$). Yet, even without theoretical argumentation, the backpressure equation received immediate, widespread acceptance and use by the gas industry.

Today we have a better understanding of the backpressure equation. We know that pressure squared accounts for the pressure dependence of fluid properties $(1/\mu_g B_g$ or $p/\mu_g Z)$. The backpressure exponent n accounts for high-velocity flow e.g., turbulence. (Note that n equals the reciprocal of the slope of the backpressure straight line.) Although the constant C has yet to be expressed analytically in terms of reservoir properties for cases other than $n = 1$, we know that it accounts for reservoir rock and fluid properties, flow geometry, and transient effects.

Several testing methods can be used to determine the backpressure relation for a gas well. They involve flowing the well at several rates, measuring flowing and buildup pressures, and plotting the results as q_g versus $p_R^2 - p_{wf}^2$ on log–log paper. The common multirate sequences include the flow-after-flow, isochronal, and modified isochronal tests. Example 1.7 (see chapter 1) illustrates the procedure for determining n and C from a flow-after-flow multirate test. The procedures for multirate testing are discussed in section 2.7. Here we shall only note that the flow-after-flow test assumes that a stabilized, pseudosteady state is reached before changing from one rate to the next. In fact, C is not a constant unless stabilized (pseudosteady-state) production exists. Isochronal tests can be at transient conditions during flow periods, but it is mandatory that shut-in periods, which separate flow periods, are of sufficient duration to reach static reservoir pressure at the wellbore. Also, isochronal tests usually are followed immediately by an extended flow period to determine the stabilized backpressure curve. Generally, multirate tests (particularly the modified isochronal test) should be run with increasing rates. Time required to reach stabilized flow varies from well to well. In general, the higher the permeability, the less time it takes to reach stabilization. On the log–log backpressure curve, a changing C is reflected by a gradual shift of the straight line to the left. The classic paper on multirate testing by Cullender (1955) reports multirate data that confirm this transient behavior of C. Cullender also shows how important it is to account for the shifting backpressure curve during a test of a slow-to-stabilize well.

The backpressure equation originated from field observations. This section will show that, for the particular case of a low-pressure gas well with a backpressure coefficient $n = 1$, the equation matches the behavior predicted by Darcy's law. Lower values of n reflect deviations from Darcy's law that affect and often dominate calculations and interpretations of gas well production.

In section 2.1 we noted that Darcy's law breaks down at high flow velocity. Many models were suggested to replace or modify Darcy's law for high-velocity flow. Several models and their experimental background are discussed by Muskat (1937). The most accepted model was proposed by Forchheimer in 1901:

$$dp/dr = av + bv^2, \tag{2.36}$$

where a and b are constants and $v = q/A$ is fluid velocity. Later work by Green and Duwez (1951) and Cornell and Katz (1953) expressed equation (2.36) in terms of fluid and rock properties

$$dp/dr = (\mu/k)v + \beta\rho v^2, \tag{2.37}$$

where

μ = gas viscosity,
ρ = gas density,
k = formation permeability,
β = high velocity coefficient.

The high-velocity coefficient in equation (2.37) is a property of the formation rock that accounts for the deviation from Darcy's law. Equation (2.37) implies that two rock parameters, permeability and the high-velocity coefficient, are needed to express high-velocity flow in reservoirs.

The deviation from Darcy's flow is more pronounced in gas wells than in oil wells. Therefore, it is introduced here for the first time. Section 3.4 is dedicated to high-velocity flow and expands the discussion beyond the short introduction in this section.

In relation to the radial flow equation we should note two major differences between gas and undersaturated oil flow: (1) gas properties have a strong pressure dependence at low and intermediate pressures, and (2) high-velocity effects are exhibited by gas flow at relatively low rates. It is possible to account for these phenomena in a gas radial flow model to establish inflow performance equations valid for the entire range of reservoir pressure and flow velocity. The gas equations are developed in terms of reservoir parameters and can be used for both production predictions and data interpretation.

We start from Darcy's law in differential form (eq. [2.4]),

$$v_g = \left(\frac{k}{\mu_g}\right)\frac{dp}{dr}.$$

Velocity can be expressed in terms of volumetric rate at standard conditions q_g and gas FVF, B_g ($= TZP_{sc}/pT_{sc}$):

$$v_g = \frac{q_g B_g}{2\pi hr} = \left(\frac{q_g}{2\pi hr}\right)\left(\frac{TZp_{sc}}{pT_{sc}}\right).$$ (2.38)

Substituting equation (2.38) in equation (2.4), separating variables (pressure p and radius r), defining inner and outer boundaries, and performing some algebraic manipulation and simple integration, the final expression for gas rate is

$$q_g = \frac{2\pi kh T_{sc}}{Tp_{sc}\ln(r_e/r_w)} \times \int_{p_{wf}}^{p_e} \frac{p}{\mu_g Z}\,dp.$$ (2.39)

Equations (2.38) and (2.39) presume that a set of consistent units has been used. Equation (2.39), written in field units for pseudosteady-state conditions, is

$$q_g = \frac{0.703kh}{T[\ln(r_e/r_w) - 0.75]} \times 2\int_{p_{wf}}^{p_R} \frac{p}{\mu_g Z}\,dp,$$ (2.40)

where terms and their units are: q_g (scf/D), k (md), h (ft), r (ft), T (°R), p (psia), and μ_g (cp). Standard conditions of 14.7 psia and 60°F (i.e., 520°R) are assumed in the constant 0.703, as is $Z = 1$ at standard conditions. The integral in equation (2.40) represents the area under the curve of $p/\mu_g Z$ versus pressure. Figure 2.10 shows a typical plot of the gas pressure function $p/\mu_g Z$.

The pressure function exhibits three distinct regions of behavior. At low pressures, usually less than 2000 psia, the $p/\mu_g Z$ curve is linear, and intercepts at the origin. This is equivalent to the observation that $1/\mu_g Z$ is essentially constant at low pressures (see fig. 2.11). At pressures higher than about 3000 psia the pressure function $p/\mu_g Z$ is nearly constant, showing some decrease at increasing pressures. Between 2000 and 3000 psia the pressure function shows distinct curvature. In review, the pressure function $p/\mu_g Z$ has three regions of behavior: low-pressure linearity, intermediate-pressure curvature, and high-pressure flattening. We might note that $p/\mu_g Z$ is directly proportional to $1/\mu_g B_g$, where $p/\mu_g Z = [p_{sc}(T/T_{sc})]$ $(1/\mu_g B_g)$.

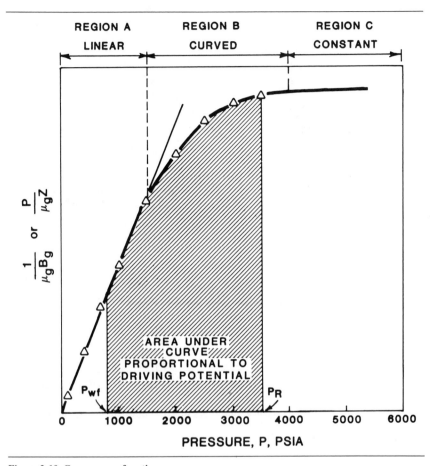

Figure 2.10 Gas pressure function.

The low-pressure behavior of $p/\mu_g Z$ results in a simple analytical solution to the pressure integral in equation (2.40):

$$2\int_{p_{wf}}^{p_R} \frac{p}{\mu_g Z}\,dp = \frac{p_R^2 - p_{wf}^2}{\mu_g Z}, \tag{2.41}$$

where p_R is assumed to be less than about 2000 psia. As indicated in figure 2.11, $1/\mu_g Z$ is essentially constant in the low-pressure region, and thus μ_g and Z can be evaluated at any pressure. By convention, we usually evaluate μ_g and Z at p_R. The radial flow equation for gas at *low pressures* can now be written

$$q_g = \frac{0.703\,kh(p_R^2 - p_{wf}^2)}{T\mu_g Z[\ln(r_e/r_w) - 0.75 + s]}, \tag{2.42}$$

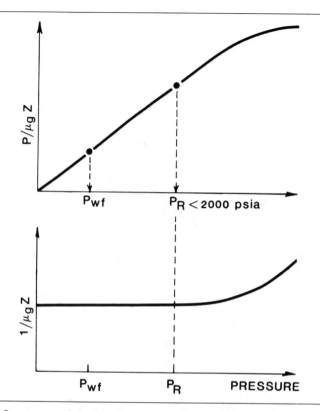

Figure 2.11 Low-pressure behavior of gas pressure function, $p/\mu_g Z$, and $1/\mu_g z$.

where skin s is defined as

$$s = \frac{0.703kh}{q_g T \mu_g Z}(p_{wf}'^2 - p_{wf}^2) \tag{2.43}$$

Recalling that p_{wf}' indicates wellbore flowing pressure for an ideal well, the skin factor in Equation (2.43) is proportional to delta pressure squared, caused by nonideal flow.

Using the Forchheimer modification to Darcy's law for high-velocity flow, equation (2.42) can be written

$$q_g = \frac{0.703kh(p_R^2 - p_{wf}^2)}{T\mu_g Z[\ln(r_e/r_w) - 0.75 + s + Dq_g]}, \tag{2.44}$$

where D is proportional to constant b in the Forchheimer equation (eq. [2.36]). The term Dq_g is commonly referred to as rate-dependent skin and is discussed in detail in section 3.4.

Although equations (2.42) and (2.44) appear similar except for the term Dq_g, they represent two different flow models. While the first one expresses the linear rate–pressure relationship of Darcy's law, the second one expresses the Forchheimer model. This similarity in form is very useful. It allows for all equations that are developed with Darcy's law to be modified to account for high-velocity effects by merely adding a rate-dependent skin term. Example 2.4 illustrates the use of the radial flow equation for gas wells producing at low reservoir pressures.

EXAMPLE 2.4 INFLOW PERFORMANCE CALCULATIONS FOR A GAS WELL PRODUCING AT LOW RESERVOIR PRESSURES

A two-rate drawdown/buildup test was run on a new gas discovery well in Kansas, the Medicine Lodge No. 1. For the first buildup following an eight-hour flow period at 6.4 MMscf/D, Horner analysis indicated a permeability-thickness (kh) of 790 md-ft and a skin of +3.62. The second buildup followed a 12-hour flow period at 8.7 MMscf/D, and Horner analysis indicated a kh of 815 md-ft and a skin of +4.63. Other reservoir data included initial reservoir pressure of 1623 psia at a temperature of 128°F. From standard gas property correlations, the initial gas viscosity and Z-factor are 0.0134 cp and 0.879, respectively.

Determine the high-velocity flow term D, used in the radial flow equation (2.44). What is the steady-state skin factor (i.e., when rate equals zero)? Write the IPR equation using the pressure-squared, low-reservoir pressure assumptions. Assume an average kh of 800 md-ft and $\ln(r_e/r_w) - 0.75 = 7$.

SOLUTION

First, we determine the rate-dependent skin coefficient D using skins reported from buildup test analysis. However, since a different kh is reported for each test, it is necessary to calculate an average kh and then correct the skin accordingly. Assuming stabilized flow, the corrected test skin s_{tc} is found from the actual test skin s_t from the relation

$$\frac{(kh)_{\text{test}}}{\ln(r_e/r_w) - 0.75 + s_t} = \frac{(kh)_{\text{avg}}}{\ln(r_e/r_w) - 0.75 + s_{tc}}$$

In this example we assume $\ln(r_e/r_w) - 0.75 = 7$ and $(kh)_{\text{avg}} = 800$ md-ft. The corrected test skin for the first test with rate of 6.4 MMscf/D is

$$\frac{790}{7 + 3.62} = \frac{800}{7 + s_{tc}}$$

or

$$s_{tc} = (800/790)(7 + 3.62) - 7$$

$$= 3.75.$$

EXAMPLE 2.4 continued

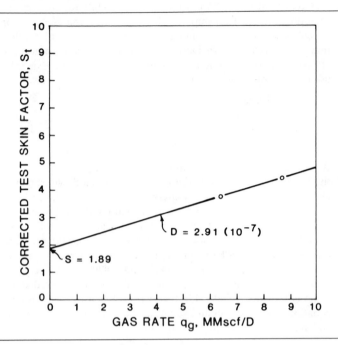

Figure E2.4a Rate-dependent skin factor in the Medicine Lodge No. 1 gas well.

For the second test with rate of 8.7 MMscf/D, corrected skin is

$$\frac{825}{7 + 4.63} = \frac{800}{7 + s_{tc}}$$

or

$$s_{tc} = (800/815)(7 + 4.63) - 7$$

$$= 4.42.$$

A plot of corrected test skin versus gas rate is shown in figure E2.4a. The slope of the straight line gives a value of $D = 2.91 \times 10^{-7}$ $(\text{scf/D})^{-1}$. The intercept at zero rate equals the steady-state skin, $s = +1.89$, indicating slight formation damage.

A common error is to plot test skin versus rate without making the kh correction. Had this been done for this example the steady-state skin would be underestimated, rate-dependent skin would be overestimated, and AOF would be underestimated by 1.0 MMscf/D (corresponding to about $700,000 per year for a gas price of $2/Mscf). *It must be emphasized that the skin-versus-rate plot is not valid if kh associated with each skin is different.*

EXAMPLE 2.4 continued

Table E2.4 Calculated Gas IPR for the Medicine Lodge No. 1 Well

p_{wf} (psia)	$p_R^2 - p_{wf}^2$ (psia^2)	q_g (MMscf/D)
0	2.63×10^6	15.8 (AOF)
500	2.38×10^6	14.7
750	2.07×10^6	13.2
1000	1.63×10^6	11.0
1250	1.07×10^6	7.78
1500	3.84×10^5	3.18
1550	2.32×10^5	1.99

The stabilized IPR equation for the Medicine Lodge No. 1 is found by substituting reservoir and test data in equation (2.44).

$$q_g = \frac{0.703(800)(1623^2 - p_{wf}^2)}{(128 + 460)(0.0134)(0.879)[7 + 1.89 + 2.91 \times 10^{-7}q_g]}$$

$$= 81.2 \frac{(2.63 \times 10^6 - p_{wf}^2)}{(8.89 + 2.91 \times 10^{-7}q_g)}$$

or

$$\frac{2.63 \times 10^6 - p_{wf}^2}{q_g} = 0.1095 + 3.58 \times 10^{-9}q_g,$$

giving $A = 0.1095$ and $B = 3.58 \times 10^{-9}$. Solving the quadratic equation for rate,

$$Bq_g^2 + Aq_g - \Delta p^2 = 0$$

$$q_g = \frac{[A^2 + 4B\Delta p^2]^{0.5} - A}{2B}$$

$$= \frac{[(0.1095)^2 + 4(3.58 \times 10^{-9})(2.63 \times 10^6 - p_{wf}^2)]^{0.5} - 0.1095}{2(3.58 \times 10^{-9})}$$

$$= \frac{[0.0120 + 1.43 \times 10^{-8}(2.63 \times 10^6 - p_{wf}^2)]^{0.5} - 0.1095}{7.16 \times 10^{-9}}.$$

Table E2.4 gives a few rates and flowing pressures, which are plotted in figure E2.4b on log–log paper. From about 5 MMscf/D to the maximum rate (AOF) of 16 MMscf/D, the IPR curve is a straight line on the log–log plot. The slope is 1.89, corresponding to a backpressure exponent of $n = 0.766$.

EXAMPLE 2.4 continued

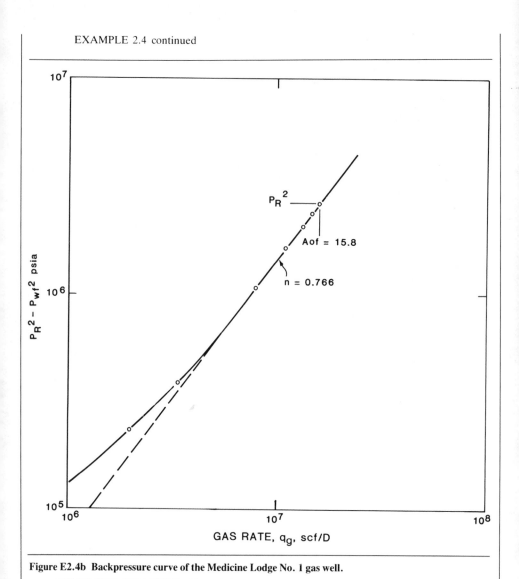

Figure E2.4b Backpressure curve of the Medicine Lodge No. 1 gas well.

At high pressures, usually greater than 3000 to 3500 psia, the pressure function $p/\mu_g Z$ is nearly constant. The pressure integral in equation (2.40) is solved analytically to give

$$2 \int_{p_{wf}}^{p_R} \frac{p}{\mu_g Z} dp = 2 \frac{p}{\mu_g Z} (p_R - p_{wf}),$$

(2.45)

where $p/\mu_g Z$ is evaluated at any pressure between p_{wf} and p_R, although we must emphasize that *both* pressures must be higher than about 3000 psia. The resulting IPR equation for gas wells producing at high flowing and static pressures is

$$q_g = \frac{1.406kh(p/\mu_g Z)(p_R - p_{wf})}{T[\ln(r_e/r_w) - 0.75 + s + Dq_g]}. \tag{2.46}$$

The high-pressure approximation of gaswell IPR is not commonly used by engineers. We mention it only to bring attention to the similarity between high-pressure gas and undersaturated oil flow.

The pressure-squared approach for low-pressure gas wells and the straight-line IPR for high-pressure gas wells are only valid in the regions of pressure for which they are designed. A more general approach to account for the pressure dependence of gas properties is to perform the integration of $p/\mu_g Z$ (eq. [2.40]) for the entire range of pressures applicable to a given well. This amounts to calculating the area under the $p/\mu_g Z$ curve from p_{wf} to p_R.

Figure 2.12 illustrates a useful property of integration that is applied to solve the integral in practical engineering problems. Let us define the area from zero pressure (vacuum) to any other pressure as $A(p)$. It can be shown that the area under the $p/\mu g Z$ curve from p_1 to p_2 is merely $A(p_2) - A(p_1)$, where $p_2 > p_1$. A special name, pseudopressure, designated $m(p)$, has been given to the quantity $2A(p)$ (Al-Hussainy, et. al. 1966). That is,

$$m(p) = 2\int_0^p (p/\mu_g Z)dp, \tag{2.47}$$

where $m(p)$ is the analog to pressure or pressure squared in equation (2.41). The differential pseudopressure, $\Delta m(p) = m(p_R) - m(p_{wf})$, represents the driving force or potential moving gas toward the well. Mathematically, $\Delta m(p)$ is given by

$$\Delta m(p) = 2\int_{p_{wf}}^{p_R} (p/\mu_g Z)dp$$

$$= 2\int_0^{r_R} (p/\mu_g Z)dp - 2\int_0^{p_{wf}} (p/\mu_g Z)dp = m(p_R) - m(p_{wf}). \tag{2.48}$$

Substituting equation (2.48) in the radial flow equation (eq. [2.40]) and including the effect of high-velocity flow, the most general gas IPR for stabilized flow is

$$q_g = \frac{0.703kh[m(p_R) - m(p_{wf})]}{T[\ln(r_e/r_w) - 0.75 + s + Dq_g]}. \tag{2.49}$$

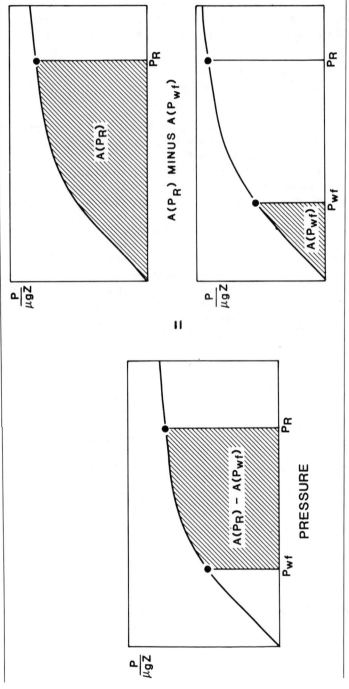

Figure 2.12 Useful property of integration shown graphically and used by the pseudopressure approach.

The relation for skin is then written

$$s = \frac{0.703kh}{q_g T} [m(p_{wf}') - m(p_{wf})],$$
(2.50)

where $m(p_{wf}')$ corresponds to the ideal wellbore flowing pressure p_{wf}', and $m(p_{wf})$ corresponds to the actual (nonzero skin) flowing pressure p_{wf}.

Two practical problems are usually associated with the pseudopressure function $m(p)$: (1) It must be calculated by tabulating p, μ, and Z, plotting $p/\mu Z$, and integrating graphically or numerically. (2) The magnitude of $m(p)$ is much larger than pressure (usually on the order of 100 times pressure-squared, or $m[p] \approx 100p^2$). These problems can be overcome with some practice, as is shown in example 2.5.

EXAMPLE 2.5 CALCULATING THE GAS PSEUDOPRESSURE FUNCTION $m(p)$

This example shows a simple procedure for calculating the gas pseudopressure function $m(p)$. The integral in equation (2.47) can usually be approximated with sufficient accuracy from the trapezoid rule of integration. This is perhaps best illustrated by a simple procedure summarized in table E2.5. Each step corresponds to a column in the table.

Basic Data:

[1] p : pressure (psia)
[2] Z : gas compressibility factor
[3] μ_g : gas viscosity (cp)

Calculate:

[4] $p/\mu_g Z$: pressure function (psia/cp)
[5] $(p/\mu_g Z)_{av}$: average for two successive entries (psia/cp)
[6] Δp : pressure difference for two successive entries (psi)
[7] $2(p/\mu_g Z)_{av}\Delta p$: incremental pseudopressure (psi²/cp)
[8] $m(p)$: the sum of products in column (7) (psi²/cp)

Table E2.5 tabulates the eight quantities. The calculated pseudopressure function is plotted in figure E2.5.

EXAMPLE 2.5 continued

Table E2.5 Calculation Procedure for Gas Pseudopressure, $m(p)$

p [1]	Z [2]	μ_g [3]	$p/\mu_g Z$ [4]	$(p/\mu_g Z)_{av}$ [5]	Δp [6]	$2([5][6])$ [7]	$m(p) = \text{Sum } [7]$ [8]
0			0				
14.7	0.998	0.0127	1,160	580[a]	14.7	1.70 E4[b]	1.70 E4
400	0.960	0.0130	32,051	16,606	385	1.28 E7	1.28 E7
800	0.925	0.0135	64,064	48,058	400	3.84 E7	5.12 E7
1200	0.895	0.0143	93,761	78,913	400	6.31 E7	1.14 E8
1600	0.873	0.0152	120,576	107,169	400	8.57 E7	2.00 E8
2000	0.860	0.0162	143,554	132,065	400	1.06 E8	3.06 E8
2250	0.856	0.0169	155,533	149,544	250	7.48 E7	3.81 E8
2500	0.857	0.0177	164,811	160,172	250	8.01 E7	4.61 E8
2750	0.860	0.0185	172,847	168,829	250	8.44 E7	5.45 E8
3000	0.867	0.0193	179,285	176,066	250	8.80 E7	6.33 E8
3150	0.872	0.0197	183,370	181,328	150	5.44 E7	6.88 E8

[a]Column [5] lists the arithmetic average of the pressure function $p/\mu_g Z$ in the pressure interval Δp.
[b]1.70 E4 is the notation for 1.70×10^4.

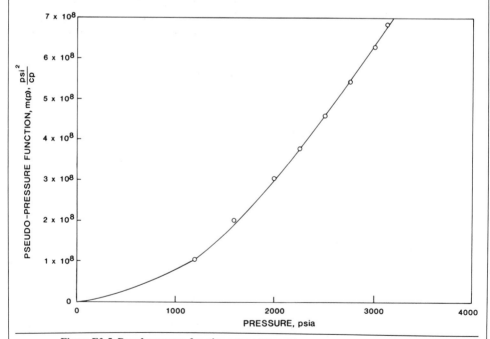

Figure E2.5 Pseudopressure function versus pressure.

An important characteristic of the pseudopressure function is that it is only necessary to calculate gas pseudopressure one time for a given field. Afterwards, it can apply to all wells in a gas field throughout the production life. Example 2.6 illustrates the use of the pseudopressure function to predict the IPR of a gas well.

EXAMPLE 2.6 GAS IPR CALCULATED USING PRESSURE-SQUARED AND PSEUDOPRESSURE METHODS

The 0.61-gravity gas considered in example 2.5 applies to the Crawford gas reservoir in northwestern Nebraska. The Crawford No. 1 produces from the Mississippi Chat at a depth of about 7040 ft. Initial reservoir pressure was 3150 psia, and the maximum temperature recorded during the well test was 148°F. The SP, gamma ray, and induction logs indicate a net pay of about 22 ft. The Chat is a clean sand with similar quality throughout the Crawford field, and usually requiries a small acid treatment to remove formation damage. Core and test permeabilities for the No. 1 well averaged about 20 md. Local graduate students from a state university studied the effect of high-velocity flow on several Chat core samples. They correlated high-velocity coefficient and permeability data and concluded that a D term of 1.5×10^{-6} 1/scf/D could be used for the Crawford No. 1 well.

The well could not be tested at high rates because no pipeline hookup was available and the No. 1 well was located on the edge of the Crawford city limits, in a residential area. Before drilling more wells, the operator requests an estimation of the well's deliverability. Make the following calculations using (a) the pressure-squared gas IPR (eq. [2.44]) and (b) the pseudopressure gas IPR.

1. Calculate and plot the gas IPR on Cartesian paper.
2. Determine the AOF.

SOLUTION

Since the spacing and estimated drainage area are not known, $\ln(r_e/r_w) - 0.75$ will be assumed equal to 7.0. Since the formation sand face has been cleaned with acid, steady-state skin of zero is assumed. Using the available rock and fluid properties the two IPR equations are

$$q_g = \frac{0.703(20)(22)(3150^2 - p_{wf}^2)}{(148 + 460)(0.0197)(0.872)(7 + 1.5 \times 10^{-6}q_g)}$$

$$= 29.6(9.92 \times 10^6 - p_{wf}^2)/(7 + 1.5 \times 10^{-6}q_g)$$

or, when rearranged

$$\frac{9.92 \times 10^6 - p_{wf}^2}{q_g} = A + Bq_g$$

$$= 0.236 + 5.07 \times 10^{-8}q_g,$$

EXAMPLE 2.6 continued

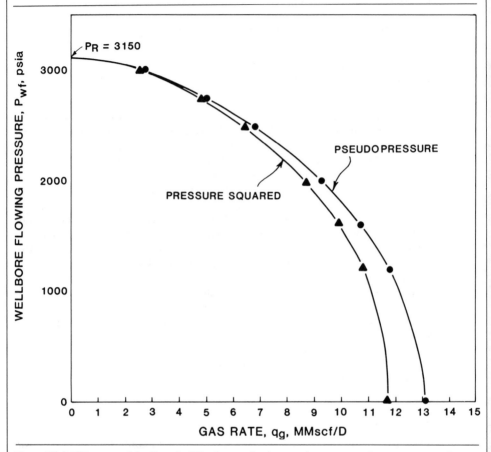

Figure E2.6 IPR curves of the Crawford No. 1 gas well using pseudopressure and pressure-squared approaches.

yielding the q_g solution

$$q_g = \frac{[A^2 + 4B\Delta p^2]^{0.5} - A}{2B}$$

$$= \frac{[0.0557 + 2.03 \times 10^{-7}(9.92 \times 10^6 - p_{wf}^2)]^{0.5} - 0.236}{1.01 \times 10^{-7}}.$$

Using the pseudopressure IPR, gas rate is expressed by

$$q_g = \frac{0.703(20)(22)[6.88 \times 10^8 - m(p_{wf})]}{(148 + 460)(7 + 1.5 \times 10^{-6}q_g)}$$

$$= 0.509[6.88 \times 10^8 - m(p_{wf})]/(7 + 1.5 \times 10^{-6}q_g)$$

EXAMPLE 2.6 continued

Table E2.6 Calculation of Gas IPR Curves for the Crawford No. 1 Well

p_{wf} (psia)	p_{wf}^2 (psia^2)	$m(p_{wf})$ (psi^2/cp)	q_g (MMscf/D) for IPR	
			PRESSURE-SQUARED	PSEUDO-PRESSURE
0	0.00	0.00	11.7	13.1
1200	1.44 E6	1.14 E8	10.8	11.8
1600	2.56 E6	2.00 E8	9.96	10.7
2000	4.00 E6	3.06 E8	8.74	9.28
2500	6.25 E6	4.61 E8	6.50	6.74
2750	7.56 E6	5.45 E8	4.89	5.01
3000	9.00 E6	6.33 E8	2.53	2.57

or by the quadratic equation with $A = 13.8$ and $B = 2.95 \times 10^{-6}$ with the direct solution

$$q_g = \frac{[190 + 1.18 \times 10^{-5}[6.88 \times 10^8 - m(p_{wf})]^{0.5} - 13.8}{5.90 \times 10^{-6}}.$$

Table E2.6 tabulates the results of the calculations needed to plot the two IPR curves as in figure E2.6. The plot indicates that IPR calculated by the pressure-squared approach is more conservative than IPR calculated by the pseudopressure approach.

Concerning the practical application of the radial flow equation including rate-dependent skin Dq_g, equation (2.44) can also be written as a quadratic equation (Forchheimer model)

$$p_R^2 - p_{wf}^2 = Aq_g + Bq_g^2, \tag{2.51}$$

where

$$A = \frac{T\mu_g Z}{0.703kh}[\ln(r_e/r_w) - 0.75 + s] \tag{2.52}$$

and

$$B = \frac{T\mu_g Z}{0.703kh}D. \tag{2.53}$$

The term $\mu_g Z$ can be evaluated at any pressure as long as $p_R < 2000$ psia.

For high-pressure gas wells with limited drawdown, pressure can be used instead of pressure-squared, in which case the Forchheimer quadratic equation is written

$$p_R - p_{wf} = Aq_g + Bq_g^2, \tag{2.54}$$

where

$$A = \frac{T}{1.407kh} \left(\frac{\mu_g Z}{p_{av}} \right) [\ln(r_e/r_w) - 0.75 + s] \qquad (2.55)$$

and

$$B = \frac{T}{1.407kh} \left(\frac{\mu_g Z}{p_{av}} \right) D. \qquad (2.56)$$

Note that $\mu_g Z$ is evaluated at $p_{av} = (p_R + p_{wf})/2$.

If pseudopressure $m(p)$ is used instead of pressure-squared, the rate equation is written

$$m(p_R) - m(p_{wf}) = Aq_g + Bq_g^2, \qquad (2.57)$$

where

$$A = \frac{T}{0.703kh} [\ln(r_e/r_w) - 0.75 + s] \qquad (2.58)$$

and

$$B = \frac{T}{0.703kh} D. \qquad (2.59)$$

The most practical solution of the Forchheimer equation is to plot $(p_R^2 - p_{wf}^2)/q_g$ versus q_g, $(p_R - p_{wf})/q_g$ versus q_g, or $[m(p_R) - m(p_{wf})]/q_g$ versus q_g on linear coordinate paper. The result is a straight line with intercept A and slope B. Figure 2.13 illustrates such a plot, using pressure-squared for a low-pressure gas well. The slope B in figure 2.13 indicates the significance of high-velocity effect on the productivity of the well. A large slope implies large rate-dependent skin. The intercept A is related to steady-state skin factor.

If rate needs to be written in terms of flowing pressure, the quadratic equations can be solved as follows:

$$q_g = \frac{[A^2 + 4B\Delta p^2]^{0.5} - A}{2B}, \qquad (2.60)$$

$$q_g = \frac{[A^2 + 4B\Delta p]^{0.5} - A}{2B}, \qquad (2.61)$$

and

$$q_g = \frac{[A^2 + 4B\Delta m(p)]^{0.5} - A}{2B}, \qquad (2.62)$$

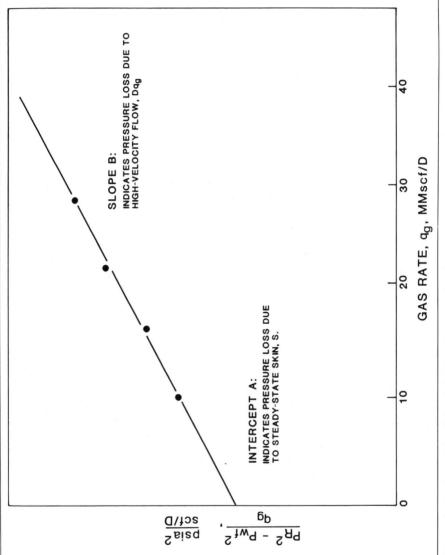

Figure 2.13 Linear plot for determining high-velocity flow effect on well performance.

where $\Delta p^2 = p_R^2 - p_{wf}^2$, $\Delta p = p_R - p_{wf}$, and $\Delta m(p) = m(p_R) - m(p_{wf})$. Obviously, values of A and B will be different, depending on whether pressure, pressure-squared, or pseudopressure is used.

Example 2.7 illustrates the linearized plot of test data for a gas well. The constant D in the rate dependent skin factor is related to the slope B of the linear plot in figure 2.13 by equations (2.53), (2.56), or (2.59). By combining equations (2.37) and (2.44) the constant is related also to rock properties,

$$D = 2.222 \times 10^{-18} \frac{\gamma_g kh}{\mu_g r_w h_p^2} \beta. \qquad (2.63)$$

EXAMPLE 2.7 LINEAR PLOT OF GASWELL TEST DATA

The Cullender No. 5 gas well produces from a shallow, low-pressure, highly productive reservoir. The well has been tested by a multirate test and the results are listed in table E2.7. One-hour duration of each flow period was enough to reach stabilization of flowing wellbore pressure. In fact, it was observed that pressures stabilized almost instantaneously after each rate change.

The three high flow rates (March 30, 1950) were obtained by flow-after-flow sequence without shut-in between flow periods. The three low flow rates were performed at three consecutive days; each flow period started from shut-in conditions. Determine the IPR and evaluate the high-velocity-flow effects in the well.

SOLUTION

The reservoir did not exhibit appreciable depletion during the test period and reservoir pressure was essentially constant. Downhole pressures listed in table E2.7 were calculated from wellhead pressures using vertical flow correlations, which probably explains the spread in static reservoir pressures. The IPR will be established by using both the backpressure equation and the quadratic equation.

The log–log backpressure plot in figure E2.7a gives a straight line which defines a backpressure exponent $n = 1/\text{slope} = 0.55$. The backpressure coefficient is calculated from the curve as

$$C = 8.737 \times 10^6/(11270)^{0.55} = 49{,}468 \text{ scf/D/psi}^2.$$

The backpressure equation then is

$$q_g = 49{,}468(p_R^2 - p_{wf}^2)^{0.55},$$

and the absolute open-flow is 39.8 MMscf/D.

A Cartesian plot of $\Delta p^2/q_g$ versus q_g (fig. E2.7b) gives a straight line (except for a small deviation and the low-rate point). The intercept of the line is

EXAMPLE 2.7 continued

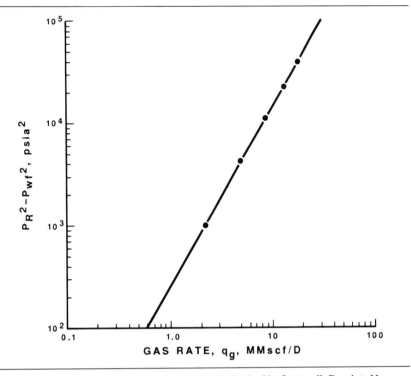

Figure E2.7a Stabilized backpressure curve of the Cullender No. 5 gas well. Reprinted by permission of the SPE-AIME from Cullender 1955. © 1955 SPE-AIME.

$$A = 0.00028 \frac{\text{psia}^2}{\text{scf/D}}.$$

The slope is

$$B = 1.26 \times 10^{-4} \frac{\text{psia}^2/\text{scf/D}}{\text{MMscf/D}}$$

or, when expressed in scf/D,

$$B = 1.26 \times 10^{-10} \frac{\text{psia}^2/\text{scf/D}}{\text{scf/D}}.$$

The low n value and the high B value indicate large rate-dependent skin.

Reservoir data were not presented by Cullender (1955) and it is therefore difficult to quantify steady-state skin s and rate-dependent skin coefficient D. It is certain, however, that rate-dependent pressure losses dictate reservoir inflow performance.

EXAMPLE 2.7 continued

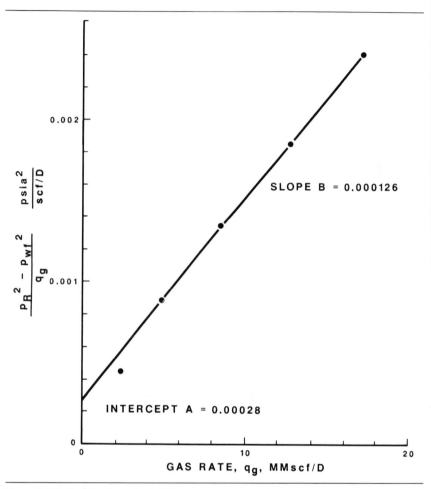

Figure E2.7b Stabilized quadratic IPR curve of the Cullender No. 5 gas well.

Table E2.7 Test Data of Cullender No. 5 Gas Well (March–April 1950)

Date	p_R psia	Δt hr	p_{wf} psia	q_g MMscf/D	$p_R^2 - p_{wf}^2$ psia^2	$\Delta p^2/q_g$ psia^2/scf/D
March 30	439.0	1	425.97	8.373	11270	0.001340
March 30	439.0	1	411.69	12.484	25250	0.001860
March 30	439.0	1	390.08	16.817	40600	0.002410
April 3	439.9	1	439.80	0.570	90	0.000158
April 4	439.6	1	438.45	2.231	1010	0.000453
April 5	439.8	1	434.86	4.841	4320	0.000892

The high velocity coefficient $\beta\,(1/\text{ft})$ can be approximated by an empirical correlation (discussed later in section 3.4)

$$\beta = 2.73 \times 10^{10} k_a^{-1.1045}, \tag{2.64}$$

where k_a is the permeability used to evaluate β, equal to the effective gas permeability near the wellbore. In equation (2.63), h_p is the formation thickness open to flow. If the near-wellbore region is not damaged or stimulated with acid, the D term is essentially independent of permeability, since β is approximately proportional to $1/k$ and D is proportional to βk. Without an estimate of permeability, D can be written (with $\beta \approx 1.69 \times 10^{10}/k$):

$$D = 3.75 \times 10^{-8} \frac{\gamma_g h}{\mu_g r_w h_p^{\,2}}. \tag{2.65}$$

The slope and intercept of the cartesian plot together with equations (2.63) and (2.49) provide a useful mean for interpreting multirate well test data in terms of formation properties and well completion data. Example 2.8 applies the quadratic rate equation to interpret test data.

EXAMPLE 2.8 HIGH-PRESSURE GASWELL MULTIRATE TEST INTERPRETATION

The McLeod No. 1A (McLeod 1983) is a high-pressure gas well producing from the Worth sandstone. During the first year of production, the average reservoir pressure dropped from 12,315 psia to 5,565 psia. Six tests have been run and relevant data are given in table E2.8a. General reservoir and well data are given in table E2.8b.

Use the quadratic equation to develop an inflow performance relation for the McLeod No. 1A at pressures encountered during the second year of production (approximately 5000 psia average reservoir pressure).

Table E2.8a Test Data for the McLeod No. 1A Well

	1	2	3	4	5	6
q_g (MMscf/D)	7.152	8.080	7.739	5.178	4.850	4.895
p_R (psia)	12,315	10,177	8,625	6,365	5,815	5,565
p_{wf}^{*} (psia)	11,458	9,070	7,691	5,915	5,260	5,082
p_{av} (psia)	11,887	9,624	8,158	6,140	5,538	5,324
Z at p_{av}	1.55	1.38	1.26	1.10	1.05	1.04
μ (cp) at p_{av}	0.0380	0.0340	0.0310	0.0265	0.0245	0.0240
$(\Delta p/q_g)(p_{av}/\mu Z)$	24.2	28.1	25.2	18.3	24.6	21.0

*Bottomhole pressures calculated from surface pressures.

EXAMPLE 2.8 continued

Table E2.8b Reservoir and Well Data for the McLeod No. 1A Well

Formation permeability* k	200 md
Net pay h	26 ft
Estimated drainage radius r_e	1320 ft
Wellbore radius r_w	0.375 ft
Gas gravity γ_g	0.635
Formation temperature T_R	245°F

* From sidewall core data.

SOLUTION

The quadratic equation (2.51) can be written

$$\left(\frac{p_R - p_{wf}}{q_g}\right)\left(\frac{p_{av}}{\mu_g Z}\right) = A' + B'q_g,$$

where

$$A' = \frac{T}{1.407kh}[\ln(r_e/r_w) - 0.75 + s]$$

and

$$B' = \frac{T}{1.407kh}D.$$

Note that μ_g and Z are evaluated at p_{av}, where

$$p_{av} = (p_R + p_{wf})/2.$$

This form of normalizing pressure accounts for severe depletion and large changes in pressure-dependent properties during the period of testing. In other words, since the term $p_{av}/\mu_g Z$ shows considerable variation as a result of depletion, it has been eliminated from the expressions of the slope and the intercept. A plot of $[(\Delta p/q_g)(p_{av}/\mu_g Z)]$ versus q_g is shown in figure E2.8.

The reservoir has high permeability and the drainage volume appears to be limited, based on the rapid depletion indicated by the test data in table E2.8a. We can assume stabilized flow for all five tests. Two interpretations of the data are possible.

The first interpretation uses rates 1, 2, 3, and 4, which define a straight line with slope $B' = 3.01 \times 10^{-6}$ and intercept $A' = 2.7$. Based on $kh = 200(26) = 5200$ md-ft and $\ln(r_e/r_w) - 0.75 = \ln(1320/0.375) - 0.75 = 7.42$, we calculate

$$D = B'1.407kh/T$$

$$= 3.01 \times 10^{-6}(1.407)(5200)/(460 + 245)$$

EXAMPLE 2.8 continued

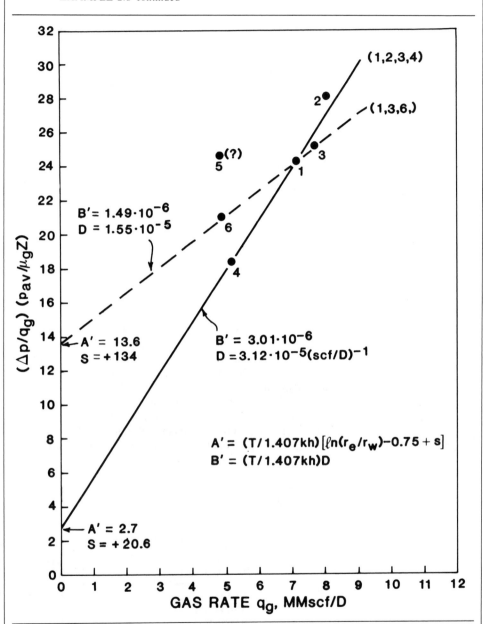

Figure E2.8 Quadratic IPR plot of test data of the McLeod No. 1 gas well.

EXAMPLE 2.8 continued

$$= 3.12 \times 10^{-5} (\text{scf/D})^{-1}$$

and

$$s = A'1.407kh/T - [\ln(r_e/r_w) - 0.75]$$

$$= 2.7(1.407)(5200)/(460 + 245) - 7.42$$

$$= +20.6.$$

The second interpretation uses rates 1, 3, and 6 to define a straight line with slope $B' = 1.49 \times 10^{-6}$ and intercept $A' = 13.6$, yielding

$$D = 1.49 \times 10^{-6}(1.407)(5200)/(460 + 245)$$

$$= 1.55 \times 10^{-5} (\text{scf/D})^{-1}$$

and

$$s = 13.6(1.407)(5200)/(460 + 245) - 8.2$$

$$= +134.$$

The two interpretations are considerably different. Table E2.8c indicates the actual difference and its impact on stabilized well performance.

The conclusion about the test data is that (1) a damaged zone appears to restrict flow near the wellbore, and (2) the high-velocity flow is exacerbated by the damaged permeability. Also, the test data show considerable scatter, indicating changing conditions near the wellbore through the first year of production, and/or bad data. Part of the scatter may result from calculating bottomhole pressures from wellhead measurements. McLeod used the test data to substantiate a high-velocity-flow model for the perforations. His model is discussed in chapter 3 (section 3.5) and in example 3.8.

Table E2.8c Results of Two Interpretations of Test Data for the McLeod No. 1A

	Total Skin $s + Dq$ (well flowing pressure)	
(MMscf/D)	$s = +20.6$, $D = 3.12 \times 10^{-5}$	$s = +134$, $D = 1.55 \times 10^{-5}$
2	82.2 (4921)*	164.0 (4849)
4	144.6 (4732)	195.0 (4644)
6	207.0 (4434)	226.0 (4384)
8	269.4 (4027)	257.0 (4071)
10	331.8 (3511)	288.0 (3703)

*$p_R = 5000$ psia, $(p_{av}/\mu_g Z) = 220{,}000$, or $1/\mu_g Z = 0.0227$ cp^{-1}.

Comparing equation (2.42) with the backpressure equation, we can write an expression for C (stabilized) in terms of reservoir properties for the case of $n = 1$:

$$q_g = C(p_R{}^2 - p_{wf}{}^2), \tag{2.66}$$

where

$$C = \frac{0.703kh}{T\mu_g Z[\ln(r_e/r_w) - 0.75 + s]}. \tag{2.67}$$

When applied for a high-pressure gas well,

$$q_g = C(p_R - p_{wf}), \tag{2.68}$$

where

$$C = \frac{1.407p_{av}kh}{T\mu_g Z[\ln(r_e/r_w) - 0.75 + s]}, \tag{2.69}$$

with $\mu_g Z$ evaluated at p_{av}. In terms of the pseudopressure function,

$$q_g = C[m(p_R) - m(p_{wf})], \tag{2.70}$$

where

$$C = \frac{0.703kh}{T[\ln(r_e/r_w) - 0.75 + s]}. \tag{2.71}$$

Equations (2.66) through (2.71) apply to stabilized flow when the Dq_g term is small and can be neglected; $Dq_g \ll [\ln(r_e/r_w) - 0.75 + s]$. At high rates, or when Dq_g has a relatively large effect, the Dq_g term dominates the skin and the resulting low-pressure gas equation (eq. [2.44]) becomes

$$q_g = \left[\frac{0.703kh(p_R{}^2 - p_{wf}{}^2)}{T\mu_g ZD} \right]^{0.5} \tag{2.72}$$

or

$$q_g = C(p_R{}^2 - p_{wf}{}^2)^{0.5}, \tag{2.73}$$

where

$$C = \left[\frac{0.703kh}{T\mu_g ZD} \right]^{0.5}. \tag{2.74}$$

Similar expressions for C can also be written for pressure and pseudopressure when Dq_g dominates the flow equation. Equations (2.66) through (2.74) apply for the two limiting conditions of inflow equations; pure Darcy flow ($D = 0$, $n = 1$) and completely turbulent flow ($D = \infty$, $n = 0.5$).

A generalized expression for the backpressure equation that is valid at the two limiting conditions and approximate for the range $0.5 < n < 1.0$ is, for low-pressure gas,

$$q_g = C(p_R^2 - p_{wf}^2)^n, \tag{1.33}$$

where

$$C = \frac{(0.703kh)^n}{(T\mu_g Z)^n D^{1-n}[\ln(r_e/r_w) - 0.75 + s]^{2n-1}}. \tag{2.75}$$

For high-pressure gas wells,

$$q_g = C(p_R - p_{wf})^n, \tag{2.76}$$

where

$$C = \frac{(1.407 p_{av} kh)^n}{(T\mu_g Z)^n D^{1-n}[\ln(r_e/r_w) - 0.75 + s]^{2n-1}}. \tag{2.77}$$

Using the pseudopressure function,

$$q_g = C[m(p_R) - m(p_{wf})]^n, \tag{2.78}$$

where

$$C = \frac{(0.703kh)^n}{T^n D^{1-n}[\ln(r_e/r_w) - 0.75 + s]^{2n-1}}. \tag{2.79}$$

Tek, Grove, and Poettman (1957) published alternative expressions for the backpressure constant C if $n < 1$, based on theoretical arguments put forth by Houpeurt (1953). Their work is not widely used by the industry because of a somewhat complicated procedure for determining C. We have found the relations presented here accurate enough for practical applications. Example 2.9 shows the use of equations (1.33) and (2.75) for a gas well in the Hugoton field in Texas.

EXAMPLE 2.9 STABILIZED MULTIRATE TEST ANALYSIS OF THE FREE NO. 4 WELL, HUGOTON FIELD, TEXAS

The Free No. 4 is a low-pressure gas well in the Texas Hugoton field. Cullender [Gas Well No. 1] (1955) and Tek et al. (1957) analyzed test data on the Free No. 4 obtained from 1944 to 1946. Table E2.9a gives relevant reservoir and well data. Using the approximate relation for backpressure constant C in equation (2.75), compare the calculated value with the field constant determined from a 24-hour test (table E2.9b).

159

EXAMPLE 2.9 continued

Table E2.9a Reservoir and Well Data for the Free No. 4 Well

Net pay thickness h^a	120 ft
Permeability k^b	30 md
Reservoir temperature T	90°F
Initial gas viscosity μ_c	0.012 cp
Initial Z-factor Z	0.925
Initial total compressibility c_{ti}	0.0016 1/psi
Gas gravity γ_g	0.712
Wellbore radius r_w	0.292 ft
Skin factor s^b	−3.2
Backpressure exponent n^b	0.867
Porosity, ϕ	0.07

[a] The zone was completed open hole with an acid treatment.
[b] Based on evaluation of all the Cullender data.

Table E2.9b 24-hour Test Data for the Free No. 4 Well

Test Reference	p_R (psia)	p_{wf} (psia)	q_g (MMscf/D)	Test C
Cullender				
10-03-44	435.2	302.8	9.900	467.1
10-24-44	436.8	390.0	4.440	467.9
12-11-45	394.7	375.8	1.947	478.5
Tek et al.[*]	424.0	357.9	5.165	423.2

[*] Last of four 24-hour rates in a flow after flow sequence.

SOLUTION

Constant C is given by equation (2.75) as

$$C = \frac{[0.703kh/T\mu Z]^n}{D^{1-n}[\ln(r_e/r_w) - 0.75 + s]^{2n-1}}.$$

In section 2.7 it is shown that the transient drainage radius is calculated from equation (2.135) as

$$r_e = 0.024[kt/\phi\mu_i c_{ti}]^{0.5}.$$

For 24-hour isochronal flow periods the drainage radius is

$$r_e = 0.024[(30)(24)/(0.07)(0.012)(0.0016)]^{0.5}$$

$$= 555 \, ft.$$

EXAMPLE 2.9 continued

This yields

$$\ln(r_e/r_w) - 3.2 = \ln(550/0.292) - 3.2$$

$$= 4.3$$

From equation (2.63)

$$D = 2.222 \times 10^{-18} \frac{\gamma_g kh\beta}{\mu_g r_w h_p^{2}}$$

$$= 2.222 \times 10^{-18} \frac{(0.712)(30)(120)(2.73 \times 10^{10})(30^{-1.1045})}{(0.012)(0.292)(120^2)}$$

$$= 7.19 \times 10^{-8}.$$

Substituting the values of r_e and D in equation (2.75) gives

$$C = \frac{[(0.703)(30)(120)/(550)(0.012)(0.925)]^{0.867}}{(7.19 \times 10^{-8})^{0.133}(4.3)^{0.734}}$$

$$= 568$$

The 24-hour rate–pressure data given by Cullender and by Tek et al. give C values that range from 423 to 479. The calculated C is higher, although it is a good approximation. A permeability of 30 md has been used here, even though Tek et al. report $k = 46.9$ md from a buildup test. The 30 md value was determined from analysis of all the transient data given by Cullender (see example 2.21). Since the Tek et al. analysis uses calculated bottomhole pressures and the buildup follows a four-point flow-after-flow sequence (24 hours each), the accuracy of their analysis can be argued. The calculated $C = 568$ represents the backpressure equation at the end of the 24-hour flow period. Example 2.21 shows that the C value in this well will continue to decrease until pseudosteady state is reached (after 21 days) and C stabilizes.

2.5   **RATE–PRESSURE RELATION FOR SATURATED OIL WELLS.** Thus far we have considered the flow of undersaturated oil and gas, both of which are considered homogeneous (single-phase) systems. Most oil wells, however, produce both gas and oil from the reservoir. The most typical two-phase gas/oil system is the solution gas drive reservoir. Gas that is initially dissolved in the oil at reservoir conditions evolves continuously as pressure drops below the bubble point. The free gas pushes the oil toward producing wells as it seeks to occupy more of the pore volume for expansion. After a sufficient gas saturation has developed in the formation the free gas also moves toward the producing wells. In many reservoirs the oil may be undersaturated at initial reservoir pressure (expansion drive), but as the oil moves toward the wellbore the pressure can drop below the bubble point, when two-phase flow results. In either case—solution gas drive or expansion drive—the inflow performance of the oil phase is reduced by the evolution of free gas.

Since the late 1920s it has been observed that measured oil rate plotted versus Δp^2 on log–log paper results in a linear relation. This implies the general oil flow equation

$$q_o = C(p_R^2 - p_{wf}^2)^n, \tag{1.33}$$

where the exponent n ranges from 0.5 to 1.0. Example 1.9 illustrates the application of equation (1.33). It is understood today that the exponent n in equation (1.33) accounts for the effect of high-velocity flow and the pressure-squared function accounts for the effect of simultaneous two-phase flow.

The Vogel equation presented in chapter 1 for saturated oils is an average of simulated hypothetical systems:

$$q_o/q_{omax} = 1 - 0.2(p_{wf}/p_R) - 0.8(p_{wf}/p_R)^2. \tag{1.34}$$

Vogel's work considers only the effect of rock and fluid properties on saturated oil systems. The Vogel relation does not account for high-velocity-flow effects that may exist in high-rate wells. Normalization of the IPR by q_{omax} was a novel idea introduced by Vogel. It gives a simple way to calculate IPR from a single-rate test, using the dimensionless curve in figure 1.15. Simplicity is probably the main feature of Vogel's relationship, which brought it favorable and wide acceptance by the industry. Example 1.8 illustrates the use of Vogel's IPR.

Unfortunately, when considering the published data on multirate oilwell tests, it is difficult to find field data to support the Vogel equation. We therefore suggest the empirical IPR equation (eq. [1.33]) suggested in the 1930s and later substantiated by Fetkovich (1973). Normalizing with $q_{omax} = Cp_R^{2n}$, equation (1.33) can be written

$$q_o/q_{omax} = [1 - (p_{wf}/p_R)^2]^n. \tag{1.35}$$

This equation contains two factors, q_{omax} and n, that characterize the productivity of a particular well. These factors can be determined if at least two rate–pressure data are available.

If only one test point is available, then we suggest that equation (1.35) be simplified by assuming $n = 1$:

$$q_o/q_{omax} = 1 - (p_{wf}/p_R)^2. \tag{1.36}$$

This equation is slightly more conservative than Vogel's IPR, but the difference is small. In fact, considering the spread in Vogel's calculated data (see his fig. 7), equation (1.36) could just as well have been chosen to give the best match to his simulated results.

Concept of Relative Permeability. The physical nature of two-phase flow does not easily lend itself to rigorous mathematical treatment. The main problem with treating multiphase flow in porous media is that the permeability of a given phase is strongly dependent on the fraction of total pore space occupied by that phase (and possibly on the fraction of the other phase[s]). In general, an increasing fraction of a given phase indicates an increasing effective permeability of that phase. It also indicates a decrease in the effective permeability of the other phase(s). Thus, when gas comes out of solution as pressure drops below the bubble point, gas occupies an increasingly larger fraction of the pore space and oil permeability decreases as a result. The reduction in oil permeability and its relation to oil saturation is important to the analytical treatment of two-phase gas/oil flow in saturated reservoirs. Unfortunately, it is very difficult to express analytically.

The fraction of a given phase occupying the pore space is defined as saturation, which for oil, gas, and water is written

$$S_o = \frac{V_{oil}}{V_{pore}} \qquad S_g = \frac{V_{gas}}{V_{pore}} \qquad S_w = \frac{V_{water}}{V_{pore}}. \tag{2.80}$$

The sum of saturations for all phases equals unity:

$$S_o + S_g + S_w = 1. \tag{2.81}$$

Relative permeability is a useful concept for quantifying the change in effective permeability of individual phases for conditions of changing saturation. Relative permeability is the ratio of effective permeability of a given phase, say oil k_o, in the presence of other phases (water and/or gas), divided by the absolute permeability. The absolute permeability k should be the same if oil, water, or gas saturates the porous media completely. By introducing a second phase, the permeability of the phase originally saturating the pores 100% is reduced to a lower value. An important observation is that the sum of effective permeabilities in a multiphase system is always less than the single-phase absolute permeability.

For practical reasons, we define relative permeabilities of gas and oil relative to the effective permeability of gas or oil at irreducible water saturation:

$$k_{ro} = k_o/k, \tag{2.82}$$

$$k_{rg} = k_g/k \tag{2.83}$$

where

k = effective oil or gas permeability at irreducible water saturation, md;

k_o = effective oil permeability, md;

k_g = effective gas permeability, md.

A general observation of relative permeabilities is that

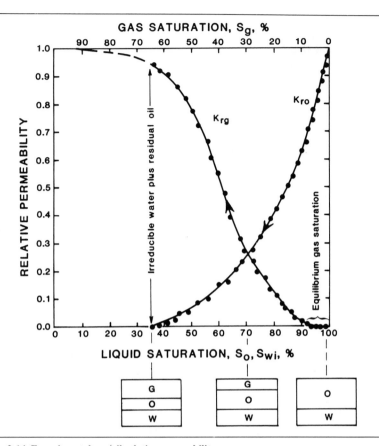

Figure 2.14 Experimental gas/oil relative permeability curves.

$$k_{ro} + k_{rg} < 1. \tag{2.84}$$

In most cases, relative permeability can be considered a function of saturation only:

$$k_r = k_r(S), \tag{2.85}$$

even though pore size distribution, saturation history, temperature, surface tension, and viscosities have been shown to affect relative permeability. Relative permeabilities cannot be measured precisely in the laboratory, and the uniqueness of experimental relative permeability data is dependent on the method used, equipment, fluids, and not least, the experience of the tester.

Figure 2.14 shows an example of a relative permeability curve, which displays measured relative permeability data for gas displacing oil in the presence of connate water. Note the significant decrease in k_{ro} for only small changes in oil saturation. The gas relative permeability changes only slightly from zero as its saturation increases. In fact, there is usually a critical gas saturation at which the gas finally starts flowing (at lower gas saturations the gas is immobile). We typically assume that k_{rg} at $S_g = 1 - S_{wi}$ equals k_{ro} at $S_o = 1 - S_{wi}$, independent of which base is used.

Development of Saturated Oil Flow Equations. The development of two-phase gas/oil flow in saturated oil wells has been studied by analytical and numerical methods; the result is shown schematically in figure 2.15. During Period I, as pressure drops below the bubble point near the wellbore, gas saturation builds up to its critical value. The critical gas saturation forms throughout the entire drainage area before substantial gas flow occurs. During this period the producing gas/oil ratio actually sinks below the initial solution GOR. To maintain a constant oil rate with the buildup of gas saturation, the flowing wellbore pressure must be reduced. Period II starts as gas saturation has reached the critical value throughout the entire drainage region. A constant rate of oil production is maintained by further drop of the flowing wellbore pressure. The reservoir pressure drops continuously, whereas gas saturation and producing gas/oil ratio increases. Period III starts when the flowing wellbore pressure drops to a minimum value, dictated by a minimum possible wellhead pressure, and the production rate starts to drop. The producing gas/oil ratio continues to increase until it reaches a peak and starts to drop again.

The effect of increasing gas saturation has three effects on oil flow:

1. relative permeability to oil decreases, due to increasing gas saturation
2. oil viscosity increases, due to loss of solution gas
3. oil FVF decreases, due to loss of solution gas.

The first two characteristics are detrimental to oil flow, and their combined effect is considerably greater than the slight improvement resulting from decreased oil FVF.

Starting once again with Darcy's equation in differential form, we can write, for an ideal radial geometry,

$$q_o = \frac{2\pi rh k k_{ro}}{\mu_o B_o} \frac{dp}{dr}. \tag{2.86}$$

Effective oil permeability k_o is written kk_{ro}, where k_{ro} is primarily dependent on oil saturation. At $S_o = 1 - S_{wi}$, k_{ro} equals 1.0 and k represents the oil permeability at irreducible water saturation. Both μ_o and B_o are directly dependent on pressure, but k_{ro} is indirectly related to pressure, through the saturation–pressure relation. That is, $k_{ro} = k_{ro}(S_o)$, $S_o = S_o(p)$, resulting in $k_{ro} = k_{ro}(p)$. The pressure-dependent properties μ_o, B_o, and k_{ro} combine to form the pressure function,

$$F(p) = k_{ro}/\mu_o B_o. \tag{2.87}$$

The analogous pressure function for gas is $p/\mu_g Z$, or $1/\mu_g B_g$. Solving equation (2.86) in terms of reservoir variables, skin factor, pseudosteady-state conditions, and radial geometry, a general flow equation for saturated oils can be written

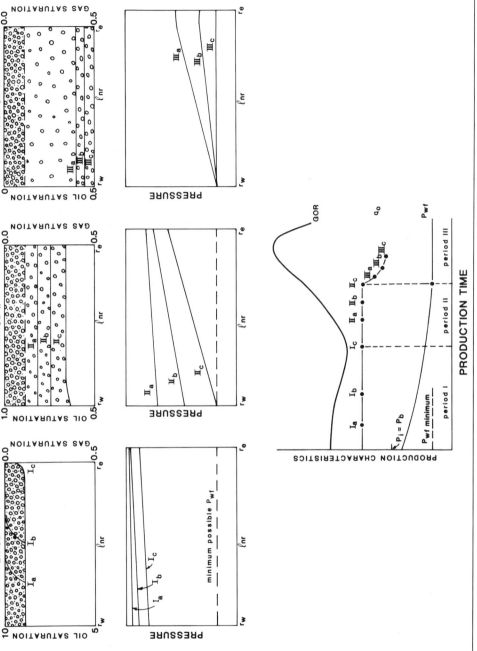

Figure 2.15 Development of pressure and saturation distributions for a well producing under solution gas drive.

$$q_o = \frac{kh}{141.2[\ln(r_e/r_w) - 0.75 + s + Dq_o]} \int_{p_{wf}}^{p_R} \frac{k_{ro}}{\mu_o B_o} dp,$$

(2.88)

or simply

$$q_o = U \int_{p_{wf}}^{p_R} F(p) \, dp,$$

(2.89)

where

$$U = \frac{kh}{141.2[\ln(r_e/r_w) - 0.75 + s + Dq_o]}.$$

(2.90)

Solving the integral of the pressure function is not a trivial procedure. Evinger and Muskat (1942) suggest a practical method for approximating the saturation–pressure relation, which allows plotting and integrating the pressure function graphically or with a simple numerical method. Because the Evinger–Muskat method is similar in complexity to material balance calculations it has never received widespread application to well performance engineering. Work by later investigators—Vogel, Fetkovich, Raghavan (1976), and others—has led to the conclusion that the pressure function $F(p)$ can be accurately represented versus pressure by a straight line ranging from $k_{ro}/\mu_o B_o$ at reservoir pressure to the origin. Figure 2.16 shows the approximate pressure function. Note that to arrive at Vogel's IPR equation the intercept of the curve should equal 1/9 of the $1/\mu_o B_o$ value at the bubble point. The integral of $F(p)$ is easily solved by calculating the area of a trapezoid under the straight line. Example 2.10 illustrates the ease of integrating the linear $F(p)$ relation.

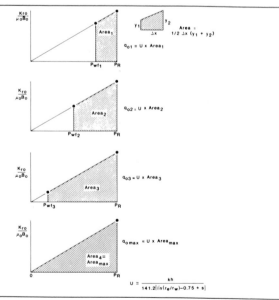

Figure 2.16 Straight-line pressure function approximation for saturated oil wells.

EXAMPLE 2.10 APPLICATION OF THE SIMPLIFIED PRESSURE FUNCTION TO CONSTRUCT THE IPR OF A SATURATED OIL WELL

The Yukon No. 3 is a well in a partially depleted, saturated oil reservoir producing from the Hunton limestone at a depth of about 9220 ft. The drawdown test stabilized at a rate of 310 STB/D at a flowing bottomhole pressure of 715 psia. Buildup analysis indicates a steady-state skin of +4.7. Average reservoir pressure is 2830 psia, calculated from the Horner extrapolation (p^*) to infinite buildup time, corrected for drainage area and shape. Fluid properties calculated from PVT correlations at average reservoir pressure are $B_o = 1.35$ bbl/STB and $\mu_o = 0.52$ cp. Based on material balance calculations, the average gas saturation is 12%, suggesting relative permeability to oil has decreased to $k_{ro} = 0.8$ from its initial value of 1.0 at S_{wi}.

Using the assumption of a straight-line pressure function $F(p) = k_{ro}/\mu_o B_o$ with intercept at the origin, calculate oil rate at several flowing pressures using simple integration [i.e., area under the $F(p)$ curve]. Plot the points on Cartesian paper and draw the IPR curve. Plot the points on log–log paper and calculate the slope.

SOLUTION

The pressure function $F(p)$ at the present average reservoir pressure is

$$F(p_R = 2830) = 0.8/(0.52)(1.35)$$

$$= 1.14 \, \text{cp}^{-1}.$$

Plotting $F(p)$ involves drawing a straight line from the origin to the point (2830, 1.14) as illustrated in figure E2.10a. The equation of the line is

$$F(p) = \frac{F(p_R = 2830)}{p_R} \times p = \frac{1.14}{2830} \times p = 0.000404 p \, (\text{psia}).$$

For the test point, $q_o = 310$ STB/D and $p_{wf} = 715$ psia, $F(p_{wf})$ is 0.000404(715) $= 0.288$ and the area under the curve from 715 to 2830 psia is

$$\text{Area} = \int_{715}^{2830} F(p) \, dp$$

$$= 0.5 \times (1.14 + 0.288) \times (2830 - 715)$$

$$= 1510.$$

The rate equation is simply $q_o = C' \times \text{Area}$, where the constant C' is calculated from the test point:

EXAMPLE 2.10 continued

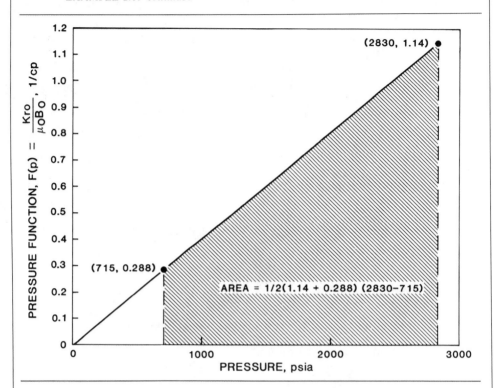

Figure E2.10a Graphical integration of the pressure function in the Yukon No. 3 oil well.

$C' = q_o/\text{Area}$

$= 310/1510$

$= 0.205.$

Note that the constant C' is *not* the backpressure coefficient. The general expression for IPR is $q_o = 0.205 \times \text{Area}$. To calculate rates at other flowing pressures it is necessary to calculate $F(p_{wf})$ or to read it from the straight-line plot of $F(p)$ in figure E2.10a. The area is given by

$$\text{area} = 0.5 \times [F(p_R) + F(p_{wf})] \times (p_R - p_{wf})$$

$$= 0.5 \times (1.14 + 0.000404 p_{wf}) \times (2830 - p_{wf}).$$

Table E2.10 gives values for the area at several flowing pressures. The rate equation, written explicitly, is

EXAMPLE 2.10 continued

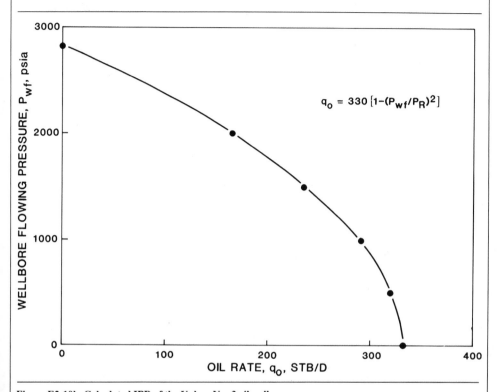

$$q_o = 330\left[1-(P_{wf}/P_R)^2\right]$$

Figure E2.10b Calculated IPR of the Yukon No. 3 oil well.

$q_o = C' \times \text{area}$

$= 0.205[0.5 \times (1.14 + 0.000404 p_{wf}) \times (2830 - p_{wf})]$

$= 0.205(0.5)[1.14 + (1.14/2830)p_{wf}][2830 - p_{wf}]$

$= 0.103(1.14/2830)[2830 + p_{wf}][2830 - p_{wf}]$

$= 4.15 \times 10^{-5}(2830^2 - p_{wf}{}^2),$

or

$q_o = 332[1 - (p_{wf}/p_R)^2].$

Figures E2.10b and E2.10c plot the calculated IPR data on Cartesian and log–log coordinates, respectively. The slope of the straight line obtained by a logarithmic plot of q_o versus Δp^2 is 1.0, as suggested by the IPR equation.

EXAMPLE 2.10 continued

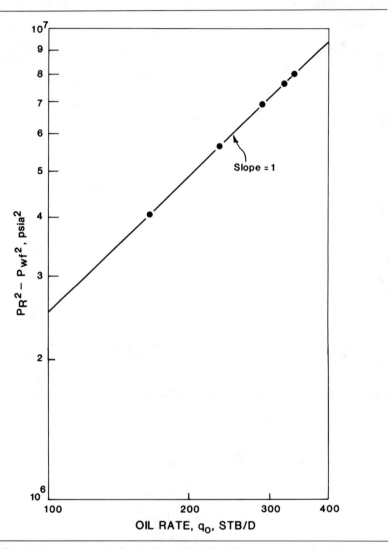

Figure E2.10c Backpressure plot for the Yukon No. 3 oil well.

EXAMPLE 2.10 continued

Table E2.10 Calculation of $F(p)$, Area, and Rate for Several Flowing Pressures—Yukon No. 3 Well

p_{wf} (psia)	$F(p) =$ $k_{ro}/\mu_o B_o$ (1/cp)	$\int F(p)\,dp =$ area (psia/cp)	q_o (STB/D)
2830	1.140	0.0	0.0
2000	0.806	807.6	165.6
1500	0.604	1159.8	237.8
1000	0.403	1411.8	289.4
500	0.201	1562.3	320.3
0	0.000	1613.1	330.7 (AOF)

The analytical solution of equation (2.88) when substituting the straight-line assumption for $F(p)$ is equivalent to the pressure-squared IPR equation

$$q_o = C(p_R^2 - p_{wf}^2),\qquad(2.91)$$

where, for $p_R \leq p_b$, C is given by

$$C = \frac{kh}{141.2[\ln(r_e/r_w) - 0.75 + s + Dq_o]}\left(\frac{1}{2p_R}\right)\left(\frac{k_{ro}}{\mu_o B_o}\right)_{p_R}\qquad(2.92)$$

and the properties μ_o and B_o are evaluated at P_R. If $D = 0$ or Dq_o is very small, then equation (2.92) can be written as $q_o/q_{omax} = 1 - (p_{wf}^2/p_R^2)$, and $C = q_{omax}/p_R^2$.

Similar to the gas equation, accounting for high-velocity flow in saturated oil wells is done by adding the term Dq_o to equation (2.92). In fact, adding this term converts the basis of the equation from Darcy's model to the Forchheimer model.

Substituting equation (2.92) in equation (2.91) and solving for q_o gives a backpressure equation with exponent n, which aproximately represents the IPR of wells in saturated oil reservoirs

$$q_o = C(p_R^2 - p_{wf}^2)^n,\qquad(2.93)$$

where the backpressure constant can be approximated by

$$C = \left[\frac{kk_{ro}h}{141.2(2\mu_o B_o p_R)}\right]^n \frac{1}{D^{1-n}[\ln(r_e/r_w) - 0.75 + s]^{2n-1}}.\qquad(2.94)$$

Fieldtest data (Millikan, Fetkovich, etc.) indicates that the effect of high-velocity flow in oil wells can be appreciable. Plotting their data as backpressure curves of q_o

versus Δp^2 indicates that the exponent n in the general IPR equation (2.93) ranges from 0.5 to 1.0. It is difficult to explain this rate–pressure behavior by pressure functions $F(p)$ alone. The only explanation is the existence of a high-velocity effect.

For oil wells, the term D in the rate-dependent skin can be estimated from reservoir and well data using a relation analogous to equation (2.63) for gas:

$$D = 1.635 \times 10^{-16} \frac{khB_o\rho_o}{\mu_o r_w h_p^2} \beta. \tag{2.95}$$

Reservoir oil density ρ_o, for saturated oil, can be written

$$\rho_o = [62.4\gamma_{STO} + 0.0136\gamma_g R_s]/B_o, \tag{1.27}$$

which gives

$$D = 1.635 \times 10^{-16} \frac{kh[0.0135R_s\gamma_g + 62.4\gamma_o]}{\mu_o r_w h_p^2} \beta, \tag{2.96}$$

where R_s = solution gas/oil ratio at the wellbore flowing pressure, γ_g = gas gravity (air = 1), and γ_o = oil gravity (water = 1). The β factor is estimated from

$$\beta = 2.73 \times 10^{10} k_a^{-1.1045}, \tag{2.64}$$

where k_a is the effective oil permeability near the wellbore. If permeability is not available, use the approximate expression

$$D = 2.76 \times 10^{-6} \frac{h[0.0135R_s\gamma_g + 62.4\gamma_o]}{\mu_o r_w h_p^2}. \tag{2.97}$$

Wells producing from undersaturated oil reservoirs also can be treated with the same methods as for saturated oil reservoirs. For such wells the pressure function $F(p)$ covers two regions, undersaturated conditions ($p > p_b$) and saturated conditions ($p < p_b$). Since oil relative permeability in the undersaturated region equals unity ($k_{ro} = 1.0$), $F(p)$ equals $1/\mu_o B_o$. Moreover, it has been observed that the variation in $F(p)$ for undersaturated oils is only slight.

Figure 2.17 shows the composite pressure function below and above the bubble point and its integration to develop a general IPR equation. The two top cases in figure 2.17 illustrate the graphical integration of the pressure function for cases when $p_{wf} \geq p_b$, the third case is for $p_{wf} < p_b$, and the bottom case is for $p_{wf} = 0$.

To show the application of the pressure function to develop an IPR equation, example 2.11 gives the derivation of the undersaturated IPR equation presented in chapter 1:

$$q_o = J(p_R - p_b) + \frac{J}{2p_b}(p_b^2 - p_{wf}^2)^{1.0}. \tag{2.98}$$

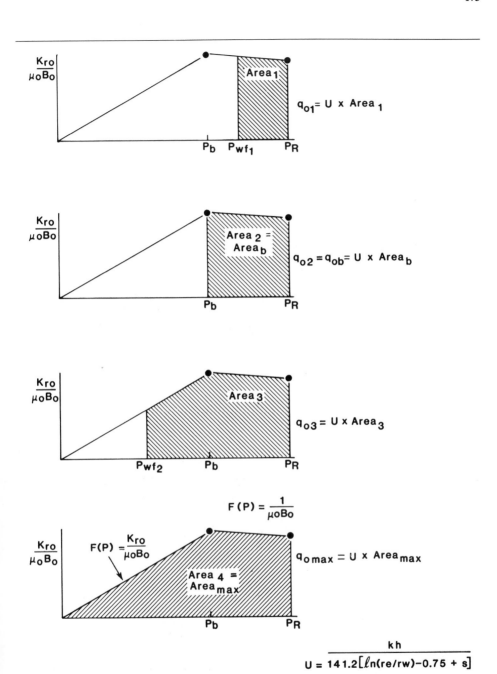

Figure 2.17 Graphical integration of the pressure function for an undersaturated oil well producing at flowing pressure below the bubble point.

The example shows that, when assuming high-velocity flow is negligible,

$$J = \frac{kh}{141.2\mu_{ob}B_{ob}[\ln(r_e/r_w) - 0.75 + s]} \tag{2.99}$$

or, assuming high-velocity flow,

$$J = \frac{kh}{141.2\mu_{ob}B_{ob}[\ln(r_e/r_w) - 0.75 + s + Dq_o]}. \tag{2.100}$$

EXAMPLE 2.11 DEVELOPMENT OF THE UNDERSATURATED IPR EQUATION USING THE GRAPHICAL PRESSURE FUNCTION

This example illustrates the simplicity of using the straight-line pressure function $F(p)$ as an assumption to develop practical IPR equations. Specifically, equation (1.38), the IPR equation for a well producing from an undersaturated oil reservoir at wellbore flowing pressures below the bubble point, is derived using simple geometric arguments and algebraic manipulation. The pressure function assumed in the development of equation (1.38) is shown in figure E2.11. It consists of a constant value $F(p) = F(p_b) = 1/\mu_{ob}B_{ob}$, extending from p_R to p_b, and a straight-line segment starting at p_b and ending at the origin.

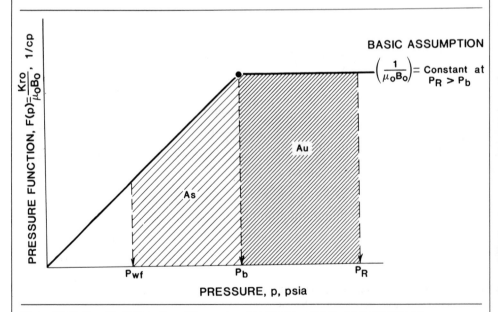

Figure E2.11 Graphical integration of the pressure function in undersaturated oil reservoirs.

EXAMPLE 2.11 continued

Consider first the undersaturated region from p_b to p_R. The area A_u under the constant $F(p)$ line is

$$A_u = F(p_b)(p_R - p_b).$$

The area under the straight line extending from p_b to any flowing pressure p_{wf} is

$$A_s = 0.5[F(p_b) + F(p_{wf})](p_b - p_{wf}),$$

where $F(p_{wf})$ is given by

$$F(p_{wf}) = [F(p_b)](p_{wf}/p_b),$$

which results in

$$A_s = 0.5F(p_b)[1 + p_{wf}/p_b](p_b - p_{wf})$$

$$= 0.5[F(p_b)/p_b](p_b + p_{wf})(p_b - p_{wf})$$

$$= 0.5F(p_b)(p_b^2 - p_{wf}^2)/p_b$$

$$= F(p_b)(p_b^2 - p_{wf}^2)/2p_b.$$

The total area $A_t = A_u + A_s$ is

$$A_t = A_u + A_s$$

$$= [F(p_b)(p_R - p_b)] + [F(p_b)(p_b^2 - p_{wf}^2)/2p_b]$$

$$= F(p_b)[(p_R - pb) + (p_b^2 - p_{wf}^2)/2p_b].$$

The flow equation for oil is

$$q_o = \frac{kh}{141.2[\ln(r_e/r_w) - 0.75 + s]}A_t.$$

If we define J as

$$J = \frac{kh}{141.2(\mu_{ob}B_{ob})[\ln(r_e/r_w) - 0.75 + s]}$$

and we note that $F(p_b) = 1/\mu_{ob}B_{ob}$, then

$$q_o = J(p_R - p_b) + (J/2p_b)(p_b^2 - p_{wf}^2).$$

The Forchheimer model (J with Dq_o) is suggested for quantifying high-velocity flow in undersaturated oil wells producing at flowing pressures below the bubble point. The problem may not be quite so simple, since the D terms for undersaturated oil and saturated gas/oil flow may differ. We suggest that D be calculated from equation (2.96) or (2.97), using $R_s = R_s(p_{wf})$ as a first approximation.

The exponent $n = 1.0$ in equation (2.98) is included intentionally to emphasize that a plot of this equation as q_o versus $p_R^2 - p_{wf}^2$ on log–log paper gives a straight line with a slope greater than 1. It appears similar to a backpressure curve of a well in a saturated reservoir with n (1/slope) less than 1. Unlike a well in a saturated reservoir, however, the slope here does not necessarily indicate high-velocity effects. It represents only a mathematical feature of the logarithmic plot of equation (2.98).

For pseudosteady-state production without rate-dependent skin, the back-pressure coefficient C changes only as a result of depletion. That is because declining average reservoir pressure results in the decline of average properties in the drainage area, $(k_{ro}/\mu_o B_o)_R$. Average reservoir properties in the drainage area are evaluated at average reservoir pressure.

The decline of the average properties is shown in figure 2.18. The figure illustrates the decline of the pressure function as obtained from three sources: as observed by Fetkovich (1973), as back-calculated from Vogel's IPR by Whitson (1983), and as calculated by Evinger and Muskat (1942). The dotted line illustrates the decline of the pressure function with declining p_R. The straight line is a plot of the pressure function between $p = 0$ and $p = p_R$ at a given depletion stage.

Generally, the straight-line pressure function $F(p)$ begins at $(k_{ro}/\mu_o B_o)_R$, defined by the material balance, and ends at or near the origin. Accordingly, the only change in the general IPR is due to changing the constant C, which includes the properties $(k_{ro}/\mu_o B_o)_R$ evaluated at p_R. Then, during depletion, the IPR equation is

$$q_o = C(p_R^2 - p_{wf}^2)^n, \tag{1.33}$$

where

$$C = \left\{ \frac{[k_{ro}/\mu_o B_o]_R k h}{141.2(2p_R)} \right\}^n \frac{1}{D^{1-n}[\ln(r_e/r_w) - 0.75 + s]^{2n-1}}. \tag{2.94}$$

Changes of IPR with depletion can be explained even more simply, using equations (2.89) and (2.90), which state that

$$q_o = U \int_{p_{wf}}^{p_R} F(p)\,dp, \tag{2.89}$$

where

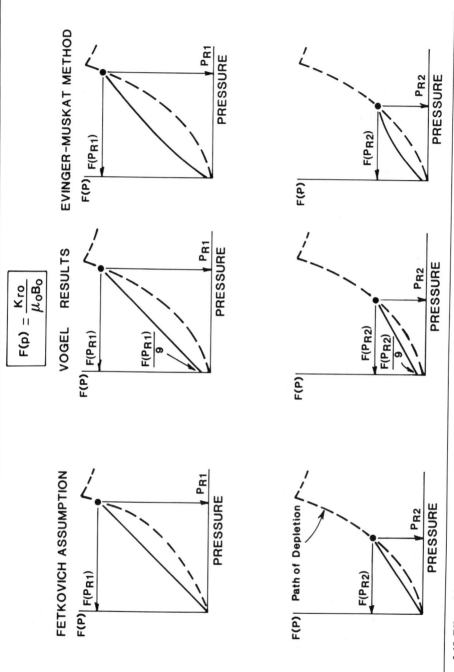

Figure 2.18 Effect of depletion on saturated oil pressure function, $F(p)$.

$$U = \frac{kh}{141.2[\ln(r_e/r_w) - 0.75 + s + Dq_o]}. \tag{2.90}$$

The coefficient U is expressed in terms of flow geometry and skin. Assuming it does not change with depletion, the only variant in equation (2.89) is the integral of the pressure function.

Figure 2.19 illustrates the integration of the pressure function at two stages of depletion. It shows that the area defining the pressure integral at a new stage of depletion is equal to the new shaded trapezoid. The new maximum oil rate is proportional to the total (triangular) area under the straight line, given by $(k_{ro}/\mu_o B_o)_{av} \times p_R/2$, where the average properties are evaluated at p_R. If C (or q_{omax}) is written at a new state of depletion in terms of C (or q_{omax}) at a previous state of depletion, then

$$C_{new} = C_{old} \times \left\{ \frac{[k_{ro}/\mu_o B_o]_{Rnew} \times p_{Rold}}{[k_{ro}/\mu_o B_o]_{Rold} \times p_{Rnew}} \right\}^n, \tag{2.101}$$

$$[q_{omax}]_{new} = [q_{omax}]_{old} \times \left\{ \frac{[k_{ro}/\mu_o B_o]_{Rnew} \times p_{Rnew}}{[k_{ro}/\mu_o B_o]_{Rold} \times p_{Rold}} \right\}^n, \tag{2.102}$$

where the exponent n is the backpressure exponent, assumed constant during depletion.

Standing (1971) develops a similar correction for the Vogel equation. In fact, Standing's correction can be expressed as equation (2.102) for $n = 1$; it is then applicable to the Vogel IPR and the pressure-squared IPR with $n = 1$.

In a similar manner, the correction for depletion when using the quadratic IPR equation is made by adjusting A and B (see eq. [2.51]).

Using a straight-line oil pressure function $F(p)$ with zero intercept, the quadratic equation can be written for saturated oils as

$$\frac{p_R^2 - p_{wf}^2}{q_o} = A + Bq_o, \tag{2.103}$$

where

$$A = \frac{141.2(2p_R)}{kh[k_{ro}/\mu_o B_o]_R} [\ln(r_e/r_w) - 0.75 + s] \tag{2.104}$$

and

$$B = \frac{141.2(2p_R)}{kh[k_{ro}/\mu_o B_o]_R} D. \tag{2.105}$$

The depletion adjustments are

$$A_{new} = A_{old} \times \frac{p_{Rnew} \times [k_{ro}/\mu_o B_o]_{Rold}}{p_{Rold} \times [k_{ro}/\mu_o B_o]_{Rnew}}, \tag{2.106}$$

$$F(p) = \frac{K_{ro}}{\mu_o B_o}$$

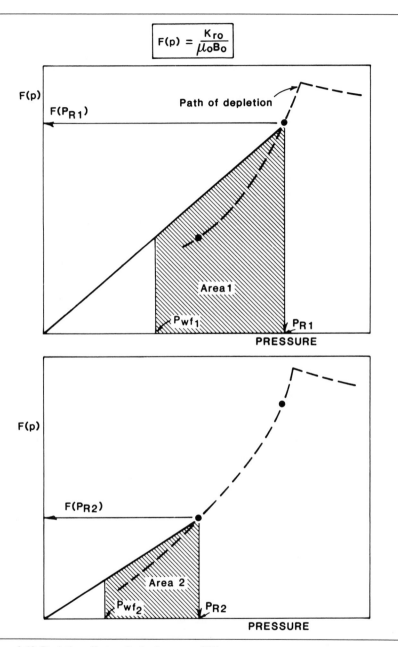

Figure 2.19 Depletion effect on the backpressure IPR.

$$B_{new} = B_{old} \times \frac{p_{Rnew} \times [k_{ro}/\mu_o B_o]_{Rold}}{p_{Rold} \times [k_{ro}/\mu_o B_o]_{Rnew}}, \tag{2.107}$$

Example 2.12 illustrates the procedure for correcting the effect of depletion on a saturated oil IPR.

EXAMPLE 2.12 EFFECT OF DEPLETION ON SATURATED OIL IPR

The Davis No. 3 well (example 1.14) had produced for about one year when a new bottomhole pressure buildup survey was run. To date, the well had produced 89,780 STB oil. The average reservoir pressure was estimated to be about 3520 psia, indicating a drop of 480 psia from the initial pressure of 4000 psia. Material balance calculations were made based on average reservoir PVT and rock properties (relative permeabilities were calculated from a correlation). Results indicated that $k_{ro}/\mu_o B_o$ has decreased from $0.223\,cp^{-1}$ at initial conditions to 0.147 at $p_R = 3520$ psia.

Estimate the new IPR relation for this well at its present stage of depletion. What flowing wellbore pressure should be expected for a stabilized rate of 180 STB/D? Plot the present and initial IPR curves on Cartesian paper.

SOLUTION

The initial calculated AOF, or q_{omax}, is reported in example 1.14 as 480 STB/D. The new AOF is less than the initial value, due to the effects of depletion. That is, the driving force p_R has declined, and the resistence to oil flow $k_{ro}/\mu_o B_o$ has increased. Assuming that the same form of IPR remains, and that the exponent $n = 0.8$ has not changed, the new IPR is written

$$q_o = [q_{omax}]_{old} \times \left\{ \frac{[k_{ro}/\mu_o B_o]_{new} \times p_{Rnew}}{[k_{ro}/\mu_o B_o]_{old} \times p_{Rold}} \right\}^{0.8} \times [1 - (p_{wf}/p_R)^2]^{0.8}$$

$$= 480 \times \left\{ \frac{(0.147)(3520)}{(0.223)(4000)} \right\}^{0.8} [1 - (p_{wf}/p_R)^2]^{0.8}$$

$$= 310[1 - (p_{wf}/p_R)^2]^{0.8}.$$

The calculated AOF is now 310 STB/D instead of 480 STB/D. The expected flowing pressure at a rate of 180 STB/D is

$$p_{wf} = 3520[1 - (180/310)^{1.25}]^{0.5}$$

$$= 2472\,psia.$$

EXAMPLE 2.12 continued

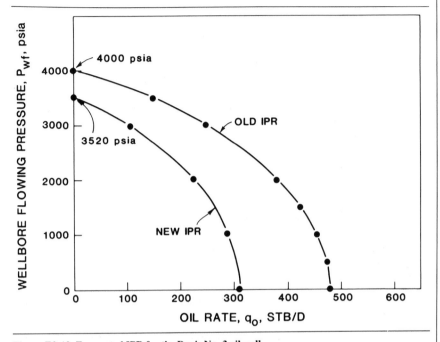

Figure E2.12 Forecasted IPR for the Davis No. 3 oil well.

Figure E2.12 shows the present and initial IPR curves. A log–log plot of the same data would appear as two parallel straight lines with slope 1.25 ($= 1/0.8$), the present one being shifted to the left by a factor of 0.65 ($= 310/480$).

Similarly, we can derive IPR corrections for changing skin (or flow efficiency) and/or drainage radius. These changes affect only the factor U in equation (2.89), while the pressure function and its integral remain unchanged. In terms of the backpressure equation (eqs. [2.91] and [2.92]), these changes affect the coefficient C according to

$$C_{\text{new}} = C_{\text{old}} \times \left\{ \frac{[E_F]_{\text{new}}}{[E_F]_{\text{old}}} \right\}^{2n-1}, \tag{2.108}$$

$$C_{\text{new}} = C_{\text{old}} \times \left\{ \frac{[\ln(r_e/r_w) - 0.75 + s]_{\text{old}}}{[\ln(r_e/r_w) - 0.75 + s]_{\text{new}}} \right\}^{2n-1} \tag{2.109}$$

In terms of q_{omax}, the corrections are

$$[q_{omax}]_{new} = [q_{omax}]_{old} \times \left\{ \frac{[E_F]_{new}}{[E_F]_{old}} \right\}^{2n-1} \tag{2.110}$$

$$[q_{omax}]_{new} = [q_{omax}]_{old} \times \left\{ \frac{[\ln(r_e/r_w) - 0.75 + s]_{old}}{[\ln(r_e/r_w) - 0.75 + s]_{new}} \right\}^{2n-1} \tag{2.111}$$

The correction for change of skin and/or drainage radius using the quadratic (Forchheimer) equation (with Dq_o) is made by changing A in equations (2.103) and (2.104):

$$A_{new} = A_{old} \times \frac{[E_F]_{old}}{[E_F]_{new}}, \tag{2.112}$$

$$A_{new} = A_{old} \times \frac{[\ln(r_e/r_w) - 0.75 + s]_{new}}{[\ln(r_e/r_w) - 0.75 + s]_{old}}. \tag{2.113}$$

Example 2.13 shows the procedure for correcting a saturated oil IPR for change in skin.

EXAMPLE 2.13 EFFECT OF CHANGING SKIN ON THE IPR OF A SATURATED OIL WELL

The Yukon No. 3 (Example 2.10) reportedly has a skin of +4.7. A service company was contacted about the well and they submitted a proposal to clean up around the wellbore with an acid wash. Because the reservoir engineer considers the minimum effect of limited perforation interval (see section 3.3) to be a skin of +2.0, it is estimated that the service company's proposed treatment will result in a new flow efficiency of 0.779 [i.e., $s = +2.0$, $\ln(r_e/r_w) - 0.75 = 7$] instead of the present flow efficiency of 0.598 ($s = +4.7$). Calculate the posttreatment IPR equation.

SOLUTION

There are two approaches to correcting the initial IPR equation: Use the ratio of new to old flow efficiencies, or use the ratio of new to old $[\ln(r_e/r_w) - 0.75 + s]$ terms. Both methods yield the same answer. There is no change in the pressure function due to a change in skin. Using flow efficiencies, equation (2.110),

$$[q_{omax}]_{new} = [q_{omax}]_{old} \times \frac{[E_F]_{new}}{[E_F]_{old}}$$

$$= 332 \times \frac{0.778}{0.598}$$

$$= 432.0 \, STB/D.$$

EXAMPLE 2.13 continued

Table E2.13 Pre- and Posttreatment Calculated Rates for the Yukon No. 3 Well

p_{wf} (psia)	Before treatment (STB/D)	After treatment (STB/D)
2830	0.0	0.0
2000	166.2	216.2
1500	238.7	310.6
1000	290.5	378.1
500	321.6	418.5
0	332.0	432.0

Using skin factors, equation (2.111),

$$[q_{o\text{max}}]_{\text{new}} = [q_{o\text{max}}]_{\text{old}} \times \frac{[\ln(r_e/r_w) - 0.75 + s]_{\text{old}}}{[\ln(r_e/r_w) - 0.75 + s]_{\text{new}}}$$

$$= 332 \times \frac{7 + 4.7}{7 + 2.0}$$

$$= 432.0 \, \text{STB/D}.$$

Then the new IPR is

$$q_o = 432[1 - (p_{wf}/p_R)^2].$$

Table E2.13 lists pre- and post-treatment rates for a few drawdowns.

This section has considered several aspects of inflow performance for saturated and undersaturated oil wells producing in the presence of free gas. We presented the existing IPR equations and commented on their use and validity. We suggested that whenever an oil well produces at high rates the IPR of the well can be obtained only by a multirate test. Plotting the test data as q_o versus Δp^2 on log–log paper determines the coefficient and the exponent of the backpressure equation. An alternative plot of the test data is $\Delta p^2/q_o$ versus q_o, which determines the coefficients of the quadratic Forchheimer equation. A single-rate test provides only limited information and requires an arbitary assumption to quantify or ignore high-velocity effects.

This section also investigated the effects of reservoir depletion and changes of skin factor and radius of drainage on the IPR equations. The general form of the IPR equation was stated as

$$q_o = U \int_{p_{wf}}^{p_R} F(p)\,dp.$$

The expression for the term U was developed by using Darcy's law in the radial flow model and adjusting it for skin factor and rate-dependent skin. Several simplifying assumptions were made regarding the behavior of the pressure function $F(p)$. These allowed integrating the function graphically (or analytically) by simple area calculations of trapezoids and triangles. The simplified pressure function assumptions and their corresponding integrals are listed in table 2.3. The resultant IPR can be arranged in the form of the backpressure equation, where the backpressure coefficient is expressed in terms of reservoir properties.

The fundamental assumption in investigating the effect of reservoir changes is that the coefficient U and the integral of the pressure function are independent. In other words, reservoir depletion affects only the value of the pressure function integral, whereas skin factor and drainage radius affect only the coefficient U. Assuming U is constant with depletion, variation in the pressure function establishes simple expressions to calculate the variation of the IPR coefficient C or q_{omax}. Similarly, considering that the pressure function does not vary with s and r_e allows establishment of simple expressions for the effect of these parameters on the coefficients C and q_{omax} of the IPR equation.

2.6   **PSEUDOSTEADY-STATE PRODUCTION: STABILIZED FLOW.** At the onset of production, a well moves from a period of transience-dominated flow into a period of stabilized flow dominated by depletion. The two periods can be visualized by considering the ripples caused by a pebble falling into a quiet pond. The outermost ripple moves radially away from the pebble's impact, finally reaching the edge of the pond. Transience coincides with the early propagation of the outer ripple. The pseudosteady state begins when the ripple reaches the edge of the pond. If the edge is not circular, the outer ripple will continue to move in all directions until it reaches the shore furthest from the initial impact.

Flow boundaries are formed when several wells are producing from a common, limited reservoir. Some no-flow boundaries are hydrodynamic and develop around wells as a result of production rate and regional variation in formation properties (permeability, thickness, etc.). These boundaries, together with permanent no-flow impermeable boundaries such as pinchouts and sealing faults, establish a drainage volume for each well. If extraneous fluids do not enter the original hydrocarbon-bearing formation (e.g., from an aquifer or injection wells), pressure continuously declines in each drainage unit. The rate of pressure decline depends on how fast the fluids are produced, the expansion of reservoir fluids, and the compaction of the pore volume. Quantifying pressure decline is a task of the reservoir engineer, and it is usually calculated from a volumetric material balance. The most important effect of depletion is the deterioration of inflow performance, reflected by decline in average reservoir pressure and increased resistance to flow.

Case	Integral form of Darcy's Equation	Pressure function	Integral of the pressure function
Ideal liquid	$q_o = \dfrac{2\pi kh}{\ln r_e/r_w - 0.75 + s + Dq} \displaystyle\int_{p_{wf}}^{p_R} \dfrac{1}{\mu B}\, dp$	$\dfrac{1}{\mu B}$	$\dfrac{p_R - p_{wf}}{\mu B}$
Undersaturated oil	$q_o = \dfrac{2\pi kh}{\ln r_e/r_w - 0.75 + s + Dq} \displaystyle\int_{p_{wf}}^{p_R} \dfrac{1}{\mu_o B_o}\, dp$	$\dfrac{1}{\mu_o B_o}$	$\dfrac{p_R - p_{wf}}{(\mu_o B_o)_{av}}$
Saturated oil	$q_o = \dfrac{2\pi kh}{\ln r_e/r_w - 0.75 + s + Dq} \displaystyle\int_{p_{wf}}^{p_R} \dfrac{k_{ro}}{\mu_o B_o}\, dp$	$\dfrac{k_{ro}}{\mu_o B_o}$	$\dfrac{p_R^2 - p_{wf}^2}{2p_R}\left(\dfrac{k_{ro}}{\mu_o B_o}\right)_{p_R}$
Low-pressure gas	$q_g = \dfrac{2\pi kh}{\ln r_e/r_w - 0.75 + s + Dq}\dfrac{T_{sc}}{p_{sc}T_R} \displaystyle\int_{p_{wf}}^{p_R} \dfrac{p}{\mu Z}\, dp$	$\dfrac{p}{\mu Z}$	$\dfrac{p_R^2 - p_{wf}^2}{2\mu Z}$
High-pressure gas	$q_g = \dfrac{2\pi kh}{\ln r_e/r_w - 0.75 + s + Dq}\dfrac{T_{sc}}{p_{sc}T_R} \displaystyle\int_{p_{wf}}^{p_R} \dfrac{p}{\mu Z}\, dp$	$\dfrac{p}{\mu Z}$	$\dfrac{p(p_R - p_{wf})}{\mu Z}$
Entire gas pressure range	$q_g = \dfrac{2\pi kh}{\ln r_e/r_w - 0.75 + s + Dq}\dfrac{T_{sc}}{p_{sc}T_R} \displaystyle\int_{p_{wf}}^{p_R} \dfrac{p}{\mu Z}\, dp$	$\dfrac{p}{\mu Z}$	$m(p_R) - m(p_{wf})$

The material balance relating the decline in average reservoir pressure p_R to cumulative oil produced N_p is

$$N_p B_o = V_p c_t(p_i - p_R)$$
$$= Ah\phi c_t(p_i - p_R),$$

(2.114)

where V_p = pore volume and c_t is the total compressibility. Physically, equation (2.114) equates the reservoir voidage caused by withdrawal of the produced oil with expansion of the remaining oil. For constant-rate production, N_p equals the product of oil rate and time, $N_p = q_o t$, resulting in the following expression for p_R:

$$p_R = p_i - \frac{q_o B_o}{Ah\phi c_t} t.$$

(2.115)

Practically, this relation suggests that average pressure declines linearly with time in a system producing from a slightly compressible oil reservoir.

By definition, volumetric average reservoir pressure p_R is given by

$$p_R = \frac{\int_{r_w}^{r_e} p \, dV}{\int_{r_w}^{r_e} dV}.$$

(2.116)

Since volume V for a radial system is written as

$$V = \pi(r^2 - r_w^2)h\phi$$

(2.117)

and dV/dr is

$$dV/dr = 2\pi rh\phi,$$

(2.118)

p_R can be expressed, with certain mathematical manipulations, as

$$p_R = \frac{2}{r_e^2 - r_w^2} \int_{r_w}^{r_e} rp(r) \, dr,$$

(2.119)

or even as a simpler expression if we assume $r_e^2 \gg t_w^2$.

The general radial pressure distribution for pseudosteady-state flow of an ideal fluid (liquid) in a closed circular reservoir (see Craft and Hawkins 1959, p.288) is

$$p(r) = p_{wf} + \frac{141.2q\mu B}{kh}[\ln(r/r_w) - 0.5(r/r_e)^2].$$

(2.120)

Substituting equation (2.120) in (2.119) and integrating gives an IPR equation that relates rate, reservoir pressure, and wellbore pressure

$$q_o = \frac{kh(p_R - p_{wf})}{141.2\mu_o B_o[\ln(r_e/r_w) - 0.75]}. \tag{2.121}$$

A practical application of equations developed for reservoir pressure decline at constant-rate production is the combination of material balance and inflow performance relations to give wellbore flowing pressure as a function of time. This gives an indication of how long the well can produce at a constant rate without adding artificial lift. Figure 2.20 shows the interrelation between material balance, IPR, and the flowing-pressure profile. For simplicity it assumes that declining reservoir pressure is the only effect of depletion on the IPR of an undersaturated oil well. Example 2.14 illustrates how to establish the depletion characteristics of an undersaturated oil reservoir.

EXAMPLE 2.14 DEPLETION CHARACTERISTICS OF AN UNDERSATURATED OIL RESERVOIR

An offshore discovery well, the Vik No. 1 (example 2.3), produces oil from a chalk at a depth of 12,350 ft. Production profiles have been requested by management to make an economic evaluation of what appears to be a marginal field. It is agreed that no more than six wells will be drilled, suggesting an average drainage per well of about 80 acres. The desired production plateau from the field is 9000 STB/D. Use the data in table E2.14 (obtained from tests on the Vik No. 1) to estimate how long the wells can produce before reaching a flowing wellbore pressure equal to the bubble point 4800 psia.

SOLUTION

The decline in average reservoir pressure with time is estimated from equation (2.115):

$$p_R = p_i - \frac{q_o B_o t}{Ah\phi c_{ti}}$$

$$= 7055 - \frac{5.615(1500)(1.50)}{80(43560)(80)(0.25)(10.7 \times 10^{-6})}t$$

$$= 7055 - 16.94t \text{ (days)}.$$

The wellbore flowing pressure p_{wf}, calculated from the radial flow equation, is

EXAMPLE 2.14 continued

Table E2.14 Reservoir and Well Data for the Vik No. 1

Initial pressure p_i	7055 psia
Oil FVF, B_o	1.50 bbl/STB
Initial total compressibility c_t	$10.7 \times 10^{-6}\,\text{psi}^{-1}$
Oil viscosity μ_o	0.31 cp
Bubble-point pressure p_b	4800 psia
Average net pay h	80 ft
Permeability to oil k	24 md
Skin due to stimulation s	-5
Wellbore radius r_w	0.29 ft
Drainage radius (80 acres) r_e	1053 ft
Porosity ϕ	0.25

$$p_{wf} = p_R - \frac{141.2 q_o \mu_o B_o}{kh} [\ln(r_e/r_w) - 0.75 + s]$$

$$= p_R - \frac{141.2(1500)(0.31)(1.50)}{24(80)} [\ln(1053/0.29) - 0.75 - 5]$$

$$= p_R - 125.5.$$

Substituting the calculated expression for p_R yields

$$p_{wf} = 7055 - 125.5 - 16.94t \text{ (days)}$$

$$= 6929.5 - 16.94t \text{ (days)}.$$

To reach $p_{wf} = 4800$ psia will require

$$t = (6929.5 - 4800)/16.94$$

$$= 125.7 \text{ days}$$

$$= 0.34 \text{ years,}$$

at which time the average reservoir pressure will be

$$p_R = 7055 - 16.94(125.7) = 4925 \text{ psia.}$$

The material balance for a gas reservoir is

$$p_R/Z_R = (p_i/Z_i)(1 - G_p/G), \tag{2.122}$$

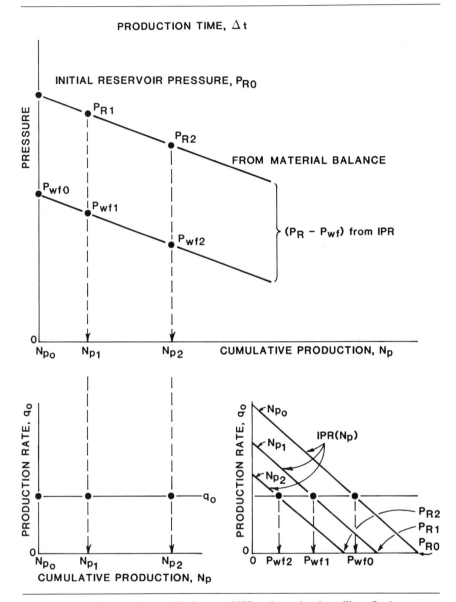

Figure 2.20 Application of material balance and IPR to determine the wellbore flowing pressure profile.

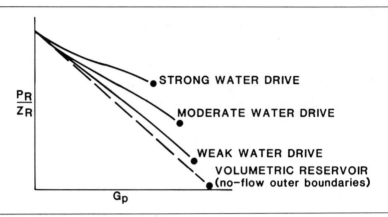

Figure 2.21 Straight-line material balance for a gas reservoir.

where G_p is the cumulative gas produced (in scf), G is the initial gas in place (scf), p_i is the initial pressure, Z_i is the compressibility factor at p_i, p_R is the average reservoir pressure, and Z_R is the compressibility factor at p_R. A cartesian plot of p_R/Z_R versus G_p is a straight line with slope $-p_i/Z_iG$ and intercept p_i/Z_i. Figure 2.21 shows an example of a gas straight-line material balance.

The general effect of water influx on gas depletion is slower pressure decline than with simple depletion. The rate of gas withdrawal affects the mechanism of water influx: accelerated production does not give the aquifer a chance to encroach and maintain pressure. The size and character of an aquifer can be a major factor in designing field development strategy for a gas reservoir. Calculation of the aquifer/ gas material balance is beyond the scope of well performance engineering, and the equations necessary to perform the calculations therefore are not presented here.

The basic IPR equation for a low-pressure gas well is

$$q_g = C(p_R^2 - p_{wf}^2)^n, \tag{1.33}$$

where n and C are determined from a stabilized multirate test (see section 2.7). The same IPR equation applies for gas wells at all stages of depletion. That is, neither C nor n changes during depletion (assuming pseudosteady state has been reached). Alternatively, equation (1.33), normalized by the calculated absolute open flow $(q_{gmax} = Cp_R^{2n})$, giving

$$q_g/q_{gmax} = [1 - (p_{wf}^2/p_R^2)]^n \tag{2.123}$$

is another common form of the gas IPR equation. The maximum gas rate q_{gmax} changes during depletion in proportion to p_R^{2n},

$$(q_{gmax})_{new} = (q_{gmax})_{old} \times \left(\frac{p_{Rnew}}{p_{Rold}}\right)^{2n} \tag{2.124}$$

or in terms of pseudopressure,

$$(q_{gmax})_{new} = (q_{gmax})_{old} \times \left[\frac{m(p_{Rnew})}{m(p_{Rold})}\right]^n \tag{2.125}$$

Combining the gas material balance and the gas IPR allows us to estimate the change in static and flowing pressures as a function of time. Explicit expressions are not usually written for pressure as a function of time, but example 2.15 shows the calculation procedure.

EXAMPLE 2.15 PERFORMANCE OF A GAS WELL DURING DEPLETION

The backpressure equation of the Medicine Lodge No. 1 gas well (example 2.4) was established using two buildup tests. The stabilized IPR equation is

$$q_g = 192(p_R^2 - p_{wf}^2)^{0.766}.$$

For the initial reservoir pressure of 1623 psia, calculated AOF is $192(1623)^{1.532} = 15.8$ MMscf/D. The Kansas state regulatory board has reduced gas allowable from 50% AOF to 25% AOF because of the present "gas bubble" (excessive gas supply).

1. Calculate and plot static and wellbore flowing pressure as a function of time, assuming a constant rate of $0.25(15.8) = 3.95$ MMscf/D.
2. Calculate the AOFs and allowable rates during the first three years of production if the commission ruling on 25% AOF is reapplied at the beginning of each year.

Well spacing is 320 acres. Use data in table E2.15a to solve the example.

SOLUTION

First, the initial gas in place (IGIP) per spacing unit is calculated. This requires the initial gas FVF, B_{gi}, calculated from equation (1.14) as

$$B_{gi} = (14.7/520)\left[\frac{(92 + 460)(0.752)}{1623}\right]$$

$$= 0.00723 \text{ ft}^3/\text{scf}.$$

IGIP for each well on a 320-acre tract is

$$G = Ah\phi(1 - S_w)/B_{gi}$$

$$= 320(43{,}560)(60)(0.17)(1 - 0.26)/0.00723$$

$$= 14.55 \text{ MMMscf,}$$

EXAMPLE 2.15 continued

Table E2.15a Reservoir and Well Data for the Medicine Lodge No. 1 Well

Initial reservoir pressure, p_i	1623 psia
Net pay thickness, h	60 ft
Porosity, ϕ	0.17
Water saturation, S_w	0.26
Reservoir temperature, T_R	92°F
Gas gravity, γ_g	0.69
Initial gas compressibility factor, Z_i	0.752
Well Spacing, A	320 acres

Table E2.15b Results of Production Forecast Calculations for the Medicine Lodge No. 1 Well

				$q_g = 2.58$ MMscf/D		
p_R (psia)	Z_R	p_R/Z_R (psia)	G_p (MMMscf)	t (days)	t (yr)	p_{wf} (psia)
1623	0.752	2158	0.00	0	0.00	1485
1500	0.764	1963	1.31	332	0.91	1350
1250	0.794	1574	3.94	997	2.73	1065
1000	0.830	1205	6.43	1628	4.46	757
750	0.870	862	8.74	2213	6.06	367

where 1 MMMscf $= 10^9$ scf $= 1$ billion scf.

Table E2.15b gives average reservoir pressure p_R, Z-factor Z_R, and p_R/Z_R for pressures from 1623 to 750 psia. The material balance equation, written in terms of G_p as a function of p_R/Z_R, is

$$G_p = [(Z_i/p_i)G][p_i/Z_i - p_R/Z_R]$$

$$= 6.742(10^6)[2158 - p_R/Z_R],$$

which is also tabulated in table E2.15b.

Assuming a constant allowable rate of 3.95 MMscf/D, the time required to deplete the reservoir to an average reservoir pressure associated with a given G_p is

$$t(\text{days}) = G_p/3.95 \times 10^6,$$

which is tabulated in table E2.15b. Wellbore flowing pressure at the end of a period t is calculated by solving the IPR for p_{wf}:

$$p_{wf} = [p_R^2 - (3.95 \times 10^6/192)^{1/0.766}]^{0.5}$$

$$= [p_R^2 - 427,500]^{0.5}$$

Values are listed in the last column of table E2.15b.

EXAMPLE 2.15 continued

2. Calculated AOF after one year's production is found by first calculating the cumulative gas produced:

$$G_p(1 \text{ year}) = 365[0.25(15.8 \times 10^6)]$$

$$= 1.442 \text{ MMMscf.}$$

From the material balance, p_R/Z_R is found to be

$$p_R/Z_R = 2158 - (G_p/6.742 \times 10^6)$$

$$= 2158 - (1.442 \times 10^9/6.742 \times 10^6)$$

$$= 1944.$$

Interpolating in table E2.15b, p_R is found to be 1488 psia. The new AOF for the second year of production is, then,

$$q_{gmax}(2) = q_{gmax}(1) \times \left[\frac{p_{Rnew}}{p_{Rold}}\right]^{2n}$$

$$= 15.8(10^6) \times (1488/1623)^{1.53}$$

$$= 13.8 \text{ MMscf/D.}$$

Production during the second year at 25% AOF (3.45 MMscf/D) results in a cumulative gas produced of

$$G_p = 365[0.25(13.8 \times 10^6)] + 1.442 \times 10^9$$

$$= 1.259 \times 10^9 + 1.442 \times 10^9$$

$$= 2.70 \times 10^9 \text{ scf.}$$

From the material balance, p_R/Z_R is

$$p_R/Z_R = 2158 - (G_p/6.742 \times 10^6)$$

$$= 2158 - (2.70 \times 10^9/6.742 \times 10^6)$$

$$= 1757.$$

Interpolation in table E2.15b gives an average pressure of 1368 psia. The new AOF for the third year of production is, then,

$$q_{gmax}(3) = 13.8 \times 10^6 (1368/1488)^{1.53}$$

$$= 12.1 \text{ MMscf/D.}$$

In saturated oil reservoirs, depletion calculations and the corrections to pseudosteady-state flow are more complicated than for undersaturated oil or gas reservoirs. The reason is that oil and gas are flowing simultaneously, and the mobility of oil, $k_{ro}/\mu_o B_o$, is decreasing continuously. The material balance of a solution gas-drive reservoir is dictated by fluid properties and gas/oil relative permeabilities. The expansion of oil and gas necessary to make up for the voidage caused by oil and gas production depends not only on phase compressibilities, but also on the phase saturations and the changing characteristics of gas and oil flow.

Perhaps the simplest calculation procedure for a solution gas-drive material balance was given by Tracy (1955) and Tarner (1944). For most large oil reservoirs numerical simulators have replaced the simple material balance. Using either method to model depletion characteristics, there are three functional relations used by the production engineer in designing well performance:

1. p_R versus N_p
2. GOR versus N_p
3. $k_{ro}/\mu_o B_o$ versus N_p

Figure 2.22 shows the general behavior of p_R, GOR, and $k_{ro}/\mu_o B_o$ as a function of depletion for a saturated oil reservoir. Two flow-related factors, p_R and $k_{ro}/\mu_o B_o$, decline with depletion. Consequently, the coefficient C in the oil backpressure equation (eqs. [1.33] or [2.91]) and $q_{o\max}$ normalized oil IPR equation (eq. [1.35]) change with depletion. The depletion correction for C is given by equation (2.101) and for $q_{o\max}$ by equation (2.102). Example 2.16 shows the combined use of material-balance-derived data with the saturated-oil IPR.

EXAMPLE 2.16 DEPLETION CHARACTERISTICS OF A WELL PRODUCING,
FROM A SATURATED OIL RESERVOIR

The Davis No. 3 (example 2.12) depletion forecast has been generated by the reservoir department of the operator (see table E2.16). Stabilized oil rate at about 275 STB/D in the first 324 days of production confirmed the forecast. During the most recent flow test a downhole pressure gauge was used to measure the pressure drop in the tubing. It averaged about 1250 psi for oil rates ranging from 80 to 120 STB/D. Wellhead pressure of 200 psia must be maintained to transfer gas into the pipeline system. This means that the minimum allowable wellbore flowing pressure is $1250 + 200 = 1450$ psia. Below this critical pressure the well can produce only with assistance of artificial lift.

Calculate how long the Davis No. 3 can maintain a rate of 100 STB/D before reaching the minimum flowing pressure of 1450 psia. Start zero time at initial production (i.e., $N_p = 0$).

SOLUTION

The column for cumulative production N_p in table E2.16 can be converted to time by dividing the cumulative production increment by the oil rate, 100 STB/D (except

EXAMPLE 2.16 continued

the first period of production, which averages 275 STB/D). Wellbore flowing pressure for the average pressure p_R is given by the IPR equation,

$$q_o = 480[1 - (p_{wf}/p_R)^2]^{0.8}.$$

The initial maximum oil rate, $q_{omax} = 480\,STB/D$, must be corrected for depletion effects:

$$[q_{omax}]_{new} = [q_{omax}]_{old} \times \left[\frac{[k_{ro}/\mu_o B_o]_{new} \times p_{Rnew}}{[k_{ro}/\mu_o B_o]_{old} \times p_{Rold}} \right]^n$$

$$= \frac{480}{[(0.223)(4000)]^{0.8}} \{[k_{ro}/\mu_o B_o]_{new} \times p_{Rnew}\}^{0.8}$$

$$= 2.09\{[k_{ro}/\mu_o B_o]_{new} \times p_{Rnew}\}^{0.8}.$$

Substituting this expression in the normalized IPR equation and solving for p_{wf} gives

Table E2.16 Production Forecast Calculations for the Davis No. 3 Well

p_R (psia)	$k_{ro}/\mu_o B_o$ (cp^{-1})	N_p (STB)	q_{omax} (STB/D)	p_{wf} (psia)	t (days)	t (yr)
				$q_o = 100\,STB/D$		
4000	0.223	0	480		0	0
3520	0.147	89,000	310		324[a]	0.89
3250	0.110	125,000	231	2616	684[b]	1.87
3000	0.092	162,000	187	2213	1054	2.89
2750	0.080	198,000	156	1799	1414	3.87
2500	0.060	220,000	115	1003	1634	4.48

[a] 324 days = 89,000 STB/275 STB/D
[b] 684 days = 324 + (125,000 − 89,000)/100

$$p_{wf} = p_R[1 - (q_o/q_{omax})^{1.25}]^{0.5}$$

$$= p_R[1 - (100/[q_{omax}]_{new})^{1.25}]^{0.5},$$

which has been tabulated in table E2.16. The well should be able to maintain the 100 STB/D rate for about 4.0 years. In fact, the rate may be sustained longer because increasing GOR during depletion will lower pressure losses in the tubing, thereby lowering the minimum wellbore flowing pressure.

In general, gas and oil wells producing by depletion experience continually decreasing average reservoir pressure, accompanied by decreasing wellbore flowing

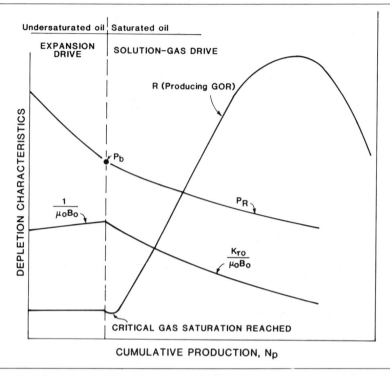

Figure 2.22 Depletion characteristics of a saturated oil reservoir.

pressure. It is noted earlier that the decreasing average pressure can be predicted by material balance calculations. The wellbore flowing pressure decline results from the combined effect of deteriorating IPR and decreasing average reservoir pressure. Flowing wells eventually reach minimum flowing pressures, when the constant rate can no longer be maintained. The rate plateau can be prolonged in an oil well by artificial lift. Otherwise, the rate starts declining as flowing pressure remains more or less constant.

According to the IPR equation, several factors can be controlled to extend the production plateau or, more generally, increase the rate for a given drawdown. The three main factors are skin factor, drainage area size, and to a lesser extent, drainage area shape. Chapter 3 covers the skin factor in some detail. Drainage area is usually controlled by well spacing, production rate, geological structures and regional variation in rock properties. Drainage area shape is determined by well location, production rate, and the structural no-flow outer boundaries defining the reservoir.

The effect of nonradial drainage boundaries is usually insignificant. The problem of well location, however, is sometimes a key element in the design of field development schemes.

If we define an equivalent radius of drainage as

$$r_e = (\text{Area}/\pi)^{0.5} \tag{2.126}$$

and assume pseudosteady-state flow, it can be shown that the effect of nonradial boundaries on the productivity is equivalent to that of a pseudosteady-state skin factor s_A. Fetkovich and Vienot (1985) showed that s_A is expressed by

$$s_A = 0.5\ln(31.62/C_A), \tag{2.127}$$

where C_A is the Dietz (1965) shape factor. Table 2.4 gives values of C_A and s_A for several nonradial drainage geometries. Other references give more complete sets of geometries and values for C_A. The radial flow equation for oil can now be expressed as

$$q_o = \frac{kh(p_R - p_{wf})}{141.2\mu_o B_o[\ln(r_e/r_w) - 0.75 + s + s_A + Dq_o]}. \tag{2.128}$$

The drainage area skin factor s_A is applied in the same way to gas wells.

Table 2.4 Shape Factors for Nonradial Outer Boundary Geometries

Geometry	C_A	s_A	t_{DAeia}[a]	t_{DApss}[b]
	31.62	0.000	0.1	0.1
	30.88	0.012	0.09	0.1
	31.60	0.000	0.1	0.1
	27.6	0.068	0.09	0.2
	27.1	0.077	0.09	0.2
	21.9	0.184	0.08	0.4
	21.84	0.185	0.025	0.3

Table 2.4 (continued)

Geometry	C_A	s_A	t_{DAeia}	t_{DApss}
	5.379	0.886	0.01	0.8
	2.361	1.298	0.025	1.0
	12.98	0.445	0.03	0.7
	4.513	0.973	0.025	0.6
	10.84	0.535	0.025	0.4
	4.514	0.973	0.06	1.5
	2.077	1.362	0.02	1.7
	2.690	1.232	0.01	0.8
	0.232	2.458	0.03	4.0
	0.115	2.806	0.01	4.0
	3.335	1.125	0.01	0.7
	3.157	1.152	0.005	0.4
	0.581	1.998	0.02	2.0

Table 2.4 (continued)

Geometry	C_A	s_A	t_{DAeia}	t_{DApss}
(figure: rectangle with marks, labeled 1, 2)	0.111	2.827	0.005	3.0
(figure: triangle, labeled 3, 4)	0.098	2.888	0.015	0.9

[a] Dimensionless time (based on area) when a well stops behaving as if it were in an infinite system (end-infinite-acting).
[b] Dimensionless time (based on area) when a well reaches pseudosteady state.
Source: After D. N. Dietz: "Determination of Average Reservoir Pressure from Build-up Surveys," *J. Pet. Tech.* (Aug. 1965) 955–959; *Trans.*, Aime, 234; by permission of the SPE-AIME.

A nonradial geometry affects flowing pressure continuously from the instant the closest boundary is felt until the entire outer boundary has been reached. In fact, it prolongs the transition between infinite-acting and pseudosteady-state flow periods. The use of the shape factor s_A to quantify the boundary shape effect on inflow performance is valid only for stabilized flow (steady- or pseudosteady-state). For calculation purposes it is possible to combine s and s_A in the IPR equation. Yet, it is important to realize that unlike the skin factor, the shape factor can not be detected by short well tests conducted to obtain transient well data. Example 2.17 shows the effect of nonradial geometry on well performance.

EXAMPLE 2.17 EFFECT OF NONRADIAL DRAINAGE AREA ON WELL PERFORMANCE CALCULATIONS

Testing of two appraisal wells, Likedda No. 1 and 2, confirms the commerciality of the Likedda offshore oil field. The reservoir is considered marginal in size (80 million barrels), for independent offshore development but it is a satellite to a much larger producing field, with access to process and transportation facilities. The ocean depth is about 370 ft, making subsea completion a viable and economic production alternative. A study has been contracted for evaluation of two alternative subsea production systems: (A) subsea satellite wells (6 wells) or (B) subsea cluster template (6 wells). The two alternatives are illustrated in figures 2.17a and 2.17b.

In alternative A, subsea satellite wells would be drilled vertically, covering the entire reservoir area, and connected by flowlines to a central subsea manifold. In alternative B, deviated wells will be drilled from a seabed integrated wellhead and manifold template. Borehole stability problems encountered during the drilling of the exploration wells limit the maximum inclination (i.e., horizontal reach) of the planned template wells. This limitation creates concern regarding the performance

EXAMPLE 2.17 continued

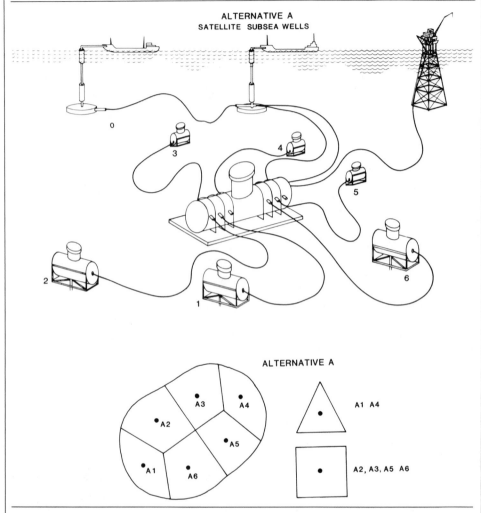

Figure E2.17a Subsea satellite-well arrangement in the Likedda field.

of the deviated wells, particularly since permeability is relatively low and the extent of natural fracturing is uncertain.

Regarding well performance, a major difference between alternatives A and B is the drainage shape and well placement of each well. The subsea satellite design should result in centered well placement with more or less regular drainage shapes (square or triangular). The template cluster design should result in triangular drainage shapes with wells located at the apices. Assuming each well produces at about the same rate, the drainage areas sketched in figures E2.17a and E2.17b should be representative.

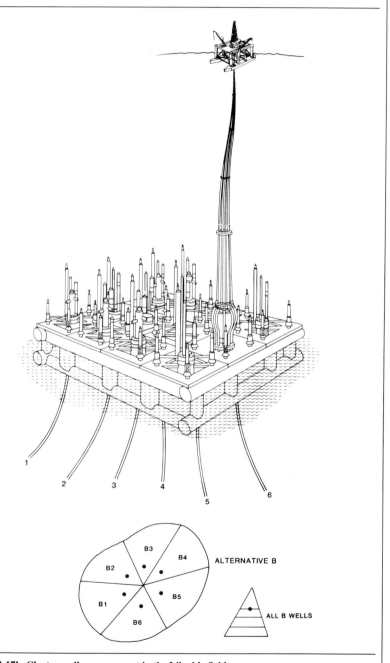

EXAMPLE 2.17 continued

Figure E2.17b Cluster-well arrangement in the Likedda field.

EXAMPLE 2.17 continued

Table E2.17 Likedda Reservoir and Well Data

Field	Likedda
Producing formation	limestone
Midperforations from ground level	10250 ft
Average permeability to oil	3.5 md
Average formation pay thickness	80 ft
Average porosity	0.24
Average water saturation	0.34
Total estimated oil in place	80 MMSTB
Desired plateau rate	1000 STB/D/well
Number of wells	6
Initial reservoir pressure	4520 psia
Bubble-point pressure	4520 psia
Initial oil viscosity	0.307 cp
Initial oil FVF	1.52 bbl/STB
Initial total compressibility	8.8E − 6 1/psi
Wellbore radius	0.29 ft
Stimulation skin	−3.5
Constant wellhead flowing pressure	1000 psia
Minimum wellbore flowing pressure	2000 psia

Material balance relations:

$$k_{ro}/\mu_o B_o = 1.228 \times 10^{-12} p_R^{3.349}$$

$$N_p/N = 0.20 - 4.42 \times 10^{-5} p_R$$

Reservoir factors not considered in this analysis include

- that permeability and porosity decrease toward the flank;
- partial penetration to avoid water coning and;
- regional variation in PVT properties.

Given the reservoir and well data in table E2.17, assume pseudosteady-state production and calculate for each alternative the length of the constant-rate plateau (1000 STB/D well) if minimum wellbore flowing pressure is 2000 psia. Note: production rate has been specified by the rule of 3% initial oil in place (IOIP) per year and an average downtime of about 10%.

SOLUTION

First calculate the average drainage area per well. The total area of the field is

$$A_{field} = 5.615NB_{oi}/(1 - S_w)\phi h$$

$$= 5.615(80 \times 10^6)(1.52)/(1 - 0.34)(0.24)(80)$$

EXAMPLE 2.17 continued

$$= 53{,}880{,}000\,\text{ft}^2$$

$$= 1237\,\text{acres}.$$

Six wells draining the field gives an average drainage area per well of

$$A_{well} = 1237/6$$

$$= 206\,\text{acres}$$

$$= 8{,}980{,}500\,\text{ft}^2.$$

Apparent drainage radius per well is

$$r_e = (8{,}900{,}500/\pi)^{0.5}$$

$$= 1690\,\text{ft}.$$

The rate equation is

$$q_o = \frac{kh(k_{ro}/\mu_o B_o)_{av}(p_R^2 - p_{wf}^2)}{141.2(2p_R)[\ln(r_e/r_w) - 0.75 + s + s_A]},$$

which, when solved for wellbore flowing pressure, is

$$p_{wf}^2 = p_R^2 - \frac{141.2(2p_R)[\ln(r_e/r_w) - 0.75 + s + s_A]}{kh(k_{ro}/\mu_o B_o)_R}q_o.$$

Substituting well and reservoir data, and 1000 STB/D plateau rate gives

$$p_{wf}^2 = p_R^2 - \frac{141.2(2p_R)[\ln(1690/0.29) - 0.75 - 3.5 + s_A]1000}{3.5(80)(1.228 \times 10^{-12})p_R^{3.349}}$$

$$= p_R^2 - 8.213 \times 10^{14}p_R^{-2.349}[4.42 + s_A].$$

For the satellite alternative, drainage areas are centered and the radial/centered shape approximation is adequate (i.e., $s_A = 0$):

$$p_{wf}^2 = p_R^2 - 3.63 \times 10^{15}p_R^{-2.349}.$$

Substituting $p_{wf} = 2000$ psia and solving for reservoir pressure yields $p_R = 4036$ psia. The corresponding cumulative production calculated by the approximation to the solution gas drive material balance is

$$N_p/N = 0.20 - 4.42 \times 10^{-5}(4036)$$

$$= 2.16\%.$$

EXAMPLE 2.17 continued

Since $N = 80 \times 10^6$ STB, cumulative STB produced is

$N_p = 1{,}728{,}000$ STB.

The production time is

$$t = \frac{N_p}{q_o} = \frac{1.728 \times 10^6}{6000} = 286 \text{ days}$$

$$= 0.8 \text{ year}$$

$$= 9\tfrac{1}{2} \text{ months.}$$

For the cluster alternative, drainage areas are triangular and the wells are located near the apices of the triangles. Using an equilateral triangle with a well centered 25% from the apex, the shape skin factor is about +2.89. The well flowing pressure equation, then, is

$$p_{wf}^2 = p_R^2 - 6.00 \times 10^{15} p_R^{-2.349},$$

which gives $p_R = 4470$ psia when $p_{wf} = 2000$ psia. The cumulative oil produced at 4470 psia is only 0.24%, or 194,080 STB. At a field rate of 6000 STB/D, the plateau can only be maintained for about 32 days (one month), or about ten times less than for the case of centered wells with near-radial geometries.

The pressure loss due to skin is approximated from

$$\Delta p_s = \frac{141.2 q_o \mu_o B_o}{kh} s_A$$

$$= \frac{141.2(1000)(0.307)(1.52)}{3.5(80)} s_A$$

$$= 235 s_A.$$

For the triangular area with a well close to the apex, $s_A = 2.89$ and the pressure loss due to skin is about 680 psi. Although this expression for pressure drop due to skin is only approximate for the two-phase gas/oil system, it gives a "ball-park" indication of the absolute effect that shape skin has on inflow performance.

2.7   **TRANSIENT PRODUCTION.** Initial reservoir pressure is dictated by depth, geological evolution, and migration of hydrocarbons. Prior to production startup, pressure is distributed uniformly from the wellbore to the outer boundary and moveable reservoir fluids are motionless. The well and reservoir system is in a state of equilibrium. Opening the well disturbs this equilibrium and creates a pressure gradient toward the wellbore. The pressure gradient results in flow of mobile oil, gas, and water through the pore channels to the wellbore.

The response of a reservoir to production is a chain reaction. Reducing pressure at the wellbore results in flow of reservoir fluid from the immediate vicinity of the wellbore and expansion of the remaining fluid in the affected zone. The pressure drop of the expanding fluid provokes a flow from yet undisturbed regions adjacent to the first one. The phenomenon repeats itself and the pressure disturbance and fluid movement propagates radially away from the wellbore. As production continues, fluid moves from greater and greater distances. It takes time, however, for the initial disturbance to affect the fluid far away from the wellbore. The gradually extending region affected by production is illustrated schematically in figure 2.23. The time-dependent propagation of pressure response will be referred to as *transient production*, during which a well's inflow performance is unstable and may not be described by the stabilized IPR equations presented earlier.

In relation to transient production, wells experience three distinct production periods:

1. *Infinite-Acting Period*, starting at the onset of production and continuing until the nearest no-flow (or constant-pressure) boundary is reached by the propagating pressure disturbance. During this period, the well behaves as if it was located in a reservoir of infinite size.
2. *Transition Period*, starting the instant that the nearest boundary is reached by the pressure disturbance and ending when the furthest outer boundary is reached. The wellbore pressure or rate response during the transition period is not easily interpreted because the exact geometry of the outer boundary is unknown. Practically, however, the transition period is very short unless the outer boundary is highly unsymmetric.
3. *Pseudosteady-State Period*, with onset at the end of the transition period, when the no-flow boundary furthest from the wellbore is reached by the pressure disturbance and the entire drainage area starts to contribute to production. Wellbore conditions (rate and pressure) tend to stabilize during pseudosteady state. Assuming constant rate production, a particular feature of the pseudosteady-state period is that pressure decreases at the same rate everywhere in the reservoir. We generally account for the transient nature of pseudosteady-state flow through the declining average reservoir pressure p_R in the stabilized IPR equation. Note that *all* IPR equations discussed earlier in the text are applicable for pseudosteady conditions.

Chapter 4 is dedicated to discussions concerning time behavior of production wells. It presents methods to calculate and analyze time behavior of wells producing at either a constant rate or at a constant flowing bottomhole pressure. This section concentrates mainly on two aspects of transient production: the length of the infinite-acting period—that is, how long before pseudosteady state is reached—and how transient behavior should be considered when conducting and interpreting short multirate tests. Our discussion of time changes of well performance considers only infinite-acting and pseudosteady-state flow for a centered well with radial outer boundary, where the transition period does not exist for practical purposes.

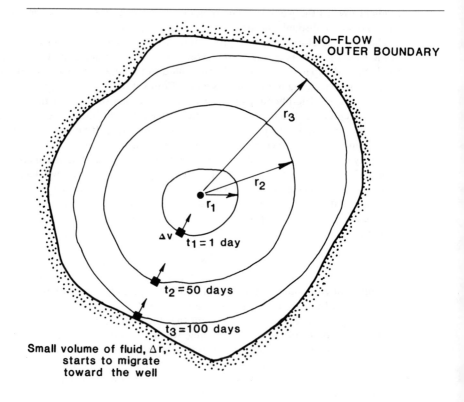

RADIAL PRESSURE PROFILES

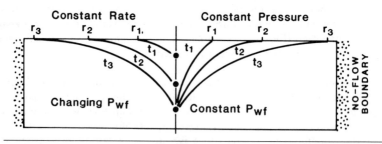

Figure 2.23 Extension of drainage boundaries versus time during transient production.

Two general observations can be made regarding transient production:

1. For medium- to high-permeability reservoirs (>10 to 50 md), the infinite-acting period may last from only a few seconds to several hours. Practically, infinite-acting production does not affect the design of well performance, and stabilized IPR equations can be used. Infinite-acting performance can, however, be important to multirate test interpretation. Rules on stabilization set out by state regulatory bodies should ensure that pseudosteady state has been reached during a test flow period. These regulations, however, are not usually applicable to low-permeability producers.
2. Wells producing from low-permeability reservoirs can require days, months, or years to reach stabilization. For such wells, infinite-acting pressure response has a significant effect on inflow performance, and the concept of stabilized IPR is no longer useful. Most low-permeability wells produce against low, constant wellhead pressure to maximize production. Constant pressure results in declining production rate. The engineering effort is thus focused on rate–time behavior rather than on rate–pressure behavior (i.e., traditional IPR).

Theoretical studies on transient well behavior (see section 4.1) suggest that the rate of propagation of a pressure/rate disturbance in a reservoir is dependent on rock and fluid properties. Thus, the time to reach pseudosteady state is dependent on these properties and, in addition, on the area of the drainage volume. *Dimensionless time* is a time-related variable used to generalize the transient behavior of wells. Actually, there are two types of dimensionless time, t_D and t_{DA}. The first is commonly used to quantify flow performance in the infinite-acting period

$$t_D = \frac{0.000264k}{\phi \mu_i c_{ti} r_w^2} t. \tag{2.129}$$

The second is used primarily to quantify flow performance during pseudosteady-state flow,

$$t_{DA} = \frac{0.000264k}{\phi \mu_i c_{ti} A} t, \tag{2.130}$$

which also implies that $t_{DA} = t_D(r_w^2/A)$. In equations (2.129) and (2.130) t is in hours, r_w is in ft, A is in ft^2, k is in md, μ_i is in cp, and c_{ti} is in 1/psi. Both dimensionless times are applicable throughout the entire transient history of production, including both infinite-acting, transition, and pseudosteady-state periods. We merely want to emphasize that t_D, which is based on wellbore radius, is more useful for describing the infinite-acting period, and t_{DA}, which is based on total drainage area, is better suited for describing the pseudosteady-state period.

Theoretical studies of transient flow (see Earlougher 1977) have shown that the dimensionless time is sufficient to define when a well reaches stabilized or pseudosteady-state flow. For a centered well with a radial outer boundary, the condition of pseudosteady-state flow is simply

$$t_{DA\text{pss}} = 0.1 \qquad\qquad\qquad (2.131)$$

or

$$t_{D\text{pss}} = 0.1\pi(r_e/r_w)^2. \qquad\qquad\qquad (2.132)$$

Equations (2.131) and (2.132) are identical, since $A = \pi r_e^2$. By substituting equation (2.131) in equation (2.130) and solving the condition for pseudosteady state in terms of real time, we find (for a radial geometry)

$$t_{\text{pss}} = 379\frac{\phi\mu_i c_{ti} A}{k} \qquad\qquad\qquad (2.133)$$

where t_{pss} is in hr, A is in ft^2, μ_i is in cp, c_{ti} is in 1/psi, and k is in md.

To generalize equation (2.133) for nonradial drainage geometries we introduce the *constant* $t_{DA\text{pss}}$:

$$t_{\text{pss}} = 3790\frac{\phi\mu_i c_{ti} A}{k}t_{DA\text{pss}}, \qquad\qquad\qquad (2.134)$$

where $t_{DA\text{pss}}$ depends on geometry and well placement. Table 2.4 gives values of $t_{DA\text{pss}}$ for several geometries and well locations, where we note that $t_{DA\text{pss}} = 0.1$ for radial geometry. The values of $t_{DA\text{pss}}$ represent the time when wellbore flowing pressure starts to decline as a linear function of time.

As mentioned earlier, the transition from infinite acting to pseudosteady state is practically instantaneous for a radial geometry. When the outer boundary has irregular shape or the well location is not centered, the transition from infinite acting to pseudosteady state may be substantial. The time at which a well stops acting as if it produced in an infinte reservoir is indicated by equation (2.134), where the constant $t_{D\text{eia}}$ in table 2.4 is used instead of $t_{D\text{pss}}$. Note that $t_{D\text{eia}} = t_{D\text{pss}}(=0.1)$ for a centered well with a radial outer boundary.

Another application of the dimensionless time to pseudosteady state is to estimate a *radius of drainage* at a given time. The concept of transient radius of drainage during the infinite—acting period is particularly useful for interpreting multirate tests and, more generally, it gives a physical meaning to "transient behavior." There are several definitions for radius of drainage, r_d, but the simplest is based on equation (2.131). Solving for r_e at a given time,

$$r_d = r_e(t) = 0.029[kt/\phi\mu_i c_{ti}]^{0.5}. \qquad\qquad\qquad (2.135)$$

A more common expression (see, for example, Earlougher 1977) uses the constant 0.024 instead 0.029, which is equivalent to $r_d/r_w = 1.5t_D^{0.5}$.

Example 2.18 shows how to use the equations defining pseudosteady state.

EXAMPLE 2.18 PREDICTION OF THE START OF PSEUDOSTEADY-STATE FLOW (STABILIZATION)

The Lambert No. 2 well has a permeability of 2.2 md, porosity of 0.28, compressibility of 0.000032 1/psi, viscosity of 0.021 cp, and area of 320 acres ($13,939,200\,\text{ft}^2$). How long will the well produce (at any rate) before pseudosteady state is reached?

SOLUTION

The dimensionless time t_{DA} corresponding to the onset of pseudosteady state is $t_{DA\text{pss}} = 0.1$ for centered radial geometry. Solving equation (2.130) for the corresponding real time t_{pss}, we find

$$0.1 = \frac{0.000264(2.2)}{0.28(0.021)(0.00032)(13,939,200)} t_{\text{pss}}$$

or

$$t_{\text{pss}} = 4518 \text{ hours}$$

$$= 188 \text{ days}.$$

The duration of the infinite-acting period is an important factor in determining drilling and spacing units for low-permeability reservoirs. Long infinite-acting production suggests that the well is not draining the entire spaced area and more wells are needed to deplete the reservoir economically and within a reasonable period of time. The balance between extra drilling and completion costs and accelerated production revenue is the basis for well spacing considerations of low-permeability reservoirs.

Interpretation of multirate tests affected by transient behavior requires basic understanding of the transient phenomenon. For that purpose, it is useful to consider transient production as a series of "steady-state" conditions with increasing radius of drainage. To facilitate a simple mathematical treatment, we will assume the case of constant rate, where flowing pressure is a function of time. Writing the steady-state IPR equation (eq. [2.9]) for constant rate in terms of $\ln(r_e/r_w)$, where $r_e = r_e(t)$, we find

$$\ln[r_e(t)/r_w] = \frac{kh}{141.2q_o\mu_oB_o}[p_i - p_{wf}(t)]. \tag{2.136}$$

The time-dependent expression, $\ln[r_e(t)/r_w]$, actually represents *dimensionless pressure*, p_D, which is related to the actual pressure drawdown, $p_i - p_{wf}(t)$, by the *definition*

$$p_D = \frac{kh}{141.2q_o\mu_oB_o}[p_i - p_{wf}(t)]. \tag{2.137}$$

Similarly for gas, p_D can be written

$$p_D = \frac{0.703kh(p_i^2 - p_{wf}^2)}{T(\mu_g Z)_i q_g}$$

(2.137a)

$$p_D = \frac{1.406kh(p/\mu_g Z)(p_i - p_{wf})}{T q_g}$$

(2.137b)

$$p_D = \frac{0.703kh[m(p_i) - m(p_{wf})]}{T q_g}.$$

(2.137c)

Thus, we can write drainage radius as a function of p_D:

$$r_e(t) = r_w \exp(p_D)$$

(2.138)

or

$$p_D = \ln[r_e(t)/r_w],$$

(2.139)

which applies until the actual drainage radius r_e is reached.

Extensive mathematical treatment of transient pressure behavior has resulted in numerous expressions for dimensionless pressure as a function of dimensionless time (for constant rate). The general radial solution for p_D is given in figure 2.24 (after Fetkovich and Vienot 1983, based on tables of the original solution by van Everdingen and Hurst 1949). The figure is a log–log plot of p_D as a function of t_D for radial flow geometry at the wellbore and at the outer no-flow boundary. In general, a log–log plot correlating dimensionless quantities is called a *type curve*.

Figure 2.24 covers both the infinite-acting and pseudosteady-state periods. The infinite-acting solution is a single smooth line with half-slope at early times (p_D proportional to $t_D^{0.5}$) and more gradual change at later times (p_D proportional to $\ln t_D$). Pseudosteady state appears as a family of stems having similar shape, each representing a different value of dimensionless radius, r_e/r_w. Each stem branches off the infinite-acting curve at a different t_D, as determined by t_{Dpss} (eq. [2.132]).

The radial p_D solution (fig. 2.24) can also be used for stimulated and damage wells by using apparent wellbore radius r_{wa} instead of r_w in the definition of t_D. The treatment of stimulated wells is discussed in some detail in section 4.3. A useful approximation of the radial p_D function for infinite-acting times is given by

$$p_D = 0.5[\ln(t_D) + 0.80907],$$

(2.140)

which applies for $t_D > 25$. (If high-velocity flow exists, then depending on the rate, eq. [2.140] may not be valid until t_D exceeds 2000.) For $t_D < 25$, equation (2.140) should not be used for infinite-acting flow. Instead, figure 2.24 can be used, or the approximate relation (Edwardson et al. 1962),

$$p_D = \frac{370.529 t_D^{0.5} + 137.582 t_D + 5.69549 t_D^{1.5}}{328.834 + 265.488 t_D^{0.5} + 45.2157 t_D + t_D^{1.5}},$$

(2.141)

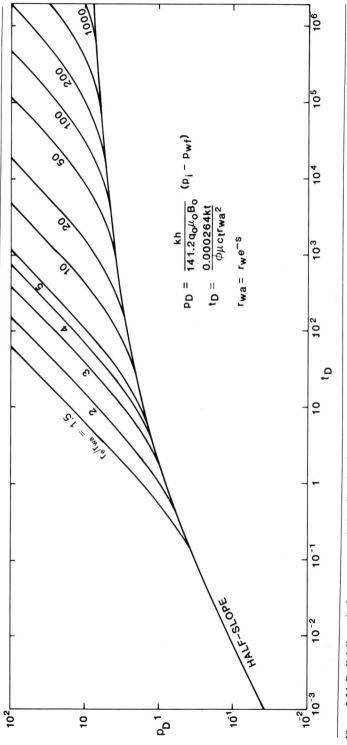

Figure 2.24 Radial dimensionless pressure solution. Reprinted by permission of the SPE-AIME from Fetkovich and Vienot 1983. © 1983 SPE-AIME.

which applies for all $t_D < 500$ (it approaches the asymptotic square-root solution at small times). Example 2.19 illustrates the use of dimensionless pressure to predict transient behavior.

EXAMPLE 2.19 APPLICATION OF DIMENSIONLESS PRESSURE

The Lipscomb No. 1 is an undersaturated oil well producing from the Morrow Sand in a field bordering the Oklahoma and Texas panhandle. The Lipscomb No. 1 is the first well drilled into what geologists believe to be a separate stratigraphic trap. The shape of the trap is approximately circular, with a diameter of one mile. Table E2.19a gives relevant data for the Lipscomb well. A permanently installed downhole pressure gauge recorded a 2244 psia stabilized flowing downhole pressure at 857 STB/D stabilized flow rate.

To substantiate the geologists' interpretation of the trap's area, a reservoir limit test is scheduled. The program is to shut in the well and let the bottomhole pressure build up to stabilization. Then the well will be open to production at a constant rate of about 450 STB/D (the allowable) and bottomhole pressures will be monitored to indicate when pseudosteady state is reached. Estimate how long the well must be produced to substantiate the drainage diameter of one mile. In addition, calculate the expected pressure decline during the transient period.

SOLUTION

The dimensionless time must be estimated from equation (2.130) as

$$t_{DA} = \frac{0.000264k}{\phi \mu c_t A} t,$$

where area A is given by

$A = \pi r_{field}^2$

$= \pi (5280/2)^2$

$= 2.19 \times 10^7 \, ft^2.$

Table E2.19a Reservoir and Well Data for the Lipscomb No. 1 Well

Net pay thickness h	22 ft
Average reservoir pressure p_R	2677 psia
Oil viscosity μ_o	0.584 cp
Oil FVF, B_o	1.5 bbl/STB
Total compressibility c_t	11.4×10^{-6} 1/psi
Wellbore radius r_w	0.3 ft
Porosity, ϕ	0.23

EXAMPLE 2.19 continued

The only information on permeability must be derived from the stabilized flow test. It may be estimated from the stabilized IPR equation (eq. [2.28]), which when solved for k is

$$k = \frac{141.2\mu_o B_o q_o[\ln(r_e/r_w) - 0.75 + s]}{h(p_R - p_{wf})}.$$

Assuming $\ln(r_e/r_w) - 0.75 + s = 8.0$, permeability is

$$k = \frac{141.2(0.584)(1.5)(857)(8.0)}{22(2677 - 2244)}$$

$$= 89 \, \text{md}.$$

Substituting the estimated permeability, reservoir data, and the condition for start of pseudosteady state, $t_{DA} = 0.1$, in the dimensionless time equation

$$t_{DA} = \frac{0.000264(89)(t_{pss})}{(0.23)(0.584)(2.19 \times 10^7)(11.4 \times 10^{-6})} = 0.1,$$

and solving for t_{pss} yields

$$t_{pss} = 142 \, \text{hr}$$

$$= 6.0 \, \text{days}.$$

The reservoir limit test should last at least six days to ensure stabilization, and probably 12 days to ensure reliable results. At a constant rate of 450 STB/D, the wellbore flowing pressure as a function of time during the transient period can be calculated by solving equation (2.137) for p_{wf}:

$$p_{wf} = p_i - 141.2q_o(\mu_o B_o/kh)p_D$$

$$= 2677 - 141.2[(450)(0.584)(1.5)/(89)(22)]p_D$$

$$= 2677 - 28.4p_D.$$

Figure 2.24 gives the relationship between p_D and t_D, where t_D is related to real time by

$$t_D = \frac{0.000264(89)}{(0.23)(0.584)(11.4 \times 10^{-6})(0.3)^2}t(\text{hr}).$$

Table E2.19b lists real time t, dimensionless time t_D, dimensionless pressure p_D, and the corresponding wellbore flowing pressure p_{wf}.

EXAMPLE 2.19 continued

Table E2.19b Calculated Flowing Pressures for the Proposed 12-Day Reservoir Limit Test

t (hr)	t (days)	t_D	p_D	p_{wf} (psia)
1	0.04	1.71×10^5	6.43	2494.4
6	0.25	1.02×10^6	7.32	2469.1
12	0.50	2.05×10^6	7.67	2459.2
24	1.00	4.09×10^6	8.02	2449.2
48	2.00	8.18×10^6	8.36	2439.6
96	4.00	1.64×10^7	8.71	2429.6
144	6.00	2.46×10^7	$(8.91)^*$	2424.0
216	9.00	3.68×10^7	(9.12)	2418.0
288	12.00	4.91×10^7	(9.26)	2414.0

*Values in parentheses are calculated from the semilog approximation, even though the indication of pseudosteady-state flow occurs at six days.

Returning to the concept of *radius of drainage*, it can be shown that substituting $r_e(t)$ given by equation (2.135) [with 0.024 instead of 0.029] in p_D given by equation (2.139), results in the logarithmic approximation for p_D (eq. [2.140]). Conceptually it is easier to use transient radius of drainage instead of dimensionless pressure. Once the transient radius of drainage equals the actual drainage radius r_e, flow stabilizes and the pseudosteady-state IPR equation can be used. This is achieved by replacing p_D by $\ln(r_e/r_w) - 0.75$ and replacing initial pressure p_i by average reservoir pressure p_R (which is an indirect function of time) in equation (2.137).

In review, we can write two IPR equations, the first for the infinite-acting period,

$$q_o = \frac{kh[p_i - p_{wf}(t)]}{141.2\mu_o B_o p_D(t_D)}, \tag{2.142}$$

where rate is assumed constant and wellbore flowing pressure varies with time. Once the physical drainage radius r_e is reached, the stabilized IPR is used,

$$q_o = \frac{kh[p_R(t) - p_{wf}]}{141.2\mu_o B_o[\ln(r_e/r_w) - 0.75]} \tag{2.15}$$

As mentioned previously, the IPR equation (q versus p_{wf}) has little practical use for transient production. If the reservoir is tight and transient production is long, then most likely constant flowing pressure rate–time behavior is of primary interest. That is, the IPR is *rate–time* instead of rate–pressure relationship.

It may be tempting to plot the IPR for infinite-acting conditions as a series of rate–pressure plots, as shown in figure 2.25. Each time curve is found by solving equation (2.142) for $p_{wf}(t)$ at different rates. When pseudosteady state is reached, the stabilized IPR is plotted. Thereafter, the IPR (rate–pressure) is dictated by changes associated with changing average reservoir pressure, as fixed by the material balance.

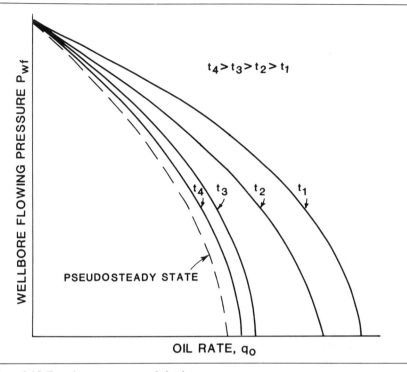

Figure 2.25 Transient rate–pressure behavior.

The problem with representing transient IPR as shown in figure 2.25 is that transient behavior is not properly accounted for when rate changes. For example, if rate is q_1 from production startup to time t_1, and q_2 from time t_1 to t_2, the flowing pressure will *not* change from p_{wf1} to p_{wf2} as indicated in the figure. Instead, the new wellbore pressure is a composite result of the transient pressure associated with q_1, together with the new pressure response related to q_2. To properly account for changing rate, the method of superposition should be used (see section 4.4).

Figure 2.25 can, despite its shortcomings, be used to illustrate the transient behavior of rate *if* flowing wellbore pressure remains somewhat constant during infinite-acting times. For example, maximum rate (AOF) declines rapidly with time until pseudosteady state is reached, after which it declines according to changes related to average reservoir pressure. Transient IPR is also reflected by a shifting backpressure curve, where constant C (eq. [1.33]) decreases with time. Likewise, transient behavior is reflected in the quadratic (Forchheimer) equation by a time-dependent constant A (eq. [2.51]).

Transient Multirate Testing. Transient behavior is a major concern in planning and interpreting multirate tests. The reason for running a multirate test is to establish the IPR and, in particular, to quantify the effect of high-velocity flow (rate-dependent skin). Flowing each rate until stabilization, gives the most reliable backpressure curve. That is, the pressure transience of an earlier flow period does not continue into subsequent flow periods. The so-called flow after flow multirate test is based on stabilized flow for each rate. Figures 2.26 and 2.27 show the typical sequence of a flow-after-flow test. The stabilized rate–pressure data are plotted as q versus Δp^2 on log–log paper. A straight line is drawn through the points with the slope defining the backpressure exponent n ($= 1/\text{slope}$) and backpressure constant C. As an alternative, a cartesian plot of q versus $\Delta p^2/q$ or (for gas) $\Delta m(q)/q$ yields a straight line used to determine constants A (intercept) and B (slope) of the quadratic Forchheimer equation. Truely stabilized flow-after-flow tests should not be influenced by the sequence used. Increasing the rates (the standard) illustrated in figure 2.26, or decreasing the rates, illustrated in figure 2.27 gives essentially the same results. In general, however, an increasing sequence multirate test is always preferred.

When infinite-acting flow lasts the entire duration of each flow period (4 to 12 hours) an alternative test procedure must be used. The isochronal test is the most reliable alternative to a stabilized flow-after-flow sequence. *Isochronal* means equal duration. A true isochronal test consists of flowing a well at several rates, each separated by a buildup period of sufficiently long duration to reach stabilized (initial or average) reservoir pressure. The wellbore flowing pressure is recorded during each flow period at a specific time. If the time is 4 hours, then the test is referred to as a 4-hour isochronal test. The actual flow periods may be of different duration, but the flowing pressure should be measured at a specific time from the start of each flow period. A true isochronal test is shown in figure 2.28. Rate–pressure data are analyzed using the log–log backpressure approach or a linear plot of $\Delta p^2/q$ versus q. If flowing pressures are measured at several times during each test (e.g., 2, 4, and 6 hours), then isochronal analysis can be made separately on data corresponding to each time. The backpressure slope should be the same at each time, and the resulting values of backpressure constant C (intercept) are correlated as a function of time. For a cartesian $\Delta p^2/q$ versus q plot, intercept A is correlated as a function of time, where slope B is held constant.

There are several methods available to determine the stabilized IPR coefficients C for the backpressure equation and A for the quadratic Forchheimer equation. If the last test is long enough to reach stabilization, the stabilized rate–pressure data marks a single point on the graph. A straight line is drawn through this point parallel to the transient curve(s), thereby maintaining the slope defined by transient data.

If a stabilized flow cannot be reached during a reasonable test period, the stabilized backpressure coefficient can be estimated from equation (2.75). An estimation of the drainage area is needed to calculate the stabilized coefficient. The corresponding time to stabilization is given by equation (2.133). Example 2.20 illustrates the procedure to establish the stabilized IPR.

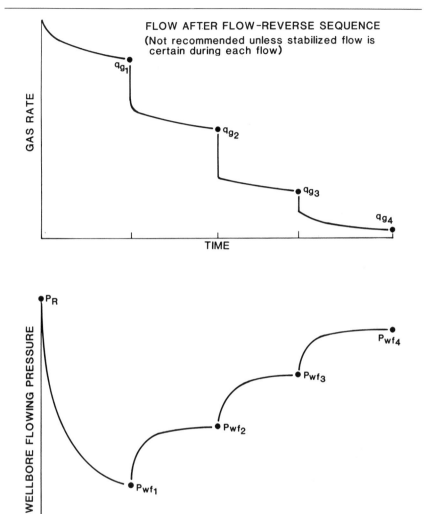

Figure 2.26 Normal flow-after-flow multirate sequence. After Fetkovich 1975 by permission of the SPE-AIME.

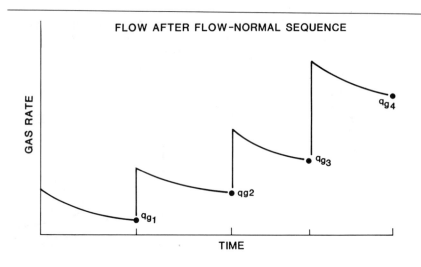

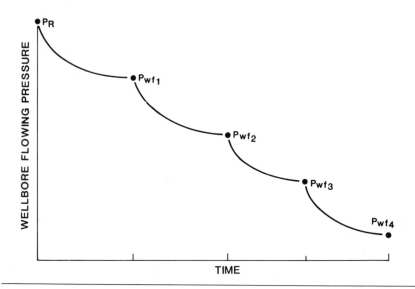

Figure 2.27 Reverse flow-after-flow multirate sequence. After Fetkovich 1975 by permission of the SPE-AIME.

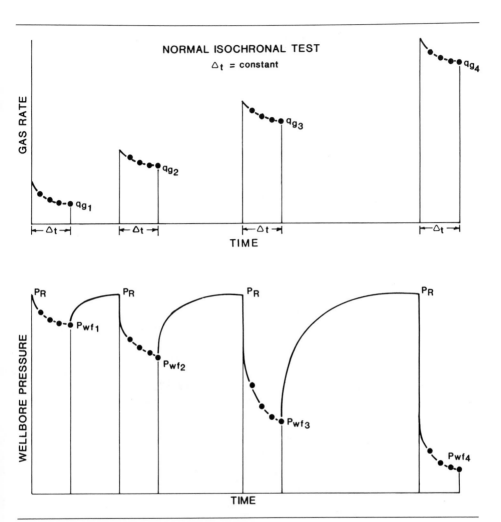

Figure 2.28 True isochronal test sequence. After Fetkovich 1975 by permission of the SPE-AIME.

EXAMPLE 2.20 ISOCHRONAL TEST USED TO DETERMINE THE IPR OF A GAS WELL

The Cullender Gas Well No. 3 was tested several times over a ten-year period, indicating a constant backpressure exponent $n = 0.948$ and a transient constant C that does not reach stabilization even after nine-day flow periods. Table E2.20a lists reservoir and well data and table E2.20b gives one-hour isochronal data for the well.

Tasks
1. Make a logarithmic backpressure plot and substantiate the reported backpressure exponent.
2. Draw the backpressure curve through the single nine-day test point.
3. Calculate t_{pss} considering that the well drains 640 acres.
4. Determine the stabilized backpressure coefficient C and draw the stabilized backpressure curve.

SOLUTION

Figure E2.20 shows the backpressure plot for one-hour test data, indicating a slope of 1.053 ($n = 0.95$). The single nine-day test point is plotted, and a straight line is drawn through it with the same slope.

The dimensionless time corresponding to stabilized pseudosteady-state flow is $t_{DA} = 0.1$ or $t_D = 0.314(r_e/r_{wa})^2$. Drainage radius $r_e = 3000$ ft for 640-acre spacing and $r_{wa} = 10$ ft ($s = -3.5$), giving $r_e/r_a = 300$. The time to reach stabilized pseudosteady-state flow is then obtained by combining equations (2.129), (2.130), and (2.131)

$$t_D = \frac{0.000264 k t_{pss}}{\phi \mu_i c_{ti} r_{wa}^2} = 0.314(r_e/r_{wa})^2$$

$$= \frac{0.000264(5.3) t_{pss}}{0.07(0.012)(0.0016)(10^2)} = 0.314(300)^2$$

or

$$10.4 t_{pss} = 18,260$$

or

$$t_{pss} = 2715 \text{ hours}$$

$$= 113 \text{ days.}$$

The stabilized backpressure coefficient is calculated by equation (2.75),

$$C = \frac{(0.703 kh)^n}{(T\mu_g Z)^n D^{1-n} p_D^{2n-1}},$$

EXAMPLE 2.20 continued

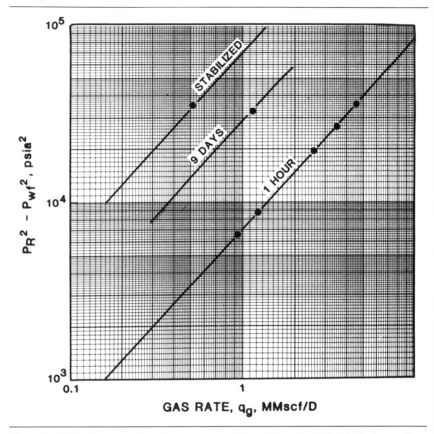

Figure E2.20 Backpressure plot of isochronal test data and the calculated stabilized curve for Cullender No. 3 gas well.

Table E2.20a   Relevant Reservoir and Well Data for the Cullender Gas Well No. 3

Porosity, ϕ	0.07
Net pay thickness h^a	110 ft
Permeability k^b	5.3 md
Reservoir temperature T	90°F
Initial gas viscosity μ_g	0.012 cp
Initial Z-factor	0.925
Initial total compressibility c_{ti}	0.0016 1/psi
Gas gravity γ_g	0.712
Wellbore radius r_w	0.292 ft
Skin factor s^b	−3.5
Backpressure exponent n^b	0.948

[a] The zone was completed open-hole with an acid treatment.
[b] Based on evaluation of all the Cullender data.

EXAMPLE 2.20 continued

Table E2.20b Test Data for the Cullender Gas Well No. 3

	p_R (psia)	p_{wf} (psia)	q_g (MMscf/D)	Test C
1-hr tests				
10-11-44	441.6	431.7	1.229	227.8
12-03-51	352.4	342.4	0.977	222.8
12-04-51	352.3	322.9	2.588	218.1
12-05-51	351.0	309.5	3.565	221.3
12-06-51	349.5	293.6	4.625	222.0
9-day test				
10-11-44	441.6	401.4	1.156	58.7
Calculated 113-day stabilized	350.0	300.0	0.508	26.3

where

$$p_D = [\ln(r_e/r_{wa})]$$

$$= [\ln(3000/10)] = 5.6,$$

and D is given by equation (2.65),

$$D = 3.75 \times 10^{-8} \frac{(0.71)(110)}{(0.012)(0.292)(110^2)}$$

$$= 6.9 \times 10^{-8} (\text{scf/D})^{-1}.$$

Substituting the data in the C expression gives

$$C = \frac{[(0.703)(5.3)(110)/(550)(0.012)(0.925)]^{0.95}}{(6.9 \times 10^{-8})^{0.05}(5.6)^{0.90}}$$

$$= 26.3.$$

The single rate–pressure time point corresponding to $C = 26.3$ is arbitrarily chosen as $p_{wf} = 300$ psia and

$$q_g = 26.3(350^2 - 300^2)^{0.95}$$

$$= 508 \, \text{Mscf/D}.$$

This point is plotted in figure E2.20 with a line passing through it with slope of 1.053 ($n = 0.95$). This is the stabilized backpressure curve.

Similar to a backpressure plot, a Cartesian $\Delta p^2/q$ versus q plot of isochronal data gives a set of parallel lines having the same slope and decreasing intercept with increasing test time. The stabilized curve can be determined by one stabilized flow point, or from calculation based on equation (2.52), with the time to reach stabilization given by equation (2.133).

An important observation regarding the transient behavior of the backpressure constant $C(t)$ and the quadratic constant $A(t)$ is that both coefficients can be related to dimensionless pressure. For low-pressure gas wells, combining equations (1.33) and (2.137a) gives

$$\frac{1}{C(t)} = \frac{\Delta p^2}{q_g} = \frac{T(\mu_g Z)_i}{0.703kh} p_D \tag{2.143}$$

such that $1/C(t)$ is proportional to p_D. For the quadratic equation, combining equations (2.55) and (2.137a) gives

$$A(t) = \frac{\Delta p^2}{q_g} - Bq_g = \frac{T(\mu_g Z)_i}{0.703kh} p_D \tag{2.144}$$

such that $A(t)$ is proportional to p_D.

A plot of $1/C(t)$ or $A(t)$ versus time on log–log paper (with the same grid size as in figure 2.24) can be matched to the radial dimensionless pressure solution. Using tracing paper, plot $1/C(t)$ or $A(t)$ versus time and match the infinite-acting p_D solution by shifting the tracing paper vertically and horizontally until the points overlay the radial solution. A depletion stem can be chosen corresponding to the known spacing (r_e/r_w) and the time to stabilization is read immediately from the curve where the depletion stem deviates from the infinite-acting curve. This allows calculation of stabilized constants C or A. Example 2.21 shows the procedure for matching the transient constant to the radial $p_D(t_D)$ solution in figure 2.24. Data are taken from Well 1 in the classic paper by Cullender.

EXAMPLE 2.21 MATCHING THE TRANSIENT IPR CONSTANTS TO DIMENSIONLESS PRESSURE SOLUTION FOR RADIAL SYSTEM

The Free No. 4 gas well (Cullender Gas Well No. 1) was discussed in example 2.9. Isochronal test data reported by Cullender are given in table E2.21a. The well showed transient behavior throughout the entire test. Cullender analyzed the test data and obtained backpressure exponent $n = 0.867$. He also reported a decreasing $C(t)$ as the period of flow increased.

Tasks
1. Determine reservoir properties and skin for the well using backpressure analysis and a match of $1/C(t)$ to the p_D versus t_D type curve.
2. Repeat the study by matching $A(t)$ to the p_D curve.
3. Determine the time t_D it takes to reach pseudosteady state, considering that the well drains 640 acres.

EXAMPLE 2.21 continued

Table E2.21a Isochronal Data for the Free No. 4 Well, as Reported by Cullender (Gas Well No. 1)

Test	Date (m-d-y)	p_R (psia)	t (hr)	q_g (MMscf/D)	p_{wf} (psia)	$q/\Delta p^2$ (scf/D/psia^2)	C^a (scf/D/psia^{2n})	A^b (psia^2/scf/D)
(a)	10-03-44	435.2	24.0	9.900	302.8	101.3	467.1	0.00839
(b)	10-24-44	436.8	1.0	4.656	410.2	206.8	784.0	0.00414
			3.0	4.587	404.4	168.3	654.5	0.00525
			23.0	4.440	390.0	114.8	467.9	0.00804
(c)	12-11-45	394.7	0.1	2.016	388.8	437.3	1343.0	0.00199
			0.2	2.009	387.4	353.7	1117.0	0.00253
			0.5	2.001	385.6	281.8	916.7	0.00325
			1.0	1.994	384.1	241.4	801.1	0.00384
			3.0	1.980	381.3	190.8	652.6	0.00494
			24.0	1.947	375.8	133.7	478.5	0.00719
(d)	01-11-46	390.7	0.1	2.991	380.8	391.5	1286.0	0.00210
			0.2	2.977	378.7	323.2	1088.0	0.00264
			0.5	2.956	375.6	255.7	887.0	0.00347
			1.0	2.941	373.3	221.5	782.9	0.00407
(e)	01-15-46	394.0	0.2	7.327	359.4	280.8	1086.0	0.00246
			0.5	7.199	352.1	230.4	912.5	0.00326
			1.0	7.092	346.0	199.7	804.5	0.00395
			3.0	6.887	335.0	160.2	662.1	0.00521
(f)	01-17-46	391.1	0.5	2.952	376.5	262.9	908.7	0.00336
			1.0	2.937	374.3	228.2	803.3	0.00394
			3.0	2.905	370.4	184.8	668.1	0.00497
(g)	12-05-46	381.0	0.1	4.158	366.8	391.9	1344.0	0.00193
			0.2	4.130	363.9	324.7	1141.0	0.00246
			0.5	4.086	359.5	256.8	930.0	0.00328
			1.0	4.052	356.0	220.2	813.0	0.00393
			3.0	3.989	350.7	179.9	681.0	0.00496

$^a C = q_g/(\Delta p^2)^{0.867}$
$^b A = \Delta p^2/q_g - 1.5(10^{-10})q_g$

SOLUTION

Backpressure Analysis
Test data are plotted as pressure-squared versus rate on log–log paper in figure E2.21a. The points are grouped in sets according to flow periods (i.e., $t = 0.1, 0.2,$ . . . 24 hrs), and each set is matched to a straight line. The backpressure exponent n and the coefficient C of each line are given in table E2.21b. The goodness of fit of the straight line for each time is excellent, as indicated by the statistical fitness parameter R computed and listed in table E2.21b ($R = 1$ indicates a perfect fit).

An average exponent $n = 0.867$ is a good indicator of the slope ($1/n$) for all the curves. The backpressure constant C is then calculated as $q_g/(\Delta p^2)^{0.867}$ for each rate data, as found in table E.21a. A log–log plot of $1/C(t)$ versus time is shown in

EXAMPLE 2.21 continuted

figure E2.21b. The plot is matched to the radial dimensionless pressure solution in figure 2.24, with a match point of

$t_M = 1\,\text{hr}$,

$t_{DM} = 80$,

$[(\Delta p^2)^{0.867}/q_g]_M = 0.001$,

$p_{DM} = 2.0$,

where the subscript M indicates match point. For a given time the spread in points (from 3 to 6 per time) is only slight, suggesting a good fit of the data. The match to the p_D curve is unique. Dimensionless time of 100 occurs after about 1.5 hours, indicating that the logarithmic approximation to p_D can be used thereafter.

The dimensionless time match is used to estimate the apparent wellbore radius,

$$r_{wa}^2 = \frac{0.000264 k t_M}{\phi \mu_i c_{ti} t_{DM}}$$

$$= \frac{0.000264(29.5)(1)}{(0.07)(0.012)(0.0016)(80)},$$

$r_{wa} = 8.5\,\text{ft}$,

which is equivalent to skin,

$s = -\ln(r_{wa}/r_w)$

$= -\ln(8.5/0.292)$

$= -3.4.$

Table E2.21b Best-fit Coefficients in the Backpressure and Forcheimer Equations for the Free No. 4 Well (Cullender Gas Well No. 1)

t	No.	Quadratic			Backpressure		
		R	A	B	R	C	n
0.1	3	0.70	0.00210	1.17×10^{-10}	0.99	1.396	0.861
0.2	4	0.95	0.00261	1.28×10^{-10}	1.00	1.242	0.855
0.5	5	0.91	0.00338	1.35×10^{-10}	1.00	0.873	0.871
1.0	6	0.89	0.00493	1.64×10^{-10}	1.00	0.783	0.869
3.0	5	0.95	0.00481	2.12×10^{-10}	1.00	0.630	0.872
24.0	3	0.95	0.00713	2.86×10^{-10}	1.00	0.539	0.854
			Avg.	1.50×10^{-10}		Avg.	0.867

EXAMPLE 2.21 continued

For 640-acre spacing, $r_e = 3000$ ft and $r_e/r_{wa} = 350$. The time to reach pseudo-steady state is, then,

$$t_{pss} = t_{DApss}(\pi r_e^2/r_w^2) \times (t_M/t_{DM})$$

$$= 0.1(\pi 350^2) \times (1/80)$$

$$= 481 \text{ hr}$$

$$= 20 \text{ days.}$$

Analysis of the pressure match point is somewhat complicated when the backpressure exponent n is less than one. When equation (2.75) is solved for kh and dimensionless pressure is used instead of $[\ln(r_e/r_w) - 0.75 + s]$, we find

$$kh = \frac{\{(D^{1-n})(p_{DM}^{2n-1})/[(\Delta p^2)^n/q_g]_M\}^{1/n} T \mu_g Z}{0.703}.$$

The ratio of p_{DM}^{2n-1} to $[(\Delta p^2)^n/q_g]_M$—and therefore kh—is *not* independent of the match point chosen. It can be shown that kh is dependent upon $\{p_{DM}/[(\Delta p^2)^n/q_g]_M\}p_{DM}^{2n-2}$. The question, then, is which p_{DM} should be chosen. Since the primary application of calculated permeability is to predict stabilized inflow performance, we suggest that p_{DM} at the start of pseudosteady state be chosen. The relation for kh can now be expressed

$$kh = \frac{\{(D^{1-n})(p_{Dpss}^{2n-2})(p_{DM})/[(\Delta p^2)^n/q_g]_M\}^{1/n} T \mu_g Z}{0.703},$$

where p_{Dpss} is p_D calculated at t_{Dpss}. Earlier in the example we calculated the time to pseudosteady state and it was found that the logarithmic approximation for p_D (eq. [2.140]) is valid up to t_{pss}. Therefore,

$$p_{Dpss} = 0.5[\ln(t_{Dpss}) + 0.809]$$

$$= 0.5[\ln 481(80/1) + 0.809]$$

$$= 5.68.$$

The high-velocity flow term is estimated from equation (2.65) as

$$D = 3.75 \times 10^{-8} \frac{\gamma_g h}{\mu_g r_w h_p^2}$$

$$= 3.75 \times 10^{-8} \frac{(0.712)(120)}{(0.012)(0.292)(120^2)}$$

EXAMPLE 2.21 continued

$$= 6.35 \times 10^{-8} (\text{scf/D})^{-1},$$

which gives

$$kh = \frac{\{(D^{1-n})(p_{Dpss}^{2n-2})(p_{DM})/[(\Delta p^2)^n/q_g]_M\}^{1/n} T\mu_g Z}{0.703}$$

$$= \frac{[(6.35 \times 10^{-8})^{0.133}(5.68)^{-0.265}(2)/0.001]^{1.153}(550)(0.012)(0.925)}{0.703}$$

$$= 2574 \, \text{md-ft}.$$

With total thickness of 120 ft, permeability is

$$k = 2574/120$$

$$= 21.4 \, \text{md}.$$

Quadratic Equation Analysis
A Cartesian plot of $\Delta p^2/q_g$ versus q_g is given in figure E2.21c. Grouping the points in sets according to flow periods and fitting each set to a straight line gives a family of parallel lines (only one line is plotted in fig. E2.21c). The slope B and the intercept A of each line are listed in table E2.21b. The slopes B should (theoretically) be constant. In fact, B ranges from 1.17×10^{-10} to 2.86×10^{-10}, increasing continuously from 0.1-hour data to 24-hour data. An average slope of 1.5×10^{-10} is used in the analysis that follows. Similar results are found for values of B from 1.0 to 2.0×10^{-10}.

The constant A in table E2.21b is calculated for the test data, using the equation

$$A(t) = (p_R^2 - p_{wf}^2)/q_g - Bq_g,$$

where $B = 1.5 \times 10^{-10}$. Values of $A(t)$ were plotted on log–log paper in figure E2.21d. The plot is matched to the dimensionless radial type-curve solution for p_D (fig. 2.24). A match point is chosen as

$$t_M = 1 \, \text{hr},$$

$$t_{DM} = 10,$$

$$A_M = 0.001,$$

$$p_{DM} = 0.4.$$

For a given time the spread in points (from 3 to 6 per time) is greater than when using the backpressure constant C (fig. E2.21b). No real improvement is shown if

EXAMPLE 2.21 continued

different values of B are chosen. No improvement in scatter is gained by including a correction term suggested by Wattenbarger and Ramey (1968):

$$A(t) = (p_R^2 - p_{wf}^2)/q_g - Bq_g(1 - 1/1.5t_D^{0.5}).$$

In general, the constant $A(t)$ shows more scatter than the backpressure constant $C(t)$ [i.e., $1/C(t)$].

The match to the p_D curve is unique. Dimensionless time of 100 is reaced after about ten hours. The logarithmic approximation should be valid thereafter. Substituting p_D for $[\ln(r_e/r_w) - 0.75 + s]$ and A_M for A in equation (2.52) and solving for kh gives

$$kh = \frac{T\mu Z p_{DM}}{0.703 h A_M}$$

$$= \frac{(550)(0.012)(0.925)(0.4)}{(0.703)(0.001)}$$

$$= 3474,$$

where $h = 120$ ft, so $k = 28.9$ md.

The dimensionless time match is used to estimate the apparent wellbore radius,

$$r_{wa} = \left[\frac{0.000264 k t_M}{\phi\mu_i c_{ti} t_{DM}} \right]^{0.5}$$

$$= \left[\frac{0.000264(28.9)(1)}{(0.07)(0.012)(0.0016)(10)} \right]^{0.5}$$

$$= 23.8 \text{ ft},$$

which is equivalent to skin,

$$s = -\ln(r_{wa}/r_w)$$

$$= -\ln(23.8/0.292)$$

$$= -4.4.$$

For 640-acre spacing $r_e = 3000$ ft and $r_e/r_{wa} = 126$. The time to reach pseudosteady state is

$$t_{pss} = t_{Dpss}(t_M/t_{DM})$$

$$= t_{DApss}(A/r_w^2) \times (t_M/t_{DM})$$

$$= 0.1(\pi 126^2) \times (1/10)$$

EXAMPLE 2.21 continued

   = 499 hr

   = 21 days.

The similarity in results obtained by the two methods is striking. Since a "right" equation doesn't exist, the backpressure and quadratic equations can be considered equally good engineering tools. Both methods have advantages, but our experience suggests the backpressure equation fits field data better than the quadratic equation.

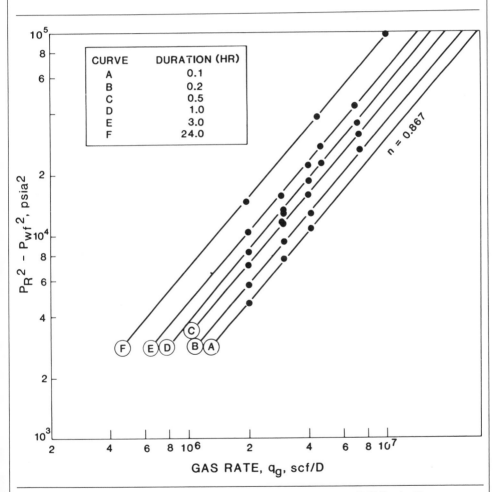

Figure E2.21a Backpressure plot of isochronal test data for Free No. 4 gas well (Cullender No. 1 gas well). Reprinted by permission of the SPE-AIME from Cullender 1955. © 1955 SPE-AIME.

EXAMPLE 2.21 continued

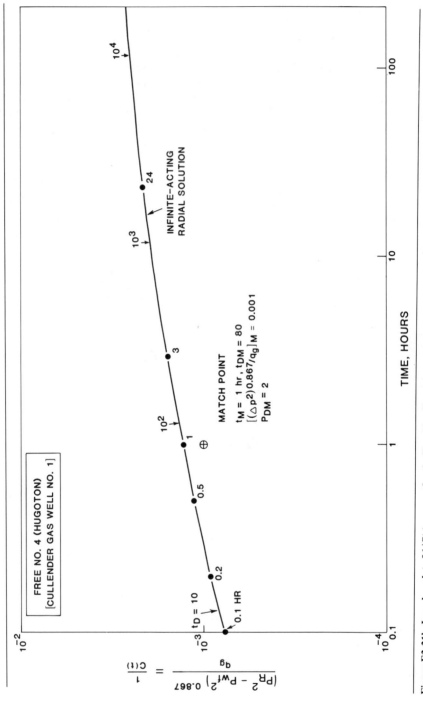

Figure E2.21b Log–log plot of $1/C(t)$ versus t for the Free No. 4 isochronal test data and a match to the dimensionless pressure type curve.

EXAMPLE 2.21 continued

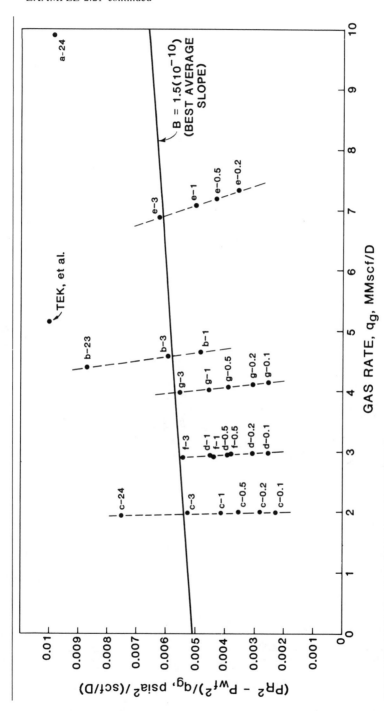

Figure E2.21c Cartesian plot of $\Delta p^2/q_g$ versus q_g to establish the quadratic IPR equation for the Free No. 4 gas well.

EXAMPLE 2.21 continued

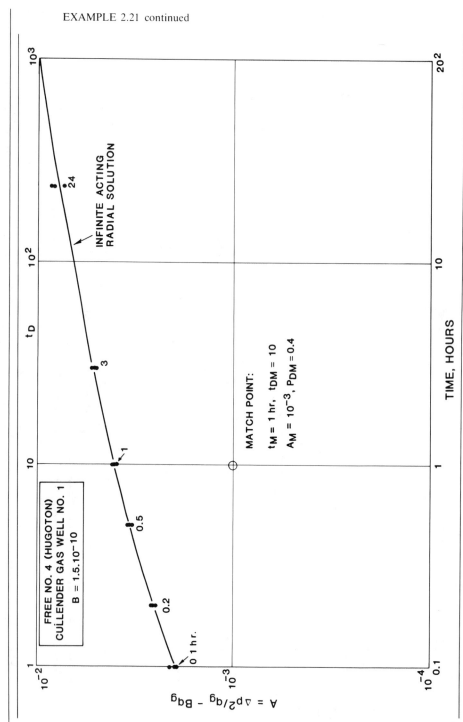

Figure E2.21d Logarithmic plot of $A(t)$ versus t for the Free No. 4 isochronal test data and a match to the dimensionless pressure type curve.

The true isochronal test is not based on superposition, a theory commonly used in transient well test analysis. The basic requirement for validity of the isochronal test is that flowing pressures be measured at the same time from the start of each flow period, and that buildup between flow periods reaches initial or average reservoir pressure. Both the normal (increasing) and reverse (decreasing) rate sequences should result in the same backpressure curve. This may not be the case, however, if problems of fines migration, condensation, or gas saturation buildup are present.

Katz et al. (1959) suggested a modification of the true isochronal sequence which shortens the testing time for low-permeability wells. The modified isochronal test consists of flowing and shut-in periods of equal duration (e.g., 4 hours). Stabilized flow does not occur during drawdown or buildup. Instead of using initial or average reservoir pressure to plot the backpressure curve, the shut-in pressure at the end of each shut-in period is used. The flowing pressure used with a shut-in pressure is that corresponding to the start of the buildup period. Figure 2.29 shows the modified isochronal sequence and how the pressures are chosen to plot the backpressure curve.

The modified isochronal test should only be run with a normal (increasing) rate sequence. The only justification for the validity of modified isochronal testing is based on use of the logarithmic approximation to p_D and application of superposition. Since modified isochronal testing is usually limited to low-permeability wells, the logarithmic approximation is not valid (t_D must be greater than 25, which may correspond to weeks or months). Apparently, the modified isochronal test gives reasonable results even at t_D less than 25 (based on theoretical studies), if the rate sequence is increasing.

2.8   **SUMMARY.** This chapter discusses some physical considerations necessary to develop practical inflow performance relations (IPR) for oil and gas wells. The basic laws of flow in porous media are stated and applied to radial flow toward a wellbore. Stabilized or pseudosteady-state flow is assumed, for the most part, in deriving the IPR equations. Darcy's law provides the basic relation between rate and pressure drop in the reservoir; simply stated, the macroscopic velocity (flux) of flow is proportional to the pressure drop along a given length of porous material. Usually, flow velocities encountered in the production of oil and gas obey Darcy's law. At high velocities, however, Darcy's law breaks down and an alternative flow equation must be used; either the empirical backpressure equation with exponent n, or the Forchheimer (quadratic) equation.

The simplest quantitative treatment of radial flow in porous media is based on the assumption of steady-state conditions for single-phase liquid in a cylindrical geometry with a centered well. The assumption of constant fluid properties (ideal fluid) simplifies the integration of Darcy's equation from the wellbore to the drainage area boundary. The steady-state condition is satisfied by specifying a constant-pressure outer boundary. A more realistic condition is the no-flow outer boundary, resulting in reservoir depletion and pseudosteady-state flow. Using either the constant-pressure, steady-state assumption or the no-flow, pseudosteady-state assumption, the resulting inflow performance relation gives rate as a linear function of flowing pressure.

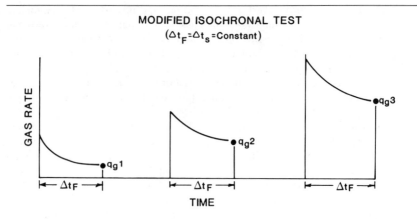

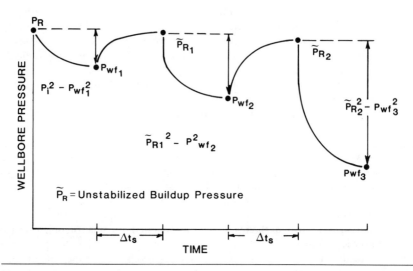

Figure 2.29 Modified isochronal test procedure. After Fetkovich 1975 by permission of the SPE-AIME.

Flow of undersaturated oil is somewhat more complicated than the ideal liquid case, because viscosity and the oil formation volume factor vary with pressure. The term $1/\mu_o B_o$ is very nearly a linear function of pressure above the bubble point, leading to the linear IPR, with $1/\mu_o B_o$ evaluated at an average pressure. Unless the oil is highly undersaturated and pressure drawdown is very large, the linear IPR is adequate for describing stabilized flow of undersaturated oil wells.

The skin effect is introduced to account for nonideal conditions of flow near the wellbore, including formation damage, partial penetration, perforations restriction, high-velocity flow, and condensate blockage. The skin factor is a pressure drop expressed in dimensionless form, indicating the additional pressure drawdown, compared with ideal drawdown, needed to produce a given rate. Alternative expressions for nonideal flow conditions are apparent radius, flow efficiency, and damage ratio, all of which can be related to skin.

Application of Darcy's law to gas wells is done by including pressure-dependent fluid properties [μ_g and Z (or B_g)] in the pressure integral. At low pressures, the pressure integral can be evaluated analytically, resulting in the widely used pressure-squared backpressure equation. At high pressures gas behaves almost like undersaturated oil, showing only slight deviation from ideal incompressible flow behavior. When pressure drawdown covers a large range in pressure, the pressure-integral is solved numerically giving the pseudopressure form of the IPR equation. High-velocity flow effects must be considered for gas wells. This is done in one of two ways, with exponent n in the backpressure equation, or with the Forchheimer modification of Darcy's equation, usually expressed as a rate-dependent skin.

The flow of saturated oil is considerably more complicated to describe analytically, because gas evolves from the oil to form a two-phase system. Relative permeabilities can be used to quantify the effect of changing saturations, but the difficulty in relating saturation to pressure makes any solution to the problem only approximate. Evinger and Muskat (1942) give perhaps the most rigorous analytical treatment of saturated oil flow for steady-state conditions. Later work by Vogel (1968), Standing (1971), and Fetkovich (1973) has greatly simplified the practical application of saturated inflow calculations. Fetkovich shows that the pressure function (including relative permeability effects) can be approximated with a straight line passing through the origin, resulting in a pressure-squared backpressure IPR (directly analogous to low-pressure gas wells). The effect of high-velocity flow is incorporated in the pressure-squared equation by the backpressure exponent n. There appears to be little advantage to the Vogel equation, since the pressure-squared approach is simpler, it fits Vogel's simulated results, and it apparently describes field data better than Vogel's equation (particularly for high-rate wells). Vogel's novel suggestion to normalize with maximum flow rate (AOF) is applied to the pressure-squared saturated oil IPR, including high-velocity flow effects. Changes in skin, drainage area, and depletion are accounted for by correction ratios to the backpressure constant C or maximum oil rate q_{omax}.

Depletion causes decline in average reservoir pressure and, as a result, change in average fluid properties. The connection between depletion and inflow performance is discussed in the context of pseudosteady-state flow. Also, the material balance equation relating average pressure to cumulative production is coupled with the IPR to predict a well's production profile.

Transient inflow performance is treated in some detail. Particular attention is given to the estimation of how long infinite-acting flow lasts, how long before pseudosteady state begins, and the necessary changes in IPR equations to account for infinite-acting conditions of long duration. Concepts of dimensionless time and pressure were introduced to generalize and simplify the treatment of transient production. For example, the criterion for start of pseudosteady-state flow is simply that dimensionless time based on area equals 0.1 (assuming radial geometry).

Approximations of the infinite-acting dimensionless pressure solution were given, to help quantify the effect of transience for low-permeability wells. The exact dimensionless pressure solution for radial flow was presented as a log–log type curve. The type curve is used to interpret transient multirate test data, and specifically to determine the stabilized backpressure constant C.

3   RESTRICTED FLOW INTO THE WELLBORE

In section 2.3 it was established that a well rarely exhibits the ideal flow conditions considered in the ideal well model in section 2.2. Three additional phenomena characterize the actual flow to a well:

1. changes in permeability near the wellbore
2. change in the radial flow geometry, caused by limited entry to the wellbore and flow convergence into the perforations
3. breakdown of Darcy's law at high flow velocities, usually localized near the wellbore

The petroleum industry has chosen the skin-factor approach to adjust the radial flow equation for the deviations from the ideal well model. This approach combines the simplicity of the flow equations of the ideal well with a more rigorous representation of real flow in an actual well. Skin factor is a dimensionless form of the pressure drop resulting from nonideal flow at or near the wellbore. This chapter will discuss skin factor as accounting for the following sources of nonideal flow:

• formation damage
• limited completion interval
• perforation effects
• high-velocity flow (turbulence)
• saturation blockage near the wellbore
• sand control

The composite skin factor in a given well is calculated from well test data. This chapter shows how to separate the observed skin factor into its components and to establish which near-wellbore flow restrictions can be removed by stimulation treatment and which require workover or recompletion. The effect of nonideal flow will be developed specifically for pseudosteady-state flow. Transient effects are not considered in detail, although some mention is made of how long production must be maintained before the transient condition of skin becomes steady state.

3.1   SKIN FACTOR AND RELATED CONCEPTS. The concept of skin factor originates from the work of Hurst (1953) and van Everdingen (1953). They proposed skin factor as a means to quantify nonideal flow. Van Everdingen's introduction of the skin concept includes two field examples that illustrate the use of skin to quantify formation damage and flow restriction due to perforations. These are the most obvious causes of near-wellbore flow restriction.

In relation to the inflow performance relationship of a well, the skin factor accounts for the difference between the ideal and the actual pressure drawdown. Figure 3.1 illustrates the significance of the skin effect in a rate–pressure plot of a well. The figure indicates that the actual IPR of a well deviates from the straight-line IPR of the ideal model by the constant skin effect, the rate-dependent skin, and the combined effects of pressure-dependent fluid properties and simultaneous flow of oil and gas. The pressure-dependent properties and the effect of simultaneous oil and gas flow are expressed by the pressure function discussed in chapter 2. The constant and rate-dependent skins are discussed in this chapter.

Generally, we are interested only in the pseudosteady-state skin and can neglect the transience of the skin effect. This also applies to the high-velocity skin. Expressed in equation form, skin is included in the calculation of total pressure drop $p_R - p_{wf}$ for pseudosteady-state conditions in an oil well as

$$p_R - p_{wf} = \underset{|\text{ideal}|}{p_R - p_{wf}'} + \underset{|\text{nonideal}|}{(p_{wf}' - p_{wf})}$$

$$= \frac{141.2 q_o \mu_o B_o}{kh} [\ln(r_e/r_w) - 0.75 + s], \tag{2.27}$$

where pressure drop due to skin is expressed as

$$\Delta p_s = p_{wf}' - p_{wf}$$

$$= \frac{141.2 q_o \mu_o B_o}{kh} s. \tag{2.26}$$

The pressure p_{wf}' represents the flowing pressure resulting from ideal radial flow (i.e., in the absence of skin),

$$p_R - p_{wf}' = \frac{141.2 q_o \mu_o B_o}{kh} [\ln(r_e/r_w) - 0.75] \tag{2.24}$$

Adding equations (2.26) and (2.24) yields the total pressure drop $p_R - p_{wf}$ given by equation (2.27).

Skin s is the composite of all nonideal conditions affecting flow, the most important of which are

s_d = formation-damage skin,
s_c = completion skin due to partial penetration,
s_p = perforation skin,
s_b = blockage skin,

239

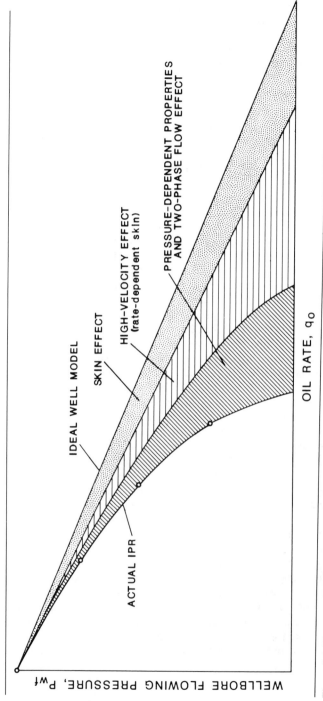

Figure 3.1 The actual IPR versus the IPR developed from the ideal well model.

s_G = gravel-pack skin,
s_A = outer boundary geometry skin.

The effect of high-velocity flow is also expressed as an equivalent skin, Dq, where $D = D_R + D_d + D_{dp} + D_G$, composed of the following elements:

D_R = reservoir high-velocity flow term in the region beyond near-wellbore damage $r > r_a$,
D_a = damaged zone high-velocity flow term at $r_w < r < r_a$,
D_{dp} = high-velocity flow term in the damaged zone immediately surrounding the perforations,
D_G = high-velocity flow term in a gravel-packed perforation.

The composite skin factor $s + Dq$ is usually calculated from analysis of drawdown and buildup test data. Methods of well test interpretation allow separate calculation of formation permeability k and the nonideal effects resulting in additional pressure loss. In relation to skin measurements, it is important to recognize that skin factor calculated from buildup analysis, such as the Horner plot, represents skin effect experienced by the wellbore at the instant the well is shut in. Therefore, if the production period prior to shut-in is short, and pseudosteady state is not reached, the calculated skin is not always the correct pseudosteady skin. In addition, to assure correct skin calculations, it is important to measure the flowing pressure and rate immediately before shut-in. Unfortunately, it is often difficult to run a pressure gauge and record the flowing pressure at the instant of shut-in.

Generally, we are interested only in the pseudosteady-state skin and can neglect the transience of the skin effect. This also applies to high-velocity skin. For low-permeability wells, however, we may need to consider the time variation in skin. This concern is covered in chapter 4, where we look at the extended transient behavior of stimulated wells. High-velocity-flow skin Dq is rate-dependent, as is blockage skin s_b due to buildup of a second (gas or oil) saturation near the wellbore. Blockage skin increases rapidly with time, and in fact it quickly reaches a plateau, after which a steady-state skin value can be used.

Methods of multirate testing have been developed to quantify the effect of changing skin with rate. Such tests can identify separately the constant skin and the rate-dependent skin. To maintain efficient flow from the reservoir into the wellbore, skin should be minimized. In fact, a well can be stimulated to produce at rates higher than predicted for the ideal model or zero-skin well, in which case the well has a negative skin.

Our ability to assess possible measures to maintain, restore, or enhance productivity depends on the ability to separate the measured skin factor into its individual components. Since individual components of the composite skin cannot be measured directly, it is necessary to calculate individual skins based on correlations developed empirically, analytically, and with numerical simulators. Having backed out the contribution of each skin component it is possible to consider corrective measures to reduce its detrimental effect, and thereby enhance the well's productivity.

3.2   NEAR-WELLBORE ALTERED PERMEABILITY. To maintain pressure control during drilling, completion, or workover of a well, the operations are usually conducted at overbalanced conditions. This implies that the hydrostatic pressure of the fluid in the wellbore is slightly higher than the formation pressure. The overbalanced condition results in influx of fluids and solids from the wellbore into the formation. Usually, the volume of invading fluids is small and the invasion is limited to short distances, from a few inches to a few feet from the wellbore. The depth of solids invasion is less than fluid invasion and usually is limited to a few inches only. The invading fluids and solids interact with the formation, creating a multitude of productivity damage effects, such as (Meyer and Vargas 1984)

- emulsion blockage
- water blockage
- change in rock wettability
- hydration and swelling of formation clays
- dispersion and migration of formation fines and grain cementation materials (clay particles)
- precipitation of inorganic salts (scaling)
- particle plugging of pores from entrained solids

The net effect of the invading fluid interaction with the formation is generally detrimental. The result is formation damage, causing additional pressure losses in the vicinity of the wellbore and a reduction in well productivity.

Damage has always been a serious problem, and there has been considerable variation in the methods for treating damage (Nowak and Krueger 1951; Bertness 1953; Krueger and Vogel 1954; Jones and Lummus 1959; Eakin and Miller 1965; Allen 1973; Bruist 1974; Maly 1975). During the last fifteen years, developments in well technology have allowed reduction and even elimination of most formation damage. The most pronounced developments are

- progress in understanding mechanisms of formation damage and in predicting formation sensitivities
- development of nondamaging drilling and completion fluids (see Millhone 1983)
- development of high viscosity, polymer-based completion fluids with good fluid-loss control properties (Meyer and Vargas 1984)
- development of effective bridging materials (filter-cake builders) that can be easily removed before production startup (King and Hollingsworth 1979; Mondshine 1981)
- development of chemical agents that inhibit formation damage tendencies (Vetter 1976; Peters and Stout 1977; Shaughnessy and Kline 1983; Tyler et al. 1985; Meyers et al. 1985)
- improvement of practices for conducting well operations in general, and for handling completion fluid in particular (Millhone 1983)
- development of underbalanced operation techniques such as workovers with snubbing units or continuous-coiled workover strings (Goeken 1958; Slator and Hanson 1965; Rike 1967; Sage 1979; Bell 1984)

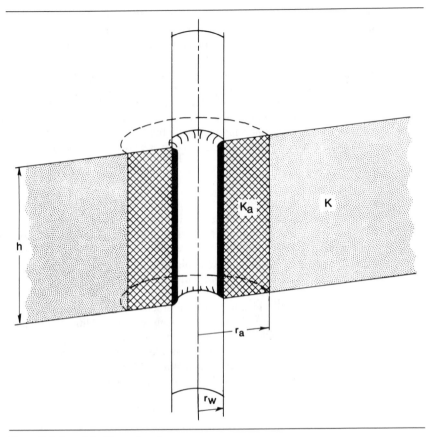

Figure 3.2 A model of formation damage.

Regardless of the methods of damage prevention, there usually exists some degree of damage that must be considered in productivity calculations. The effect of formation damage on productivity has plagued the petroleum industry since its inception. It was treated analytically by Muskat (1937), using a model of a well producing from a formation with two concentric annular regions of different permeability. Muskat's model of a damaged well is illustrated in figure 3.2. He notes that the physical model of discontinuous radial variation in the permeability corresponds to "*a well which was initially drilled into a homogeneous sand, the (induced) inhomogeneity having been caused by a partial plugging or mudding off of the region immediately surrounding the sand face during the course of production or in the process of drilling*" (p. 404).

Craft and Hawkins (1959) were the first to translate the Muskat model of a near-wellbore altered permeability into an expression for skin factor:

$$s_a = (k/k_a - 1)\ln(r_a/r_w), \tag{3.1}$$

where k is the formation permeability and k_a is the altered permeability extending from the wellbore radius r_w to a radius r_a. We select the subscript a denoting an altered permeability, rather than d denoting formation damage, to emphasize that equation (3.1) is valid also for cases of increased near-wellbore permeability (stimulation). A problem inherent with the practical use of equation (3.1) is that the altered zone is very difficult to quantify in terms of k_a and r_a. That is, altered permeability and radius cannot be measured directly. At best, if the skin of the altered zone can be backed out of the total skin (calculated from well test analysis), an estimate of the radius of the altered zone r_a allows calculation of the altered-zone permeability, by simple rearrangement of equation (3.1).

Other expressions relating the skin to altered-zone permeability and radius are obtained by simple rearrangement of equation (3.1):

$$k_a = k \left[1 + \frac{s_a}{\ln(r_a/r_w)} \right]^{-1} \tag{3.2}$$

Solving for radius of the altered zone gives

$$r_a = r_w \exp \left[\frac{s_a}{(k/k_a - 1)} \right]. \tag{3.3}$$

Simplified expressions for the typical situation of a stimulated well when $k_a \gg k$ are

$$r_a = r_w \exp[-s_a], \quad k_a \gg k \text{ (stimulation)}; \tag{3.4}$$

$$s_a = -\ln(r_a/r_w), \quad k_a \gg k \text{ (stimulation)}. \tag{3.5}$$

Example 3.1 illustrates the use of equation (3.1). Formation damage is associated with two phenomena that reduce effective permeability: reduction in relative permeability of oil and gas around the wellbore, and reduction in absolute permeability due to plugging of flow paths in the porous rock. Part of the original productivity of a damaged well is usually restored by simply flowing the well. Plugging material in the near-wellbore region tends to be removed during a cleanup flow period (see example 3.13). In addition, the saturation of oil or gas near the wellbore—and thus also its relative permeability—increases during the initial flow period, because the water-based filtrate is "washed" away. The main concern in relation to formation damage is, then, the prevention of permanent damage that does not clean up by itself. Numerous publications describe causes and remedies for formation damage. Many of them are reviewed by McLeod (1984). Microscopically, causes for permanent alteration of formation permeability can be classified in three categories: chemical, physical, and biological incompatibility between invading fluids and the formation.

EXAMPLE 3.1 ESTIMATING FORMATION DAMAGE FROM SKIN FACTOR

The Everdingen No. 2 is a well analyzed by van Everdingen (1953) in his classic paper on skin effect. The formation has a low permeability, 7.0 md. Producing

EXAMPLE 3.1 continued

thickness is 69 ft and average oil rate is 250 STB/D. Table E3.1a gives other relevant well data.

After 58 days of stabilized production, the well was shut in for a pressure buildup test. A Horner plot of the test data is given in figure 7 of van Everdingen's paper. A +5.6 skin factor is calculated from the plot. After 70 production days, production was shut down to perform stimulation treatment in the well. Poststimulation test indicated a skin factor of −3.7 and 4425 psia reservoir pressure.

Tasks
1. Calculate the steady-state, pressure loss due to prestimulation skin when the well produces 250 STB/D. Assume pseudosteady-state flow and a drainage area of 80 acres to calculate the total pressure drop for a rate of 250 STB/D. Note the fraction of pressure drop due to damage.
2. Calculate the altered-zone permeability before stimulation, assuming several values of damage radius: 0.25, 1, and 2 ft.
3. For a rate of 255 STB/D, calculate the stabilized flowing bottomhole pressure after stimulation.

SOLUTION

1. The pressure loss due to skin is given by

$$\Delta p_s = \frac{141.2 q_o \mu_o B_o}{kh} s$$

$$= \frac{141.2(250)(0.80)(1.136)}{(7.0)(69.0)}(5.6)$$

$$= 372 \text{ psia.}$$

The pressure loss due to ideal radial flow in the reservoir is

$$\Delta p_R = \frac{141.2 q_o \mu_o B_o}{kh}[\ln(r_e/r_w) - 0.75],$$

where

Table E3.1a Data for the Everdingen No. 2 Well

Total (producing) thickness h	69 ft
Oil formation volume factor B_o	1.136 bbl/STB
Oil viscosity μ_o	0.80 cp
Initial total compressibility c_{ti}	6.8×10^{-6} psi^{-1}
Porosity ϕ	0.039
Wellbore radius r_w	0.198 ft
Permeability k	7.0 md
Prestimulation skin s	+5.6
Poststimulation skin s	−3.7
Initial reservoir pressure p_i	4600 psia

EXAMPLE 3.1 continued

Table E3.1b Calculated Altered-Zone Permeability for Several Assumed Values of Damage Radius, Everdingen No. 2 Well

r_a (ft)	k_a (md)	k_a/k (%)
0.25	0.280	4.0
1.00	1.570	22.4
2.00	2.046	29.2

$$r_e = [80(43560)/\pi]^{0.5}$$

$$= 1053 \, \text{ft},$$

giving

$$\Delta p_R = \frac{141.2(250)(0.80)(1.136)}{(7.0)(69.0)} [\ln(1053/0.198) - 0.75]$$

$$= 520 \, \text{psia}.$$

Thus the total pressure drop at 250 STB/D is $520 + 372 = 892$ psia. Pressure drop due to skin accounts for 41.7% of the total.

2. Altered-zone permeability k_a for a given altered-zone radius r_a is

$$k_a = k \left[1 + \frac{s}{\ln(r_a/r_w)} \right]^{-1}$$

$$= 7.0 \left[1 + \frac{5.6}{\ln(r_a/0.198)} \right]^{-1},$$

which has been tabulated in table E3.1b for several values of damage radius.

3. The flowing wellbore pressure after stimulation and slight depletion is

$$p_{wf} = p_R - \frac{141.2 q_o \mu_o B_o}{kh} [\ln(r_e/r_w) - 0.75 + s]$$

$$= 4425 - \frac{141.2(255)(0.80)(1.136)}{(7.0)(69.0)} \times [\ln(1053/0.198) - 0.75 - 3.7]$$

$$= 4425 - 279$$

$$= 4146 \, \text{psia}.$$

In the category of chemical incompatibility it is possible to list the effects of

1. dislodgement and suspension of clay particles that are transported with the fluid until they reach a restriction in the pore channels and plug it

2. precipitation of products resulting from a chemical reaction between the invading fluid and native formation brines or solid formation materials
3. precipitation of scales from formation brines, due to changes in equilibrium that reduce the amount of minerals that can be held in solution

To illustrate an example of chemical incompatibility, figure 3.3 shows the results of a laboratory experiment reported by Veley (1969) and Peters and Stout (1977), showing two sequences of fluid passing through an undamaged Berea sandstone.

The tests are conducted with a multifluid permeameter illustrated in figure 3.4. The apparatus allows continuous recording of core permeability while flowing any of several fluids that are passed sequentially through the core. In the first illustrated flow sequence the core was cleaned with hexane and alcohol, followed by calcium chloride brine (3% $CaCl_2$), distilled water, sodium chloride brine (3% NaCl), and distilled water. The second flow sequence was identical to the first, except that a hydrolyzed zirconium salt solution ($ZrOCl_2$) was added following the calcium·chloride brine. In the first test no damage was observed at the first part of the flow sequence. Continuing the flow sequence, a 95% permeability reduction was observed when distilled water passed through the core following the 3% sodium chloride brine. In the second experiment a 5% permeability reduction was observed when distilled water passed through the core following (1) a $ZrOCl_2$ solution and (2) a 3% sodium chloride brine.

The two tests illustrate (Veley 1969) that the sensitivity to fresh water of Berea sand, and most sand formations is increased by exposure to monovalent cations (e.g., Na^+ and K^+) and decreased by exposure to divalent cations (e.g., Ca^{++}, Mg^{++}, Ba^{++}). Therefore, fresh water is more likely to cause permeability damage when it follows sodium chloride brine than when it follows calcium chloride brine. Formation treated with highly charged cations, such as tetravalent zirconium (Zr^{++++}) shows even greater permeability stability. The phenomenon reflects the different capacity of hydrolized metal ions to dislodge and disperse clay particles originally attached to a surface consisting of sand grains. In addition to the plugging of small passages by dispersed clays, passages may be restricted, though to a lesser extent, by the swelling tendency of clay minerals in the presence of fresh water. Rock cementing materials (calcareous and siliceous) may also be dissolved or dispersed by acids or alkaline solutions and damage the formation (Mungan 1965).

Another pronounced example of chemical incompatibility is damage by deposition of calcium carbonate ($CaCO_3$) scale. Several recent publications (Shaughnessy and Kline 1983; Meyers et al. 1985; Tyler et al. 1985, document the effect and the treatment of severe scaling in the sandstone formation around many wells (more than 50%) in the Prudhoe Bay field in Alaska. At Prudhoe Bay, investigations have shown that formation damage can occur as a result of incompatibility of certain drilling, completion, workover, and stimulation fluids with formation water. Furthermore, scales may precipitate from formation-connate water with a decrease in pressure.

Physical incompatibility occurs when an invading fluid contains entrained solid particles, which, if too small to pass through the pores of the rock, plug the formation and reduce the absolute permeability. Two types of plugging are generally observed: In *bridging*, large particles, too large to penetrate even the largest pores, accumulate on the face of the formation at the wellbore, forming a

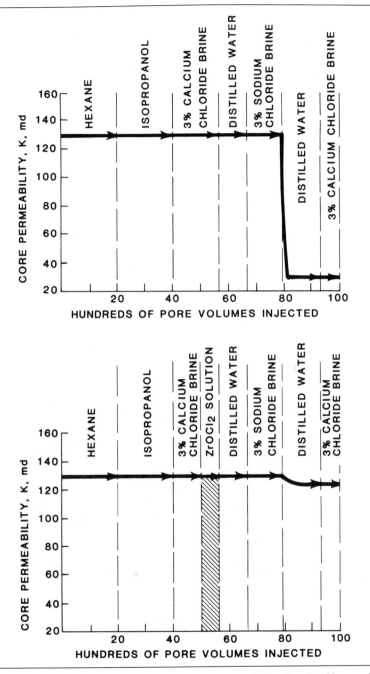

Figure 3.3 Laboratory flow test illustrating chemical incompatibility. Reprinted by permission of the SPE-AIME from Peters and Stout 1977, figs. 6, 7, pp. 187–194, © 1977 SPE-AIME.

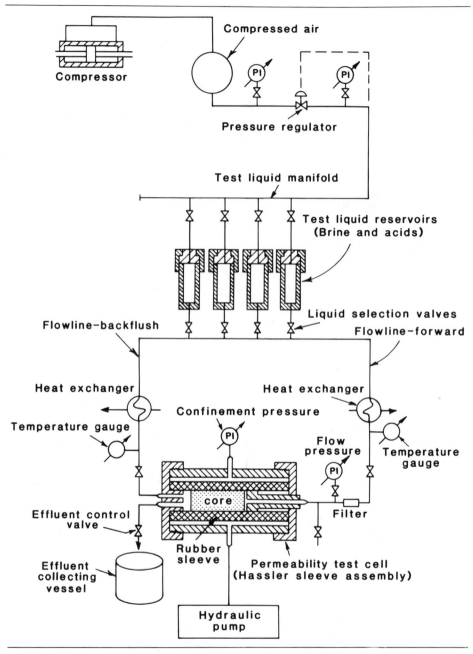

Figure 3.4 **Multifluid permeameter.**

"cake", and *plugging* smaller particles penetrate into the pore structure, lodging themselves into place and reducing the flow of oil and gas through the rock. Bridging is usually easy to remove by acid wash or a cleanup flow. Plugging may be permanent in the worst case, requiring expensive stimulation treatment to open new channels of flow to the wellbore.

Soft invading solids, such as bentonite, are the most damaging, as they can extrude into the pore throat, making them almost impossible to remove. Hard solids, such as salt crystals, $CaCO_3$, or barite, may only wedge on the entrance to the pore throat, making them easier to backflush out of the formation. Unlike plugging, bridging is often introduced intentionally to provide fluid-loss control during well operations. Properly sized, hard particles, large enough to bridge on the sand surface are added to the wellbore fluid to form a sealing layer on the sandface. The bridging particles may be acid soluble granulated ($CaCO_3$), easily dissolved in HCl acid, or water soluble salts (crystaline salts described by Mondshine 1981) easily dissolved in fresh water or in undersaturated brine. In either case, the particles can be removed completely without any residual effect on productivity.

Biological incompatibility between the formation fluids and the invading fluids occurs when microorganisms found in the fluids produce a precipitate that accumulates and plugs the interconnected pores. Practically, this problem arises in water injection wells where large quantities of water pass through the wellbore over a long period of time.

Another restriction to flow, though not readily classified as formation damage, is the possibility of a major increase in viscosity near the wellbore, due to emulsification by invading fluids. A special test (API RP 42, section 1) quantifies the tendency of formation fluids to form emulsions in the presence of various invading fluids. Viscosity increase is not usually included in the traditional definition of damage skin (eq. [3.1]), but the effect is analogous to reduced permeability.

Some types of formation damage are not induced from the wellbore. Rather, they are the results of the plugging effect of moving particles dragged by produced fluids. Formation plugging by migratory fines has been demonstrated by Krueger et al. (1967), who related the phenomena to the drag forces of the flowing fluid. Holden et al. (1981) described the severe damage from fines migration in the Wilcox sand in the Fordoche field, Louisiana and related the severity of the damage to an increase in water/oil ratio. In either case, the plugging damage occurred away from the wellbore. This kind of damage is very difficult to control. Control might require a combination of

1. restricted production rate
2. limited completion interval, to avoid water coning and production of clay-contaminated zones
3. deep injection of clay-stabilizing solutions
4. treatment with retarded, deep-penetrating acids

Perhaps the easiest way to identify deep damage due to fines or clay migration is to run a multirate test. If the backpressure curve at increasing rates does not "trace" the backpressure curve at decreasing rates, then particle movement is probably the problem. The type of multirate test chosen will depend on the permeability of the formation: High-permeability reservoirs can be tested with a flow-after-flow sequence, whereas low-permeability reservoirs should be tested with a true isochronal sequence, having adequate shut-in periods to erase the transients of previous flows.

Many measures are available today to avoid or mitigate formation damage.

Table 3.1 lists the main mechanisms of formation damage, well operations that may produce the damage, precautions to prevent it, and methods to cure it. Avoiding formation damage is of paramount importance to the completion engineer. Yet, measures to prevent formation damage are costly and often more expensive than treatments to cure the damage. Avoiding formation damage involves costs for determining specifications for nondamaging fluid, obtaining the fluid, filtering the fluid, cleaning the well, and placing the fluid. Therefore, the strategy for handling formation damage is usually a matter of economics. (Bell 1985)

Finally, a treatment to cure formation damage should be planned and executed only after a skin due to damage is verified. That is, after skin components attributable to other effects have been subtracted from the measured composite skin. The procedure for this skin analysis is covered in detail in section 3.8.

3.3   **PARTIAL PENETRATION AND LIMITED ENTRY.** Since the beginning of petroleum production, wells have been drilled and completed through only a fraction of the total formation, to avoid contact with the water zone that may underlie the oil or gas zone, or perhaps because of difficulties in controlling mud circulation in the pay zone.

A completion arrangement where only limited pay-zone interval is open to production is referred to as partial penetration or limited entry. Numerous cases of partial penetration are mentioned and discussed in the petroleum literature. One example is the completion of wells in the North Antioch field in Oklahoma (Culter and Rees 1970). The wells were completed in the Oil Creek reservoir and were perforated only 5–10 ft near the top of approximately 100 ft of a fairly uniform and clean sandstone pay zone. The partial penetration reflects the concern regarding water coning from bottom water that underlies the oil reservoir.

Another example is the high-rate (50 MMscf/D) gas wells of the North Sea Frigg field (Barril and Gay 1983). They are only partially penetrated so as to keep the production interval a safe distance above the water level. High-rate oil wells in the Statfjord field (Norway) completed in the Brent sandstone formation are not perforated close to the gas–oil contact at the top of the formation, nor close to the oil–water contact, to avoid both gas and water coning. Furthermore, the wells are perforated only across intervals where the sandstone is highly consolidated, to avoid sand production.

In many wells the problem of gas and water coning restricts the production interval to a small fraction of the oil zone located near the midpoint of the formation. In general, reasons for limited entry into the hydrocarbon-bearing formation are:

Table 3.1 Causes of Formation Damage and Precautions to Control It

Operation	Causes of formation damage	Accelerating factors	How to prevent it	How to cure the damage
1. Drilling	— mud filtrate invasion — mud solids invasion — sealing of pores and flow tunnels by the trowelling action of the bit, drill collars, and drill pipes — plugging by rock cuttings	— high-permeability formation — water-based mud — abrupt reduction in salinity — drilling with high water loss — bentonite mud — strongly overpressured drilling — high solids mud	— drilling the production zone with nondamaging fluids — use of removable bridging loss and of circulation material — use of clay-migration and clay-swelling inhibitors	— backflush — acid wash, matrix acidizing
2. Running casing and cementing	— plugging/blockage of pore space by mud or cement solids — filtrate invasion — chemical reactions with cement additives and spacers	— high-permeability formation	— use fluid-loss additives — pretreat for clay stabilizing	— deep perforations — matrix acidizing, acid wash
3. Perforating	— plugging of perforations and formation with debris — compaction of pores around perforations	— use of low performance or expendable guns — perforate overbalanced in drilling mud	— perforate underbalanced — use of clean, solid-free fluid — use premium charges and large guns — use deep-penetrating charges	— backflow — acidizing
4. Running completion string	— plugging by solids from completion fluids and diverting agents — filtrate invasion — **dissolutions** of rock cementing materials	— overbalanced conditions with damaging completion fluids — improper bridging materials — high-permeability formation — uncleaned wellbore and production equipment	— underbalanced operation — remove all bulk solids — clean casing and tubing before use — use nondamaging fluids and bridging materials	— acid treatment — solvent wash — same as for drilling

Table 3.1 (continued)

Operation	Causes of formation damage	Accelerating factors	How to prevent it	How to cure the damage
5. Production	— fines movement — clay migration — condensate and water blockage — deposits of salt crystals, wax, and paraffines — hydrate and emulsions forming	— high production rates — increase water/oil ratio — pressure decrease — communication with water zones — poor gravel-packing or sand-control measures	— control water/oil ratio — inject clay-migration inhibitors — inject scale inhibitors — keep clean wellbore — avoid abrupt increase of production rate	— acidizing — chemical treatments
6. Gravel packing	— invasion of filtrate from gravel-pack slurries — invasion of solids and contaminations — mixing of gravel with formation sand — plugging by diverting agents	— variation of permeability along the producing interval — nonuniform sand — clay-rich sand	— use nondamaging clean fluids — operate in clean wellbore — properly designed pre- and post-gravel-packing acidizing — proper design and placement of gravel and gravel-pack equipment	— acidizing (through gravel pack) — replace the gravel pack

7. Acidizing	— insoluble precipitates — iron precipitation in the wellbore — plugging by solids scoured from the tubing	— incompatibility between acid, acid additivies, and formation materials — damaging diverting agents — large variations in permeability	— proper injection sequence — use only nondamaging additives — proper diverting procedure — use damage-inhibition additives	— reacidize with proper additives
8. Fracturing	— plugging by formation fines or damaged by gelled frac fluids	— poorly designed frac	— clean, properly sorted and sized proppant — use of proper and sufficient breakers in the fracturing fluids and slurries	— soak with gel breaker
9. Workover	— residual cement plugging — wireline loosened iron scale or paraffin from tubing plugging — plugging by metallic particles resulting from casing repair operations — damaging workover fluids — damaging bridging materials	— operate at overpressured conditions — high-permeability formation — large variation in permeabilities — uncleaned wellbore — use of corrosion inhibitors or emulsion breakers	— underpressured workover operation — use of nondamaging fluids — operate in clean wellbore — clean the working string	— acid stimulation — chemical treatment

1. to avoid coning of water and/or gas
2. the well cannot be drilled throughout the pay zone for mechanical or safety reasons
3. to avoid producing sand or other friable formation particles
4. to test an exploratory well in selected intervals
5. to leave portions of the casing unperforated for future needs of setting mechanical assemblies such as packers, spacers, bridge plugs, and centralizers
6. erroneous log interpretation that fails to define the true total pay zone
7. plugged perforations that do not contribute to production

Most of the reasons for partial penetration and limited entry are intentional, designed to improve the overall performance of a well or reservoir (though not necessarily productivity). The last two reasons listed are not planned, and in fact the operator may not be aware of the unintended restriction to flow.

The general characteristics of a well with limited entry are shown in figure 3.5. Flow lines converge from above and below the open interval, gradually changing to radial flow away from the wellbore. Because of the deformed flow path and localized pressure gradients near the ends of the open interval, lower wellbore flowing pressure is required to produce a given rate. Muskat's original work (1932) on partial penetration serves as the fundamental solution to the steady-state problem. He illustrated the influence of partial penetration, as a plot of rate versus flowing pressure, for the case of limited entry without any other flow restriction. Figure 3.6 reproduces some of Muskat's results. Muskat (1937) also discussed the effect of rock unisotropy on a partially penetrating well. In unisotropic rock, permeability in various directions may vary considerably. Corresponding to the particular sedimentation process, permeability in the direction of the bedding plane is in most cases larger than permeability in a direction perpendicular to the bedding plane.

In relation to partial penetration, when the vertical permeability is less than the horizontal permeability, the anisotropy acts to hinder convergence to the limited completion interval and will attempt to keep the radial nature of the flow. Consequently, it tends to limit the contribution of the part of the reservoir not penetrated by the well and thus decreases the production capacity. In conclusion, anisotropy, where k_v is less than k, acts to reduce production capacity, a reduction that is magnified as the penetrating ratio becomes smaller.

Brons and Marting (1961) suggested that the effect of partial penetration and limited entry can be expressed as a skin factor. They gave the simple relation

$$s_c = (1/b - 1)[\ln(h_D) - G(b)], \tag{3.6}$$

where

b $= h_p/h$,
h_D = dimensionless pay thickness, $(k/k_v)^{0.5}(h/r_w)$,
h_p = limited interval open to flow (ft),
h = total formation thickness (ft),
k = horizontal formation permeability (md),

255

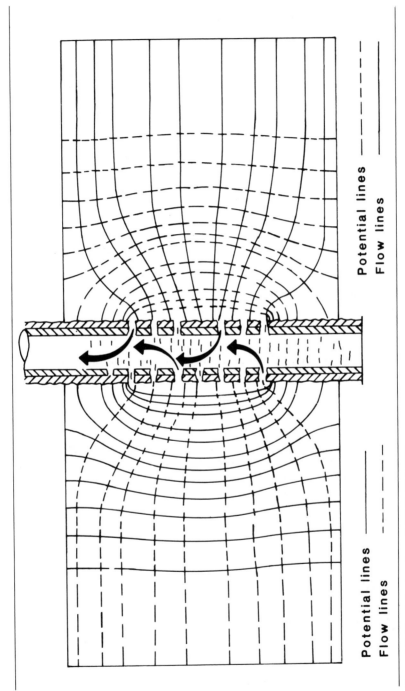

Potential lines ‒ ‒ ‒
Flow lines ⎯⎯

Potential lines ⎯⎯
Flow lines ‒ ‒ ‒

Figure 3.5 Flow behavior of a well with limited entry.

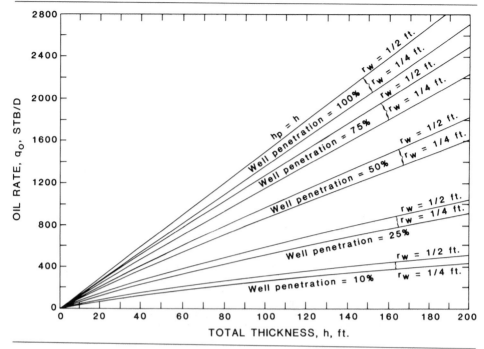

Figure 3.6 Effect of partial penetration on productivity of a well. Reprinted by permission of IHRDC Press from Muskat 1981, fig. 5.12.

k_v = vertical formation permeability (md),
$G(b)$ is a function of the fractional penetration b.

Brons and Marting solved Nisle's (1958) analytical formulation by numerical integration, to arrive at a table of values for $G(b)$. Their table is given in example 3.2, together with the analytical expression for $G(b)$ found directly by algebraic manipulation of Muskat's original solution (1932) as developed in Example 3.2. An approximate relation for $G(b)$ is

$$G(b) = 2.948 - 7.363b + 11.45b^2 - 4.675b^3. \tag{3.7}$$

EXAMPLE 3.2 DEVELOPMENT OF THE BRONS AND MARTING (1961) SKIN EQUATION, BASED ON MUSKAT'S ORIGINAL SOLUTION

Muskat (1932) studied the effect of partial penetration on well performance and proposed the following expression as a reasonable approximation to the general steady-state equation for isotropic sand:

$$q = \frac{2\pi kh\Delta p/\mu B}{\{2\ln(4h/r_w) - \ln[C(b)]\}/(2b) - \ln(4h/r_e)},$$

EXAMPLE 3.2 continued

where $b = h_p/h$ (penetrating interval divided by the total thickness), and

$$C(b) = \frac{\Gamma(0.875b)\Gamma(0.125b)}{\Gamma(1-0.875b)\Gamma(1-0.125b)}$$

where $\Gamma(x)$ is the gamma function of x. If field units are used (STB/D, md, ft, etc.), the constant 2π is replaced by $(141.2)^{-1} = 0.00708$. Note that the isotropic assumption implies that $k/k_v = 1.0$ and $h_D = h/r_w$. However, as noted by Muskat, the same solution is valid for anisotropic systems by using the transformation $(k/k_v)^{0.5}$ multiplied by h/r_w [i.e., $h_D = (k/k_v)^{0.5}h/r_w$].

Tasks
1. Show that it is possible to use Muskat's solution to derive the Brons and Marting expression $G(b)$ for the partial-penetration skin factor relation

$$s_c = (1/b - 1)[\ln(h/r_w) - G(b)].$$

   Based on the results, comment on the statement by Brons and Marting (1961), "Since this function $[G(b)]$ cannot be expressed analytically, it has been calculated numerically."
2. How would you apply the Muskat or Brons and Marting skin factor expression if the producing interval is in the middle of the formation?

SOLUTION

1. The derivation of the function $G(b)$ in terms of Muskat's analytical solution is obtained by arranging Muskat's flow equation so it explicitly expresses the skin factor. Equating Muskat's denominator with $[\ln(r_e/r_w) + s_c]$ and solving for s_c gives

$$s_c = (1/b - 1)\ln(4h/r_w) - \ln[C(b)]/(2b)$$

$$= (1/b - 1)\ln(h/r_w) + (1/b - 1)\ln(4) - \ln[C(b)]/(2b)$$

$$= (1/b - 1)\{\ln(h/r_w) + \ln(4) - [b/(1-b)]\ln[C(b)]/(2b)\}$$

$$= (1/b - 1)\{\ln(h/r_w) + \ln(4) - \ln[C(b)]/[2(1-b)]\}$$

$$= (1/b - 1)[\ln(h/r_w) - G(b)],$$

where

$$G(b) = -\ln(4) + \frac{\ln C(b)}{2(1-b)}.$$

Table E3.2 shows values of $G(b)$ from the Muskat analytical approximation compared with the numerically calculated values by Brons and Marting. It is

EXAMPLE 3.2 continued

Table E3.2 Comparison of Analytical (Muskat 1932) and Numerical (Brons and Marting 1961) Values of the $G(b)$ Function

b	Brons–Marting $G(b)$	Muskat $G(b)$	Muskat $C(b)$
0.1	2.337	2.337	814.16
0.2	1.862	1.862	180.65
0.4	1.569	1.569	34.71
0.6	1.621	1.620	11.08
0.8	1.995	1.992	3.86

obvious that the statement of Brons and Marting regarding the possibility of analytical solution is unjustified in cases of isotropic sand. A similar procedure can be developed for anisotropic sand, where the horizontal permeability is larger than the vertical permeability. The procedure for anisotropic formation, however, is beyond the scope of this example.

2. The skin factor developed by Muskat and by Brons and Marting assumes the open interval is at the top of the formation and penetrates a fraction $b = h_p/h$ of the total thickness. Symmetry is used to apply the skin factor to a situation when the open interval is located near the midpoint of the formation (e.g., when avoiding both water and gas coning).

   Basically, the formation is cut in two layers, split at the midperforations. Assuming the upper and lower sections are of equal thickness, the definition of b for each layer is $[(h_p/2)/(h/2)]$ or h_p/h, the same as for penetration from the top of the formation. The expression h/r_w [or more correctly, $(k/k_v)^{0.5}(h/r_w)$] becomes $(h/2)/r_w$ or $h/2r_w$, half the value used when penetration starts at the top of the formation. This value results in a lower skin, which is reasonable, considering the convergence in flow lines toward the wellbore. For an interval at the midperforations there is less flow convergence than for penetration from the top of the formation.

Figure 3.7 plots skin s_c versus fractional penetration b for several values of h_D. These curves are useful for three types of limited-entry configurations, shown in figure 3.8:

1. a well penetrating the top of the formation
2. a well open to flow from the midsection of the formation
3. a well with open intervals equally spaced along the entire height of the formation

For each case the value of b remains unchanged, but h_D is different for each configuration. For limited entry starting at the top of the formation, total formation thickness h is used to define h_D.

If the well is open at the midsection of the formation, $h/2$ is used to define h_D

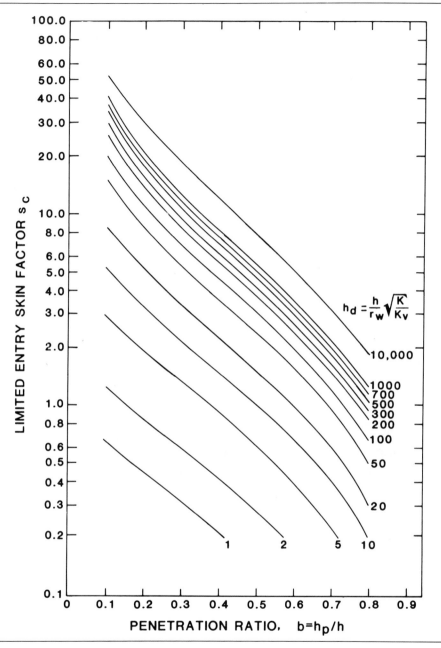

Figure 3.7 Partial-penetration skin factor. Reprinted by permission of the University of Trondheim from Standing 1980, fig. 5; after Brons and Marting 1961.

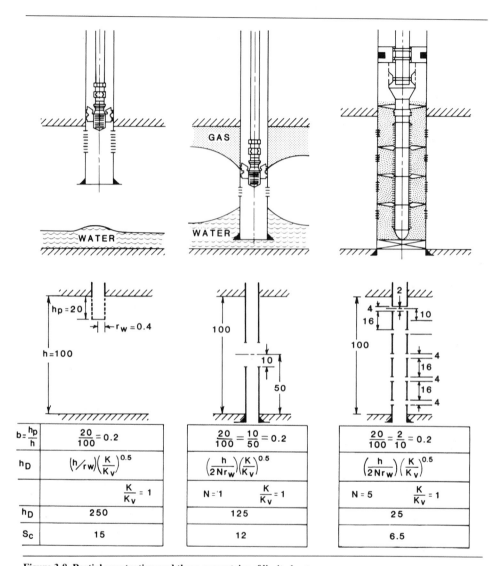

Figure 3.8 Partial penetration and three geometries of limited entry.

[i.e., $h_D = (k/k_v)^{0.5}(h/2r_w)$]. For N sections of open interval located symmetrically about the middle of the formation, with equal thickness and equally spaced, the correct expression for h_D is $(k/k_v)^{0.5}(h/2Nr_w)$. The definition of the dimensionless pay thickness, h_D, for the three configurations in figure 3.7 is also valid when using equation (3.6). Example 3.3 shows the use of figure 3.7 for estimating the skin due to limited entry.

EXAMPLE 3.3 ESTIMATION OF PARTIAL-PENETRATION SKIN FROM THE CHARTS OF BRONS AND MARTING (1961)

The Java No. 2 is a low-pressure, high-permeability gas well reported by Fetkovich (1975). An eight-point multirate test was run to determine the backpressure curve. Buildup analysis indicates a permeability thickness of 306,060 md-ft. Total thickness is 313 ft, giving a permeability of 978 md. The interval open to flow is only 70 ft (open from the top to avoid water coning from the underlying aquifer). Table E3.3 gives relevant rock and fluid data for the Java No. 2 well. The complete analysis of the test is given in example 3.13. However, we may indicate here that only the last four points of the eight test points were used to draw and interpret the backpressure curve, since cleanup had not been completed prior to the fifth point.

A plot of $(p_R^2 - p_{wf}^2)/q_g$ versus q_g given in Example 3.13 indicates an intercept of $A = 0.000966\,\text{psia}^2/(\text{scf/D})$, which calculates a steady-state skin factor of $s = +22.18$. Since the plot is based on one-hour isochronal test data, the skin is calculated from the intercept using the transient rather than the steady-state intercept expression.

The transient expression for A obtained by substituting equation (2.139) in equation (2.144) is

$$A(t) = \frac{T\mu_g Z}{0.703kh} \{0.5[\ln(t_D) + 0.80907] + s\},$$

Table E3.3 Reservoir Data for the Java No. 2 Well

Initial reservoir pressure p_i	1370 psia
Reservoir temperature T	120°F
Total reservoir thickness h	313 ft
Perforated thickness h_p	70 ft
Permeability (buildup) k	978
Horizontal/vertical permeability ratio (assumed) k/k_v	10
Gas gravity γ_g	0.655 (air = 1)
Wellbore radius r_w	0.33 ft
Initial gas viscosity μ_{gi}	0.0144 cp
Initial gas compressibility c_{gi}	832×10^{-6} 1/psia
Initial total compressibility c_{ti}	582×10^{-6} 1/psia
Initial gas Z-factor Z	0.837

EXAMPLE 3.3 continued

and t_D is given by

$$t_D = \frac{0.000264kt}{\phi \mu_{gi} c_{ti} r_w^2}$$

$$= \frac{0.000264(978)(1)}{(0.181)(0.0144)(0.000582)(0.33)^2}$$

$$= 1.56 \times 10^6,$$

so

$$A(t = 1\text{hr}) = 0.000966$$

$$= \frac{(120 + 460)(0.0144)(0.837)}{0.703(978)(313)} \times \{0.5[\ln(1.56 \times 10^6) + 0.80907] + s\}$$

or

$$0.000966 = 3.25 \times 10^{-5}(7.54 + s).$$

Solving for s yields the steady-state skin:

$$s = 29.72 - 7.54$$

$$= +22.18.$$

Task
Compare the back-calculated skin factor ($s = +22.18$) with a predicted partial-penetration skin factor.

SOLUTION
The fraction of total thickness open to flow is 70/313 or 0.22, and h_D is given by

$$h_D = (k/k_v)^{0.5}(h/r_w)$$

$$= (10)^{0.5}(313/0.33)$$

$$= 3000.$$

From the Brons and Marting figure (Fig. 3.7), $s_c = +21.0$, which checks with the back-calculated skin. Based on equation (3.7) for $G(b)$, where $b = 70/313 = 0.22$.

$$G(b) = 2.948 - 7.363b + 11.45b^2 - 4.675b^3$$

EXAMPLE 3.3 continued

$$= 2.948 - 7.363(0.22) + 11.45(0.22)^2 - 4.675(0.22)^3$$

$$= 1.833.$$

The Brons and Marting equation for skin gives

$$s_c = (1/b - 1)[\ln(h_D) - G(b)]$$

$$= (1/0.22 - 1)[\ln(3000) - 1.833]$$

$$= +21.9,$$

which closely matches the steady-state skin back-calculated from multirate data ($s = +22.18$). Example 3.13 gives a more detailed discussion of the entire test performed on the Java No. 2, including the first four points in the multirate test, which were dominated by a large damage skin.

Several other publications give expressions for s_c, among the more relevant being Odeh (1968), and Streltsova-Adams (1979). A discussion of approximate analytical expressions developed prior to Muskat's (1932) solution is given by Muskat (1937, 1982). Odeh (1980) gives an empirical relation for skin due to an arbitrarily located open interval h_p:

$$s_c = 1.35(1/b - 1)^{0.825}$$
$$\{\ln(r_w h_D + 7) - 1.95 - [0.49 + 0.1\ln(r_w h_D)]\ln(r_{wc})\}, \tag{3.8}$$

where

$$r_{wc} = r_w \exp[0.2126(2.753 + z_m/h)], \quad 0 < z_m/h < 0.5, \tag{3.9}$$

$$r_{wc} = r_w, \quad y = 0, \tag{3.10}$$

$$z_m = y + h_p/2, \tag{3.11}$$

y = distance from the top of the formation to the top of the open interval.

If z_m/h is greater than 0.5, then use $1 - z_m/h$ instead of z_m/h in the equation for r_{wc} (eq. [3.9]). Example 3.4 shows use of Odeh's correlation for partial-penetration skin.

EXAMPLE 3.4 ODEH CORRELATION FOR ESTIMATING PARTIAL-PENETRATION SKIN

Arthur (1944) gives data for a well perforated only in the lower middle section of a 160-ft formation (fig. E3.4). An overlying gas cap and an underlying aquifer posed the problem of coning. This led to a completion interval with perforations in only

EXAMPLE 3.4 continued

62 ft of the total thickness (38.8%). Arthur claimed that as a result of the close proximity to the water–oil contact a pressure drop of only 1.3 psi would lead to water coning. Arthur also reported that up to 103 psi drawdown could be tolerated without gas coning from above.

Additional hypothetical well data, $kh = 83,200$ md-ft ($k = 520$ md); $\mu_o = 0.85$ cp; $B_o = 1.32$ bbl/STB; $\ln(r_e/r_w) - 0.75 = 7.73$ ($r_e = 1000$ ft); and $k/k_v = 1.0$.

Calculate (1) the oil rate resulting in the 1.3-psi pressure drop to produce a water cone; (2) the oil rate resulting in the 103-psia pressure drop to produces a gas cone. Assume in the second case that water coning is not a problem if a shale break separates the oil zone from the aquifer.

SOLUTION

We use the Odeh equation, equation (3.8), which is valid for calculating limited-entry completion skin for a single completion interval located anywhere within the formation. The distance from the top of the formation to the top of the perforations is $y = 7623 - 7535 = 88$ ft. The perforated interval is

$$h_p = 7685 - 7623$$

$$= 62 \, \text{ft},$$

which calculates

$$z_m = y + h_p/2$$

$$= 88 + 62/2$$

$$= 119 \, \text{ft}.$$

The effective pay zone is

$$h = 7695 - 7535$$

$$= 160 \, \text{ft},$$

which calculates

$$z_m/h = 119/160$$

$$= 0.744.$$

Since z_m/h is larger than 0.5, we use the symmetry of r_{wc}/r_w about $z_m/h = 0.5$ to substitute

EXAMPLE 3.4 continued

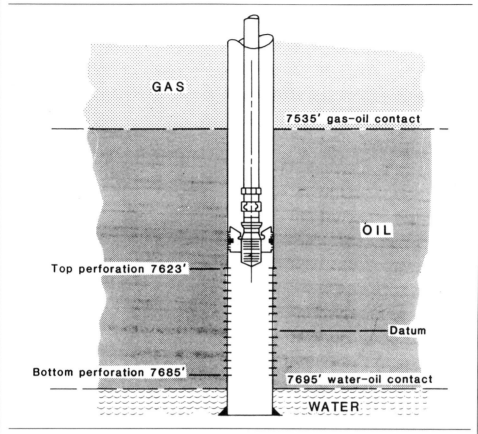

Figure E3.4 Pay zone and perforated interval reported by Arthur (1944) to study the water-coning problem.

$$1 - z_m/h = 1 - 0.744$$

$$= 0.256$$

for z_m/h in equation (3.9). The calculated r_{wc} is

$$r_{wc} = 0.2083 \exp[0.2126(0.256 + 2.753)]$$

$$= 0.394.$$

The dimensionless pay-zone thickness h_D is

$$h_D = (k/k_v)^{0.5}(h/r_w)$$

EXAMPLE 3.4 continued

$$= 1.0(160/0.2083)$$

$$= 768.1$$

and

$$r_w h_D = 0.2083(738.1)$$

$$= 160.$$

Substituting the calculated $r_w h_D$ and r_{wc} in equation (3.8) gives the limited-entry skin factor

$$s_c = 1.35(1/b - 1)^{0.825}$$
$$\{\ln(r_w h_D + 7) - 1.95 - [0.49 + 0.1 \ln(r_w h_D)]\ln(r_{wc})\}$$

$$= 1.35(1/0.388 - 1)^{0.825}$$
$$\{\ln(167) - 1.95 - [0.49 + 0.1 \ln(160)]\ln(0.394)\}$$

$$= 8.056.$$

Substituting s_c and well data in the oil IPR equation (eq. [2.28]) gives

$$q_o = \frac{83,200 \, \Delta p}{141.2(0.85)(1.32)[7.73 + 8.056]},$$

or

$$q_o = 33.27 \, \Delta p.$$

If a pressure drop of 1.3 psi results in a water cone, then the maximum oil rate that can be produced before water begins to cone is

$$q_o = 33.28(1.3)$$

$$= 43 \, \text{STB/D}.$$

Clearly, the perforated interval in this well has been chosen without regard to the limitation imposed on production by water coning. Arthur notes, however, that water coning in the well is negligible even at higher oil rates, because of low vertical permeability that restricts coning movement.

Assuming a shale barrier separates the oil zone from the aquifer, water-free production is maintained independent of oil rate. Gas coning, however, can be expected at a pressure drop of 103 psi, corresponding to an oil rate of

$$q_o = 33.28(103)$$

$$= 3427 \, \text{STB/D}.$$

An important feature of partial penetration is that s_c is always positive. That is, limited entry always reduces the productivity of a well.

The transient effect of partial penetration and limited entry may be important for low-permeability wells. Considerable work has appeared in the literature concerning the transient behavior of partially penetrating wells, including discussions on drawdown and buildup analysis. The characteristic of early-time flow in a partially penetrating well is exactly identical to a well producing from a formation of thickness h_p instead of h. That is, the well behaves as if it were draining only the interval open to flow. After some time, a transition to flow from the entire formation is observed, after which the steady-state skin s_c applies.

The transient behavior of the limited entry ends when flow lines have more or less stabilized, indicating the entire formation thickness is contributing to production. Streltsova-Adams and McKinley (1981) claim that the following relation predicts the time when the partial-penetration skin effect stabilizes to the value that can be used in the pseudosteady-state IPR equations

$$t_{Dc} = h_D^2/16, \tag{3.12}$$

where

$$t_{Dc} = \frac{0.000264 k t_c}{\phi \mu_i c_{ti} r_w^2}. \tag{3.13}$$

The real time t_c corresponding to this dimensionless time condition is expressed (in hours), as

$$t_c = 237 \frac{\phi \mu_i c_{ti} h^2}{k_v}. \tag{3.14}$$

Large values of t_c result if the total formation thickness is large and/or the vertical permeability is small. The condition given by equations (3.12) and (3.14) is used to determine the time when partial penetration no longer affects the *transient* behavior of a well. At times greater than t_c the effect of partial penetration is steady state. Practically, this means that drawdown or buildup analysis made only on data at times greater than t_c ($t_p > t_c$ or $\Delta t_{SI} > t_c$) should result in total formation thickness kh and total composite skin s, as discussed in section 2.8.

Most offshore wells are deviated wells drilled directionally from a central platform to reach a large lateral distance from the platform. These wells usually penetrate the pay zone at a certain inclination angle. By simple intuition, the productivity of these wells exceeds that of vertical wells if all other conditions are identical. Compared with a vertical well perforated along a given vertical interval, a deviated well is analogous to a well with a larger wellbore radius and a larger entry interval. Both effectively enhance well productivity.

Experiments with analog electrical models by Roemershauser and Hawkins (1955) confirmed the increase in productivity. For their model well they obtained increases in productivity from 5% to 25% for well inclinations of 20° to 50°, respectively. Their results, which ignore the ratio of horizontal to vertical permeabilities, tend to overestimate the increase in productivity. However, their results can give a rough indication of the degree of productivity increase.

3.4   **HIGH-VELOCITY FLOW.** In sections 2.4 and 2.5 we considered the effect of high-velocity flow on inflow performance relations for gas and oil wells, using the Forchheimer and backpressure equations. In this section we will investigate high-velocity flow and in particular the Forchheimer model when stated in terms of rate-dependent skin.

Experimental flow tests through different porous materials indicate that Darcy's law applies over a wide range of flow velocities. Darcy's linear relation of pressure drop to rate is certainly the simplest model of flow in porous media, and for many applications it is sufficiently accurate. At high flow rates the linear relation between pressure drop and rate is no longer valid. Instead, pressure drop increases more rapidly as velocity increases. Results of flow experiments can apparently be described by several mathematical models, the most popular model being Forchheimer's, as stated in equation (2.36).

Probably the most instructive pressure–velocity relationship for experiments of flow through porous media was presented by Fancher, Lewis, and Barnes (1933). They reported velocity and pressure drop data for different porous materials, including consolidated and unconsolidated sands. Their data are given in table 3.2, and in figure 3.9 as a log–log plot of dimensionless pressure (a type of friction factor) versus dimensionless rate (a type of Reynold's number). The data were obtained with different fluids; oil, water, and air. The plot is analogous to the Moody diagram (1944) used extensively in the calculation of pressure loss in pipe flow.

Table 3.2 Sand Porosity Data for Pressure/Velocity Experiments

Sample No.	Sand	Porosity
1	Bradford	12.5
2	Bradford	12.3
3	3rd Venango	16.9
4	Ceramic A	37.0
5	Robinson	20.3
6	Ceramic B	37.8
7	Woodbine	19.7
8	Wilcox	15.9
9	3rd Venango	11.9
10	Robinson	19.5
11	Robinson	18.4
12	3rd Venango	22.3
13	Wilcox	16.3
14	Warren	19.2
15	3rd Venango	21.4

Table 3.2 (continued)

Sample No.	Sand	Porosity
16	Robinson	20.6
17	Ceramic C	33.2
18	3rd Venango	21.9
19	Woodbine	23.8
20	Woodbine	26.9
21	Woodbine	27.7
22	Woodbine	22.1
23	Woodbine	28.8
24	Flint*	38.5
25	Ottawa*	30.9
26	20–30 Ottawa*	34.5
27	Lead Shot*	34.5

Note: *Unconsolidated sand.
Source: Reprinted, by permission of the publisher, from M. Muskat, *Physical Principles of Oil Production* (Boston: IHRDC Press, 1981).

The friction factor (i.e., dimensionless pressure) f is defined in consistent units as

$$f = \frac{d\Delta p}{2L\rho v^2},$$ (3.15)

and the modified Reynold's number (dimensionless rate) R_e is defined in consistent units as

$$R_e = \frac{\rho v d}{\mu}.$$ (3.16)

Average grain diameter d is expressed as

$$d = \left[\frac{\Sigma n_i d_i^3}{\Sigma n_i} \right]^{1/3},$$ (3.17)

where d_i is the arithmetic mean of the openings in any two consecutive sieves of the Tyler or U.S. Standard sieves series and n_i is the number of grains with diameter d_i, as defined by sieve analysis. Average grain diameter ranges from 0.001 to 0.02 in. (25 to 500 μm), and in general increases with increasing permeability.

Muskat (1937) states that a Reynold's number from 1 to 8 marks the point of deviation from Darcy's law and the start of high-velocity flow. In fact, Muskat claimed that *"it will suffice to accept as a safe lower limit where deviations from Darcy's law will become appreciable as given by a Reynold's number of 1, with d chosen as any reasonable average diameter of the sand grains."* Figure 3.9, based on experimental tests performed in the 1920s and 1930s, supports this statement.

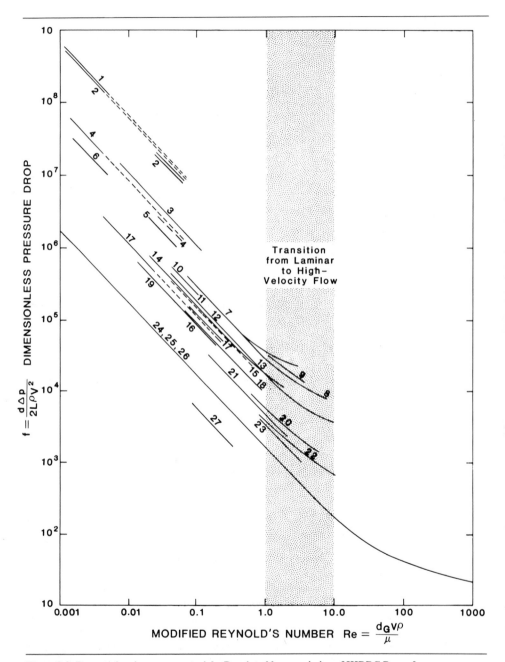

Figure 3.9 Pressure loss in porous materials. Reprinted by permission of IHRDC Press, from Muskat 1981, fig. 3.5.

We suggest the following relations for determining the oil and gas production rates that mark the onset of high-velocity flow and the start of considerable deviation from Darcy's law:

$$q_{oHVF} = 1.90 \times 10^4 \frac{\mu_o r_w h_p^2 (7 + s)}{\rho_o B_o h (k/k_a)}, \tag{3.18}$$

$$q_{gHVF} = 1.40 \times 10^6 \frac{\mu_g r_w h_p^2 (7 + s)}{\gamma_g h (k/k_a)}, \tag{3.19}$$

where

r_w = wellbore radius (ft),
h_p = perforated interval open to flow (ft),
h = total thickness (ft),
μ = gas or oil viscosity (cp),
γ_g = gas gravity (air = 1),
ρ_o = oil density at flowing pressure (1b/ft^3),
B_o = oil FVF at flowing pressure (bbl/STB),
k = formation permeability (md),
k_a = near-wellbore permeability (md),
s = formation damage or stimulated skin factor.

Equations (3.18) and (3.19) are derived from the radial flow equations by arbitrarily assuming that q_{oHVF} occurs when the fraction of total pressure drop due to high-velocity flow is 5% of the total pressure drop. During the transient production period the value of 7 in equation (3.19) should be replaced by an appropriate value for p_D.

In solution gas-drive reservoirs, both oil and gas flow simultaneously. By analogy to permeability, we might expect that the presence of a second phase would magnify the high-velocity effect of the first phase. This aspect of high-velocity skin has so far not been properly investigated. Until such investigation establishes the true effect, we shall assume no interference between the high-velocity effects of the two phases. Considering that gas may begin to deviate from Darcy flow before oil, we shall use gas to mark the onset of high-velocity flow. The surface gas rate q_g (scf/D) corresponding to gas flow at the wellbore is given by

$$q_g = q_o (R - R_s), \tag{3.20}$$

where q_o = the surface oil rate (STB/D), R is the producing gas/oil ratio (scf/STB), and R_s is the solution gas/oil ratio (scf/STB) at flowing bottomhole pressure. Comparing q_g from equation (3.20) with q_{gHVF} (eq. [3.19]) gives an indication of whether free gas flow has reached conditions deviating from Darcy flow. In fact, it is possible to back-calculate the producing gas/oil ratio R_{HVF} at which free gas begins to encounter high-velocity flow.

Example 3.5 illustrates the prediction of high-velocity flow conditions. Perhaps the most important use of the predictive equations is to decide, for a particular well, whether multirate testing should be considered to determine the effects of high-velocity flow. We should emphasize that oil wells can be dominated by high-velocity flow if one or all of the following conditions exist: (1) Rates are high; (2) damage is significant (i.e., k/k_a is large); or (3) the perforated interval is only a fraction of the total thickness; (4) perforation density is low and/or perforation size is small; and (5) perforations are packed with gravel.

EXAMPLE 3.5 PREDICTING HIGH-VELOCITY FLOW CONDITIONS IN A WELL PRODUCING FROM A SOLUTION GAS-DRIVE RESERVOIR

The Oklahoma City Field, discovered on March 26, 1930 (Katz 1941) produces from the Wilcox sandstone. Initial open-flow potentials exceeding 100,000 STB/D were reported from the Field, and average daily rates in excess of several thousand barrels per day were not unusual in the early years of production. The reservoir oil was initially at its bubble point, equal to the initial reservoir pressure of 2686 psia at a 5260-ft datum. Reservoir temperature was reported at 132°F; relevant PVT data are given in table E3.5.

Permeabilities in the wells range from 200 to 1500 md, and producing thickness averages 100 to 200 ft. Porosity ranges from 10% to 25%, with an average of about 20%. Very low water saturations have been reported, and a value of 5% is used here. Table E3.5 summarizes the average rock properties for a Wilcox producer in the Field.

1. Calculate the oil rate above which high-velocity flow effects should be present. Since drilling mud in the early 1930s was generally of poor quality, some formation damage was probably present. Assume a 2-in. thick damage zone ($r_a = 0.47$ ft) with 25% of the formation permeability ($k_a = 0.25k$).
2. For an oil rate of 500 STB/D with flowing bottomhole pressure of 1380 psia and a producing gas/oil ratio of 1250 scf/STB, calculate the free gas rate, compare it with q_{gHVF}, and comment on the high-velocity-flow effect.

Table E3.5 Average Properties for the Oklahoma City Field

Initial reservoir pressure p_i	2686 psia
Bubble-point pressure p_b	2686 psia
Reservoir temperature T_R	132°F
Initial solution gas/oil ratio R_{si}	725 scf/STB
Initial oil FVF B_{oi}	1.388 bbl/STB
Initial oil viscosity μ_{oi}	0.586 cp
Stock-tank gravity γ_{API}	40°API
Total gas gravity γ_g	0.70 (air = 1)
Initial water saturation S_{wi}	0.50
Average porosity ϕ	0.20
Average permeability k	500 md
Average thickness h	100 ft
Open interval h_p	40 ft
Wellbore radius r_w	0.33 ft
Drainage radius r_e (20-acre spacing)	527 ft
Horizontal to vertical permeabilities k/k_v	1.0

EXAMPLE 3.5 continued

SOLUTION

1. The oil rate at which the onset of high-velocity flow can be expected is given by equation (3.18)

$$q_{oHVF} = 1.90 \times 10^4 \frac{\mu_o r_w h_p^2 (7+s)}{\rho_o B_o h(k/k_a)}.$$

The term $\rho_o B_o$ is calculated from surface properties by equation (1.27):

$$\rho_o B_o = 0.0136 R_s \gamma_g + 62.37 \gamma_o$$

$$= 0.0136(725)(0.70) + 62.37(0.825)$$

$$= 58.31 \text{ lb/ft}^3.$$

Damage-zone skin is calculated by equation (3.1):

$$s_a = (1/0.25 - 1)\ln(0.47/0.33)$$

$$= +1.061$$

Partial-penetration skin s_c is calculated from the penetration ratio

$$b = h_p/h = 40/100$$

$$= 0.4,$$

the dimensionless pay-zone thickness

$$h_D = (k/k_v)^{0.5}(h/r_w)$$

$$= (1.0)(100/0.33)$$

$$= 303,$$

and the partial-penetration function

$$G(b) = 2.948 - 7.363b + 11.45b^2 - 4.675b^3$$

$$= 1.536,$$

which when substituted in equation (3.6) gives

$$s_c = (1/b - 1)[\ln(h_D) - G(b)]$$

$$= (1/0.4 - 1)[\ln(303) - 1.536]$$

$$= +6.22.$$

EXAMPLE 3.5 continued

In section 3.8 it is shown that the composite effect of s_c and s_a is (eq. [3.47])

$$s = s_c + (h/h_p)s_a,$$

which calculates

$$s = 6.22 + (100/40)1.06 = 9.5$$

Substituting the skin value and well data in equation (3.18) yields the rate that marks the onset of rate-dependent skin effect,

$$q_{oHVF} = 1.90 \times 10^4 \frac{(0.586)(0.33)(40)^2(7+9.5)}{58.31(100)(4.0)}$$

$$= 4158\,\text{STB/D}.$$

2. At a flowing pressure of 1380 psia, solution gas/oil ratio is 334 scf/STB. The free-gas rate is given by

$$q_g = q_o(R - R_s)$$

$$= 500(1250 - 334)$$

$$= 458,000\,\text{scf/D}.$$

The critical gas rate is given by

$$q_g = 1.40 \times 10^6 \frac{\mu_g r_w h_p{}^2(7+s)}{\gamma_g h(k/k_a)}$$

$$= 1.40 \times 10^6 \frac{(0.015)(0.33)(40)^2(7+9.5)}{0.7(100)(4.0)}$$

$$= 653,400\,\text{scf/D},$$

which is higher than the free-gas flow rate. Based on these calculations we can conclude that high-velocity-flow effects are probably not prevalent at the 500-STB/D rate.

The Forchheimer equation is the most popular flow model used to describe high-velocity-flow effects in petroleum reservoirs. The equation appears to match *laboratory* results best, including the gradual transition from laminar Darcy flow to "nonlinear" flow at high velocities. The backpressure equation form, with single values for the coefficient and the exponent, does not seem to match laboratory data at both low and high velocities, but it has certainly been substantiated as an adequate equation for matching *field* data for large ranges of rate and flowing pressure (the only exception we have found is fig. 5 in Cullender's [1955] paper).

The Forchheimer equation adds a second velocity term to Darcy's equation, giving

$$dp/dr = av + bv^2. \tag{3.21}$$

At low velocities, bv^2 is neglible and Darcy's law applies. At high velocities av is neglible and pressure drop is proportional to the square of velocity (analogous to turbulent flow in pipe). Through the transition from low to high velocities the two terms av and bv^2 provide sufficient fitting capabilities to match laboratory behavior. Early work by Green and Duwez (1951), and Cornell and Katz (1952) expressed the Forchheimer equation (eq. [3.21]) in terms of rock and fluid properties and provided the necessary form to apply the equation as a predictive tool. The authors concluded that the constant a is defined by Darcy's law ($a = \mu/k$), and the constant b consists of fluid density and an empirical constant β, giving

$$dp/dr = (\mu/k)v + \beta\rho v^2 \tag{2.37}$$

As discussed in sections 2.4 and 2.5, the Forchheimer equation is generally expressed as the radial Darcy flow equation with a rate-dependent skin Dq, where D is proportional to the high-velocity-flow constant β. Recent field data (Fetkovich 1973; Blacker 1982) give conclusive evidence that oil wells may be as vulnerable to high-velocity flow as are gas wells. The contribution of high-velocity flow throughout a reservoir with uniform permeability is expressed by D_R, where for gas wells

$$D_{Rg} = 2.222 \times 10^{-18} \frac{\gamma_g k h}{\mu_g r_w h_p^2} \beta_R, \tag{3.22}$$

and for oil wells

$$D_{Ro} = 1.635 \times 10^{-16} \frac{k h \rho_o B_o}{\mu_o r_w h_p^2} \beta_R, \tag{3.23}$$

or

$$D_{Ro} = 1.635 \times 10^{-16} \frac{k h (0.0135 R_s \gamma_g + 62.4 \gamma_o)}{\mu_o r_w h_p^2} \beta_R, \tag{3.24}$$

where β_R is a property of the reservoir rock, which can be estimated from

$$\beta_R = 2.73 \times 10^{10} k^{-1.1045} \tag{2.64}$$

and k is the formation permeability.

Since most of the pressure drop is localized near the wellbore, a better value of permeability to use for calculating β_R is the effective permeability k_a of the considered phase near the wellbore. If a region near the wellbore has altered permeability to some radius r_a (which can be determined or estimated), then the correct expression for high-velocity flow is $D = D_a + D_R$, where for gas wells

$$D_{ag} = 2.222 \times 10^{-18} \frac{\gamma_g kh}{\mu_g h_p^2} (1/r_w - 1/r_a)\beta_a, \tag{3.25}$$

and for oil wells

$$D_{ao} = 1.635 \times 10^{-16} \frac{kh\rho_o B_o}{\mu_o h_p^2} (1/r_w - 1/r_a)\beta_a, \tag{3.26}$$

or

$$D_{ao} = 1.635 \times 10^{-16} \frac{kh(0.0135 R_s \gamma_g + 62.4\gamma_o)}{\mu_o h_p^2} (1/r_w - 1/r_a)\beta_a, \tag{3.27}$$

where β_a is given by

$$\beta_a = 2.73 \times 10^{10} k_a^{-1.1045}. \tag{3.28}$$

The high-velocity effect beyond the altered radius is calculated using equation (2.64) for β_R and the expression $(1/r_a - 1/r_e)$ instead of $1/r_w$ in equations (3.22) to (3.24). Usually, if a damaged zone exists, the altered zone high-velocity term D_a is much larger than D_R and we can assume $D \simeq D_a$.

Many correlations for β exist in the literature. Most authors consider permeability as the main correlating parameter for β. Other physical properties that have been used are porosity, irreducible water saturation, rock type, average pore size, and pore-size distribution. Tessem (1980) presented some recent data measured with air in 112 cores of sandstone and carbonate rock. Several of his measured data are listed in Table 3.3. Use of the data in attempts to develop correlations for β is presented in figures 3.10 and 3.11. Figure 3.10 plots both Tessem's data and that of Tek et al. (1962), Figure 2. In figure 3.11 there is an attempt to develop two separate correlations, one for rocks with small pores and the other for rocks with large pores.

Firoozabadi and Katz (1979) give an excellent review of the state of the art of high-velocity flow for gas wells. (Caution: equations for β given by Firoozabadi and Katz, in their table 2, contain typographical errors.) They review the existing explanations of the phenomenon. It is obvious, however, that the true nature of the high-velocity flow has yet to be verified.

A general observation concerning β and its relation to other properties is that the wide spread in experimental data makes an accurate estimate of β almost impossible. Also, difficulties in back-calculating values of β from fieldtest data

Table 3.3 High-Velocity Coefficient versus Permeability, Porosity, and Mean Pore Size

Sample No	k (md)	ϕ	$k \times \phi$	β (ft^{-1})	d_{50} (μm)	$\beta\sqrt{k}$
1	8.5	0.162	1.38	1.102×10^9		3.21×10^9
2.1	113.2	0.184	20.83	3.87×10^7	185	4.12×10^8
2.2	98.5	0.202	19.90	2.59×10^7	203	2.57×10^8
2.3	227.6	0.188	42.80	1.89×10^7	160	2.85×10^8
2.4	24.2	0.202	4.89	4.35×10^8		2.14×10^9
2.5	13.9	0.149	2.07	7.70×10^8		2.87×10^9
2.6	12.0	0.169	2.03	5.84×10^8		2.02×10^9
2.7	165.9	0.192	31.85	2.47×10^7		3.18×10^8
3.1	149.3	0.147	21.95	3.17×10^7	155	3.87×10^8
3.2	164.3	0.173	28.42	2.41×10^7		3.09×10^8
5.1	97.0	0.201	19.50	4.30×10^7	155	4.24×10^8
5.2	298.9	0.237	70.84	1.40×10^7		2.42×10^8
6.1	168.0	0.192	32.31	2.14×10^7		2.77×10^8
6.2	162.4	0.201	32.64	1.98×10^7		2.52×10^8
7.1	333.4	0.183	61.01	9.76×10^6	138	1.78×10^8
8.1	11.1	0.210	2.33	1.80×10^8	145	6.00×10^8
8.2	44.3	0.174	7.71	1.34×10^8		6.92×10^8
9.1	356.2	0.165	58.77	1.07×10^7	225	2.02×10^8
9.2	650.9	0.204	132.78	3.66×10^6	215	9.34×10^7
9.3	51.2	0.185	9.47	3.49×10^7		2.50×10^8
9.4	390.7	0.162	63.29	7.32×10^6	135	1.45×10^8
9.5	2.0	0.161	0.32	2.18×10^{10}	25	3.08×10^{10}
9.6	275.0	0.239	65.73	6.41×10^6	43	1.06×10^8
10.1	8.6	0.178	1.53	2.20×10^8	142	6.45×10^8
10.2	5.1	0.152	0.78	5.08×10^8		1.15×10^9
102	65.5	0.264	17.29	6.34×10^7	450	5.13×10^8
104	724.8	0.196	142.06	3.66×10^6		9.85×10^7
105	231.8	0.171	39.63	7.02×10^6		1.07×10^8
106	2.4	0.149	0.36	8.53×10^8	23	1.32×10^9
108	7.4	0.167	1.24	2.58×10^8	42	7.02×10^8
110	128.9	0.209	26.94	1.77×10^7		2.01×10^8
111	140.0	0.222	31.08	1.46×10^7	130	1.73×10^8
114	24.8	0.185	4.59	1.10×10^8		5.48×10^8
117S	43.6	0.246	10.73	1.12×10^8	360	7.40×10^8
117L	2.2	0.151	0.33	1.14×10^{10}		1.69×10^{10}
118	3.7	0.203	0.75	8.39×10^8		1.61×10^9
119	423.6	0.208	88.11	5.19×10^6		1.07×10^8
206	2.4	0.296	0.71	9.50×10^9		1.47×10^{10}
214	0.7	0.325	0.23	1.15×10^9		9.62×10^8
215	0.6	0.321	0.19	6.76×10^8		5.24×10^8

Source: R. Tessem, "High Velocity Coefficient's Dependence of Rock Properties: A Laboratory Study." *Thesis.* (Pet. Inst., NTH, Norway Dec. 1980), 26.

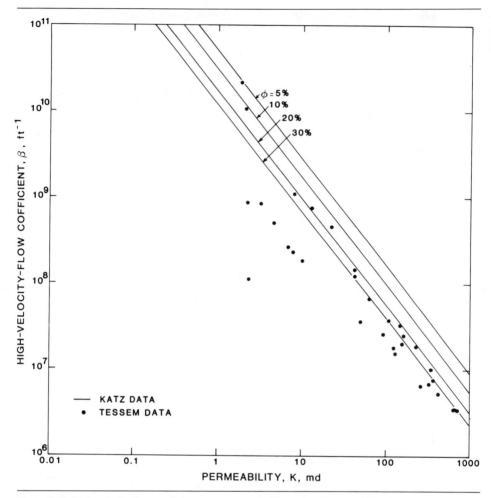

Figure 3.10 High-velocity-flow coefficient versus permeability. After Tessem 1980, fig. 11, by permission of the University of Trondheim.

hinder verification of the conclusions of laboratory experiments. It is difficult to develop physical or mathematical models that isolate the effect of the formation from the effect of the perforation so that β can be back-calculated. In addition, it is difficult to account for the effect of bedding, shale streaks, permeability anisotropy, and plugged perforations, which might affect the flow in actual wells. Only if these effects are small, the prediction of D from the β correlation can be reasonably accurate. We observe two common errors that usually impair the accuracy of the predictions: (1) Instead of calculating D with the term h/h_p^2, only the total formation thickness is considered. That is, $1/h$ is used in equations (3.22) to (3.27) instead of h/h_p^2, resulting in large errors for D. (2) Instead of using the permeability near the wellbore, k_a, formation permeability k is incorrectly used to

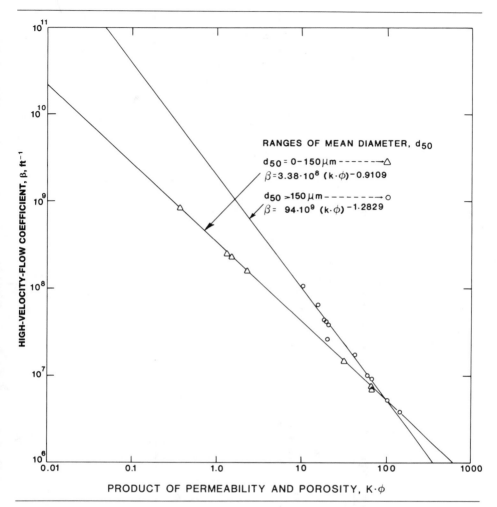

Figure 3.11 High-velocity-flow coefficient versus the product of permeability and porosity for ranges of mean diameter. After Tessem 1980, fig. 14, by permission of the University of Trondheim.

estimate β. If these two errors are avoided when predicting D from a β correlation, the calculated value of D should be a reasonable estimate. If the D back-calculated from multirate test data is still much larger than D as calculated from the β correlation, high-velocity-flow effects in the perforations may be causing the additional pressure losses and should be accounted for. The effect of high-velocity flow through perforations and gravel pack are considered separately in the next two sections.

The IPR equation in terms of the rate-dependent skin is cumbersome to work with when compared with the backpressure equation or the quadratic equation. Since, however, most engineers have adopted the rate-dependent skin for accounting for high-velocity-flow effects, table 3.4 lists the expressions relating the

Table 3.4 Calculating Rate-Dependent Skin Factor from the Quadratic Equation or from Multirate Test Data

	Gas			Oil	
	Low-pressure reservoir	High-pressure reservoir with small drawdown	Pseudopressure approach	Undersaturated reservoir	Saturated reservoir
Flow equation	$p_R^2 - p_{wf}^2 = Aq_g + Bq_g^2$	$p_R - p_{wf} = Aq_g + Bq_g^2$	$m(p_R) - m(p) = Aq_g + Bq_g^2$	$p_R - p_{wf} = Aq_o + Bq_o^2$	$p_R^2 - p_{wf}^2 = Aq_o + Bq_o^2$
Plot of test data	$\dfrac{p_R^2 - p_{wf}^2}{q_g}$ vs. q_g	$\dfrac{p_R - p_{wf}}{q_g}$ vs. q_g	$\dfrac{m(p_R) - m(p)}{q_g}$ vs. q_g	$\dfrac{p_R - p_{wf}}{q_o}$ vs. q_o	$\dfrac{p_R^2 - p_{wf}^2}{q_o}$ vs. q_o
Rate-dependent skin from the plot	$B = \dfrac{T\mu_g Z}{0.703kh}D$	$B = \dfrac{T\mu_g Z}{1.407p_{av}kh}D$	$B = \dfrac{T}{0.703kh}D$	$B = 141.2\dfrac{B_o\mu_o}{kh}D$	$B = 141.2\dfrac{2p_R}{kh(k_{ro}/\mu_o B_o)}D$
Constant skin from the plot where $[\ ] = [\ln r_e/r_w - 3/4 + s]$	$A = \dfrac{T\mu_g Z}{0.703kh}[\ ]$	$A = \dfrac{T\mu_g Z}{1.407p_{av}kh}[\ ]$	$A = \dfrac{T}{0.703kh}[\ ]$	$A = 141.2\dfrac{B_o\mu_o}{kh}[\ ]$	$A = 141.2\dfrac{2p_R}{kh(k_{ro}/\mu_o B_o)}[\ ]$

coefficient D to the constants A and B in the quadratic equation. Example 3.6 gives an instance of predicting D based on the β correlation.

EXAMPLE 3.6 PREDICTING THE EFFECT OF HIGH-VELOCITY FLOW BASED ON THE β CORRELATION

Consider again the Oklahoma City Field. Example 3.5 indicates that an initial production of approximately 4200 STB/D should mark the onset of high-velocity flow—the point when non-Darcy flow must be considered in reservoir performance.

1. Based on the β correlation, calculate the percentage of total pressure drop resulting from high-velocity flow for the rate of 4200 STB/D.
2. Repeat the calculation, assuming the damaged zone around the wellbore has been cleaned up and initial permeability restored by continuous production at high rates.

SOLUTION

The permeability in the invaded zone near the wellbore is 125 md (assuming 25% of the original 500 md). An estimate of β_a from the Firoozabadi and Katz (1979) correlation, equation (3.28), is

$$\beta_a = 2.73 \times 10^{10} k_a^{-1.1045}$$

$$= 2.73 \times 10^{10} (125)^{-1.1045}$$

$$= 1.32 \times 10^8 \, \text{ft}^{-1}.$$

From example 3.5 we know that $\rho_o B_o = 58.31$, so D_a can be calculated from equation (3.26):

$$D_a = 1.635 \times 10^{-16} \frac{kh\rho_o B_o}{\mu_o h_p^2} (1/r_w - 1/r_a)\beta_a$$

$$= 1.635 \times 10^{-16} \frac{(500)(100)(58.31)}{(0.586)(40)^2} (1/0.33 - 1/0.47) 1.32 \times 10^8$$

$$= 6.0 \times 10^{-5} \, (\text{STB/D})^{-1}.$$

The high-velocity-flow coefficient beyond the invaded zone is

$$\beta_R = 2.73 \times 10^{10} k^{-1.1045}$$

$$= 2.73 \times 10^{10} (500)^{-1.1045}$$

$$= 2.85 \times 10^7 \, \text{ft}^{-1},$$

EXAMPLE 3.6 continued

So D_R for the reservoir beyond the invaded zone can be calculated from

$$D_R = 1.635 \times 10^{-16} \frac{k h \rho_o B_o}{\mu_o h_p^2} (1/r_a - 1/r_e) \beta_R$$

$$= 1.635 \times 10^{-16} \frac{(500)(100)(58.31)}{(0.586)(40)^2} (1/0.47 - 1/527) 2.85 \times 10^7$$

$$= 3.08 \times 10^{-5} (\text{STB/D})^{-1}.$$

The total D, equal to the sum of D_a and D_R, thus is

$$D = 0.000060 + 0.0000308$$

$$= 0.000091 (\text{STB/D})^{-1}.$$

Since the reservoir is initially saturated, the IPR equation is

$$\frac{p_R^2 - p_{wf}^2}{q_o} = A + B q_o,$$

where A and B are expressed in terms of reservoir parameters (eqs. [2.104] and [2.105]):

$$A = \frac{141.2(2 p_R)}{k h [k_{ro}/\mu_o B_o]_R} [\ln(r_e/r_w) - 0.75 + s],$$

$$B = \frac{141.2(2 p_R)}{k h [k_{ro}/\mu_o B_o]_R} D.$$

Initially, $p_R = p_b = 2686$ psia, and $k_{ro} = 1.0$. Assuming 20-acre spacing, which corresponds to $r_e = 527$ ft,

$$\ln(r_e/r_w) - 0.75 + s = \ln(527/0.33) - 0.75 + 6.22 + (100/40)1.06$$

$$= 16.2,$$

where $s = 6.22 + (100/40)1.3$ is as calculated in example 3.5.

Pressure drawdown due to laminar (darcy) flow alone is $A q_o$. When substituting reservoir parameters and the rate of 4200 STB/D we obtain

$$p_R^2 - p_{wfL}^2 = \frac{141.2(2)(2686)}{(500)(100)[1/(0.586)(1.388)]} (16.2)(4200),$$

EXAMPLE 3.6 continued

or a flowing wellbore pressure of

$$p_{wfL} = [7.21 \times 10^6 - 8.45 \times 10^5]^{0.5}$$

$$= 2525 \, \text{psia}.$$

Similarly, pressure drop due to high-velocity flow is Bq_o^2. For a production rate of 4200 it gives

$$p_R^2 - p_{wf\,HVF}^2 = \frac{141.2(2)(2686)(0.000091)}{(500)(100)[1/(0.586)(1.388)]}(4200)^2,$$

or

$$p_{wf\,HVF} = [7.21 \times 10^6 - 1.98 \times 10^4]^{0.5}$$

$$= 2681 \, \text{psia}.$$

Pressure drawdown due to laminar flow alone is $2686 - 2525 = 161 \, \text{psi}$, and pressure drawdown due to high-velocity flow alone is $2686 - 2681 = 5 \, \text{psi}$, or only $5/(161 + 5) = 3.0\%$. Total pressure drawdown is 166 psi, or the sum of laminar and high-velocity-flow pressure drops.

2. Assume the damage zone has cleaned up with production and permeability near the wellbore is restored to the 500-md value of the reservoir itself. The expression for D throughout the reservoir from the wellbore to drainage radius (assuming $1/r_w \gg 1/r_e$) is equation (3.23), or

$$D_R = 1.635 \times 10^{-16} \frac{kh\rho_o B_o}{\mu_o r_w h_p^2}\beta_R,$$

$$= 1.635 \times 10^{-16} \frac{(500)(100)(58.31)}{(0.586)(0.33)(40)^2}2.85 \times 10^7$$

$$= 4.39 \times 10^{-5}\,(\text{STB/D})^{-1}.$$

Damage skin of 1.3 is now set equal to zero, and thus $s = s_c = 6.22$. The steady-state expression becomes

$$\ln(r_e/r_w) - 0.75 + s = \ln(527/0.33) - 0.75 + 6.22$$

$$= 12.8.$$

Pressure drop due to laminar flow is Aq_o or, for 4200 STB/D,

$$p_R^2 - p_{wfL}^2 = \frac{141.2(2)(2686)}{(500)(100)[1/(0.586)(1.388)]}(12.8)(4200),$$

EXAMPLE 3.6 continued

which gives

$$p_{wfL} = [7.21 \times 10^6 - 6.63 \times 10^5]^{0.5}$$

$$= 2559 \, \text{psia}.$$

Pressure drop due to high-velocity flow is Bq_o^2 or, for 4200 STB/D,

$$p_R^2 - p_{wf\,HVF}^2 = \frac{141.2(2)(2686)(4.93 \times 10^{-5})}{(500)(100)[1/(0.586)(1.388)]}(4200)^2,$$

which gives

$$p_{wf\,HVF} = [7.21 \times 10^6 - 1.07 \times 10^4]^{0.5}$$

$$= 2683 \, \text{psia}.$$

Pressure drawdown due to laminar flow alone is $2686 - 2559 = 127 \, \text{psi}$, and pressure drawdown due to high velocity alone is $2686 - 2683 = 3 \, \text{psi}$, or only $3/(127 + 3) = 2.3\%$. Total pressure drop is 130 psi, or 36 psi less than calculated with a 0.47-ft damage-zone radius near the wellbore.

In review, the existence of high-velocity effects in a well is substantiated by a multirate test that indicates either a value for the coefficient D of the rate-dependent skin or an exponent n smaller than 1 for the backpressure equation. The measured rate-dependent skin can be related to formation permeability and the degree of formation damage, but back-calculation of the altered near-wellbore permeability from measured skin requires some estimation of the effects of perforations or other flow restriction at the entry to the wellbore.

3.5   **PERFORATION PENETRATION, GEOMETRY, AND DENSITY.** Most wells today are completed with production casing cemented in place and perforated to allow reservoir fluids to enter the wellbore. The current perforating techniques use shaped charges to produce penetrating jets, which perforate through the casing and the cement sheath. The jets are usually ⅜ in. or ½ in. in diameter, with a density of 4 to 8 shots per foot. Highly productive formations may be shot with ⅝-in. or ¾-in. jets, having densities as high as 8 to 12 shots per foot. The shaped charges are assembled and run into the well in an assembly referred to as a *perforating gun*. Each charge in the gun consists of a container, an explosive element, and a conical metallic liner. When detonated, the explosion creates a high-pressure wave that moves through the cone liner and disintegrates it to form a high-velocity jet stream, which penetrates the casing, cement sheath, and formation. Figure 3.12 shows a schematic of a shaped charge and penetrating jet.

It is important to recognize that the penetration does not occur by pulverizing material in the path of the jet, but by crushing and compaction of the casing,

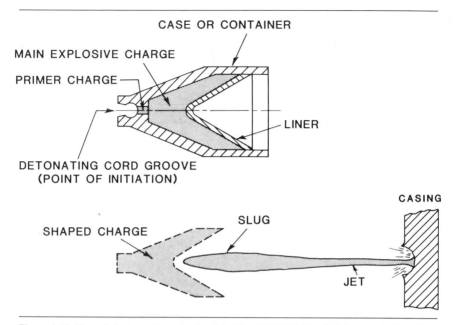

CASE OR CONTAINER

MAIN EXPLOSIVE CHARGE

PRIMER CHARGE

LINER

DETONATING CORD GROOVE
(POINT OF INITIATION)

CASING

SLUG

SHAPED CHARGE

JET

Figure 3.12 Shaped charge and penetrating jet. After Bell 1972, figs. 1, 8, by permission of the
SPE-AIME, © 1972 SPE-AIME.

cement, and formation. The jet is usually followed by a slow-moving slug of
materials from the charge, which does not form a jet. This slug does not affect the
penetration, but it can hinder the flow capacity of the perforation by partially
plugging it.

Three techniques are used to perform the perforating task:

1. *Wireline-conveyed casing gun*—usually a large-diameter gun is run through the
casing on an electrical wireline. It perforates with pressure overbalance where the
fluid in the well creates a pressure differential toward the formation, ensuring that
the well will not flow immediately after perforation. The operation is performed
with the drilling rig on location and under full blowout preventor (BOP)
protection.

2. *Wireline-conveyed-through-tubing gun*—A small-diameter gun run through the
x-mas tree and the tubing string, after the tubing has already been landed and a
packer set above the perforating interval. The gun is usually fired with
underbalanced conditions, where the wellbore fluid is underpressured in relation to
formation pressure, allowing the formation to produce immediately after
perforating.

3. *Tubing-conveyed gun*—A large-diameter gun installed on a tail pipe at the
bottom of the tubing and run together with the tubing string. After installing the
x-mas tree and setting the packer, the gun is activated by dropping a detonating
bar. Either underbalanced or overbalanced perforating can be performed. After
perforating, the gun is left hanging or dropped off into the rathole.

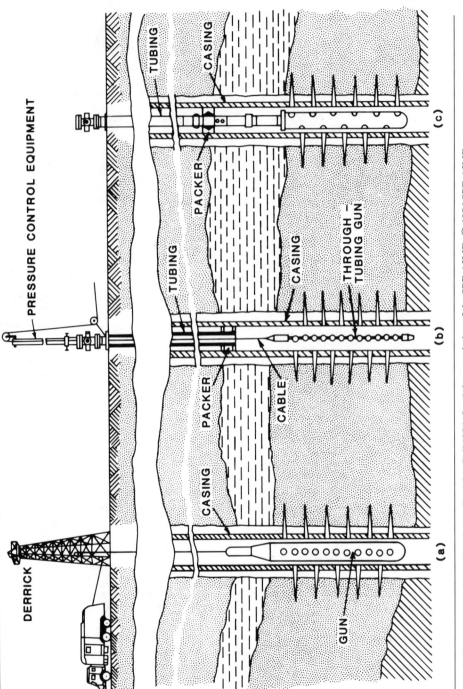

Figure 3.13 Techniques for perforating wells. After Bell 1984, fig. 6, by permission of the SPE-AIME, © 1984 SPE-AIME.

Figure 3.13 shows the three types of perforating gun. Each gun has its own advantage, but the industry seems to be leaning toward the idea that perforating underbalanced has distinct advantages from the view of well productivity and perforation flow effectiveness (Bell 1984, 1985), so the through-tubing and tubing-conveyed guns are gaining wide use by the industry. Large-diameter casing guns carrying large-diameter, deeper-penetrating charges provide substantially higher performance than smaller through-tubing guns. Their penetration may be twice that of through-tubing guns and their shot phasing (angular shot arrangement) is the favorable 90° helix-shaped pattern compared with the unfavorable 0° shot phasing for most through-tubing guns.

Two major disadvantages with wireline-conveyed casing guns are: (1) the overbalanced condition will usually create skin damage due to influx of wellbore fluid into the formation, and (2) the need to kill the perforated well for running the tubing string, removing the BOP and installing the x-mas tree.

A recent discussion by Kelly (1985) and Bell (1985) addresses the issues of perforating under- and overbalanced, the advantages of shot penetration and angular phasing versus the potential disadvantages involving an overbalanced condition. Clearly there is not a general consensus about a "best" method for perforating, and only fieldtest results under controlled conditions can help substantiate controversial conclusions by different sources.

Flow through perforations affects the productivity of a well primarily by changing the local flow geometry near the wellbore. This is shown in figure 3.14. Unlike the effect of limited entry, which always impedes inflow, perforations may result in enhanced productivity if the operation is successful. Field results suggest, however, that, compared with open-hole completions, perforations most often have a negative effect on flow, particularly if only some of the perforations are open to flow. The effect of perforations on well performance is usually expressed as a skin factor. In fact, Muskat (1943) proposed the first expression for perforation skin and discussed its resemblance to an apparent wellbore radius.

Perforation skin factor s_p depends on perforation geometry and perforation quality. The specific geometrical parameters affecting the productivity of the perforated interval have been studied analytically by Muskat (1943), with analog models by McDowell and Muskat (1950) and Howard and Watson (1950), and with numerical simulators by Harris (1966), Hong (1975), and Locke (1981). The most important parameters reognized by the studies are

1. *Penetration depth*: The deeper the penetration, the better the performance.
2. *Perforation diameter*: The larger the diameter of the perforation tunnel, the better the flow performance (although the effect is only slight as compared with penetration depth).
3. *Shot density*: The more shots per foot, the better the performance, although beyond 4 shots per foot improvement diminishes and the danger of casing damage is increased.
4. *Phasing*: The phasing, the angular pattern of shots around the wellbore, has an effect on productivity. In relation to flow capacity the worst phasing is 0°, or strip shooting, where all shots are along the same side of the wellbore, yet zero phasing

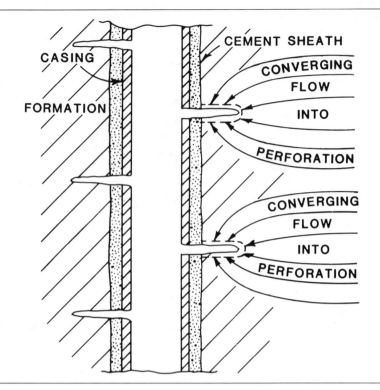

Figure 3.14 Flow geometry near the perforations.

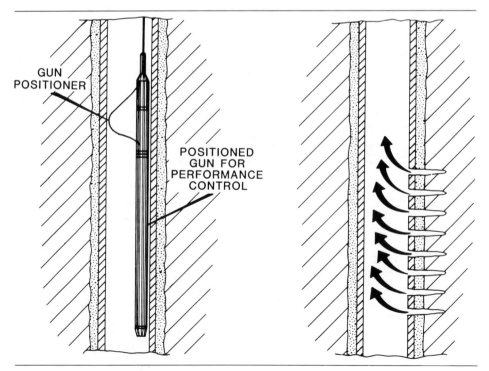

Figure 3.15 Zero phasing with positioned gun. After Bell 1972, fig. 71, by permission of the SPE-AIME, © 1972 SPE-AIME.

is common for through-tubing guns because it can achieve good penetration (fig. 3.15). For a given shot density, the phasing that provides the greatest distance between perforations, and thus the least interference between them, is the most flow-effective.

The Harris (1966) study is one of the more comprehensive on the effect of perforation on productivity. Standing (1980) rearranged the Harris's results into two handy charts (figs. 3.16 and 3.17) that give skin as a function of perforation depth beyond the casing (0 to 30 in.), density (1, 2, or 4 shots per ft), and phasing (0° or 180°). Standing notes that the 180° chart can also be used for 120° phasing, and work by Locke suggests that the 180° chart should also apply to 90° phasing without much error. Since the work by Harris assumes all perforations lie in the same horizontal plane, skin factors in figures 3.16 and 3.17 will be slightly different from those where successive perforations are arranged in angular phasing over the 1-ft interval. According to Locke, Harris's skin factors are too large for shallow penetration and too small for deep penetration, but the differences are small.

Probably the only advantage of figures 3.16 and 3.17 over the original dimensionless curves of Harris is that they give a quick-look picture of the relative importance of the various perforation parameters. Harris's work does not consider the possibility that formation damage exists near the wellbore. Intuitively, penetration that exceeds the depth of the damage significantly improves the inflow. It is impossible, however, to estimate the magnitude and the extent of formation damage after the well has been cleaned up by acid. We therefore omit formation damage considerations in calculating perforation skin factor.

The Standing–Harris curves are specifically for one-half-inch perforations through cemented casing in 9½-in. wellbore (bit diameter). The depth of penetration is measured from the sand face. To account for a wellbore with a different diameter d, the actual penetration L_p is corrected to an apparent penetration, $L_{pa} = L_p(9.5/d)$. The effect of a difference in perforation diameter (from ½-in.) is neglible.

To make a reasonable estimate of perforation skin, the depth of penetration must be evaluated. At best, we can only hope for an approximate estimate of penetration depth. Perforating companies usually provide standard depths of penetration for their charges, based on experimental work following procedures and specifications listed in API RP 43. Figure 3.18 shows the API test assembly, and the standard Berea sandstone target.

In actual wells, the deviation from the API test depth of penetration can result from a number of problems, including

1. variation in clearance between the gun and the casing
2. variation in well fluid density
3. mechanical properties of the casing
4. mechanical properties of the formation
5. effective stress and/or compressive strength of formation rock at reservoir conditions
6. crushed (compacted) zone around the perforation

Thompson (1962) has developed an empirical correlation relating perforation

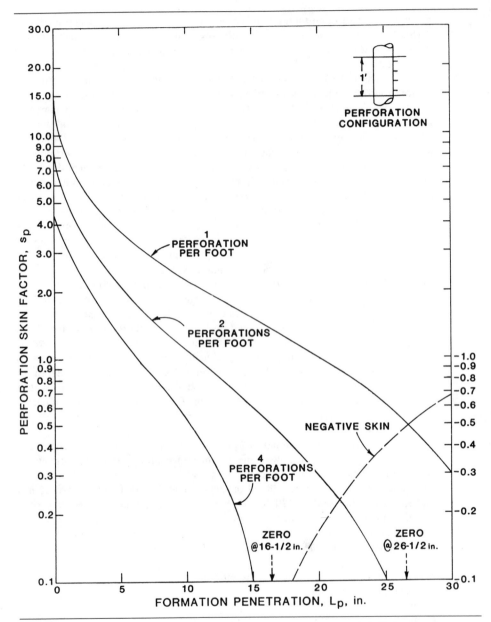

Figure 3.16 Perforation skin factor for 0° phasing. Reprinted by permission of the University of Trondheim from Standing 1980, fig. 7; after Harris 1966.

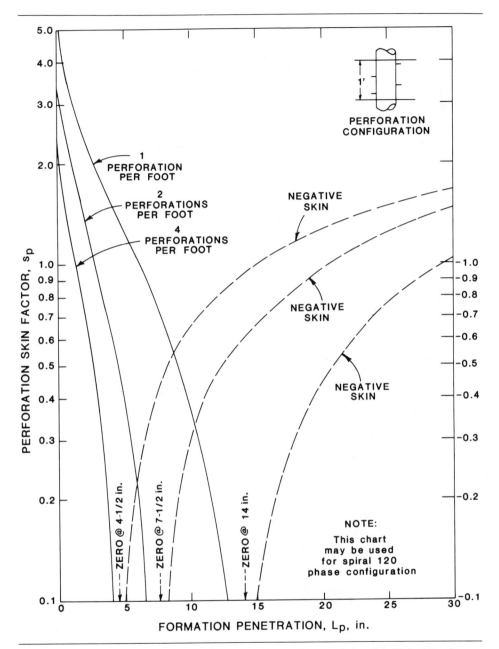

Figure 3.17 Perforation skin factors for 180° phasing. Reprinted by permission of the University of Trondheim from Standing 1980, fig. 8; after Harris 1966.

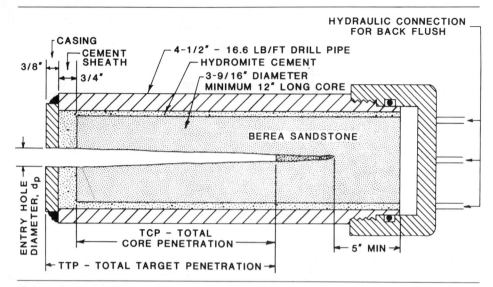

Figure 3.18 Standard API test assembly for evaluation of perforation depth. Courtesy Schlumberger Well Services.

penetration to rock compressive strength. He gives a simple equation for estimating the correction from standard Berea penetration L_{pB} to actual penetration L_p (in.):

$$L_p = [L_{pB} \times 10^{3.7(10^{-5})(C_B - C)}] - (T_s + T_c), \tag{3.29}$$

where

L_p = depth of penetration from the formation face (in.) (total core penetration = TCP),

L_{pB} = depth of penetration from the inside of the casing, through a ⅜-in. casing and a ¾-in. cement sheath (in.) (total target penetration = TTP),

C_B = Berea compressive strength ≈ 6500 psia,

C = rock compressive strength (psia),

T_s = cement sheath thickness (in.) (usually 0.75 in.),

T_c = casing thickness (in.) (usually 0.375 in.).

Equation (3.29) applies only to jet guns with shaped charges. The calculated perforation depth L_p (from the formation face to the tip of the effective perforation) can be used directly with figures 3.16 and 3.17 to estimate the perforation skin factor.

Saucier and Lands (1978) suggest that formation stress is a more suitable parameter to correlate the correction for API penetration depth. With only limited data, they present a correlation for the ratio $M_p = L_p/0.7[L_{pB} - (T_c + T_s)]$, shown in figure 3.19. Three rock types are identified: the Austin limestone (chalk), Wasson dolomite, and Berea sandstone. Note that the Berea curve moves from 1.0

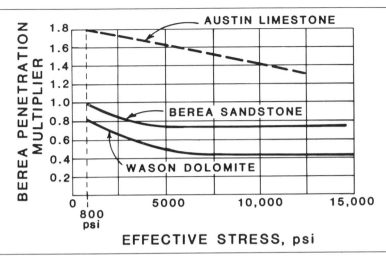

Figure 3.19 Correction to standard Berea penetration depth suggested by Saucier and Lands. Reprinted by permission of the SPE-AIME from Saucier and Lands 1978, fig. 13, pp. 1347–1353, © 1978 SPE-AIME.

at 800 psia to 0.73 at about 5000 psia, thereafter remaining constant. The Berea curve can be used for all sandstones in the absence of a better correlation.

The procedure for using the Saucier and Lands correlation is as follows:

1. Request from the perforation charge manufacturer data on the Berea total target penetration (TTP) L_{pB} as obtained in the API test for the specific gun being used.
2. Correct L_{pB} for cement and casing of the API target, to obtain the total core penetration (TCP), measured from the face of the formation to the tip of the perforation.
3. Multiply the TCP by 0.7 to account for the penetration reduction observed with actual casings and cement compared to the API penetration obtained with the thin casing and cement sheath used in the API target.
4. Determine the effective formation stress, equal to overburden minus pore pressure. Overburden can be estimated by multiplying depth by an overburden gradient of 1.1 psi/ft. Pore pressure is the reservoir pressure at the time of perforating.
5. Determine the formation rock type. Enter figure 3.19 at the effective stress, choose one of the three rock types, and read the correction for penetration due to effective stress.
6. Multiply the correction factor in step 5 by the depth from step 3. This equals the actual rock penetration from the face of the formation to the tip of the perforation, L_p.

In equation form the procedure for correcting perforation depth is

$$L_p = 0.7[L_{pB} - (T_s + T_c)]M_p, \tag{3.30}$$

where correction factors for Berea sandstone, Austin limestone, and Wasson dolomite are given in figure 3.19.

A problem with the Saucier and Lands correlation is that it is not general, and many rock formation types are not included. The authors themselves noted that much more experimental work is needed to substantiate their conclusions. Example 3.7 compares the estimation of penetration depth and skin factor using the Thompson equation with that using the Saucier and Lands procedure.

EXAMPLE 3.7 ESTIMATING PENETRATION DEPTH

The Soter No. I-25 has been drilled to a depth of 13,940 ft in the Arkoma Basin, Oklahoma. The production interval has been cased with a 6⅝-in. liner run into the 7⅞-in. hole (bit diameter). The Spiro sand was perforated from 13,850 to 13,880 feet with half-inch charges at 4 shots/ft density with 180° phasing. The 3⅛-in. gun reportedly has a 6.5-in. total target penetration in Berea sandstone, when tested by the manufacturer according to API RP 43 specifications. A special rock mechanics (mechanical properties) study was performed on the 4-in. cores taken from 13,829 to 13,890 feet, and the results are reported in table E3.7.

Use the available data to calculate the skin due to perforations. Make comments on the skin effect and compare results with (1) a completion having 4 shots/ft with 0° phasing and (2) a completion with 2 shots/ft with 0° phasing.

SOLUTION

The compressive strength of the Spiro formation ranges from 6000 to 18,000 psi, corresponding to a range in permeability from 0.15 to 0.01 md, respectively. Given the large range in compressive strength, corrections of the API Berea penetration depth are made for the two extreme values. Based on the Thompson correlation (eq. [3.29]), the actual formation penetration is

$$L_p = L_{pB} \exp[8.6 \times 10^{-5}(C_B - C)] - T_c - T_s$$

$$= 6.5 \exp[8.6 \times 10^{-5}(6500 - C)] - 0.38 - (7.875 - 6.625)/2.$$

Table E3.7 Special Core Analysis of the Soter No. I-25 Well

No.	Depth interval (ft)	Compressive strength C (psia)	Young's modulus (psia)	Poisson's ratio	Porosity ϕ (%)	Permeability k (md)	Rock type
1	13,842.4–842.6	16,190	5.80×10^6	0.11	0.088	0.242	Sand
2	13,851.6–851.8	11,165	4.21×10^6	0.27	0.036	0.024	Sand
3	13,859.7–859.9	18,386	3.45×10^6	0.35	0.007	0.008	Sand
4	13,869.7–869.9	17,909	5.15×10^6	0.27	0.034	0.011	Sand
5	13,871.5–871.7	9,665	2.13×10^6	0.17	0.023	0.134	Sand
6	13,878.3–878.5	6,081	1.19×10^6	0.29	0.029	0.123	Lime

Note: The entire interval is interspersed with limestone and dolomite.

EXAMPLE 3.7 continued

Note that in order to simplify the writing of equation (3.29), we write the exponential form, $\exp(2.302x) = e^{2.302x}$, which equals 10^x.

Substituting the lowest compressive strength value, $C = 6000\,\text{psi}$,

$$L_p = 6.79 - 0.38 - 0.62$$

$$= 5.79\,\text{in.}$$

Substituting the maximum value, $C = 18{,}000\,\text{psi}$,

$$L_p = 2.42 - 0.38 - 0.62$$

$$= 1.42\,\text{in.}$$

On the average, a formation perforation depth of 3 in. can be expected, but a wide spread in penetration depth is probable.

According to Saucier and Lands (1978), effective stress rather than compressive strength, should be used to correct Berea penetration. Overburden pressure is simply

$$p_{\text{overburden}} = 1.1(\text{psi/ft}) \times 13{,}890\,\text{ft}$$

$$= 15{,}279\,\text{psi},$$

and pore pressure is reported from DST data as 6550 psia. Effective stress is the difference between overburden and pore pressure, $15279 - 6550 = 8729\,\text{psi}$. Entering figure 3.19 with 8729 psi effective stress, the Berea penetration multiplier is found to be 0.72. According to Saucier and Lands, this calculates the actual penetration depth:

$$L_p = [6.5 - 0.38 - (7.875 - 6.625)/2](0.7)(0.72)$$

$$= 5.495(0.7)(0.72)$$

$$= 2.77\,\text{in.}$$

To calculate perforation skin, we assume an average formation penetration of 3 in. To use the Harris–Standing chart for 180° phasing (fig. 3.17), an equivalent penetration depth must be calculated to correct for the difference between the actual wellbore diameter and the 9½-in. wellbore assumed in the development of figures 3.16 and 3.17:

$$L_p = 3.0\frac{9.5}{7.875}$$

$$= 3.62\,\text{in.}$$

With 4 shots/ft, skin equals +0.45. For 0° phasing with 4 shots/ft, skin equals +1.5 and for 0° phasing with 2 shots/ft, skin equals +2.5.

Several authors (Klotz et al. 1974; Locke 1981; McLeod 1983) have suggested that the crushed zone or the compacted zone surrounding the perforation should be accounted for in the skin effect. The API RP 43 test expresses the crushed zone effect in terms of the core flow efficiency (CFE). The CFE is the ratio of the permeability k_p of a core perforated with a jet charge to depth L_p divided by permeability k_i of the same core with an "ideal" (i.e., drilled) perforation of length L_p. A standard API test measures k_p directly after a cleanup flow, as well as the permeability to the Berea sandstone without a perforation, k_o. A computer program offered by the API (appendix A, API RP 43, 3rd ed., October 1974) calculates the ratio k_i/k_o as a function of perforation depth L_p and diameter d_p. The CFE is then calculated as

$$\text{CFE} = k_p/k_i = (k_p/k_o)/(k_i/k_o).$$

Figure 3.20 is a schematic illustration of the API RP 43 flow tests in terms of k_o, k_p, and k_i.

A CFE near 1.0 indicates a relatively clean, undamaged perforation, and a CFE < 1.0 indicates a dirty or damaged perforation. Published CFE values for most perforating guns range from 0.65 to 0.85. Visual observations of API perforation targets suggest that the crushed zone around the perforation has a thickness of about 0.5 in. Back-calculated permeability of the crushed zone using CFE values of 0.65–0.85 ranges from 10% to 35% of the original formation permeability. Figure 3.21 shows an approximate relation that can be used to determine the permeability of a 0.5-in. crushed zone from a reported CFE value.

Experiments conducted with API targets show that CFE increases gradually with backflush through the perforation, finally reaching a stabilized value as reported on the API form. The residual crushed zone that may exist in the target core after backflush is illustrated in figure 3.22. The backflush performed in the API test consists of flowing kerosene at 200 psi pressure differential until the CFE stabilizes. Figure 3.23 illustrates the observed trend of increasing CFE with increasing backflush pressure until a 200 psi differential is reached. Complete perforation cleanup has been observed both in API backflow tests and in actual wells. It is uncertain, however, whether the backflow in the API test that leaves the crushed zone partly intact does simulate the actual flow conditions that exist in a well, particularly a gas well which flows at very high local velocities near the wellbore. It is therefore difficult to assess whether the crushed zone remains, or is washed out during production.

Certain trends are evolving in the practice of perforating, aimed toward achieving flow-effective perforations. These trends, as summarized by Bell (1984) are

1. selecting charges and guns that ensure deeper penetration
2. preferring charges with high reported CFE
3. increasing shot density, not less than 4 shots per foot and up to 8 and even 12 shots per foot in gravel-packed completions
4. perforating at substantially higher underbalance pressure and maximizing initial flow rate across perforations

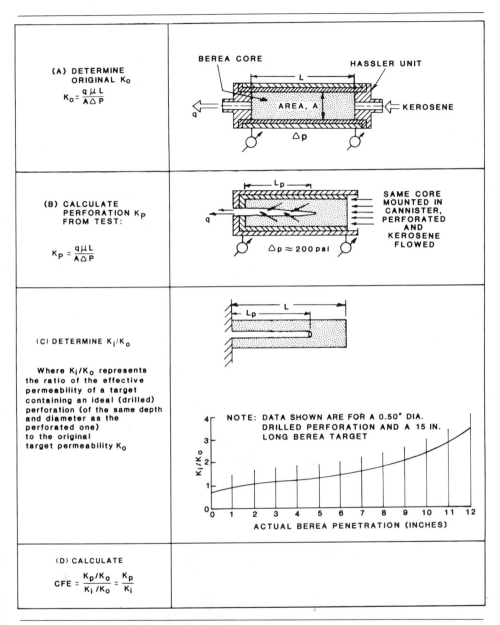

Figure 3.20 Flow tests to quantify perforation effect according to API Recommended Practice 43. After Bell 1972, fig. 20, by permission of the SPE-AIME, © 1972 SPE-AIME.

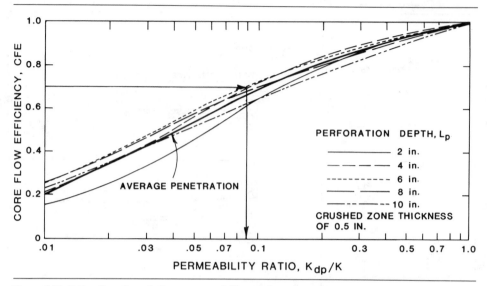

Figure 3.21 Estimation of crushed-zone permeability relative to formation permeability in the region surrounding a perforation. After Klotz et al. 1974, fig. 6, by permission of the SPE-AIME, © 1974 SPE-AIME.

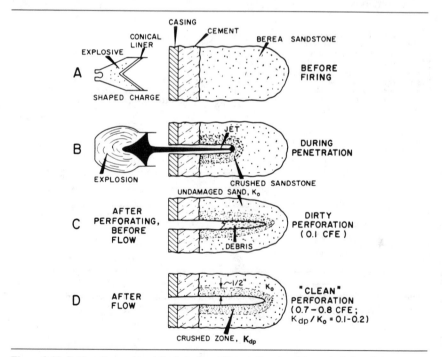

Figure 3.22 Perforation and backflush during API test. Reprinted by permission of the SPE-AIME from Bell 1984, fig. 2, © 1984 SPE-AIME.

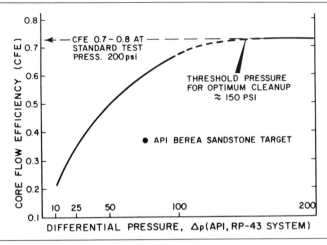

Figure 3.23 Core flow efficiency versus backflush pressure. Reprinted by permission of the SPE-AIME from Bell 1984, fig. 1, © 1984 SPE-AIME.

5. if the perforated interval is long and heterogenous, perforating and backflowing the low-permeability intervals of a production zone first, and thereafter perforating and flowing from higher permeability intervals

Several authors (Locke 1981; McLeod 1983) suggest that the effect of a crushed zone can be quantified as a skin factor and included in IPR calculations. McLeod used a model of a "horizontal microwell" with formation damage around it as an analogy to a perforation surrounded by a crushed zone. His model gives the following relation for steady-state skin due to a reduced crushed-zone permeability:

$$s_{dp} = \left(\frac{k}{k_{dp}} - \frac{k}{k_a}\right)\left(\frac{12h_p}{nL_p}\right)\ln(r_{dp}/r_p), \qquad (3.31)$$

where

k = formation permeability (md),
k_{dp} = crushed-zone permeability (md),
k_a = damage-zone permeability near the wellbore (md),
r_{dp} = crushed-zone radius (in.),
r_p = perforation radius (in.),
L_p = depth of penetration (in.),
h_p = perforated interval (ft),
n = total number of perforations.

The parameters in equation (3.31) are also illustrated in figure E3.8b. Using equation (3.31) requires knowledge of many parameters that we cannot estimate with any certainty: actual damage-zone permeability, effective number of shots, actual depth of penetration, and permeability of the crushed zone around the perforations. It is therefore difficult to see the practical usefulness of such a complicated model, other than for preparing sensitivity analysis.

Part of the rate-dependent skin measured in wells is attributed to the effect of the perforations. Several authors reported changes in rate-dependent skin resulted from changes in perforating programs. McLeod (1983) used such observations to substantiate a model that predicts rate-dependent skin due to perforations. In fact, he suggested that most of the rate-dependent skin in gas wells results from high-velocity flow through the crushed zone around perforations. By analogy to a damaged well, he developed an equation for calculating the high-velocity flow term D_{dp}:

$$D_{dp} = 3.84 \times 10^{-15} \left(\frac{kh\gamma_g}{\mu_g} \right) \left(\frac{\beta_{dp}}{n^2 L_p^2 r_p} \right),$$
(3.32)

where β_{dp} is the turbulence factor of the crushed zone and can be estimated by

$$\beta_{dp} = 2.73 \times 10^{10} k_{dp}^{-1.1045}.$$
(3.33)

The other parameters in equation (3.32) are as in equation (3.31). Example 3.8 illustrates the procedure for evaluating the effect of the crushed zone around perforations (when all the necessary parameters can be guessed or estimated).

EXAMPLE 3.8 APPLYING MCLEOD'S (1983) CRUSHED-ZONE MODEL TO ANALYZE PRODUCTION DATA OF A HIGH-PERMEABILITY GAS WELL

Consider the well McLeod 1-A, presented in example 2.8. The well has been tested, and the test points are as indicated in fig. E3.8a. The well produces from a high-permeability formation. Additional reservoir and well data are given in table E3.8a.

Over a one-year period the McLeod 1-A was tested five different times at rates that varied from 4.85 to 8.08 MMscf/D. During the year's production, depletion had claimed 55% of the initial reservoir pressure, from 12,315 psia to 5,565 psia. There are no records on recompletion, stimulation, or workover jobs that might have been conducted during this period, and therefore it is assumed that except for depletion, the status of the wellbore is unchanged.

Use the McLeod (1983) model to predict the skin and the IPR of the well from the given data and compare the prediction with the actual well test data. Comment on the assumptions used in the predictions.

SOLUTION

The solution of this example follows essentially the procedure presented by McLeod, with additional comments. The model of a single perforation is illustrated in figure E3.8b. It separates formation damage into two distinct regions, the near-wellbore region and the near-perforation region (crushed zone) and calculates the contribution of each zone separately.

EXAMPLE 3.8 continued

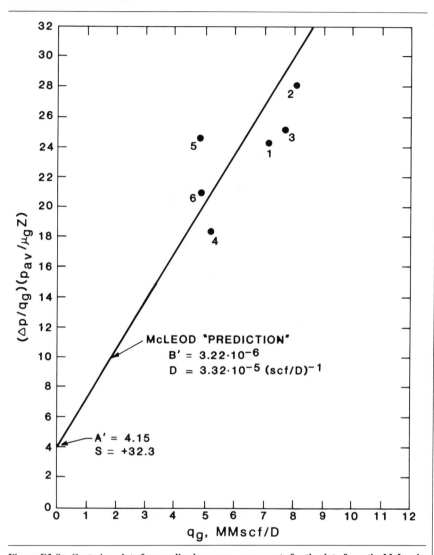

Figure E3.8a Cartesian plot of normalized pressure versus rate for the data from the McLeod 1-A gas well.

EXAMPLE 3.8 continued

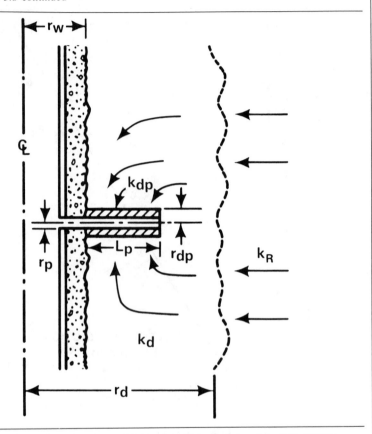

Figure E3.8b McLeod's perforation model. Reprinted by permission of the SPE-AIME from McLeod 1983, fig. 1, pp. 31–39, © 1983 SPE-AIME.

Perforation-skin factor due to perforation-flow convergence can be estimated, according to Harris (1966), based on perforation penetration, shot density, etc. Table E3.8a gives a perforation depth of penetration $L_p = 9$ in. without comment as to how it was calculated. As shown in the previous example, compressive strength and/or effective stress may play an important role in the actual penetration depth. In general, however, skin due solely to flow convergence to the perforation is of little significance in high-permeability wells. McLeod calculates a value for perforation skin of $s_p = +0.45$. Using figure 3.17 with $L_{pa} = 9(9.5/9) = 9.5$ in., we obtain $s_p = -0.25$.

Table E3.8a reports two arbitrary assumptions regarding the formation damage around the wellbore: (1) Damaged permeability is 25% of formation permeability; and (2) the radius of the damage is 1.375 ft, (i.e., the damage penetrates 1 ft beyond the wellbore). The formation-damage skin, according to these assumptions, is

EXAMPLE 3.8 continued

Table E3.8a Well Data for the McLeod A-1 Gas Well

Net pay h	26 ft
Drainage radius r_e	1320 ft
Wellbore radius r_w	4.5 in. (0.375 ft)
Initial reservoir pressure p_i	10,177 psia
Reservoir permeability k	200 md
Reservoir temperature T_R	245°F
Initial gas Z-factor	1.415
Initial gas viscosity μ_g	0.035 cp
Perforation shot density	2 shots/ft
Perforation phasing	180°
Perforation penetration L_p	9.0 in.
Perforation tunnel diameter	0.38 in.
Radius of formation damage (assumed) r_a	1.375 ft
Crushed-zone thickness (assumed)	0.5 in.
Damage-zone permeability (assumed) k_a	50 md
Crushed-zone permeability (assumed) k_{dp}	5 md

$$s_a = (k/k_a - 1)\ln(r_a/r_w)$$

$$= (200/50 - 1)\ln(1.375/0.375)$$

$$= +3.9.$$

The somewhat arbitrary choice of damage-zone radius and permeability may not seem important in the damage-skin calculation. It should be emphasized, however, that formation-damage assumptions are not universal and should be adjusted to the specific conditions in each well or field.

Additional expected pressure drop is due to the compacted (crush) zone immediately surrounding the perforation. According to observation of perforated samples in the laboratory, McLeod suggests that the radius of this damage zone is about 0.5 in. Back-calculating permeability from core flow efficiency (CFE), in the standard API test, he also suggests that the permeability of this region is on the average one-tenth of the damage-zone permeability, or $k_{dp} = 0.1 k_a = 0.1(0.25k) = 0.1(0.25)(200) = 5$ md. Table E3.8b, (table 6 in McLeod's paper), relates CFE and the back-calculated permeability around the perforations to wellbore conditions during the perforating operation.

The skin due to the crushed zone surrounding the ⅜-in. perforation is, according to equation (3.31),

$$s_{dp} = \left(\frac{12h}{nL_p}\right)\left(\frac{k}{k_{dp}} - \frac{k}{k_a}\right)\ln\left(\frac{r_{dp}}{r_p}\right)$$

$$= \left[\frac{12(26)}{(52)(9)}\right]\left(\frac{200}{5} - \frac{200}{50}\right)\ln\left(\frac{0.19 + 0.5}{0.19}\right)$$

$$= +30.95.$$

EXAMPLE 3.8 continued

Table E3.8b Typical Core Flow Efficiencies for Perforating Conditions and the Corresponding Crushed-Zone Permeabilities

API test		Perforating conditions		
CFE	Perforator	Fluid	Pressure	k_{dp}/k
0.3	Average	High solids	$+\Delta p$	0.01–0.03
0.4	Average	Low solids mud	$+\Delta p$	0.02–0.04
0.5	Poor	Unfiltered salt water	$+\Delta p$	0.04–0.06
0.7	Average	Filtered salt water	$+\Delta p$	0.08–0.16
0.8	Average	Filtered salt water	$-\Delta p$	0.15–0.25
0.9	Best	Clean, nondamaging fluid Best techniques available	$-\Delta p$	0.30–0.50
1.0	Ideal	Clean, nondamaging	$-\Delta p$	1.00–1.00

Note: $+\Delta p$ = wellbore pressure > formation pressure
$-\Delta p$ = wellbore pressure < formation pressure
k_{dp}/k = ratio of the permeability of a perforation's compacted zone to the permeability of a core before perforating (from API testing)
Source: Reprinted, by permission, from H. O. McLeod, Jr.: "The Effect of perforating conditions on Well Performance," *J. Pet. Tech.* (Jan. 1983); after Klotz et al. 1973.

McLeod adds the steady-state skin factors due to laminar-type flow, to give

$$s = s_a + s_d + s_{dp}$$

$$= 0.45 + 3.9 + 30.95$$

$$= +35.3.$$

In section 3.8 it is shown that the composite skin factor can be obtained by merely adding skin factors only in cases where the entire effective pay zone is perforated. Apparently, this is the case in this well.

Turbulence parameter D For the example well, McLeod suggests that the high-velocity flow of gas through the zone surrounding the perforations dominates the rate-dependent skin and therefore neglects the other effects. Based on the β correlation he gives, which is slightly different from the β correlation in equation (3.28),

$$\beta_{dp} = 2.6 \times 10^{10} k_{dp}^{-1.2}$$

$$= 2.6 \times 10^{10}(5)^{-1.2}$$

$$= 3.77 \times 10^{9} \, \text{ft}^{-1},$$

EXAMPLE 3.8 continued

resulting in

$$D_{dp} = 3.84 \times 10^{-15} \left(\frac{kh\gamma_g}{\mu_g}\right) \frac{\beta_{dp}\gamma_g}{n^2 L_p^2 r_p}$$

$$= 3.84 \times 10^{-15} \left[\frac{(200)(26)(0.635)}{(0.035)}\right] \times \left[\frac{3.77 \times 10^9}{(52)^2 (9.0)^2 (0.375/2)}\right]$$

$$= 3.285 \times 10^{-5} \, (\text{scf/D})^{-1}.$$

To assess the assumption that D_{dp} is much larger than the reservoir contribution D_R and the damage-zone contribution D_a, we calculate

$$D_R = 2.222 \times 10^{-18} \frac{\gamma_g kh}{\mu_g h_p^2} \beta_R (1/r_a - 1/r_e),$$

and for the near-wellbore zone

$$D_a = 2.222 \times 10^{-18} \frac{\gamma_g kh}{\mu_g h_p^2} \beta_a (1/r_w - 1/r_a).$$

From reservoir permeability

$$\beta_R = 2.6 \times 10^{10} k^{-1.2}$$

$$= 2.6 \times 10^{10} (200)^{-1.2}$$

$$= 4.51 \times 10^7 \, \text{ft}^{-1}$$

and

$$D_R = 2.222 \times 10^{-18} \frac{(0.635)(200)(26)}{(0.035)(26)^2} (4.51 \times 10^7)(1/1.375 - 1/1320)$$

$$= 1.02 \times 10^{-8} \, (\text{scf/D})^{-1}.$$

In the damaged zone near the wellbore,

$$\beta_a = 2.6 \times 10^{10} k_a^{-1.2}$$

$$= 2.6 \times 10^{10} (50)^{-1.2}$$

$$= 2.38 \times 10^8 \, \text{ft}^{-1},$$

which gives

EXAMPLE 3.8 continued

$$D_a = 2.222 \times 10^{-18} \frac{(0.635)(200)(26)}{(0.035)(26)^2}(2.38 \times 10^8)(1/0.375 - 1/1.375)$$

$$= 1.43 \times 10^{-7} (\text{scf/D})^{-1}.$$

The total high-velocity flow term, then, is

$$D = 1.02 \times 10^{-8} + 1.43 \times 10^{-7} + 3.285 \times 10^{-5}$$

$$= 3.32 \times 10^{-5} (\text{scf/D})^{-1}.$$

In this particular well, D_R and D_a are several orders of magnitude smaller than D_{dp} and do not affect the rate-dependent skin.

The quadratic IPR equation can be written

$$\frac{p_R - p_{wf}}{q_g}\left(\frac{p_{av}}{\mu_g Z}\right) = A' + B'q_g,$$

where

$$A' = \frac{T}{1.407kh}[\ln(r_e/r_w) - 0.75 + s],$$

$$B' = \frac{T}{1.407kh}D,$$

This equation form is advantageous for plotting test data that include depletion effects.

Substituting well data, s, and D gives

$$A' = \frac{(250 + 460)}{1.407(200)(26)}[\ln(1320/0.375) - 0.75 + 35.3]$$

$$= 4.15,$$

$$B' = \frac{(250 + 460)}{1.407(200)(26)}(3.32 \times 10^{-5})$$

$$= 3.22 \times 10^{-6}.$$

Figure E3.8a shows the plot of the IPR equation as predicted by the McLeod model. The straight-line is shown, together with the actual test data. The five test data exhibit considerable scatter, and the predicted line represents a kind of best fit.

Several comments should be made regarding the test and the solution:

1. Test data on the well can be fitted to match McLeod's model where a permanent crushed zone surrounding each individual perforation dominates the skin effect.

EXAMPLE 3.8 continued

2. Recalling example 2.7, the test data can also be fitted to a model where only wellbore formation damage dominates the skin effect.
3. It is obvious that the actual situation is somewhere between the two models.
4. In general, using a skin model to predict well performance requires several arbitrary assumptions that depend very much on the particular experience of the engineer.

The perforation effect is magnified if the perforations penetrate into a damaged zone surrounding the wellbore. Large pressure losses across the damaged zone are reduced if the perforations pass beyond the damaged zone into the undamaged formation. Since damaged-zone thickness is difficult if not impossible to measure, this effect on perforation skin is not usually quantified.

In review, the effect of perforations on well performance is difficult to quantify using simplified models with analytical, analog, or numerical solutions. The skin factor is a convenient method for quantifying perforation effects, as was first suggested by Muskat in 1943. The main parameters related to perforation skin are depth of penetration, density, phasing, shot diameter, crushed-zone permeability, wellbore pressure conditions during perforation, and formation damage surrounding the wellbore. Depth of penetration and perforation density are usually the most important factors, although other effects may dominate in particular wells.

In relation to the crushed zone, it is felt that more investigation is needed to assess the effect of the crushed zone around the perforation and to substantiate that it is (1) permanent (2) a substantial impediment to flow, and (3) the dominating region regarding high-velocity flow restriction. Particularly, it appears that more field investigations are needed to study the effect of the various parameters on the perforation effectiveness of actual wells.

3.6   SAND CONTROL CONSIDERATIONS. Oil and gas are produced in many areas of the world from unconsolidated or poorly consolidated sandstones. In such formations, sand may be produced with the fluids—either in surges or gradually over longer periods of time. It is well known that as fluids flow through a porous material, drag forces are created along the path of flow. Depending on the degree of natural intergranular cementation, compaction, intergranular friction, and cohesion of particles making up the porous material, flowing fluid may carry with it considerable quantities of loose and friable sand grains. In general, high flow rates result in larger quantities of sand production. Sand production is undesirable for many reasons, the most important being erosion damage and plugging of the well and surface production equipment. It is therefore important to understand the conditions that promote sand production and the measures that prevent it. Both sand production and sand control are related to the productivity and the production rate of the well.

Figure 3.24 illustrates sand production during a four-rate flow test. Sand production is monitored by a surface sonic device that counts the impingement of

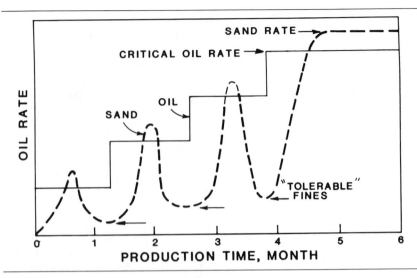

Figure 3.24 Sand production during a four-rate test.

sand grains on an in-line probe (Mullins et al. 1974). Output from the device reflects the kinetic energy of the entrained solids, and when combined with measurement of fluid velocity, it determines the rate of sand production and its concentration in the flow stream. The sand production record in figure 3.24 indicates that a new sand production peak occurs after each increase in oil rate. The peak is followed by a decline to a minimum level that is essentially sand-free production. The minimum solids level recorded results from small fines carried by the oil that do not support any load in the formation and do not usually cause damage to the system hardware. While at the three lowest oil rates sand production reaches a peak and drops off to essentially sand-free production, at the highest oil rate, sand production continues indefinitely. This oil rate at which sand production becomes uncontrollable, is called the critical sand-free oil rate.

A popular model for explaining such field observations is the sand arch model (Hall and Harrisberger 1970). It is substantiated also by laboratory experiments that indicate that stable sand arches are created around the perforations in poorly cemented sandstones at oil rates below a critical value (Bratli and Risnes 1981). Up to the critical rate, a sequence of increasing flow rates causes the formation of stable arches of increasing size, each arch corresponding to a particular flow rate. After the critical oil rate is reached, a stable arch can no longer be sustained and sand production becomes uncontrollable. To stop sand production, then, oil production must be reduced significantly below the critical value to allow arches to reform, after which the oil rate can be increased again to a value somewhat below the critical rate. The model appears to match observed field performance of sand production, such as the tests reported by Risnes et al. (1982).

The arch model is valid for poorly consolidated sands. Different models are used to explain sand production in consolidated sandstones. Here, flow erosion is the destructive force, creating cavities in the rock that periodically collapse and create free sand production. Several causes increase the tendency of sand production. The most important are

1. decline of reservoir pressure which increases the overburden that must be supported by the sand grains, thereby weakening the cementation of the grains
2. increasing water production that dissolves and destroys the intergranular cementing material. (Also decreases the capillary forces that tend to retain sand particles together)
3. formation damage that increases the pressure gradient near the wellbore, and thus increases the destabilizing stress on sand grains

In most cases the field operator first becomes aware of sand problems during the initial testing of the first discovery well. Usually the test string sands up, which may make it difficult to conclude the test. In spite of the evidence of sand problems during the test, the presence of sand alone can not reveal the nature of sand production. Special tests such as the one illustrated in figure 3.24, are needed to gain more information and to establish the critical sand-free oil rate. These tests can be combined with empirical correlations to correlate density and sonic logs to mechanical properties and to sand production tendencies (Stein et al. 1974; Stein 1976).

Operators have four alternatives to control sand production:

1. *Reduce producing oil and gas rates* below the critical rate for sand production. This approach requires identification of sand production characteristics and a test to establish the critical production rate. In addition it requires special completion and production practices, including: (1) high perforations density—8 to 12 shots per foot—(2) long perforation intervals; (3) perforating only selected intervals with high degree of sand cementation; (4) completing and treating the wells with nondamaging fluids that do not reduce the stability of the sandstone; (5) avoiding sudden flow rate changes or "surge flow."

2. *Prevent sand production mechanically* by a screen or gravel pack thereby retaining formation sand in place around the wellbore.

3. *Chemically consolidate the formation sand near the wellbore* using resinous materials. The resin glues sand grains together, forming a stable, consolidated, permeable rock mass near the wellbore. If successful, the resin should not impair permeability by more than about 10%, although considerable damage may result if the resin is incompatible with clays and minerals in the formation, or if the injection sequence was not performed properly. Details of sand consolidation techniques are described in many publications, such as ones by Strohm et al. (1967), Hamby and Richardson (1968), and Richardson and Hamby (1970).

4. *Inject resin-coated gravel into the perforation* to pack and stabilize the perforations. The gravel is sized to hold back the formation, and the coating resin bonds the gravel grains together in the perforations (Knapp et al. 1977; Saunders and McKinzie 1979).

Numerous publications, describing the preceding approaches for sand control, have been presented since the 1930s. Review papers by Tausch and Corley (1958), and Suman et al. (1983) list most of these publications.

Based on field experience, operators usually develop a particular preference for the method of controlling sand in their particular region. Mechanical sand retention is by far the most common sand control method. Figure 3.25 illustrates the conventional methods for mechanical sand retention. Either gravel pack (case a or b) is used to retain formation sand (with a screen to retain the gravel), or a screen liner (case c) is used directly to retain the formation sand (without gravel). Gravel pack is the more commonly used method. Since it was first introduced in oil and gas wells in the 1930s, the art of gravel packing has advanced considerably. Studies of proper gravel size, improvements in design and manufacturing of screens, development of efficient methods and a multitude of tools to place the gravel, all have established the present state of the art that can ensure durable sand-free production without significant hindrance to the well's productivity. In particular cases, such as the Frigg gas field offshore Norway, where sand is uniform, clean (without clays), and consists of large-size particles, a screen liner is sufficient to provide efficient sand control (Barril and Gay 1983).

Generally, mechanical retention of sand particles is achieved by either bridging or filter-size retention (Stein 1983), both illustrated in figure 3.26. Bridging is the ability of sand grains to deposit across porous materials or screen openings in such a manner that only fluid can pass through the connected openings. Large particles are retained first and continue to retain small particles, building out in a pyramid-like structure that eventually creates an effective control for sand production. Openings in the sand layer that formed from bridging across the gravel pack, and the openings in the gravel pack itself are large enough to allow the small clay particles entrained by reservoir fluid to pass through without plugging of flow passages.

Filter-size retention is accomplished by preventing all individual sand particles from entering the pores. This mechanism requires that screen opening size or gravel pore size be smaller than the smallest grain size of the formation rock. For sand retention purposes, filter-size retention is safer than bridging, but it may create problems of excessive flow restriction and possible plugging by clay particles. In review, an effective sand retention measure holds the sand particles in place but allows small impurities, usually suspended in reservoir fluids, to pass without plugging.

A general observation in relation to sand retention is that large uniform formation particles can be effectively retained by a properly sized screen, whereas small nonuniform formation particles can be effectively retained only by uniform, properly sized gravel. This observation explains the distinction between use of screen retention in uniform sand and gravel pack in nonuniform sand. The whole idea behind gravel packing is that the gravel may be sized to effectively retain the formation sand and the screen may be sized to retain the gravel.

There are two methods of arranging the gravel in front of the pay zone, inside-casing pack and underreamed-casing pack. Inside-casing pack is obtained by placing gravel in the annular space between the casing and a screen installed inside the casing opposite the perforations (see case a in fig. 3.25). The underreamed-casing pack technique is based on underreaming the casing in the pay section to obtain an openhole interval. The gravel is placed between the sandface of the open hole and a screen is suspended in the center of the borehole (see case b in fig. 3.25). The underreamed arrangement is favorable from a productivity point of view, since it eliminates flow

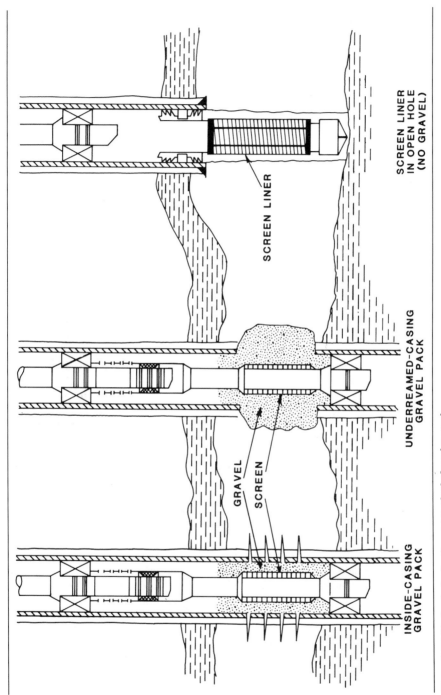

INSIDE-CASING
GRAVEL PACK

UNDERREAMED-CASING
GRAVEL PACK

SCREEN LINER
IN OPEN HOLE
(NO GRAVEL)

GRAVEL

SCREEN

SCREEN LINER

Figure 3.25 Mechanical retention as a method of sand control.

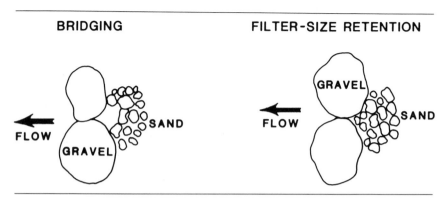

Figure 3.26 Two mechanisms of mechanical retention.

restriction in the perforation and actually increases the wellbore radius. A drawback with underreaming, however, is that only single-zone completions can be managed. Also, openhole completions (underreamed-gravel pack and screen without gravel) reduce the capability of workover operations—e.g., squeezing the lower production interval in case of water breakthrough from water coning. A tradeoff between inside-casing pack, which is mechanically reliable, and underreamed-casing pack, which results in minimum restriction to flow, must be evaluated for each well individually. The main parameter is usually productivity loss, and if the additional skin created by inside-casing pack is not severe, then this more stable mechanical arrangement can be chosen.

Observing the flow path from the reservoir into the wellbore for an inside-casing pack (fig. 3.27), it is obvious that, in relation to a regular cased well, additional pressure losses occur through the gravel-packed perforations and screen slots. Flow tests with commercial screens show that pressure losses through screen slots are negligible, unless they become plugged (Penberthy and Cope 1979). Pressure-loss calculations suggest that the effect of the gravel in the annulus between the screen and the casing is also rather small (Williams 1972), and thus, the only significant pressure loss occurs in the gravel-packed perforations. Further, the calculations show that flow through gravel-packed perforations, when expressed by the Forchheimer equation, is dominated by high-velocity flow.

It was observed that properly packed perforations exhibit relatively small resistance to flow. This resistance increases significantly if the gravel is mixed with formation sand or is invaded by small formation fines. Recent progress in gravel-packing techniques has concentrated primarily on achieving and maintaining durable plugging-free perforations (Sparlin 1969; Penberthy and Cope 1979). Measures to achieve this objective include:

1. applying properly sized gravel
2. shooting large-diameter perforations to allow effective placement of gravel without bridging
3. cleaning and washing the perforations to remove debris from the perforation tunnel and from behind the casing

313

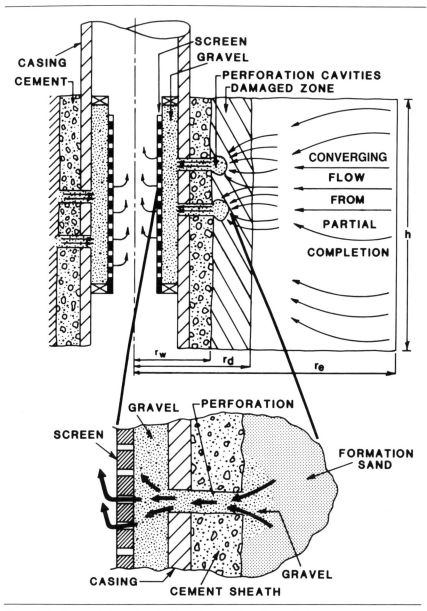

Figure 3.27 Flow path through an inside-casing gravel-pack completion.

4. ensuring effective transport and placement of gravel in the perforations while avoiding mixing with formation sand (achieved by suspending the gravel in viscous fluid [800 cp], using extremely high gravel concentration [15 lb/gal], and pumping it at a low rate [$\frac{1}{4}$–$\frac{1}{2}$ barrels per minute])
5. prepacking the perforations in an attempt to fill cavities behind the casing with gravel
6. pressurizing and squeezing gravel in the perforation to restress loosened sand
7. maintaining clean wellbore fluids throughout the gravel-packing operation.

Applying the preceding measures, it is reasonable to assume that flow in the perforation tunnels is controlled by the permeability and the high-velocity co-efficient of the gravel. Permeabilities and β_G coefficients of commercial gravels are listed in table 3.5. The size of gravel is expressed in mesh units. The mesh units are related to the opening size of a standard series of screens (sieves). Mesh unit is the number of openings per linear inch, counting from the center of any wire in the sieve to a point exactly 1-in. distant. Table 3.6, adopted from the *Chemical Engineers Handbook* (Perry 1963) correlates mesh numbers with actual sieve opening. Gravel permeability data in table 3.5 were adopted from measurements by Sparlin (1974) and Gurley et al. (1977). By convention, a 20–40-mesh commercial gravel passes through a 20-mesh sieve and is retained by a 40-mesh sieve. This size gravel has a typical permeability of 120 darcy (120,000 md) and a β_G of 3×10^4 ft^{-1}. To quantify the effect of a gravel packing on productivity, we will express the pressure loss in packed perforations in terms of a skin factor.
    Applying Darcy's law for linear flow in packed perforations gives, for the steady-state skin term due to gravel pack for both oil and gas wells,

$$s_G = 96 \frac{(k/k_G)hL_p}{d_p^2 n}. \qquad (3.34)$$

Table 3.5 Commercial Gravel Data

Sand/Gravel Size (in.)		U.S. Mesh Size	Approx. Median Dia. (in.)	Porosity (%)	Permeability (md)	$\beta_G = bk_G^{-a}$	
						a	b
0.006	0.017	40/100	0.012				
0.008	0.017	40/70	0.013				
0.010	0.017	40/60	0.014	32–39	1.2×10^5–1.7×10^5	1.6	2.12×10^{12}
0.017	0.033	20/40	0.025	35–40		1.54	3.37×10^{12}
0.023	0.047	16/30	0.035				
0.033	0.066	12/20	0.050				
0.039	0.066	12/18	0.053				
0.033	0.079	10/20	0.056	32–40	5×10^5–6.5×10^5	1.34	8.4×10^{11}
0.047	0.079	10/16	0.063	35–40	17×10^5–20×10^5		
0.066	0.094	8/12	0.080	36–40	17×10^5–	1.24	5.31×10^{11}
0.079	0.132	6/10	0.106	–42			

Table 3.6 Standard Sieve Designations

Mesh		Sieve Opening		Mesh		Sieve Opening	
U.S. std.	Tyler	(in.)	(mm)	U.S. std.	Tyler	(in.)	(mm)
2½		0.315	8.00	25		0.0280	0.710
	2½	0.312	7.925		24	0.0276	0.701
3		0.265	6.73	30	28	0.0232	0.589
	3	0.263	6.68	35		0.0197	0.500
3½		0.223	5.66		32	0.0195	0.495
	3½	0.221	5.613	40		0.0165	0.420
4		0.187	4.76		35	0.0164	0.417
	4	0.185	4.699	45	42	0.0138	0.351
5		0.157	4.00	50		0.0117	0.297
	5	0.156	3.962		48	0.0116	0.295
6		0.132	3.36	60		0.0098	0.250
	6	0.131	3.327		60	0.0097	0.246
7		0.111	2.83	70		0.0083	0.210
	7	0.110	2.794		65	0.0082	0.208
8		0.0937	2.38	80		0.0070	0.177
	8	0.093	2.362		80	0.0069	0.175
10		0.0787	2.00	100		0.0059	0.149
	9	0.078	1.981		100	0.0058	0.147
12		0.0661	1.68	120	115	0.0049	0.124
	10	0.065	1.651	140	150	0.0041	0.104
14		0.0555	1.41	170	170	0.0035	0.088
	12	0.055	1.397	200	200	0.0029	0.074
16		0.0469	1.19	230	250	0.0024	0.062
	14	0.046	1.168	270	270	0.0021	0.053
18		0.0394	1.00	325	325	0.0017	0.044
	16	0.0390	0.991	400	400	0.0015	0.037
20		0.0331	0.840				
	20	0.0328	0.833				

Source: J. H. Perry, Ed., *Chemical Engineers Handbook*, 4th ed. (New York: McGraw Hill Book Company 1963).

Similarly, according to Forchheimer's equation, the high-velocity-flow effect is, for gas wells,

$$D_{Gg} = 2.45 \times 10^{-13} \frac{\gamma_g k h L_p}{\mu_g d_p^4 n^2} \beta_G, \tag{3.35}$$

and for oil wells,

$$D_{Go} = 1.80 \times 10^{-11} \frac{B_o \rho_o k h L_p \beta_G}{\mu_o d_p^4 n^2}, \tag{3.36}$$

where β_G is related to permeability by a correlation suggested by Cooke (1973)

$$\beta_G = bk_G^{-a}, \tag{3.37}$$

where b and a (for k_G and β_G expressed in field units) are listed in table 3.5.

Brown (1984, p.134) suggested, without giving reference, the use of $b = 1.47 \times 10^7$ and $a = 0.55$ for all sizes of gravel. The variables in equations (3.35) and (3.36) are; L_p = perforation depth (in.), d_p = perforation diameter (in.), n = total number of perforations, k_G = gravel-pack permeability (md), kh = formation permeability × thickness (md-ft), β_G = gravel high-velocity-flow coefficient, μ = viscosity (cp), B_o = oil FVF (bbl/STB), and ρ_o = oil density (lb/ft^3). The empirical correlation in equation (3.37) is valid only for 100% liquid or gas saturation. In the presence of a second phase, for example water in case of gas production, β_G values will be much higher.

Geertsma (1974) discussed the effect of liquid saturation on the β_G factor in gas–liquid systems. He used data from various sources to relate β_G to the water saturation. He suggested, for dry gravel,

$$\beta_G = 1.746 \times 10^7 \times k_G^{-0.5}\phi^{-1.5}, \tag{3.38}$$

and for wet gravel

$$\beta_G = \frac{1.746 \times 10^7 k_G^{0.5}\phi^{-1.5}}{k_{rg}^{0.5}(1 - S_w)^{1.5}}, \tag{3.39}$$

where k_{rg} is the gas relative permeability at S_w water saturation. Table 3.5 lists β_G values for the most useful gravel sizes. Example 3.9 illustrates the calculation of gravel-pack pressure losses for a Gulf Coast well.

EXAMPLE 3.9 PRESSURE LOSSES IN PACKED PERFORATIONS

A Gulf Coast well, OCS-G-X4, is located in the Vermelion block and produces from a high-permeability Miocene sandstone. The well started to sand up after eight months of sand-free production. Analysis of formation sand (see example 3.10) concluded that 20–40 mesh gravel is suitable for controlling sand production. Figure E3.9 illustrates the proposed gravel-pack design. Table E3.9 gives relevant reservoir rock and fluid data for OCS-G-X4. Predict the steady-state and high-velocity flow components of skin due to the proposed gravel pack.

SOLUTION

The IPR equation for an undersaturated oil well with gravel pack is

$$q_o = \frac{kh(p_R - p_{wf})}{141.2\mu_o B_o[\ln(r_e/r_w) - 0.75 + s + Dq_o]},$$

EXAMPLE 3.9 continued

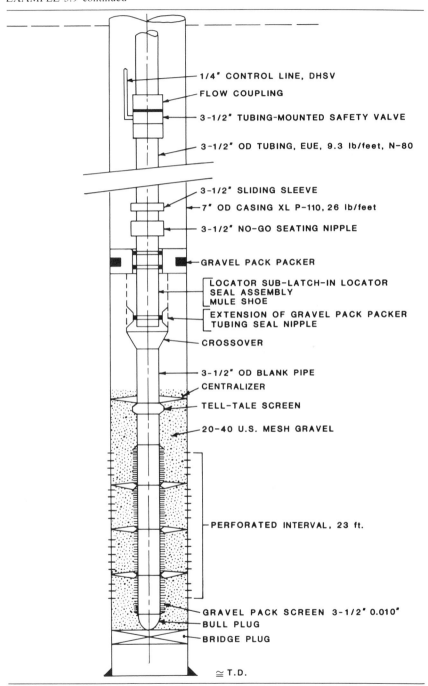

1/4″ CONTROL LINE, DHSV
FLOW COUPLING
3-1/2″ TUBING-MOUNTED SAFETY VALVE
3-1/2″ OD TUBING, EUE, 9.3 lb/feet, N-80

3-1/2″ SLIDING SLEEVE
7″ OD CASING XL P-110, 26 lb/feet
3-1/2″ NO-GO SEATING NIPPLE
GRAVEL PACK PACKER
LOCATOR SUB-LATCH-IN LOCATOR
SEAL ASSEMBLY
MULE SHOE
EXTENSION OF GRAVEL PACK PACKER
TUBING SEAL NIPPLE
CROSSOVER

3-1/2″ OD BLANK PIPE
CENTRALIZER
TELL-TALE SCREEN

20-40 U.S. MESH GRAVEL

PERFORATED INTERVAL, 23 ft.

GRAVEL PACK SCREEN 3-1/2″ 0.010″
BULL PLUG
BRIDGE PLUG

≅ T.D.

Figure E3.9 Gravel-pack completion of the OGS-G-X4 oil well.

EXAMPLE 3.9 continued

Table E3.9 Reservoir and Well Data for the OCS-G-X4 Well

Total (producing) thickness h	23 ft
Reservoir permeability k	578 md
Initial reservoir pressure p_i	6200 psia
Reservoir temperature T	254°F
Oil gravity γ_{API}	35°
Gas gravity γ_g	0.75 (air = 1)
Producing (initial) gas/oil ratio R	1100 scf/STB
Bubble-point pressure p_b	5820 psia
Initial oil viscosity μ_o	0.310 cp
Bubble-point oil viscosity μ_{ob}	0.301 cp
Initial oil FVF, B_{oi}	1.636 bbl/STB
Bubble-point oil FVF, B_{ob}	1.644 bbl/STB
Casing outer diameter	7.0 in.
Tubing outer diameter	3.5 in.
Perforation density	8 shot/ft
Perforation diameter d_p	0.5 in.
Calculated perforation penetration L_p	6 in.
Gravel size	20–40 mesh
Average gravel diameter d_{G50}	0.025 in.
Gravel permeability k_G	120,000 md
Screen size	0.010 in.

where s and D are assumed, for this example, to be only a result of the gravel pack; i.e., $s = s_G$ and $D = D_G$. Steady-state skin is given by

$$s_G = 96 \frac{(k/k_G)hL_p}{d_p^2 n}$$

$$= 96 \frac{(578/120,000)(23)(6)}{(0.5)^2(8 \times 23)}$$

$$= +1.39.$$

The high-velocity-flow term D_G is given by

$$D_G = 1.80 \times 10^{-11} \frac{B_o \rho_o k h L_p \beta_G}{\mu_o d_p^4 n^2},$$

where

$$\beta_G = 1.5 \times 10^7 (120,000)^{-0.55}$$

$$= 2.41 \times 10^4 \, \text{ft}^{-1},$$

Stock-tank oil gravity (eq. [1.6]) is

EXAMPLE 3.9 continued

$$\gamma_o = \frac{141.5}{131.5 + 35} = 0.85$$

and reservoir oil density is (eq. [1.27])

$$\rho_o = \frac{62.4(0.85) + 0.0136(0.75)(1100)}{1.632} = 39.27 \, \text{lb/ft}^3$$

which when substituted, together with β_G, in the D_G equation gives

$$D_G = 1.80 \times 10^{-11} \frac{(1.636)(39.27)6(578)(23)(1.5 \times 10^7)(120{,}000)^{-0.55}}{(0.310)(0.5)^4(8 \times 23)^2}$$

$$= 0.00339 \, (\text{STB/D})^{-1}.$$

Since typical producing rates from the Miocene sand range from 2000 to 3000 STB/D, total skin due to the gravel pack is about $1.39 + 2500(0.00339) = +9.9$, or an equivalent pressure drop of

$$\Delta p_s = \frac{141.2 q_o \mu_o B_o}{kh}[s_G + D_G q_o]$$

$$= \frac{141.2(2500)(0.310)(1.636)}{(578)(23)}[1.39 + 0.00339(2500)]$$

$$= 13.5(9.9) = 133.65 \, \text{psi}.$$

Generally, 8 shots per foot is uncommon. To show the impact of lower shot density, the same calculations are made on the basis of 4 shots per foot. It is easy to show that

$$s_G(4 \, \text{shots/ft}) = s_G(8 \, \text{shots/ft}) \times \frac{8}{4}$$

$$= 1.4 \times 2$$

$$= +2.8$$

and

$$D_G(4 \, \text{shots/ft}) = D_G(8 \, \text{shots/ft}) \times \frac{8^2}{4^2}$$

$$= 0.00339 \times (64/16)$$

$$= 0.01356 \, (\text{STB/D})^{-1},$$

EXAMPLE 3.9 continued

giving a total skin of $2.8 + 0.01356(2500) = 36.7$ at 2500 STB/D and an equivalent pressure drop of $13.5(36.7) = 495.45$ psi. The rule of thumb in the Gulf Coast area is that 150 to 300 psi pressure drop through the gravel pack is acceptable. The increase from 4 to 8 shots per foot is necessary.

The main considerations in designing and executing gravel-pack completions include

1. proper sampling and analysis of formation sand to determine average grain size and grain-size distribution
2. optimizing gravel size with respect to mean diameter of the formation sand
3. optimizing screen-opening size to retain the gravel but allow clear passage of clay particles
4. designing effective gravel placement into the perforations and across the screen
5. performing the gravel pack with nondamaging fluids.

Concerning the selection of gravel size, laboratory experiments indicate that gravel permeability is decreased significantly if small amounts of formation particles (sand grains and clay) plug the gravel pack. Saucier (1974) developed a curve where permeability reduction is quantified as a function of the ratio of gravel size to formation-sand grain size (fig. 3.28). Gravel permeability is maintained as long as the gravel size is small enough to retain the formation sand. Increasing gravel size allows formation sand to penetrate and plug the gravel. According to the figure, there exists an optimal gravel size to maintain the initial permeability. The optimum is $d_{G50} = 5\,d_{F50}$ where d_{G50} and d_{F50} are gravel and formation average grain sizes (geometric average). Coarser gravel will be plugged by formation sand, and smaller gravel will be plugged by small formation fines.

The first steps in gravel-pack design are sampling of formation sand and performing sieve analysis to determine the distribution of sand grains. Gravel size is then chosen so that mean gravel diameter d_{mG} is four to six times larger than the formation-sand mean diameter d_{mR} (Saucier 1974; Maly 1971).

Formation sand grains vary considerably from region to region, both in average size and uniformity. Particle size and distribution is determined by laboratory sieve analysis. Samples are crushed, dried, weighed, and sorted through a set of screens with varying opening (mesh size). The U.S. Standard Sieve Series (ASTM Specification E1170) or the Tyler Sieve Series are typically used.

Normally, 35, 60, 120, 230, and 325 U.S. mesh screens are used to analyze formation sands. The material retained by each sieve is weighed and reported versus sieve-opening size or corresponding grain diameter. This gives a representative grain-size distribution that can be interpreted with different statistical methods. Figure 3.29 shows the common ways to present sieve analysis results. As shown in figure 3.29(a) the weight-% or frequency versus grain diameter plot is skewed to the right (i.e., the hump is on the right side, at low grain sizes). If the same data are plotted as weight-% versus log of grain size, as in figure 3.29(b), the distribution appears normal, symmetric about some average grain size. The average grain size defining the point of symmetry (at 50%) is, in fact, the geometric average.

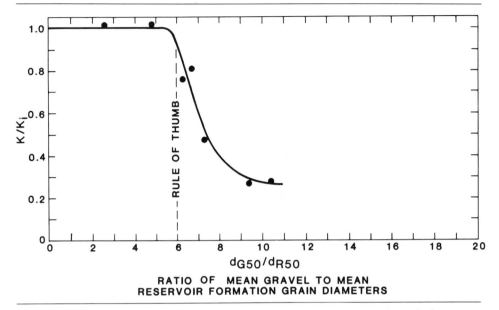

Figure 3.28 Permeability reduction as a function of the ratio of gravel size to formation grain size. Reprinted by permission of the SPE-AIME from Saucier 1974, fig. 5, © 1974 SPE-AIME.

A plot of cumulative weight-% $\geq$ grain size versus grain size has an S shape, as shown in figure 3.29(c). When plotted on log–probability paper, cumulative weight-% $\geq$ grain size versus grain size plots as a straight line (fig. 3.29[d]). The grain size at 50% (d_{50}) is the geometric average. In relation to distribution of formation properties, we might note that permeability measured in cores from a certain interval also has a log-normal distribution (based on simplified models, it is generally held that permeability is proportional to the square of average grain diameter). Porosity, on the other hand, has a normal distribution in most cases.

Note that the sieve analysis data is customarily displayed with increasing cumulative weight as grain size decreases. This corresponds to the series of sieves, with the large openings at the top and the smallest opening at the bottom. The cumulative weight is measured from top to bottom. Nonuniform sands would be typical of California formations, where the slope of a log–probability plot is relatively steep. Uniform sands are typical in the Gulf Coast and central Oklahoma areas, where the slope of a log–probability plot is relatively flat. Grain-size distributions for sand samples from the Dominguez field in California and the Oklahoma City Field, Oklahoma, are plotted on semilog paper (fig. 3.30) and on log–probability paper (fig. 3.31).

The grain diameters that have been widely used by investigators for defining rock properties and sizing gravel for sand control include

1. 50% diameter—gravel-size design (geometric average)
2. 10% diameter—bridging retention
3. 15% diameter—filter-size retention (approximately one standard deviation).

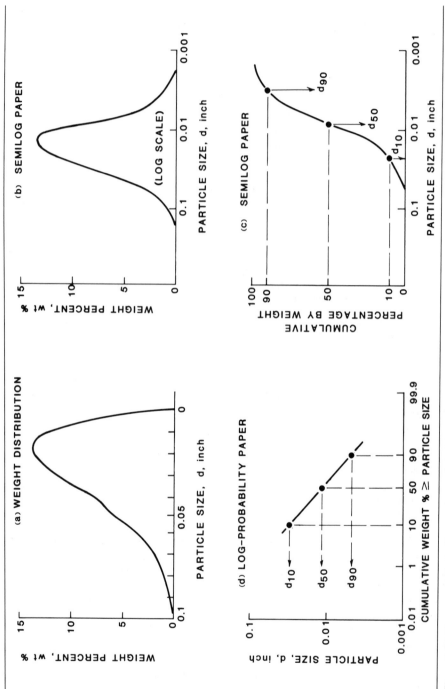

Figure 3.29 Common methods of presenting statistical distribution.

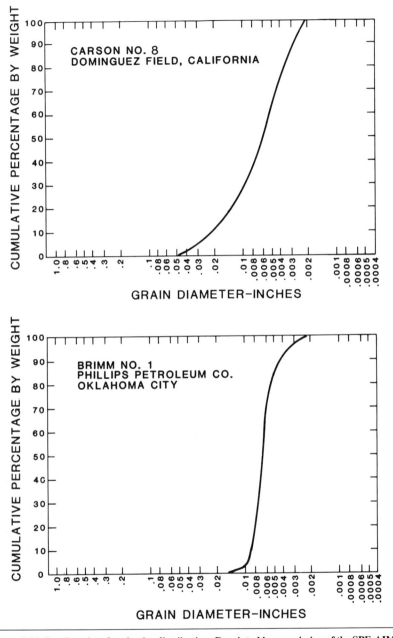

Figure 3.30 Semilog plot of grain-size distribution. Reprinted by permission of the SPE-AIME from Coberly and Wagner 1937, figs. 4, 5, © 1937 SPE-AIME.

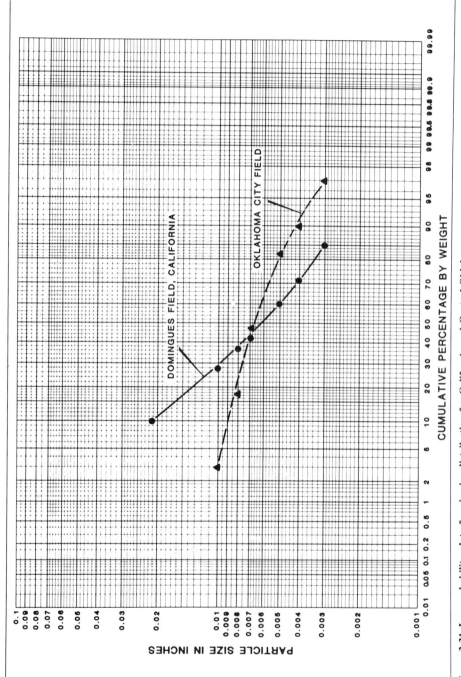

Figure 3.31 Log-probability plot of grain-size distribution for California and Central Oklahoma areas.

The 40%, 70%, and 85% diameters have also been used by various investigators for gravel-pack design calculations. Three of the better-known gravel-size design criteria are

Saucier (1974)   : $d_{G50} = 5$ to $6 \times d_{F50}$
Schwartz (1969): $d_{G40} = 6 \times d_{F40}$
Stein (1983)   : $d_{G85} < 4 \times d_{F15}$.

Practically, similar results should be expected using any of the three criteria. We suggest Saucier's relation, since it is simplest and has apparently been found successful in many field applications. In general, oversized gravel results in plugging by formation sand, while undersized gravel results in plugging by formation fines.

Concerning the analysis and the reports of sand and gravel, it is very important to use the same grain-size quantities for describing formation sand and gravel sizes. Example 3.10 illustrates the procedure for analyzing a sand sample to determine the gravel size for an inside-casing gravel pack.

EXAMPLE 3.10 SIZING GRAVEL BASED ON FORMATION GRAIN-SIZE DISTRIBUTION

The OCS-G-X4 well considered in example 3.9 is to be gravel packed with a 20–40 mesh gravel to stop sand production which started about eight months after coming on line. A sidewall sample is available to determine the grain characteristics of the producing Miocene formation (table E3.10). Suggest gravel and screen for gravel-pack design for the well.

SOLUTION

Figure E3.10 plots the sieve analysis data on log–probability paper to determine the mean grain diameter and grain-size distribution characteristics. From the straight line we can conclude that the log-normal distribution is representative of the reservoir formation and the average grain diameter is the geometric mean, read directly from the curve at 50% cumulative weight percent, $d_{R50} = 0.0046$ in. Using the Saucier criterion for optimal gravel size,

$d_{G50} = 5$ to $6 \times d_{R50}$

$= 0.023$ to 0.028 in.

Reading from table 3.5, we select commercial gravel size 20–40 mesh, which has a minimum grain diameter $d_{Gmin} = 0.0165$ in. and a maximum grain diameter $d_{Gmax} = 0.031$ in. The gravel-pack screen necessary to retain the gravel is $0.5 \, d_{Gmin}$, or 0.0083 in.

EXAMPLE 3.10 continued

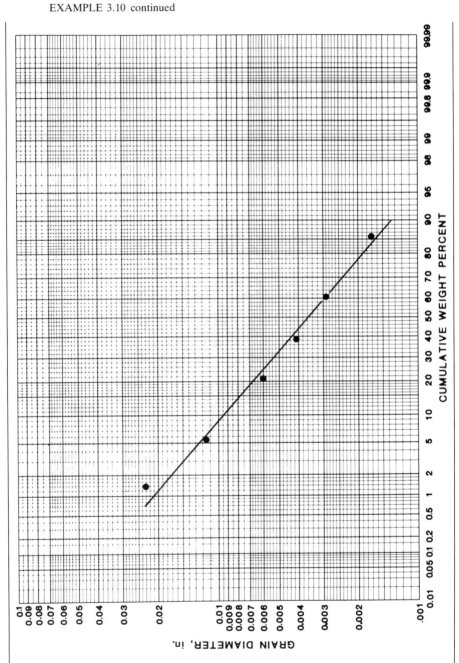

Figure E3.10 Log–probability plot of the sieve-analysis data of sidewall samples from the OGS-G-X4 oil well.

EXAMPLE 3.10 continued

Table E3.10 Sieve Analysis Results for the OCS-G-X4 Well

U.S. sieve number (mesh)	Grain diameter (in.)	Weight retained (gm)	Weight percent	Cumulative weight percent
8	0.093			
12	0.0661			
16	0.0469			
20	0.0331			
30	0.0232	0.25	1.4	1.4
40	0.0165			
50	0.0117	0.79	4.3	5.7
100	0.0059	2.81	15.4	21.1
140	0.0041	3.25	17.8	38.9
200	0.0029	4.10	22.5	61.4
270	0.0021			
325	0.0017	4.52	24.8	86.2
Pan		2.52	13.8	100.0
		18.24	100.0	

The gravel-pack screen should be designed properly to avoid plugging but retain the gravel. Screen opening is specified by slot width. The API recommends slot width to be specified in thousandths of an inch—a slot width of 15 would correspond to 0.015-in. screen openings. Mesh should not be used to specify slot width. Screen slot size should basically be about half the size of the smallest gravel particle if the screen is used to retain gravel in a gravel pack. If a screen liner is used to prevent sand production without gravel, one of two design criteria is recommended: For nonuniform sand (Coberly 1937), opening $= 2 \times d_{F10}$. For uniform sand (Flanigan 1980; Suman et al. 1983) opening $= d_{F10}$.

Samples of formation sand can be collected in several ways, including (1) rubber-sleeve cores, (2) conventional cores, (3) sidewall cores, (4) produced sand from the separator or sand trap, and (5) sand bailers. The best sample retrieval is from rubber-sleeve core holders. Although this special core type is expensive, it secures the most accurate information about in-situ formation grain properties.

Conventional cores offer the next best type of sample (Maly and Krueger 1971). If the sand is friable, as would be expected where sand production is a problem, then much of the formation sample will be lost when retrieving the core. Sidewall cores are small, but they are much less expensive to obtain. Grain analysis of sidewall cores may be less representative than full-core or rubber-sleeve core samples, but usually they provide an acceptable compromise solution to the sampling problem.

It is not good practice to use produced sand to determine sand grain-size distribution, because erosion, bypass, and gravity segregation may have altered the original distribution. Sieve analysis of produced sand will usually indicate a larger percentage of fines and small-particle sand than is representative of the native formation.

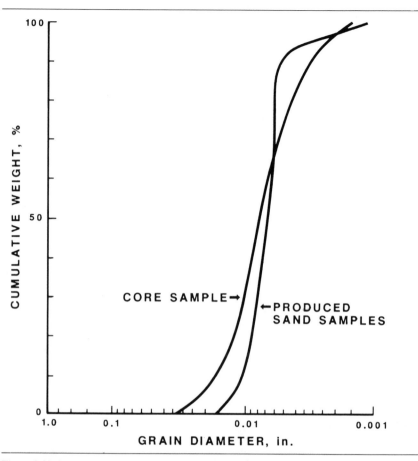

Figure 3.32 Sieve analysis on core and produced sand samples from the Frigg gas field offshore Norway. Reprinted by permission of Gulf Publishing Company from Barril and Gay 1983, fig. 2, pp. 52–56.

Bailed samples, captured at the bottom of the well by a wireline-run sand bailer, should also be used with caution. Typically, bailed samples represent larger particles that have dropped out of the produced sand from the formation. It is not uncommon that sand bailed from the top of the rathole has smaller particles than sand bailed thereafter at the bottom of the rathole. A typical separation in results related to the difference in sampling method is illustrated in figure 3.32. The figure is adapted from a publication by Barril and Gay (1983), which describes the complex considerations, and the novel design aspects of the sand-control system in Frigg gas wells. These wells are individually producing successfully at over 50 MMscf/D from an unconsolidated sand reservoir with a screen liner sand control. Obtaining and analyzing representative samples was a key issue in proper sizing of the screen.

To summarize, sand-control measures will always impair, to a certain extent, the productivity of wells. Fortunately, recent improvement of sand-control techniques allows minimizing productivity impairment and provides acceptable alternatives for safe and effective well completion.

3.7   **CONDENSATE BLOCKAGE SKIN FACTOR.** Condensate blockage results from the buildup of a liquid saturation around the wellbore as flowing pressure drops below the dewpoint pressure of a saturated gas-condensate fluid. Several investigators (Muskat 1949; Gondouin et al. 1967; Odell and Miller 1967; Fussell 1973) have studied the effect of liquid accumulation on wet gas productivity in condensate wells. Fetkovich (1973) developed Muskat's (1949) work into the form of a blockage skin factor, which appears to be the most accurate correction to the gas IPR equation. The modified gas pseudopressure function (Odell and Miller; Fussell) is more complicated and does not appear to offer any advantage over the Fetkovich blockage skin factor.

Blockage skin is developed from the rate of buildup of the condensate saturation suggested by Muskat:

$$\frac{dS_o}{dt} = \frac{q_g}{2\pi rh\phi} \frac{dp}{dr} \frac{dC}{dp}, \tag{3.40}$$

where

S_o = condensate saturation (fraction),
t = time (days),
q_g = wet gas rate (scf/D),
r = radius (ft),
h = formation thickness (ft),
ϕ = porosity (fraction),
p = pressure (psia),
r = radius (ft),
C = condensate content per wet gas unit volume (res. ft^3/scf),
p = pressure (psia).

To evaluate dp/dr, recall the steady-state pressure distribution $p(r)$:

$$p(r) = p_R - \frac{25.15 q_g \mu_g B_g}{kh} \ln(r/r_w), \tag{3.41}$$

which, when differentiated with respect to radius, gives

$$dp/dr = \frac{25.15 q_g \mu_g B_g}{khr}. \tag{3.42}$$

Gas formation volume factor and viscosity should be evaluated at the prevailing pressure $p(r)$, given by equation (1.14), but we suggest p_R, since it simplifies the calculation. The expression for B_g is

$$B_g = 0.02827 ZT/p_R. \qquad (1.14)$$

Substituting equations (3.42) and (1.14) in equation (3.40) gives

$$\frac{dS_o}{dt} = 0.1132 \frac{q_g^2 \mu_g ZTY}{r^2 h^2 \phi k p_R}, \qquad (3.43)$$

where $Y = dC/dp$ is the retrograde condensation factor. It is calculated from constant-volume depletion data and usually ranges from 10^{-6} to 10^{-7} vol/vol/psi. Since the procedure for determining Y is somewhat complicated, we suggest using a constant, $Y = 3 \times 10^{-7}$, as a reasonable approximation. The resulting deviation in skin is quite small (only $\pm 6\%$) considering the approximate nature of the entire solution to the blockage problem.

We assume that the critical condensate saturation S_{oc} builds outward from the wellbore at a rate given by solving the preceding relations,

$$r_b^2 = 0.1132 \frac{q_g^2 \mu_g ZTYt}{S_{oc} h^2 \phi k p_R}, \qquad (3.44)$$

where r_b is the radius of blockage to which the critical condensate saturation has reached. The blockage effect can be quantified in terms of skin by using the damage skin factor relation

$$s_b = \left(\frac{1}{k_{rgc}} - 1 \right) \ln(r_b/r_w), \qquad (3.45)$$

where k_{rgc} is the relative permeability to gas at critical condensate saturation S_{oc}. The largest effect of blockage is the reduction in gas permeability due to condensate accumulation. The gas relative permeability is a single point on the imbibition curve at $S_g = 1 - S_{wi} - S_{oc}$. It is easily shown that the logarithmic expression quickly increases and then remains relatively constant. This results in a singular blockage skin dominated for the most part by the magnitude of k_{rgc}. Example 3.11 demonstrates calculation of the blockage skin factor.

EXAMPLE 3.11 BLOCKAGE-SKIN FACTOR

A gas-condensate well, the Little Thumb No. 2, has been discovered in Utah. Initial well-test data indicate a relatively low permeability, about 3.2 md. Since the reservoir is initially saturated at its dew point, condensate accumulation near the wellbore is considered a potential hazard to the well's deliverability. Calculate the blockage skin factor for a rate of 2 MMscf/D after one month of production, based on the reservoir rock and fluid data given in table E3.11.

EXAMPLE 3.11 continued

Table E3.11 Reservoir Data for the Little Thumb No. 2 Well

Initial reservoir pressure p_R	7030 psia
Initial gas viscosity μ_g.	0.0571 cp
Initial gas Z-factor Z	1.159
Reservoir temperature T	261
Condensate factor Y	3×10^{-7} psi^{-1}
Critical condensate saturation S_{oc}	0.35
Reservoir thickness h	210
Porosity ϕ	0.25
Permeability k	3.2 md
Wellbore radius r_w.	0.375 ft

SOLUTION

The radius of blockage propagation is given by

$$r_b = \left(0.1132 \frac{q_g^2 \mu_g ZTYt}{S_{oc}h^2 \phi k p_R} \right)^{0.5}$$

$$= \left[0.1132 \frac{(2 \times 10^6)^2 (0.0571)(1.159)(261 + 460)(3 \times 10^{-7})(30)}{(0.35)(210)^2(0.25)(3.2)(7030)} \right]^{0.5}$$

$$= 1.5 \, \text{ft}.$$

For the reduction in relative permeability to gas from 1.0 to 0.34 at the critical oil saturation of 0.35, blockage skin after one month's production at 2 MMscf/D is

$$s_b = (1/0.34 - 1)\ln(1.5/0.375)$$

$$= +2.7.$$

After one year of production, $r_b = 5.2$ ft and $s_b = +5.1$, which in terms of pressure drop is substantial.

3.8 **COMPOSITE SKIN FACTOR.** Thus far we have considered individual flow restrictions near the wellbore and quantified each as a skin factor. The total effect of all nonideal conditions near the wellbore is a composite of the individual effects. Total skin factor is *not* merely the sum of all individual skin factors. It reflects also the existence of some degree of interaction between the different flow restrictions that may magnify or dampen their composite effect.

It is rather difficult to quantify the interference between two or more near-wellbore flow restrictions. On the one hand, it is impossible to treat the problem rigorously by mathematical methods. On the other hand, it is impossible to determine the interference from field observations. Apparently, the simplest aspect to consider is the interference due to limited entry and partial penetration. Simply stated, flow restricted by limited entry creates higher flow velocities in the proportion h/h_p. The higher velocity is reflected in a higher total skin factor. Rowland (1969), and Jones and Watts (1971) proposed simple models for adjusting individual skin factors for the effect of limited entry. They considered the flow model shown in figure 3.33, in which flow convergence into the open interval is already completed before reaching the "near-wellbore" region where damage, high-velocity flow, blockage, and perforation effects become important. The higher local flow velocity magnifies the pressure drawdown caused by the other skin factors.

Using the formal definition of skin factor (eq. [2.25]), and the h/h_p gain in local velocity (in relation to ideal radial flow), pressure drawdowns corresponding to the ideal radial flow and the various skins are

$$\Delta p_1 = \frac{141.2 q_o \mu_o B_o}{kh}[\ln(r_e/r_w) - 0.75] \qquad \text{for Ideal Flow (Darcy)}$$

$$\Delta p_2 = \frac{141.2 q_o \mu_o B_o}{kh} s_c \qquad \text{for Partial Penetration (Darcy)}$$

$$\Delta p_3 = \frac{141.2 q_o \mu_o B_o}{kh} s_A \qquad \text{for Drainage Area Shape (Darcy)}$$

$$\Delta p_4 = \frac{141.2 q_o \mu_o B_o}{kh} s_G \qquad \text{for Gravel Pack (Darcy)}$$

$$\Delta p_5 = \frac{141.2 q_o \mu_o B_o}{kh} s_{dp} \qquad \text{for Damage Perforation (Darcy)}$$

$$\Delta p_6 = \frac{141.2 q_o \mu_o B_o}{kh} (h/h_p) s_p \qquad \text{for Perforation (Darcy)}$$

$$\Delta p_7 = \frac{141.2 q_o \mu_o B_o}{kh} (h/h_p) s_a \qquad \text{for Damage/Stimulation (Darcy)}$$

$$\Delta p_8 = \frac{141.2 q_o \mu_o B_o}{kh} D_R q_o \qquad \text{for Reservoir (High-Velocity Flow)}$$

$$\Delta p_9 = \frac{141.2 q_o \mu_o B_o}{kh} D_a q_o \qquad \text{for Damage/Stimulation (High-Velocity Flow)}$$

$$\Delta p_{10} = \frac{141.2 q_o \mu_o B_o}{kh} D_{dp} q_o \qquad \text{for Damage Perforation (High-Velocity Flow)}$$

$$\Delta p_{11} = \frac{141.2 q_o \mu_o B_o}{kh} D_G q_o \qquad \text{for Gravel Pack (High-Velocity Flow)}$$

which, when added, yields

$$\Delta p_t = \frac{141.2 q_o \mu_o B_o}{kh}[\ln(r_e/r_w) - 0.75 + s + Dq_o], \tag{3.46}$$

where s is given by

$$s = s_c + s_A + s_G + s_{dp} + (h/h_p)s_p + (h/h_p)s_a \tag{3.47}$$

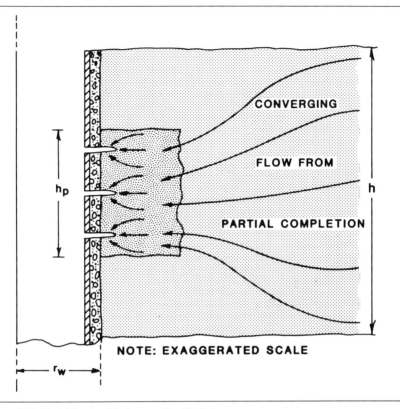

Figure 3.33 Model for simplified composite skin factor.

and D is given by

$$D = D_R + D_a + D_{dp} + D_G. \tag{3.48}$$

Equations (3.47) and (3.48) are equally applicable to gas wells using pressure-squared, pressure, or pseudopressure. Note that s_c, s_A, s_G, and s_{dp} are not corrected for limited entry. This is because limited entry is inherently considered when these skin factors are calculated individually. A similar condition holds for the individual elements D.

Although approximate, the Rowland, and Jones and Watts model is probably accurate enough for most engineering calculations. It may, however, give erroneous results in cases where certain individual skin factors are negative. For example, consider a case where perforation skin $s_p = -1.2$, damage skin $s_a = -1.0$ (acid wash), and $s_c = +11$ (for $h_p/h = 0.2$, $h/h_p = 5$, and $h_D = 100$). Applying equation (3.47) for total skin, we obtain

$s = 5(-1.2) + 5(-1.0) + 11$

$= 0.$

That is, by perforating only 20% of the total formation, we have obtained a zero total skin factor. Consider, then, the case of only 10% perforated interval ($h/h_p = 10$ and $s_c = 20$), the total skin factor from equation (3.47) is

$s = 10(-1.2) + 10(-1.0) + 20$

$= -2,$

which erroneously says the well has been stimulated by reducing the section open to flow! Clearly, this is an incorrect conclusion resulting from a situation more complex than accounted for by the total skin model. (Surprisingly, Jones and Slusser [1974] imply that partial penetration increases productivity; see their discussion.) We caution against improper use of the simplified partial-penetration correction and refer to Odeh's (1977) criticisms for a better understanding of its limitations.

Example 3.12 illustrates the use of the composite skin-factor equation when all individual skin factors are positive. Skin-factor correlations may be used in productivity prediction calculations, and in interpretation of well testing data. Considering the wide range of possible input, prediction calculations of total skin and well productivity have very low certainty level, unless supported and substantiated by well testing. Even then, total skin calculations and skin-factor analyses are usually very involved and demand a certain intuition for correct interpretation of all available data. Example 3.13 indicates the extent of such considerations.

EXAMPLE 3.12 COMPOSITE SKIN FACTOR

A Gulf Coast gas well, XM-13, producing from a low-pressure gas reservoir, was tested in a multirate test. From pressure buildup data it was calculated that $s = +47.2$ and $k = 80$ md. The stabilized multirate data were plotted as $(p_R^2 - p_{wf}^2)/q_g$ versus q_g, which gave a close fit to a straight line. The test engineer analyzed the intercept of the curve and used it to calculate a steady-state skin $s = 45$. The slope of the curve determined a rate-dependent skin coefficient D, which was used to back-calculate a high-velocity coefficient, $\beta = 1.12 \times 10^9$ ft^{-1}. For calculating β the engineer assumed that the entire rate-dependent skin was due to high-velocity flow in the reservoir. Other well and formation data are listed in table E3.12.

The following additional tasks have to be carried out:

1. Estimate the constant skin factor s_a due to formation damage.
2. If the radius of formation damage is estimated as 1 ft, calculate the altered permeability k_a in the damage zone.

EXAMPLE 3.12 continued

Table E3.12 Well and Formation Data for the XM-13 Gas Well

Bit diameter	8.5 in.
Casing diameter (OD)	7 in.
Pay-zone thickness	66 ft
Perforation interval	12 ft in the center of the pay zone
Perforation program	0.5-in. jet, 180° phasing, 4 shots per foot, 6.5-in. total target penetration in Berea sandstone
Formation permeability	80 md
Horizontal-to-vertical permeability ratio	5
Measured formation compressive strength	10,000 psia
Effective formation stress (calculated)	8,000 psia
Formation temperature	135 °F (595°R)
Initial reservoir pressure	2100 psia
Initial gas compressibility factor Z	0.821
Initial gas viscosity μ_g	0.0168 cp
Drainage radius r_e	2100 ft
gas gravity γ_g	0.72 (air = 1.0)

3. Compare the high-velocity coefficient β_a calculated for the damaged zone with the coefficient of the undamaged reservoir, β_R, and with the average β calculated by the test engineer from the multirate test data.

SOLUTION

The constant skin factor due to formation damage, s_a, is back-calculated by subtracting the effects of perforation and partial penetration from the total constant skin obtained by the test.

Perforation skin factor s_p
given:
a. $L_{pB} = 6.5$ in.
b. effective formation stress $= 8000$ psia
c. Berea penetration multiplier $= 0.72$
calculate:
d. $L_p = (L_{pB} - T_c - T_s)0.7 \times 0.72$
$= [6.5 - 0.375 - \frac{1}{2}(8.5 - 7)]0.7 \times 0.72 = 2.7$ in.
e. correcting penetration for wellbore diameter

$L_{pa} = L_p(9.5/8.5) = 3.01$ in.

f. from figure 3.17, for 4 shots/foot, 180° phasing,

$S_p = +0.14$.

Partial-penetration skin factor s_c
a. $b = h_p/h = 6/33 = 0.18$

EXAMPLE 3.12 continued

b. $h_D = (h/r_w)(k/k_v)^{0.5}$
   $= (33/0.354)5^{0.5} = 208$

c. from figure 3.7, $s_c = 15$.

Formation-Damage Skin Factor s_a

a. given total skin factor,

$$s = 45 = (h/h_p)s_p + (h/h_p)s_a + s_c$$

b. Solving for s_a,

$$s_a = (45 - s_c)(h_p/h) - s_p$$

$$= (45 - 15)(6/33) - 0.14$$

$$= 5.3.$$

The second task is to determine the k_a that corresponds to the calculated s_a. From equation (3.3) we obtain

$$k_a = k\left[1 + \frac{s_a}{\ln(r_a/r_w)}\right]^{-1}$$

$$= 80\left[1 + \frac{5.3}{\ln(1/0.354)}\right]^{-1} = 13.1 \, \text{md}.$$

For task 3 we first calculate β_a and β_R from the corresponding permeabilities:

a. β coefficient with altered permeability:

$$\beta_a = 2.73 \times 10^{10} k_a^{-1.1045}$$

$$= 2.73 \times 10^{10} \times 13.1^{-1.1045}$$

$$= 1.59 \times 10^9 \, \text{ft}^{-1}.$$

b. β_R coefficient with formation permeability:

$$\beta_R = 2.73 \times 10^{10} k^{-1.1045}$$

$$= 2.73 \times 10^{10} \times 80^{-1.1045}$$

$$= 2.16 \times 10^8 \, \text{ft}^{-1}.$$

Comparing the coefficient determined from the test, β_T, with β_a and β_R allows us to conclude that since $\beta_T \gg \beta_R$, and since $\beta_T \approx \beta_a$, then most of the high-velocity effect occurs in the near-wellbore region and the formation damaged region probably dominates the high-velocity-flow effect.

EXAMPLE 3.13 INTERPRETATION OF TEST DATA

The central production platform of the Java field collects and processes the production of several small satellite fields. Each satellite field is owned and operated by a different consortium of companies. For production allocation all the wells of the field are tested routinely to establish the contribution of each well to the total commingled production.

The Java No. 2 (example 3.3) was tested with a multirate sequence to define the average backpressure curve for allocation of company A's production in the Java field. During the test the well-site engineer was clever enough to plot the backpressure points as the testing proceeded (subsurface readout gauges were used, although wellhead flowing pressures would have been sufficient). The test sequence is illustrated in figure E3.13a.

The first flow at 11.3 MMscf/D lasted 16 hours, during which the cleanup was thought to have been completed. The next rate was half the first (6.7 MMscf/D) and lasted 2 hours, as did the third rate at 11.85 MMscf/D. The first three data plotted as a straight line on log–log paper, with a backpressure exponent of $n = 0.643$.

During the fourth 2-hour flow at 14.78 MMscf/D, the engineer noticed that the point fell to the right of the first three data. This indicated to him that perhaps cleanup had not yet been completed. The engineer ordered an additional 6-hour cleanup flow, at a rate of 52.5 MMscf/D. As seen in figure E3.13b, the fifth point plotted far to the right of the first four data. Three 1-hour tests at 13.3, 20.65, and 29.4 MMscf/D were then run. These last four points plotted as a straight line on log–log paper, indicating a backpressure exponent of $n = 0.658$.

Had the engineer neglected the shift of the fourth data point on the backpressure curve, the final deliverability curve used to determine average well performance for company A would have been much lower than the actual (after cleanup) deliverability. The difference in AOF is 90 versus 310 MMscf/D!

Example 3.3 shows that the last four points define an IPR equation with a steady-state skin of about $+23$, which is the expected skin due to partial penetration. We can conclude, therefore, that the necessary rate to cleanup this high-permeability formation is as high as 52.5 MMscf/D.

This example facilitates a discussion on total skin factor. The well has several components of nonideal flow, including damage, partial penetration, and high-velocity flow (the well was completed openhole, so perforation effects do not need to be considered). The factual story behind this example illustrates how important on-site test evaluation can be.

1. Use the last four test data (post-cleanup) to evaluate the high-velocity-flow terms D and β, considering that damage skin is zero.
2. Use the first three test data (pre-cleanup) to evaluate formation-damage skin before cleanup.
3. Use the first three data (pre-cleanup) to evaluate the high-velocity-flow terms D and β, where damage is assumed to extend to an arbitrary radius r_a. Reservoir and well data are listed in table E3.3 in example 3.3.

EXAMPLE 3.13 continued

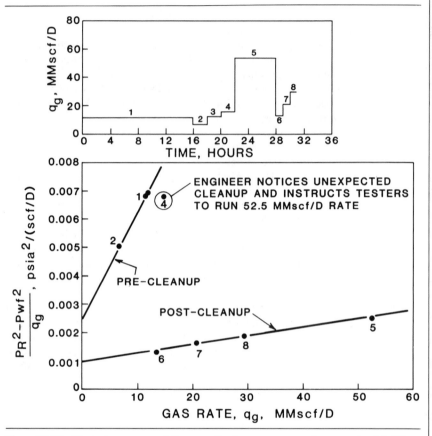

Figure E3.13a The test sequence and the normalized pressure-squared versus rate plot of the Java No. 2 gas well.

SOLUTION

1. The high-velocity-flow effect is reflected in the slope, $B = 2.94 \times 10^{-11}$, of the $\Delta p^2/q_g$ versus q_g curve in figure E3.13a. This value can be converted to the high-velocity flow term D_R by (eq. [2.53]):

$$D_R = \frac{0.703kh}{T\mu_g Z} B$$

$$= \frac{0.703(978)(313)}{(120 + 460)(0.0144)(0.837)} 2.94 \times 10^{-11}$$

$$= 9.05 \times 10^{-7} (scf/D)^{-1}.$$

The β_R term is then given by (eq. [2.63]):

EXAMPLE 3.13 continued

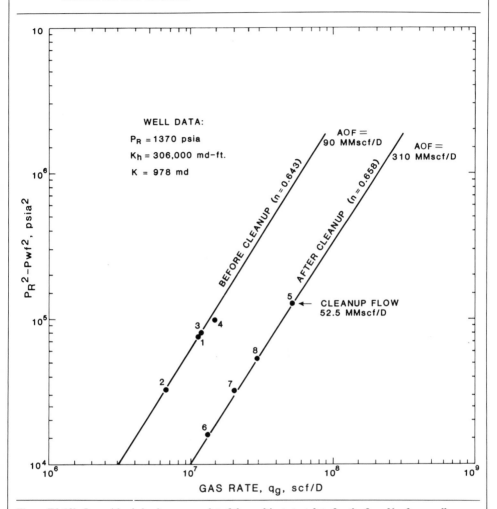

Figure E3.13b Logarithmic backpressure plot of the multirate test data for the Java No. 2 gas well.
Reprinted by permission of the authors from Fetkovich 1975, fig. 8.

$$\beta_R = 4.50 \times 10^{17} \frac{\mu_g r_w h_p^{\,2}}{\gamma_g kh} D_R$$

$$= 4.50 \times 10^{17} \frac{(0.0114)(0.33)(70)^2}{(0.655)(978)(313)} 9.05 \times 10^{-7}$$

$$= 3.75 \times 10^7 \, \text{ft}^{-1}.$$

Using the β correlation in equation (2.64) with the permeability determined
from the buildup test,

EXAMPLE 3.13 continued

$$\beta_R = 2.73 \times 10^{10} k^{-1.1045}$$

$$= 2.73 \times 10^{10} (978)^{-1.1045}$$

$$= 1.36 \times 10^7 \, \text{ft}^{-1},$$

which is about 36% of the back-calculated β_R value. Considering the scatter in data used to establish the generalized Firoozabadi–Katz correlation, the difference in β's is not unexpected.

2. The first three test data plotted as $\Delta p^2 / q_g$ versus q_g in figure E3.13a indicate an intercept $A = 0.00248$ and a slope $B = 3.78 \times 10^{-10}$. The intercept gives an indication of steady-state skin. The interpretation of the two-hour isochronal flow period is

$$A(t) = \frac{T \mu_g Z}{0.703 kh} \{0.5[\ln(t_D) + 0.80907] + s\},$$

and t_D is given by

$$t_D = \frac{0.000264 kt}{\phi \mu_{gi} c_{ti} r_w^2}$$

$$= \frac{0.000264(978)(2)}{(0.181)(0.0144)(0.000582)(0.33)^2}$$

$$= 3.12 \times 10^6,$$

so

$$A(t = 2\text{hr}) = 0.00248$$

$$= \frac{(120 + 460)(0.0144)(0.837)}{0.703(978)(313)} \times \{0.5[\ln(3.12 \times 10^6) + 0.80907] + s\},$$

or

$$0.00248 = 3.25 \times 10^{-5}(7.88 + s).$$

This yields a steady-state skin

$$s = 76.31 - 7.88$$

$$= +68.43.$$

The fact that the first flow period was 16 hours in duration has little effect. Dimensionless pressure, $p_D = 0.5[\ln(t_D) + 0.80907]$, only changes from 7.88 at two hours to 8.78 at 16 hours, or a change in skin from +68.43 to +67.53. Skin

EXAMPLE 3.13 continued

due to partial penetration was determined in example 3.3 as $s_c = +22$. Total skin is given by

$$s = s_a(h/h_p) + s_c.$$

Solving for s_a to obtain the skin due to damage,

$$s_a = (s - s_c)(h_p/h)$$

$$= (68 - 22)(0.22)$$

$$= +10.$$

3. The effect of damage on high-velocity flow is indicated by (1) the lower backpressure exponent for pre-cleanup flows (fig. E3.13b) and (2) the steeper slope B for pre-cleanup flows shown in figure E3.13a. Theoretically, a damaged zone will affect high-velocity flow through D and β. In the damaged zone with radius r_a and permeability k_a, the damage component of D is D_a, given by (eq. [3.25])

$$D_a = 2.222 \times 10^{-18} \frac{\gamma_g k h}{\mu_g h_p^2}(1/r_w - 1/r_a)\beta_a,$$

where

$$\beta_a = 2.73 \times 10^{10} k_a^{-1.1045}$$

and the reservoir component of high-velocity flow is D_R, given by

$$D_R = 2.222 \times 10^{-18} \frac{\gamma_g k h}{\mu_g h_p^2}(1/r_a - 1/r_e)\beta_R,$$

where

$$\beta_R = 2.73 \times 10^{10} k^{-1.1045}.$$

The total high-velocity flow term predicted from β correlations is, then, $D = D_a + D_R$. Back-calculated from multirate data, the term D is given by

$$D = \frac{0.703 k h}{T \mu_g Z} B$$

$$= \frac{0.703(978)(313)}{(120 + 460)(0.0144)(0.837)} 3.78 \times 10^{-10}$$

$$= 1.16 \times 10^{-5} \, (\text{scf/D})^{-1}.$$

EXAMPLE 3.13 continued

Table E3.13 Calculated High-Velocity Flow Factor for the Java No. 2 Well with Pre-Cleanup Damage Skin of +10

	Damage-zone permeability (md)		
	100	50	10
r_a (ft)	1.03	0.566	0.366
$r_a - r_w$ (in.)	8.40	2.83	0.43
D_a (scf/D)$^{-1}$	2.16×10^{-6}	2.82×10^{-6}	4.04×10^{-6}
D_R (scf/D)$^{-1}$	8.33×10^{-8}	1.51×10^{-7}	2.34×10^{-7}
D (scf/D)$^{-1}$	2.25×10^{-6}	2.97×10^{-6}	4.24×10^{-6}
D/D_{test}[a]	0.194	0.256	0.366[b]

[a] $D_{test} = 1.16 \times 10^{-5}$ (scf/D)$^{-1}$.
[b] The same ratio as reported for the post-cleanup analysis of multirate data having zero damage skin.

Thus we know composite D and skin s, as well as damage skin s_a.

This establishes four equations for the four unknowns D_R, D_a, k_a, r_a. The equations are

$$D_a = 2.222 \times 10^{-18} \frac{\gamma_g k h}{\mu_g h_p^2} (1/r_w - 1/r_a)\beta_a$$

$$= 2.222 \times 10^{-10} \frac{(0.655)(978)(313)}{(0.0144)(70)^2} (1/0.33 - 1/r_a)\beta_a$$

$$= 1.724 \times 10^{-4} (3 - 1/r_a)k_a^{-1.1045};$$

$$D_R = 2.222 \times 10^{-18} \frac{\gamma_g k h}{\mu_g h_p^2} (1/r_a - 1/r_e)\beta_R$$

$$= 2.222 \times 10^{-18} \frac{(0.655)(978)(313)}{(0.0144)(70)^2} (1/r_a)\beta_R$$

$$= 8.58 \times 10^{-8}/r_a;$$

$$D = D_a + D_R = 1.16 \times 10^{-5},$$

$$s_a = (1/k_a - 1)\ln(r_a/r_w)$$

$$= (1/k_a - 1)\ln(r_a/0.33) = 1.0.$$

Table E3.13 gives D_a, D_R, and $D = D_a + D_R$ for several combinations of k_a and r_a that correspond to a damage skin of +10. Comparing the calculated value of D with the back-calculated test value, we see once again that the β correlation tends to underpredict the actual high-velocity flow-effect. For the 0.43-in. damage zone, the calculated high-velocity-flow factor (D or β) is 36% of the

EXAMPLE 3.13 continued

back-calculated value. The post-cleanup calculated β was also about 36% lower than the back-calculated value. We might, therefore, conclude that the 0.43-in. damage zone is the best model (having a permeability about 10% less than formation permeability), and that the modified β correlation for this reservoir is

$$\beta = 2.73 \times 10^{10}(0.36)k^{-1.1045}$$

or

$$\beta = 1.0 \times 10^{10}k^{-1.1045}.$$

3.9 **NET PAY ZONE, HETEROGENEITIES, AND FLOW BARRIERS.** In reality, reservoir rocks are *not* homogeneous or isotropic. "Homogeneous" implies uniformity in properties such as porosity, saturation, and thickness. "Isotropic" implies uniform permeability in all directions of flow. By virtue of the dynamic nature of the geologic evolution that created hydrocarbon-bearing formations, rock and fluid properties usually vary in both horizontal and vertical directions.

The most important effects of reservoir heterogeneity, for well performance, are

1. contributing thickness ("net pay zone"), defining the interval that will effectively produce hydrocarbons
2. average permeability in the horizontal direction
3. contrast of horizontal to vertical permeability (anisotropy)
4. capillary pressures and vertical saturation distribution (related to water and gas coning problems)
5. relative permeability characteristics
6. the occurrence and areal extent of tight shale, carbonate, or coal streaks, that can be of sufficient extension to separate the main formation rock into noncommunicating layers.
7. the occurrence and areal extent of very-high permeability zones (thief zones).

Several of these effects are illustrated in figure 3.34, which is adapted from Amyx, Bass, and Whiting (1960). The figure illustrates a pay zone with impermeable confining layers at the top and at the bottom that prevent the migration of oil and gas away from the trap. It shows the effect of capillary pressure on vertical saturation distribution at the transition zone between water and oil. At the bottom of the transition zone, water saturation is 100%, which corresponds to zero capillary pressure (or a minimum entry pressure). Above this level water saturation decreases gradually until it reaches a minimum irreducible value.

The relative permeability corresponding to saturation distribution in the transition zone indicates that at the bottom of the transition zone only water may flow, and at the top only oil may flow. Customarily, the bottom of the water/oil transition zone, where only water can flow, is referred to as the oil/water contact. Similarly, at the transition between oil and gas, the level where only gas flows is referred to as the gas/oil contact. The gross effective oil zone is usually defined between the oil/water contact and the gas/oil contact. If the transition zone is large,

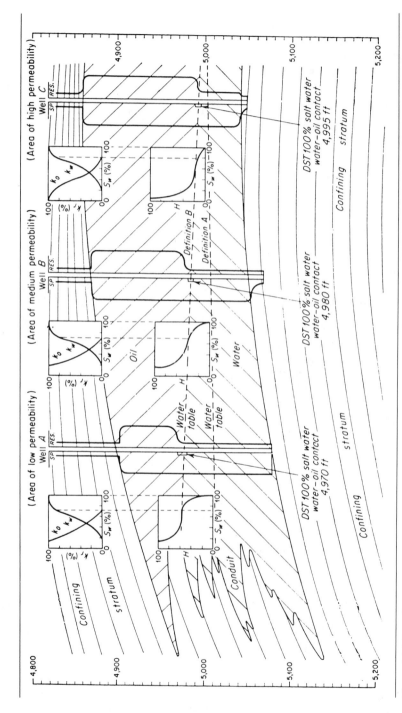

Figure 3.34 Schematic reservoir description showing the effects of saturation distribution. Reprinted by permission of McGraw-Hill Book Company from Aymx et al. 1960, fig. 3.62.

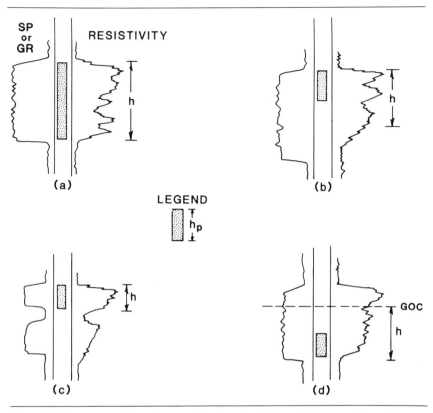

Figure 3.35 Net pay-zone determination. After Standing 1980, p. 18, by permission of the University of Trondheim.

it is customary to consider only a fraction of it, or even to ignore it completely, when considering the net effective zone. Certain companies arbitrarily define the lower limit of the zone at the level where $S_w = 50\%$. Other companies define it at the point of irreducible water saturation, that is, neglect the contribution of the transition zone.

In general, definition of the net pay zone for inflow calculations follows the four guidelines or four cases set out in figure 3.35. The figure indicates water saturation through a resistivity log and intervals of impermeable shale layers and porous zones through a gamma ray (GR) or spontaneous potential (SP) log. These two indicators suggest which parts of the formation contribute substantial quantities of oil and gas and which have negligible contributions. The figure also indicates the most reasonable perforation interval to avoid excessive water and gas production from an oil well. Figure 3.35 adopts the conservative approach, which neglects the contribution of the water/oil transition zone.

The simplest case in figure 3.35 is when the entire thickness is saturated with oil and water or gas coning is not a consideration (fig. 3.35[a]). The next most common situation is a formation with oil and water, where the water saturation changes in the transition zone from an irreducible value at the top of 100% near the zero-capillary-pressure point at the bottom (fig. 3.35[b]). In this case the figure suggests neglecting the contribution of the transition zone and avoiding perforating it.

When a tight shale streak separates an otherwise continuous oil-saturated formation, the net pay is separated into several intervals, depending on the continuity of the shale streak and the saturations in each interval of the hydrocarbon-bearing formation. Figure 3.35(c) gives an example in which the shale streak appears continuous (as supported by correlation with logs from neighboring wells) and the lower section of sand is mainly water bearing. In this case the net pay zone is only the upper, oil-bearing sand and only this interval is considered worth-while perforating.

An oil zone with an overlying gas cap is indicated in figure 3.35(d). The total net pay or contributing oil zone includes everything below the gas cap (there is no underlying water zone). Only the lower interval of the oil zone should be produced, as a precaution against gas coning. If perforations are too close to the gas/oil contact, coning is likely to occur.

Example 3.14 applies considerations used to select the perforation interval.

Another aspect related to the perforated interval is the hydraulic seal performed by the cement. Good cement seal is essential to prevent channeling of gas and/or water from bordering zones. The true criterion for a cement seal, either the cement bonding to the casing and the formation, or the compressive stresses between the cement and the formation, is yet to be proven (Cooke et al. 1982). Yet, the current practice adopts a rule of thumb that states that 5 to 15 ft of "good" bond is required to separate the oil zone from bordering gas and/or water.

EXAMPLE 3.14 SELECTION OF COMPLETION INTERVAL FOR A WELL INTERSECTING A GAS CAP, OIL COLUMN, AND WATER ZONE

The ABW No. 1 is a well discussed by Amyx, Bass, and Whiting (1960). Information from drilling records and electrical logs is given in figure E3.14a. Core analysis and other formation characteristics are given in figure E3.15 and table E3.15.

From the log data given by Amyx et al., the producing formation is a 60-ft thick sandstone at a depth of 6800 ft, with a gas cap in the upper 18 ft, 36-ft oil zone, and a 6-ft water interval. The gas/oil and water/oil transition zones are very abrupt, indicating a uniform pore-size distribution. Permeability is high, averaging about 500 md for the three sections, separated by shale streaks (see example 3.15).

The ABW No. 1 well gives a unique opportunity to discuss some basic rules for selecting perforation interval. This example gives a general discussion of log data and formation characteristics. It also selects an interval to be perforated. The available data include

1. drilling-mud log
2. drilling-rate record
3. lithology from drill cuttings

347

EXAMPLE 3.14 continued

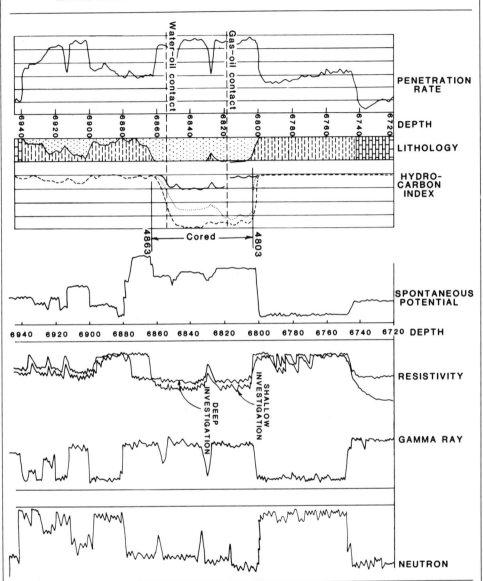

Figure E3.14a Drilling records and electrical logs for the ABW No. 1 well. Reprinted by permission of McGraw Hill Book Company from Amyx, Bass, and Whiting 1960, figs, 7.21, 22.

EXAMPLE 3.14 continued

4. hydrocarbon detector records
5. spontaneous potential (SP) log
6. resistivity logs: shallow and deep investigation
7. gamma ray (GR) log
8. neutron log (induced gamma radiation).

Use all the available data to select an interval for perforating.

SOLUTION

Drill cuttings analyzed by the wellsite geologist are used to define the basic lithology:

Limestone formation	−6740 ft
Shale layer	6740–6800 ft
Clean sandstone	6800–6860 ft
(1st shale streak)	6826–6828 ft
(2nd shale streak)	6851–6853 ft
Shaly sandstone	6860–6940 ft
Limestone formation	6940– ft

The open-hole logs support the sample analysis, indicating lithology, porosity, and saturations:

Shale Formation: 6740–6800 ft

SP log	Indicates uniform potential along the shale baseline.
GR log	Records a high gamma-ray count, typical of high potassium found in mica-bearing marine shales.
Neutron	Records a low count, indicating high porosity typical to most shales.
Resistivity	No separation between shallow and deep investigation, indicating low permeability.

Clean Sandstone Formation: 6800–6860 ft

SP log	High negative potential along the sand reference line.
GR log	Uniformly low radiation count.
Neutron	Medium count indicates medium to good porosity relative to "average" sandstone. The abrupt change in neutron count at the transition from gas to oil (6818 ft) is due to an increase in the density of hydrogen atoms in the oil zone. A separation between neutron and density logs (density not given in this example) usually is the best indicator of gas-bearing formations.
	The transition zone from oil to water is not seen on the neutron log because hydrogen concentration is essentially the same in oil and water.
Resistivity	The shallow resistivity reads higher than the deep-investigation resistivity. In fresh mud (pH = 8.8) this indicates a permeable zone. That is, fresh mud filtrate has displaced the reservoir fluid, diluting

EXAMPLE 3.14 continued

the connate salinity near the wellbore. There is no change in resistivity at the transition from gas to oil, because the resistive characters of oil and gas are not dissimilar. An abrupt change is, however, noticed in the transition from oil to water. Such a change, in the absense of a simultaneous change in porosity response from the neutron log, indicates transition from oil to water.

Shaly Sandstone Formation: 6880–6900 ft

SP log   Fluctuations of the SP between the shale and sand baselines indicates a shaly sandstone. In particular, the interval between 6880 and 6900 ft is very shaly.

GR log   Fluctuation of the GR between the shale and sand beselines indicates a shaley sandstone, and in most cases the GR is a better indicator of shaliness than the SP.

Neutron log   The interval from 6880 to 6900 ft is a low-porosity interval.

Resistivity   Generally low resistivity with alternating zones of resistivity separation.

Several basic arguments concern the choice of perforation interval:

1. The oil zone is apparently separated into two sections by a shale streak.
2. The upper zone is thin (6 ft) and is overlain by a gas cap.
3. The lower zone is thicker (24 ft) and is underlain by a water zone.
4. A thin shale streak at the bottom of the 24-ft oil interval may separate the oil from the water zone.

Perforating the upper sand zone, which is in communication with the gas cap, will almost certainly result in gas coning. On the other hand, it will be necessary to delineate with other wells whether the shale section is continuous. If the shale section is continuous, the oil will be left in the ground unless the upper sand is perforated. If the shale streak is discontinuous, the oil can be drained by production from the lower oil zone and the barrier will in fact function as an impediment to gas coning. In summary, we do not recommend perforating the upper oil zone unless the shale barrier is definitively continuous, and even in this case it is probably best to come back to the zone after the lower section has been at least partially depleted.

Perforating the lower 24-ft oil section is the obvious choice for this well. It is probably best to avoid perforating too near the water/oil contact, even though the shale streak appears to separate the oil from the water.

Given a more complicated completion design as illustrated in figure E3.14b, both the lower and the upper oil zones could be perforated providing a selective production arrangement designed to allow production from one or both of the zones. A sliding-sleeve completion arrangement would allow testing of the upper section for a period of time after depletion of the lower section. If pressure has declined in the upper zone during production from the lower zone, then drainage from both intervals is certain.

EXAMPLE 3.14 continued

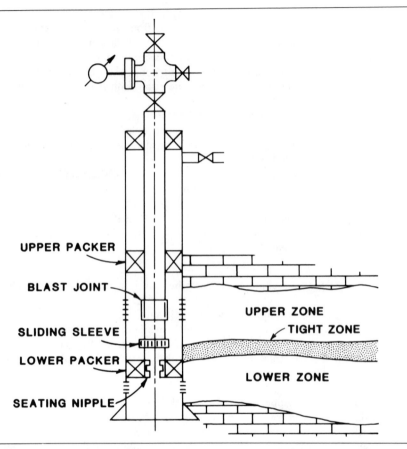

UPPER PACKER

BLAST JOINT

SLIDING SLEEVE

LOWER PACKER

SEATING NIPPLE

UPPER ZONE

TIGHT ZONE

LOWER ZONE

Figure E3.14b Recommended completion interval for the ABW No. 1 well, using a selective production arrangement.

The quality of the cement bond is recorded by a wireline cement bond log (CBL). The CBL uses a sonic device that transmits a sonic pulse through the casing and cement sheath to the formation. A receiver records the travel time, arrival amplitude, and wave train. These signals are processed to calculate a bond index factor, which indicates the quality of the bond. A good bond is considered to be achieved when the bond index factor is at values greater than 0.8. Quantitative and qualitative interpretations of CBL are presented in numerous publications, such as publications by Gromangin et al. (1961), Pradue et al. (1963), Walker (1968), Fertl et al. (1974), Fitzgerald et al. (1983), and Bigelow (1985).

Once the quality of the cement bond is established, the length of good cement bond required to isolate an oil zone in a well with a given casing size is given in figure 3.36.

A poor cement job requires a squeeze operation to secure isolation of the oil

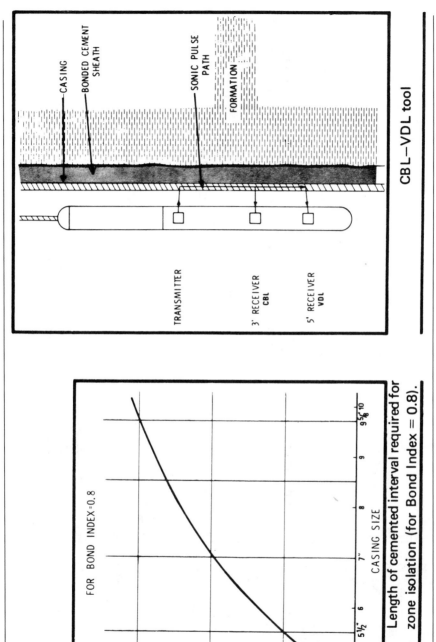

CBL—VDL tool

Figure 3.36 Length of effective cement bond required to isolate an oil zone from gas and/or water. Courtesy Schlumberger Well Services.

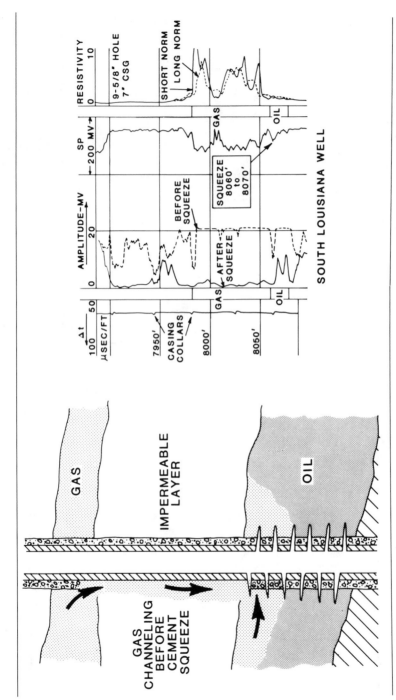

Figure 3.37 Example CBL log indicating need for cement squeeze. After Grosmangin et al. 1961, fig. 12, by permission of the SPE-AIME, © 1961 SPE-AIME.

zone from gas and/or water. Figure 3.37 illustrates a CBL log for a well in southern Louisiana (Grosmangin et al. 1961). The perforated interval (8061–8079 ft) initially produced gas through a channel in the casing annulus. A squeeze cement job was used to isolate the gas and oil zones, after which the well produced only oil. Note that the indicated squeeze interval included part of the oil-producing zone. This practice is undesirable, since it can lead to excessive formation damage and the possibility of a lost hole. As a rule, avoid squeezing directly into the producing interval.

Another important aspect related to productivity calculations is permeability distribution. Permeability distribution can be measured from core data along the pay-zone interval. Statistically, the permeability distribution along a cored interval is usually log-normal. That is, when frequency is plotted versus the log of permeability, a normal distribution results. (Frequency is the number of core samples having a given permeability or the number within a range of permeabilities.) The variation or spread of the permeabilities is often quantified by the Dykstra–Parsons (1950) variation factor V. A plot of permeability distribution on log–probability paper results in a straight line, from which V is defined as

$$V = \frac{k_{50} - k_{84.1}}{k_{50}}. \tag{3.49}$$

Figure 3.38 illustrates the log-probability plot. Average permeability for a log-normal distribution is the geometric average.

$$k_G = (k_1 \times k_2 \times k_3 \times \cdots \times k_n)^{1/n} \tag{3.50}$$

or

$$k_G = \exp[(1/n) \sum_{i=1}^{n} \ln(k_i)], \tag{3.51}$$

which can be shown to equal k_{50} at the 50% cumulative frequency point. Cardwell and Parsons (1945) and Warren and Price (1961) showed that the geometric average permeability is, in fact, the most representative average for an unlayered formation with random permeability distribution (see fig. 3.39).

If layering is prevalent (fig. 3.39[a]), the average permeability of the composite formation is an arithmetic average.

$$k_A = \frac{k_1 h_1 + k_2 h_2 + \cdots + k_n h_n}{h_1 + h_2 + \cdots + h_n} \tag{3.52}$$

or

$$k_A = \frac{\sum_{i=1}^{n} k_i h_i}{\sum_{i=1}^{n} h_i}, \tag{3.53}$$

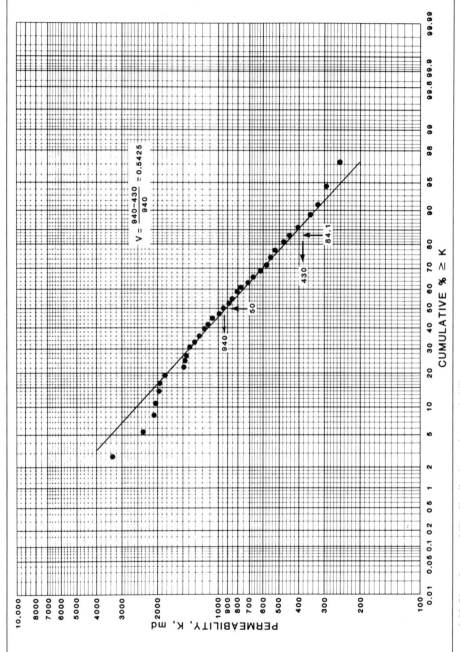

Figure 3.38 Plot of permeability distribution on log–probability paper.

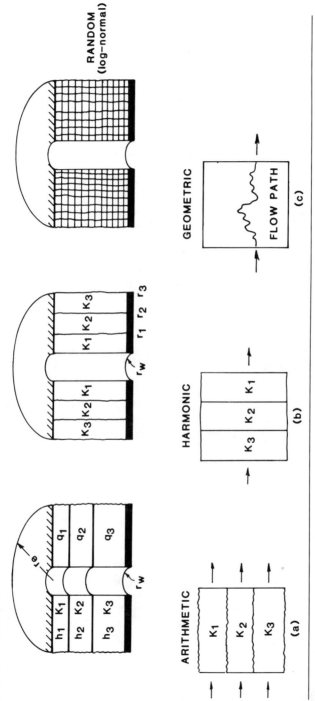

Figure 3.39 Layered reservoir, illustrating arithmetic and harmonic average permeabilities.

where k_i is the geometric average of layer i with thickness h_i. The layers are separated by impermeable barriers, across which flow does not occur.

When radial discontinuities exist (fig. 3.39[b]), the harmonic average may be used:

$$k_H = \frac{\ln(r_e/r_w)}{\displaystyle\sum_{i=1}^{n} \frac{\ln(r_i/r_{i-1})}{k_i}}, \qquad (3.54)$$

where $r_0 = r_w$ and $r_n = r_e$. Practically, the permeabilities of radial discontinuities are unknown and the harmonic average cannot be used. The most common radial discontinuity is damage near the wellbore, which we generally recognize in the form of a skin factor.

Apparently, there is widespread consensus that the geometric average permeability of unlayered formations (fig. 3.39[c]) is the most representative. The effect of anisotropy and flow path is negligible and need not be considered unless other factors such as partial penetration and coning exist. We might note that the geometric average is smaller than the arithmetic average and greater than the harmonic average: $k_A > k_G > k_H$. Example 3.15 illustrates calculation of average permeability in a pay zone.

EXAMPLE 3.15 CALCULATION OF AVERAGE PERMEABILITY FOR A COMPLEX RESERVOIR

The ABW No. 1 (example 3.14) has been perforated in the lower oil zone from 6828 to 6848 ft. Using the core analysis reported in table E3.15, and plotted in figure E3.15, calculate the geometric average permeability that should be used for reservoir calculations (and that should be compared with buildup-calculated permeability).

SOLUTION

Table E3.15 gives air permeabilities for the interval that has been perforated. We assume that only this section contributes to flow and permeabilities in the adjoining sand are not relevant.

The best average permeability is the geometric average. Using the products of air permeabilities to calculate this average may produce numbers larger than can be operated on by pocket calculators or computers. A better method of calculation is therefore to sum the logarithms of permeabilities, divide by the total number of samples, and take the resulting number to the power of the logarithm base. Using the natural logarithm,

$$k_G = \exp\{[\ln(k_1) + \ln(k_2) + \cdots + \ln(k_n)]/n\}$$

$$= \exp\{[\ln(347) + \ln(572) + \cdots + \ln(961)]/18\}$$

EXAMPLE 3.15 continued

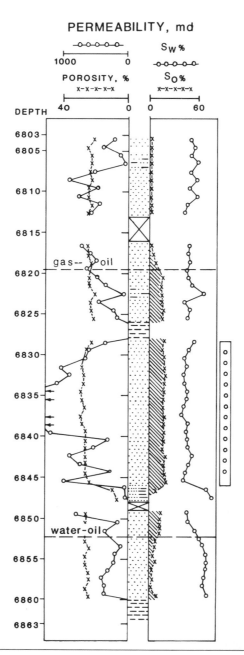

Figure E3.15 Core analysis of the ABW No. 1 well. Reprinted by permission of McGraw-Hill Book Company from Amyx, Bass, and Whiting 1960, fig. 7.24.

EXAMPLE 3.15 continued

Table E3.15 Core Analysis Report of ABW Well No. 1

Sample no.	Depth (ft)	Permeability (md)	Porosity (%)	Residual liquid saturation (% pore space)		Probable production
				Oil	Total Water	
43	6803.5	201	20.3	2.0	51.5	Gas/Cond.
44	04.5	354	23.6	2.0	57.2	Gas/Cond.
45	05.5	106	22.1	1.9	53.4	Gas/Cond.
46	06.5	25	22.2	2.0	59.0	Gas/Cond.
47	07.5	498	23.1	2.0	50.0	Gas/Cond.
48	08.5	906	22.0	2.1	58.4	Gas/Cond.
49	09.5	146	23.3	2.1	48.5	Gas/Cond.
50	10.5	747	23.9	2.0	60.0	Gas/Cond.
51	11.5	410	21.9	2.1	46.5	Gas/Cond.
52	12.5	536	23.7	2.0	44.1	Gas/Cond.
53	6816.5	693	23.8	2.0	50.3	Gas/Cond.
54	17.5	560	23.2	6.8	48.6	Gas/Cond.
55	18.5	448	22.0	8.0	50.7	Gas/Cond.
56	19.5	612	23.1	14.1	46.3	Oil
57	20.5	448	22.9	18.3	48.9	Oil
58	21.5	327	22.6	16.2	52.3	Oil
59	22.5	25	20.1	16.5	68.2	Oil
60	23.5	418	21.7	16.1	44.2	Oil
61	24.5	203	22.0	17.8	51.0	Oil
62	25.5	146	21.2	16.0	48.9	Oil
63	6828.5	347	21.7	17.6	56.3	Oil
64	29.5	572	24.0	16.4	49.4	Oil
65	30.5	628	24.9	18.9	43.0	Oil
66	31.5	981	26.6	20.0	46.1	Oil
67	32.5	862	25.6	20.3	42.5	Oil
68	33.5	1040	26.0	20.1	45.4	Oil
69	34.5	2200	28.1	18.6	47.6	Oil
70	35.5	3200	27.3	17.9	47.7	Oil
71	36.5	1162	25.8	19.0	44.2	Oil
72	37.5	1320	27.8	20.0	40.9	Oil
73	38.5	1282	27.2	18.6	49.2	Oil
74	39.5	1141	26.2	18.0	46.4	Oil
75	40.5	257	25.6	18.3	47.2	Oil
76	41.5	482	24.7	16.3	48.1	Oil
77	42.5	844	24.8	20.0	52.1	Oil
78	43.5	665	24.1	17.8	47.6	Oil
79	44.5	221	24.8	19.3	44.3	Oil
80	45.5	961	23.9	19.8	42.7	Oil
81	46.5	0.0	9.8	7.7	68.5	
82	47.5	0.0	6.9	0.0	76.0	
83	49.5	793	25.0	14.0	47.2	Oil
84	50.5	137	26.1	11.9	48.7	Oil
85	51.5	323	25.2	12.6	56.1	Oil

EXAMPLE 3.15 continued

Table E3.15 (continued)

Sample no.	Depth (ft)	Permeability (md)	Porosity (%)	Residual liquid saturation (% pore space) Oil	Total Water	Probable production
86	52.5	127	25.1	7.6	60.6	Water
87	53.5	97	23.9	7.3	65.2	Water
88	54.5	196	25.8	4.0	67.8	Water
89	55.5	202	24.9	6.3	69.2	Water
90	56.5	301	24.0	1.9	68.1	Water
91	57.5	396	23.9	4.1	65.5	Water
92	58.5	340	24.7	2.0	63.9	Water
93	59.5	336	23.9	6.9	67.8	Water

$$= \exp(121/18)$$

$$= 816 \, \text{md}.$$

This permeability is for air at low pressures. The actual permeability is smaller than this value because of slippage (gas molecules flow through the pores at a faster velocity than a nonreactive liquid). Correction for the so-called Klinkenberg effect should be applied to the 816-md value before using it in reservoir calculations. Also, correction should be made for the effect of an irreducible water saturation.

Assuming there is communication between the lower and the upper oil zones, the best average permeability is the arithmetic average of the geometric averages of each zone. The upper oil zone, from 6820 to 6826 ft, has a geometric average permeability of 189 md, giving a total average for the entire oil zone of

$$k = \frac{k_1 h_1 + k_2 h_2}{h_1 + h_2}$$

$$= \frac{(816)(18) + (189)(6)}{18 + 6}$$

$$= 659 \, \text{md}.$$

In review, several reservoir data are needed to define net pay zone, estimate its productivity and calculate the hydrocarbon pore volume:

1. porosity from log and core data
2. water saturation from log data
3. permeability from core and well test data
4. capillary pressure from core and log data

5. relative permeabilities from core data
6. isopach map from log and core data
7. structure map from log, core, and seismic data

These data are prepared by geologists, log analysts, and reservoir engineers and are usually readily available for well productivity calculations.

3.10   **SUMMARY.** This chapter discussed flow restrictions that affect flow toward the wellbore and, in general, reduce the productivity of a well. Compared with the radial model well, flow restrictions create additional pressure drops that require lower flowing pressures to maintain a desired rate of production. Skin factor has been chosen to characterize nonideal conditions, because it is simple to use and it has general applicability. Skin factor (in its traditional definition) represents a dimensionless pressure drop occurring near or at the entry to the wellbore.

Skin factor is a quantitative measure used to evaluate the performance of a well relative to an ideal well producing from a fully open, unrestricted formation. The magnitude of skin indicates the need to stimulate the well or perform remedial workover. In his classic paper on skin effect, van Everdingen (1953) gives two examples showing that detrimental skin can be recognized by proper well test interpretation, and that remedial action can improve reservoir well performance. The most important types of flow restriction quantified in terms of skin are

1. formation damage
2. limited completion interval
3. high-velocity flow (turbulence)
4. perforation effects
5. saturation blockage near the wellbore
6. sand control measures

Rate-dependent skin is the concept adopted by the petroleum industry to express the most general flow equation for flow in porous media, the Forchheimer equation. It extends the radial flow equations developed from Darcy's law, the simplest and most fundamental law governing flow in porous media. In terms of skin, two types Darcy (steady-state) skin and non-Darcy (high-velocity-flow) skin, are required to account for flow restrictions.

Perhaps the most important use of skin is to determine whether a well's performance can be improved by remedial efforts such as reperforation or stimulation. The skin factor determined by well test analysis is a composite of all nonideal conditions of flow. Useful models have been presented that allow back-calculation of the elements of the composite skin that cannot be changed by stimulation treatment. For example, if a well penetrates only 25% of the total formation thickness to avoid coning, then a skin due to limited entry should be expected. Well test data may indicate a positive skin, on the order of +23, but if the back-calculated contribution of limited entry is a skin of only +13, then the additional skin may be attributed to formation damage near the wellbore. This

Effect	Constant skin factor	Rate-dependent skin
Radial flow in the reservoir	$\ln(r_e/r_w) - 0.75$	$$D_{Rg} = 2.222 \times 10^{-18}\,\frac{\gamma_g kh}{\mu_g h_p^2}\left(\frac{1}{r_a} - \frac{1}{r_e}\right)\beta_R$$ or $$D_{Rg} = 2.222 \times 10^{-18}\,\frac{\gamma_g kh}{\mu_g r_w h_p^2}\,\beta_R$$ $$D_{Ro} = 1.635 \times 10^{-16}\,\frac{B_o \rho_o kh}{\mu_o h_p^2}\left(\frac{1}{r_a} - \frac{1}{r_e}\right)\beta_R$$ or $$D_{Ro} = 1.635 \times 10^{-16}\,\frac{kh\rho_o B_o}{\mu_o r_w h_p^2}\,\beta_R$$
Formation damage	$s_a = (k/k_a - 1)\ln(r_a/r_w)$	$$D_{ag} = 2.222 \times 10^{-18}\,\frac{\gamma_g kh}{\mu_g h_p^2}\,(1/r_w - 1/r_a)\,\beta_a$$ $$D_{ao} = 1.635 \times 10^{-16}\,\frac{kh\rho_o B_o}{\mu_o h_p^2}\,(1/r_w - 1/r_a)\,\beta_a$$
Partial penetration, limited entry	$s_c = (1/b - 1)[\ln(h_D) - G(b)]$	expressed by substituting h_p instead of h in D_R and D_a
Convergence to perforations	from s_p charts	not considered
Perforation crushed zone	$s_{dp} = \left(\dfrac{k}{k_{dp}} - \dfrac{k}{k_a}\right)\left(\dfrac{12h_p}{nL_p}\right)\ln(r_{dp}/r_p)$	$$D_{dp} = 3.84 \times 10^{-15}\left(\frac{kh\gamma_g}{\mu_g}\right)\left(\frac{\beta_{dp}}{n^2 L_p^2 r_p}\right)$$
Linear flow in packed perforations	$s_G = 96\,\dfrac{(k/k_G)hL_p}{d_p^2 n}$	$$D_{Gg} = 2.45 \times 10^{-13}\,\frac{\gamma_g khL_p}{\mu_g d_p^4 n^2}\,\beta_G$$ $$D_{Go} = 1.80 \times 10^{-11}\,\frac{B_o\rho_o khL_p}{\mu_o d_p^4 n^2}\,\beta_G$$
Condensate blockage	$s_b = 0.5\left(\dfrac{1}{k_{rgc}} - 1\right)\ln[(r_b/r_w)^2]$ $r_b = r_b(q_g, t)$	

Note: Total constant skin:
$s = s_c + s_G + s_{dp} + (h/h_p)s_p + (h/h_p)s_a$
Total rate-dependent skin:
$D = D_R + D_a + D_{dp} + D_G$

damage can probably be removed by chemical treatment, thereby improving the well's performance.

A simple model that relates the individual components of the composite skin factor helps in back-calculation of restrictions that can be eliminated. It also helps in predicting the performance of wells in the planning stage of field development. Sensitivity analysis can be performed, to investigate factors that are likely to contribute the most pronounced effect on reservoir performance (perforating shot density, gravel pack, stimulation, etc.). In this simplified model, interaction of the individual restrictions is not accounted for. The effect of limited entry is included, however, by assuming that the increase in velocity near the wellbore will be in proportion to the ratio of total thickness to the open interval, h/h_p. This model seems to be adequate for most engineering calculations.

Table 3.7 lists the individual skin effects and their corresponding skin-factor expressions. We emphasize that these expressions are only approximate and that they must be used with a degree of conservatism. The most accurate estimate of steady-state skin s is from buildup test data. The best estimate of the high-velocity-flow term D is from accurate multirate test data. In general, field data should always be considered more valuable for quantifying skin than predictive mathematical expressions based on simplified models.

4   RATE DECLINE ANALYSIS

The IPR equation for stabilized production presented in the previous three chapters, together with vertical flow performance as discussed in chapter 1, are adequate to predict flow rate and wellhead conditions at a given time. Furthermore, the ability to calculate changes in IPR equations and vertical flow performance during depletion of a reservoir adds a time dimension to the analysis and allows determination of:

1. the decrease of wellhead pressure needed to maintain constant production rate, and the duration for which a constant rate can be maintained
2. the decline of production rate if wellhead pressure is maintained constant

So far such depletion-governed calculations can be performed only if changes in the reservoir during depletion can be forecast by reservoir material balance calculations.

The first four sections of this chapter consider particular cases of production decline in wells producing with constant wellhead pressure that can be treated *without* explicit material balance calculations. Production with constant wellhead pressure is typical for low-productivity wells producing against the constant pressure of a separator or a pipeline without restriction or control by a wellhead choke. It is also typical for "old" high-rate wells when wellhead pressure has already reached the minimum delivery pressure required to sustain flow against a constant separator and flowline backpressure. In either case, constant wellhead pressure implies decline in production rate.

The constant flowing wellhead pressure that exists in practical problems does not correspond rigorously to a constant flowing bottomhole pressure, which is assumed in developing the methods in this chapter. In fact, bottomhole pressure does change if the flow rate declines gradually and wellhead pressure is maintained constant. These changes, however, are often insignificant, so neglecting them allows a considerable simplification of the calculations with only a minor loss of accuracy.

The basis for calculating rate decline in the first four sections is a set of characteristic curves, referred to as *type curves*, developed by Fetkovich (1980).

These curves result from mathematical and empirical investigations and are suggested here as quick solutions to a variety of production rate decline problems. Two distinct periods of rate decline in a well are considered in the chapter:

1. *Transient decline* ("infinite-acting"), which is the natural decline caused by expansion of oil, gas, and water in a drainage region with continuously increasing radius (section 4.1).
2. *Depletion decline* ("pseudosteady state"), which is the natural decline following transient decline; it occurs after the radius of drainage has reached the outer boundaries and the well is draining a constant reservoir volume (section 4.2).

For practical purposes, transient decline is only observed in wells with effective permeability less than about 100 md. Depletion decline, on the other hand, is observed for all wells producing by expansion, solution-gas, gravity drainage, or partial water drive.

The methods presented in the first four sections have a multitude of applications. They can be used to identify a production decline trend in a well or a field and to extrapolate it into the future. They also provide tools to interpret rate decline in terms of the reservoir properties of permeability, skin, and the size of the drainage region. They can also be used to extrapolate the immediate changes of rate decline caused by stimulation treatments or adjustments in surface backpressure, which may occur at any time during the life of the well.

Special consideration is given to the effect of stimulation treatment on the production profiles of oil and gas wells. Section 4.3 describes the various methods of well stimulation and explains techniques to apply type curves to forecasting the production of stimulated wells. Other particular cases where wellbore pressure is not constant with time are treated in section 4.4. It considers cases of gradual decrease and abrupt changes in pressure.

The chapter concludes with a section discussing the role of production forecasting for field planning and economical analysis. It particularly addresses the planning of offshore fields and certain onshore fields where considerable initial investment is required prior to production start-up.

4.1   **TRANSIENT RATE DECLINE.** In section 2.7 it was established that opening a well to production disturbs the equilibrium state of the reservoir and creates a pressure response at the wellbore. The pressure disturbance propagates gradually away from the wellbore, increasing the area drained by the well. As long as the pressure disturbance propagates toward the outer boundaries, production conditions at the wellbore change rapidly. Production during this period is referred to as transient production, or production from an infinite-acting reservoir.

When the pressure disturbance reaches all outer boundaries and the entire drainage area starts to contribute to production, wellbore conditions tend to stabilize at a pseudosteady state. Pseudosteady state is characterized by slow changes in production condition resulting from depletion of the entire well's drainage volume.

Two modes of transient production are usually considered and treated mathematically: constant production rate and constant flowing wellbore pressure. These two production modes are illustrated schematically in figure 4.1. The figure illustrates that constant rate implies a decline in wellbore pressure and that constant pressure implies a decline in production rate. Section 2.7 develops equations for pressure transience at constant flow rate. This section quantifies the transient rate decline for a well with constant flowing wellbore pressure.

For the purpose of expressing rate versus time, it is useful to consider transient production as a series of "steady-state" productions with increasing radius of drainage. Thus, writing the steady-state radial flow equation, equation (2.9), for constant pressure drawdown and an increasing drainage radius gives

$$q_o(t) = \frac{kh(p_e - p_{wf})}{141.2\mu_o B_o \ln[r_e(t)/r_{wa}]},$$
(4.1)

where r_{wa} is an apparent wellbore radius, defined in chapter 2 (eq. [2.34]) as $r_{wa} = r_w e^{-s}$. Equation (4.1) indicates that increasing drainage radius results in rate decline. Figure 4.2 shows the typical transience of $r_e(t)$ and $q_o(t)$ and illustrates the increasing drainage radius and the corresponding decline of duction rate.

The problem of quantifying $r_e(t)$ and $q_o(t)$ has received extensive mathematical treatment, starting with formulating the governing physical phenomena as a differential equation, and then solving the equation for relevant boundary and initial conditions. The solution obtained is usually given in the form of dimensionless rate q_D versus dimensionless time t_D, where

$$q_D = \frac{141.2\mu_o B_o}{kh(p_i - p_{wf})} q_o,$$
(4.2)

$$t_D = \frac{0.000264k}{\phi\mu_i c_{ti} r_{wa}^2} t,$$
(2.129)

and real time t is given in hours,

k = permeability (md)
ϕ = porosity (fraction)
μ_i = initial viscosity (cp)
c_{ti} = initial total compressibility (1/psi)
and r_{wa} = apparent wellbore radius (ft).

If t is given in days, then dimensionless time is written

$$t_D = \frac{0.00634k}{\phi\mu_i c_{ti} r_{wa}^2} t.$$
(4.3)

A graphical presentation by Earlougher (1977) of the general solution for infinite-acting transient conditions obtained originally by Jacob and Lohman (1952) is given in figure 4.3. It is a plot of dimensionless variables on log–log paper. Such a

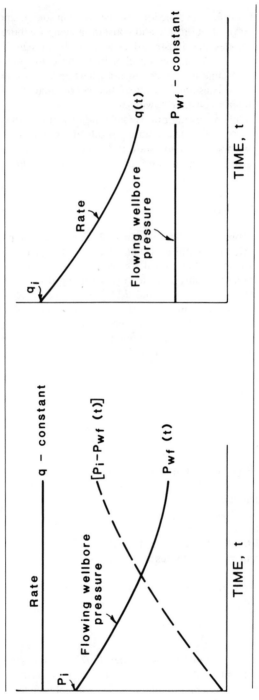

Figure 4.1 Transient pressure and transient rate decline.

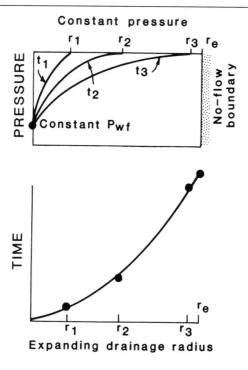

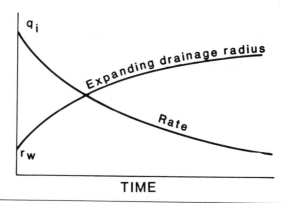

Figure 4.2 Rate behavior of a well producing against a constant backpressure, and the concept of an expanding drainage radius.

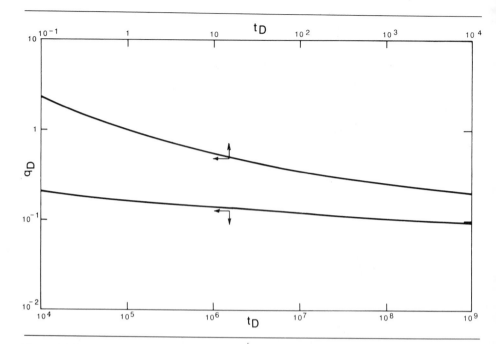

Figure 4.3 Infinite-acting dimensionless-rate solution. Reprinted by permission of the SPE-AIME from Earlougher 1977, fig. 4.12, p. 5. © 1977 SPE-AIME. Data from Jacob and Lohman 1952.

plot has particularly useful features that are discussed later in this section. Customarily, this type of plot is referred to as a *type curve*. The solution in figure 4.3 presents the behavior of a well during the transient period, where it behaves as if it drains an infinite reservoir. Accordingly, this decline solution is referred to as "infinite-acting." Note that the terms "infinite-acting decline" and "transient decline" are used interchangeably.

The definition of q_D in equation (4.2) implies that the transient drainage radius is related to the dimensionless rate by

$$r_e(t) = r_{wa}\exp(1/q_D).\tag{4.4}$$

It is important to recognize that the concept of an expanding drainage radius is valid only during the infinite-acting period.

The calculation of transient rate decline with constant wellbore pressure is similar to the previously discussed calculation of the wellbore pressure decline at constant production rate. The pressure decline case is treated in section 2.7, where it is expressed, by rearranging equation (2.136), as

$$p_i - p_{wf}(t) = \frac{141.2q_o\mu_o B_o}{kh}\ln\left[\frac{r_e(t)}{r_{wa}}\right],\tag{4.5}$$

or, when combined with the definition of p_D in equation (2.137), it is expressed as

$$p_i - p_{wf}(t) = \frac{141.2 q_o \mu_o B_o}{kh} p_D, \qquad (4.6)$$

and the p_D versus t_D solution is given in figure 2.24. Thus, according to the actual production mode of the well, the engineer has the option to use either the p_D or the q_D general solution.

In section 2.7 it is also shown that the condition for reaching pseudosteady state for a well in the center of a radial geometry is

$$t_{DApss} = 0.1, \qquad (2.131)$$

or

$$t_{Dpss} = 0.1 \pi (r_e/r_{wa})^2. \qquad (2.132)$$

In terms of real time, the condition in equations (2.131) and (2.132) becomes

$$t_{pss} = 379 \frac{\phi \mu_i c_{ti} A}{k}, \qquad (2.133)$$

where

t_{pss} is expressed in hrs
A is expressed in ft^2
μ_i is expressed in cp
c_{ti} is expressed in 1/psi
k is expressed in md.

Equation (2.133) states an important conclusion, that the time to the end of the transient period is a function of the permeability, but not a function of the skin or the apparent wellbore radius.

Assuming that oil fields are typically developed with 40-acre spacing and gas fields with 160-acre spacing, equation (2.133) used with "typical" oil and gas reservoir data gives a rule of thumb valid for oil and gas wells:

$$t_{pss} = \frac{2000}{k},$$

where t_{pss} is given in hours. This rule of thumb should be used only for estimation of the order of magnitude of the transient period.

Example 4.1 illustrates the use of the general infinite-acting solution and reservoir properties, to calculate wellbore conditions during the transient production period of the well.

EXAMPLE 4.1 CALCULATING DIMENSIONLESS QUANTITIES AND
ESTABLISHING THEIR RELATION TO PHYSICAL QUANTITIES

Typical well and reservoir data for oil wells completed in the Pennsylvanian Strawn
sand in the KWB field, Tom Green County, Texas, are given in table E4.1a.

As a part of a preliminary production study, it is required to estimate the time for
the end of the transient production and the start of depletion. It is also desired to
calculate the production characteristics during the transient period if the wells are
to be produced

1. at a constant production rate $q = 60 \, \text{STB/D}$
2. at a constant flowing wellbore pressure $p_{wf} = 1200 \, \text{psia}$

SOLUTION

Using equation (2.132), the dimensionless time for start of pseudosteady state flow
is calculated as

$$t_{Dpss} = 0.1\pi \left(\frac{r_e}{r_{wa}}\right)^2$$

$$= 0.1\pi \left(\frac{744}{0.33}\right)^2 = 1.6 \times 10^6.$$

In real time, by using equation (2.129), this condition corresponds to

$$t_{pss} = \frac{1.6 \times 10^6 \times 0.117 \times 0.2 \times 30 \times 10^{-6} \times 0.33^2}{0.000264 \times 0.25}$$

$$= 1850 \text{ hours}$$

$$= 77 \text{ days}.$$

Table E4.1a Reservoir Data for a Typical KWB Well

p_i = 2600 psia
μ_{oi} = 0.2 cp
B_{oi} = 1.642 bbl/STB
h = 66 ft
r_w = 0.33 ft
c_{ti} = 30 × 10^{-6} psi^{-1}
ϕ = 0.117
S_w = 0.32
r_e = 744 ft (40-acre spacing)
k = 0.25 md

EXAMPLE 4.1 (continued)

For the case of constant rate production, pressure versus time will be calculated according to the following procedure:

a. List the production time in days, from 1 to 70, in 10-day increments.
b. Calculate the corresponding dimensionless time t_D using equation (4.3), which states:

$$t_D = \frac{0.00634k}{\phi\mu_i c_{ti} r_{wa}^2}t = \frac{0.00634 \times 0.25}{0.117 \times 0.2 \times 30 \times 10^{-6} \times 0.33^2}t$$

$$= 20,733t \text{ (days).}$$

c. Read p_D values from the type curve in figure 2.24 corresponding to t_D values.
d. Calculate $[p_i - p_{wf}(t)]$ using equation (2.137), which gives:

$$\Delta p = \frac{141.2 q_o \mu_o B_o}{kh}p_D = \frac{141.2 \times 60 \times 0.2 \times 1.642}{0.25 \times 66}p_D$$

$$= 169 p_D.$$

e. Calculate $p_{wf}(t)$ by subtracting Δp from p_i, which gives:

$$p_{wf} = p_i - \Delta p = 2600 - 169 p_D.$$

The resulting p_{wf}'s are tabulated in table E4.1b.
For the case of constant pressure, production declining rate is calculated according to the following procedure:

a. List production time (in days) in 10-day increments.
b. Calculate the corresponding dimensionless time t_D using equation (4.3).
c. Read q_D from figure 4.3 at the corresponding values of t_D.
d. Calculate the corresponding rates $q_o(t)$ from q_D using equation (4.2), which gives

$$q_o(t) = \frac{kh(p_i - p_{wf})}{141.2\mu_o B_o}q_D$$

$$= \frac{0.25 \times 66(2600 - 1200)}{141.2 \times 0.2 \times 1.642}q_D = 498 q_D.$$

The results are tabulated in table E4.1c.

EXAMPLE 4.1 continued

Table E4.1b Pressure Decline with Constant Production Rate, 60 STB/D

t (days)	t (hours)	t_D	p_D	Δp (psia)	p_{wf} (psia)
1	24	2.07×10^4	5.37	908.0	1692.0
10	240	2.07×10^5	6.50	1096.0	1504.0
20	480	4.15×10^5	6.87	1158.4	1441.6
40	960	8.29×10^5	7.20	1214.1	1385.9
60	1440	1.24×10^6	7.40	1247.8	1352.2
70	1680	1.45×10^6	7.50	1264.7	1335.4

Table E4.1c Rate Decline with Constant Production Pressure, $p_{wf} = 1200$ psia

t (days)	t (hours)	t_D	q_D	q_o (STB/D)
1	24	2.07×10^4	0.182	90.7
10	240	2.07×10^5	0.150	74.7
20	480	4.15×10^5	0.144	71.7
40	960	8.29×10^5	0.140	69.7
60	1440	1.24×10^6	0.133	66.3
70	1680	1.45×10^6	0.130	64.8

The dimensionless-rate solution is not limited to undersaturated oil wells. It can be applied for other oil and gas systems by appropriate definitions of dimensionless rate.

Oil wells, undersaturated:

$$q_D = \frac{141.2\mu_o B_o}{kh(p_i - p_{wf})} q_o. \tag{4.2}$$

Oil wells, saturated (pressure-squared):

$$q_D = \frac{141.2(2p_i)}{kh(k_{ro}/\mu_o B_o)_i(p_i^2 - p_{wf}^2)} q_o. \tag{4.7}$$

Gas wells, low-pressure (pressure-squared):

$$q_D = \frac{\mu_i Z_i T}{0.703 kh(p_i^2 - p_{wf}^2)} q_g. \tag{4.8}$$

Gas wells, general (pseudopressure):

$$q_D = \frac{T}{0.703kh[m(p_i) - m(p_{wf})]} q_g. \tag{4.9}$$

In these equations defining dimensionless rate, the driving potential is expressed as $(p_i - p_{wf})$, $(p_i^2 - p_{wf}^2)$, or $[m(p_i) - m(p_{wf})]$, and is assumed constant when used with the dimensionless rate–time solution.

For computing purposes, the dimensionless rate–time solution given in figure 4.3 can be expressed as a set of aproximate equations. Van Everdingen and Hurst (1949) gave the asymptotic infinite-acting q_D solution that applies for $t_D \leqslant 0.01$:

$$q_D = \frac{1}{(\pi t_D)^{0.5}}. \tag{4.10}$$

Two approximate equations for infinite-acting q_D are given by Edwardson et al. (1962), for $t_D > 200$:

$$q_D = \frac{26.7544 + 43.5537t_D^{0.5} + 13.3813t_D + 0.492949t_D^{1.5}}{47.4210t_D^{0.5} + 35.5372t_D + 2.60967t_D^{1.5}} \tag{4.11}$$

for $200 > t_D > 0.01$:

$$q_D = \frac{3.90086 + 2.02623t_D[\ln(t_D) - 1]}{t_D[\ln(t_D)]^2}. \tag{4.12}$$

At large dimensionless times the infinite-acting q_D solution approaches the inverse of the p_D logarithmic approximation and can be expressed for $t_D > 5,000$ as

$$q_D = \frac{2}{\ln(t_D) + 0.80907}, \tag{4.13}$$

which Earlougher (1977) claims is correct within 0.1% for $t_D > 5 \times 10^{11}$, within 1% for $t_D > 80,000$, and within 2% for $t_D > 5,000$.

In example 4.1 the general rate solution and reservoir properties are used to predict rate–time behavior. A different use of the general solution is when production data exists and can be matched to the type curve to identify the reservoir parameters and to extrapolate rate decline into the future. Type-curve matching utilizes the proportion between real and dimensionless properties. This proportion implies that the logarithm of real properties is equal to the logarithm of dimensionless properties plus a constant. Considering dimensionless rate and time, from figure 4.3,

$$q_D = \frac{141.2\mu_o B_o}{kh(p_i - p_{wf})} q_o \tag{4.2}$$

and

$$t_D = \frac{0.000264k}{\phi\mu_i c_{ti} r_{wa}^2} t. \tag{2.129}$$

Taking the logarithm of each, the proportionality constant relating real to dimensionless variables is given by a linear shift:

$$\log q_D = \log\left[\frac{141.2\mu_o B_o}{kh(p_i - p_{wf})}\right] + \log q_o \tag{4.14}$$

$$\underset{\text{log–log paper}}{\underbrace{\text{linear shift on}}}$$

and

$$\log t_D = \log\left(\frac{0.000264k}{\phi\mu_i c_{ti} r_{wa}^2}\right) + \log t. \tag{4.15}$$

$$\underset{\text{log–log paper}}{\underbrace{\text{linear shift on}}}$$

Plotting q_o versus t on tracing paper with the *same log–log scale* used for the $q_D(t_D)$ solution, it is possible to fit the rate–time data to the dimensionless type curve. The fit is made by laying the tracing paper with rate–time data over the type curve and shifting it horizontally and vertically, making sure that axes for rate and time are parallel with the axes for their dimensionless equivalents. Once a match is achieved, the ratio of real variables (q_o and t) and dimensionless variables (q_D and t_D) at any chosen match point can be used to calculate the constants of proportionality between q_o and q_D and t and t_D. In equation form, the match point states that

$$\left(\frac{q_D}{q_o}\right)_{\text{match}} = \frac{141.2\mu_o B_o}{kh(p_i - p_{wf})}, \tag{4.16}$$

$$\left(\frac{t_D}{t}\right)_{\text{match}} = \frac{0.000264k}{\phi\mu_i c_{ti} r_{wa}^2}. \tag{4.17}$$

The match point and the values of q_D/q_o and t_D/t used for the match point are chosen arbitrarily from the type-curve match. In fact, any point on the plot can be chosen after the match is made and it does not need to lie on the actual rate–time curve match. It is common to choose $q_D = 1$ and $t_D = 1$ for quick relocation of the fit after the tracing paper has been removed.

From the match of rate (eq. [4.16]) it is possible to calculate permeability, which for undersaturated oil wells is

$$k = \frac{141.2\mu_o B_o}{h(p_i - p_{wf})}\left(\frac{q_o}{q_D}\right)_{\text{match}}. \tag{4.18}$$

and by analogy, for low-pressure gas wells is

$$k = \frac{\mu_{gi} Z_i T}{0.703h(p_i^2 - p_{wf}^2)}\left(\frac{q_g}{q_D}\right)_{\text{match}}. \tag{4.19}$$

From the match of time it is possible to calculate skin factor, which in terms of apparent wellbore radius is

$$r_{wa}^2 = \frac{0.000264k}{\phi\mu_i c_{ti}} \left(\frac{t}{t_D}\right)_{match},$$

(4.20)

where

$$r_{wa} = r_w e^{-s}$$

(2.34)

and solved for skin factor

$$s = -\ln(r_{wa}/r_w).$$

(4.21)

Example 4.2 illustrates a type-curve match for an undersaturated oil well using the infinite-acting dimensionless rate solution in figure 4.3. A similar procedure is applied in example 4.3 for the analysis of a gas well producing from a low-permeability reservoir.

EXAMPLE 4.2 SEVEN-DAY OPEN-FLOW TEST OF AN UNDERSATURATED OIL WELL WITH MODERATE PERMEABILITY

An appraisal well M-4x (Fetkovich et al. 1984) drilled to the Carbonate Middle Cretaceous Mishrif structure (Middle East) has been treated with acid and tested for 7 days. The well and reservoir data are given in table E4.2a. During the 7-day production test, rate declined severely from an initial rate of 2361 STB/D to 1045 STB/D. Considering the moderate permeability of the formation, the decline was first suspected to be depletion, or more specifically, depletion of the natural fractures and vugs observed in cores of the Mishrif formation.

Rate decline during the test is listed in table E4.2b. It was also observed during the test that wellhead pressure was essentially constant (55 psia). Considering that the reservoir fluid is highly undersaturated and that hydrostatic head, rather than friction losses, dominate pressure losses in the tubing, wellbore pressure during the entire test was practically constant.

One engineer suspected, in contrast to the depletion theory, that the rapid rate decline was actually the expected behavior of a successfully stimulated well producing high-viscosity oil from a reservoir of moderate to low permeability. To check this, it is necessary to investigate whether the test data match the transient period of a type curve for constant-pressure rate decline. Based on the analysis, what is the right conclusion?

SOLUTION

The rate–time data from table E4.2b are plotted on tracing paper having the same log–log scale as the type curve in figure 4.3. The plot of the test data in figure E4.2

EXAMPLE 4.2 continued

Table E4.2a Well Data for the M-4x Oil Well

Wellbore radius r_w	0.328 ft
Drainage radius r_e	3000 ft
Initial gas–oil ratio	112 scf/STB
Initial oil viscosity μ_{oi}	2.3 cp
Oil gravity	22 API
Depth (midperforations)	7000 ft
Net pay-zone thickness h	30 ft
Initial reservoir pressure p_i	3360 psia
Flowing wellhead pressure p_{wh}	55 psia
Flowing wellbore pressure p_{wf}	2660 psia
Average flowing gradient G_f	0.38 psi/ft
Formation volume factor B_{oi}	1.1
Reservoir porosity ϕ	0.25
Total reservoir compressibility c_{ti}	$3 \times 10^{-6}\,\text{psi}^{-1}$

**Table E4.2b Rate Decline Data for the M-4x Oil Well with
Constant Flowing Wellbore Pressure, $p_{wf} = 2626$ psia**

t (hours)	q_o (STB/D)
6	1924.9
8	1845.2
9	1731.9
11	1653.3
12	1625.6
14	1591.6
16	1558.3
18	1525.8
19	1493.9
22	1493.9
34	1344.1
42	1305.0
48	1288.5
51	1261.6
69	1209.4
82	1159.4
106	1111.4
115	1088.2
125	1065.4
136	1043.2
149	1032.2
155	1021.3

EXAMPLE 4.2 continued

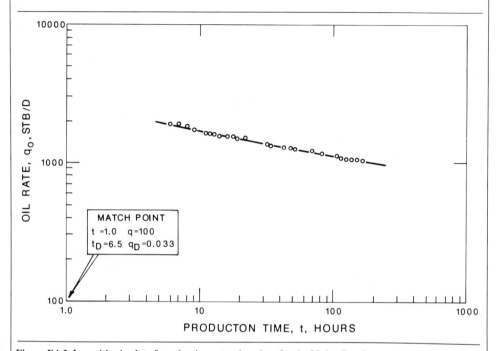

Figure E4.2 Logarithmic plot of production rate–time data for the M-4x oil well.

matches very well the radial q_D solution in figure 4.3. The conclusion is that the rapid rate decline is normal transient behavior rather than depletion. The match point is:

$t = 1$ hour, $\qquad t_D = 6.5$;

$q = 100\,\text{STB/D}$, $\qquad q_D = 0.033$.

From the match point it is possible to calculate the permeability using equation (4.18), which gives

$$k = \frac{141.2(2.3)(1.1)}{30(3360 - 2660)}\left(\frac{100}{0.033}\right) = 52\,\text{md}.$$

The apparent wellbore radius is calculated from equation (4.20):

$$r_{wa}^{2} = \frac{0.000264 \times 52}{0.25 \times 2.3 \times 3 \times 10^{-6}} \times \left(\frac{1}{6.5}\right) = 1224,$$

or

$r_{wa} = 35\,\text{ft}.$

EXAMPLE 4.2 continued

The apparent radius corresponds to a skin factor of

$$s = -\ln\frac{35}{0.328} = -4.7.$$

The cause of the relatively long transient period observed in the well is partly due to high viscosity of the oil. In fact, the effect of high oil viscosity is similar to the effect of low permeability in gas wells, where we usually expect a long transient period.

EXAMPLE 4.3 PRODUCTION HISTORY OF A LOW-PERMEABILITY LIMESTONE GAS WELL IN ALFALFA COUNTY, OKLAHOMA

The 1–4 Oare gas well has produced from the low-permeability Oswego limestone formation for 30 months at essentially constant wellhead pressure. Production data for the first 30 months are given in table E4.3a. The well was stimulated upon completion. Additional well and reservoir data are given in table E4.3b.

Use the type-curve matching technique to predict the time and the rate at the end of transient production. Use the match point to calculate permeability and skin factor for the well.

SOLUTION

The 30-month production data are plotted on logarithmic graph paper in figure E4.3 and matched on the type curve in figure 4.3. The point selected as a match point is

$$t_D = 1.0, \quad t = 3.1 \text{ months};$$

$$q_D = 0.1, \quad q = 0.48 \text{ mmscf/month}.$$

Substituting the match point in equation (4.19) calculates a formation permeability of

$$k = \frac{50.36 \times 2275 \times 0.0175 \times 0.00611}{13(2275^2 - 140^2)}\left(\frac{0.48}{0.1}\right) \times \frac{10^6}{30} = 0.0292 \text{ md}.$$

Substituting the match point and the calculated permeability in equation (4.20) gives

$$r_{wa}{}^2 = \frac{0.000264 \times 0.0292}{0.074 \times 0.0175 \times 0.0002686}\frac{(3.1 \times 30 \times 24)}{1.0} = 46{,}326,$$

or

$$r_{wa} = 215 \text{ ft},$$

EXAMPLE 4.3 continued

Table E4.3a Production Data for the First 30 Months of Production, 1–4 Oare Gas Well, Alfalfa County, Oklahoma

Data	Time (months)	q_g (MMscf/m)	G_p (MMscf)
1975 June	1	7.021	7.021
July	2	5.010	12.031
Aug.	3	5.607	17.638
Sep.	4	4.970	22.608
Oct.	5	3.546	26.154
Nov.	6	3.406	29.560
Dec.	7	3.246	32.806
1976 Jan.	8	3.489	36.295
Feb.	9	3.093	39.389
March	10	3.143	42.532
April	11	3.143	45.675
May	12	3.019	48.695
June	13	2.877	51.572
July	14	3.068	54.640
Aug.	15	3.019	57.660
Sep.	16	2.924	60.584
Oct.	17	3.220	63.804
Nov.	18	2.947	66.751
Dec.	19	2.995	69.747
1977 Jan.	20	3.019	72.766
Feb.	21	2.720	75.486
March	22	2.720	78.206
April	23	2.947	81.153
May	24	2.809	83.962
June	25	2.551	86.513
July	26	2.947	89.460
Aug.	27	2.613	92.073
Sep.	28	2.742	94.815
Oct.	29	2.720	97.535
Nov.	30	2.551	100.085

Table E4.3b Well Data for the 1–4 Oare Gas Well

Initial reservoir pressure p_i	2275 psia
Constant flowing wellbore pressure p_{wf}	140 psia
Net pay zone h	13 ft
Initial gas viscosity μ_{gi}	0.0175 cp
Initial gas formation volume factor B_{gi}	0.00611 ft³/scf
Total compressibility c_{ti}	0.0002686 psi⁻¹
Porosity ϕ	0.074
Reservoir temperature	138°F
Initial compressibility factor Z	0.82
Wellbore radius r_w	0.33 ft
Drainage radius r_e	2134 ft

EXAMPLE 4.3 continued

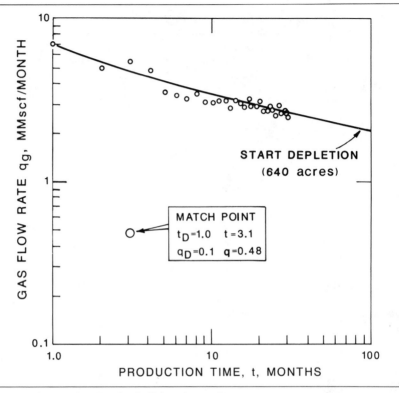

Figure E4.3 Rate–time data for the Oare 1-4 gas well.

which corresponds to a skin factor of

$s = -6.4$.

An estimated time for the start of pseudosteady state is calculated from equation (2.133) as

$$t_{pss} = 379 \times \frac{0.074 \times 0.0175 \times 0.0002686 \times 3.14 \times 2134^2}{0.0292}$$

$$= 64,558 \text{ hours} = 2689 \text{ days} = 89 \text{ months} = 7.5 \text{ years}.$$

Figure E4.3 extrapolates the infinite-acting rate decline to 100 months (8.3 years).

4.2   **DEPLETION RATE DECLINE.** In section 2.6 it was established that, following the early period of infinite-acting production, the production assumes more stable characteristics dominated by gradual reservoir depletion. Considering the concept of a series of "steady-state" productions to describe the behavior of a well, the onset of depletion is marked by the time the expanding drainage radius has reached the no-flow outer boundaries. Thereafter as production proceeds, the entire region drained by a well starts being depleted, and thus the pressure drops throughout the entire drainage area, as indicated in figure 4.4.

The figure illustrates two cases of depletion, constant-rate depletion and constant-pressure depletion. These two cases can be treated by relatively simple mathematical relations. In reality, other cases with simultaneous rate and pressure variations may occur. These other cases are discussed in section 4.4. Constant-rate depletion is treated in section 2.6. It is shown there that average reservoir pressure for undersaturated oil reservoirs with no-flow boundaries decreases during depletion according to the following relation:

$$p_R = p_i - \frac{q_p B_o}{Ah\phi c_t} t. \tag{2.115}$$

In cases of constant-pressure depletion, the expression for undersaturated reservoir pressure decline is more complicated. The production rate in depleting reservoirs is expressed by the radial flow equation

$$q_o(t) = \frac{kh[p_e(t) - p_{wf}]}{141.2\mu_o B_o[\ln(r_e/r_{wa})]}, \tag{4.1}$$

where the pressure at the external boundary $p_e(t)$ declines as a function of time. A material balance equation relates the cumulative production N_p to the pressure $p_e(t)$. It expresses the cumulative production as a function of the apparent total compressibility of the system c_{ta}, the hydrocarbon pore volume $V_p(1 - s_w)$, and the pressure drop in the reservoir $p_i - p_e(t)$. In equation form it is written

$$N_p = V_p(1 - S_w)c_{ta}[p_i - p_e(t)], \tag{4.2}$$

where c_{ta} is apparent total compressibility, which varies with $p_e(t)$.

Calculating production rate or pressure decline in saturated oil reservoirs is far more complicated and requires reservoir material balance calculations. Calculating procedures by Tracy (1955) and Tarner (1944) are perhaps the simplest procedures available. Yet, in spite of their relative simplicity, they may be unavailable when performing well performance analysis.

Rate–time behavior during depletion has been treated rigorously by mathematicians who solve the flow equations analytically for particular boundary conditions of no-flow at the outer boundary and constant pressure at the inner boundary (i.e., at the wellbore). A useful form of this solution has been presented by Fetkovich (1980), who utilized the mathematical solution of Tsarevich and

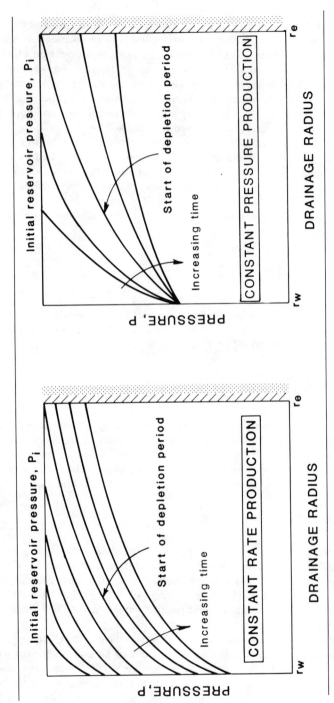

Figure 4.4 Pressure decline in constant rate and constant pressure production.

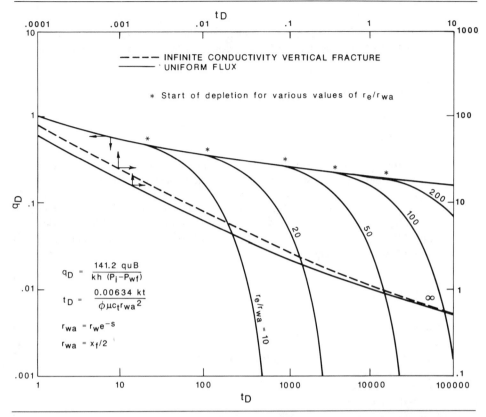

Figure 4.5 Full analytical, constant-pressure, dimensionless-rate solution showing pseudosteady-state depletion stems. Reprinted by permission of the authors from Fetkovich and Therasher 1979, fig.1.

Kuranov (1966), originally presented in table form. Fetkovich prepared a type curve of dimensionless rate versus dimensionless time. His plot is given in figure 4.5. The figure also includes the transient or infinite-acting period prior to depletion.

As can be observed from the curves, transition from the infinite-acting period to the pseudosteady state is instantaneous for a circular outer geometry. The instantaneous change occurs at t_{pss}, which can be estimated from equation (2.133) (these points are marked with asterisks in fig. 4.5). An irregular outer geometry or an off-center well location may shorten the infinite-acting period and postpone true pseudosteady-state decline, creating a period of transition between transient and pseudosteady-state production. Transition decline is not considered here and for most practical needs can be neglected.

A general expression for pseudosteady-state decline for constant pressure production, according to the analytical solution, is

$$q_D = Ae^{-Bt_D},$$ (4.23)

where A and B are constants defined by the ratio r_e/r_{wa}. Fetkovich (1980) developed expressions for A and B in equation (4.23) and stated that

$$A = \frac{1}{\ln(r_e/r_{wa}) - 0.5}.$$ (4.24)

$$B = \frac{2A}{(r_e/r_{wa})^2 - 1}.$$ (4.25)

The expressions for A and B reflect the observation that different ratios of r_e/r_{wa} give different depletion stems in figure 4.5. The higher the ratio, the larger is t_{Dpss}, and the lower is q_D at the start of depletion.

Exponential decline, according to the analytical solution, is substantiated by many field observations. The primary observation is included in Arps's (1945) classic study of field production data, which suggests that all conventional depletion *declines* can be expressed by the equation

$$q_o = \frac{q_{oi}}{(1 + bDt)^{1/b}},$$ (4.26)

where

q_{oi} = initial oil rate (neglecting transient decline),
q_o = rate at time t,
D = decline constant,
b = decline exponent.

In relation to his equation, Arps classifies three types of decline, referred to as exponential, hyperbolic, and harmonic. He observed that production data can be fitted to equation (4.26) with q_{oi}, D, and the coefficient b, which takes on one of the following values:

1. exponential decline: $b = 0$
2. hyperbolic decline: $0 < b < 1$
3. harmonic decline: $b = 1$.

For exponential decline ($b = 0$)

$$q_o = q_{oi}e^{-Dt},$$ (4.27)

and for harmonic decline ($b = 1$)

$$q_o = q_{oi}\frac{1}{(1 + Dt)}.$$ (4.28)

Arps did not give physical reasons for the three observed declines. He only indicated that exponential decline ($b = 0$) is the most common, and that the exponent b generally ranges from 0 to 0.5. Work by other investigators suggests that $b = 0.3$ is typical for solution gas-drive reservoirs and $b = 0.5$ indicates water drive or gravity drainage. In fact, exponential decline is most severe and the production rate declines "faster" than for hyperbolic and harmonic declines. Exponential decline is therefore used as a standard to forecast production trends for economic evaluation requiring conservative forecast assumptions. The harmonic decline equation gives the most "optimistic" depletion forecast, whereas the hyperbolic decline includes a family of decline curves that lie between the exponential and harmonic curves.

Fetkovich managed to express Arps's exponential decline, equation (4.27), in terms of reservoir variables and thus to provide a physical reasoning to Arps's observations. He obtained the following expressions for Arps's empirical constants q_{oi} and D:

$$q_{oi} = \frac{kh(p_i - p_{wf})}{141.2\mu_o B_o[\ln(r_e/r_{wa}) - 0.5]},$$ (4.29)

$$D = \frac{2(0.000264)k}{\phi\mu_i c_{ti}(r_e^2 - r_{wa}^2)[\ln(r_e/r_{wa}) - 0.5]}.$$ (4.30)

These expressions can be used to forecast rate decline if production data are not available to identify the actual decline trend.

Example 4.4 applies the exponential decline model to field data, showing the relation between Arps's empirical constants and dimensionless production quantities.

EXAMPLE 4.4 CALCULATIONS FOR FIELD DATA SHOWING EXPONENTIAL DECLINE

An A-13 oil well is producing with a downhole pump from a high pressure, highly undersaturated, low-permeability oil sand in the Alta field. The pumping rate is adjusted weekly to maintain a constant flowing fluid level in the casing/tubing annulus corresponding to a flowing wellbore pressure of 800 psia. The rate decline data observed in the well are listed in table E4.4a.

An initial buildup pressure test has been conducted on the well to identify reservoir parameters. Well data and buildup test results are given in table E4.4b. A production study requires the following information:

1. Identify the rate decline pattern of the well and extrapolate it to the point when production declines to 10 STB/D.
2. Use the decline data to calculate the terms q_{oi} and D to be used with Arps's decline equation.
3. Compare the calculated constants q_{oi} and D from point 2 with the values calculated from equations (4.29) and (4.30), using the buildup test.

EXAMPLE 4.4 continued

Table E4.4a Rate Decline of an A-13 Oil Well with Constant p_{wf} = 800 psia

t (months)	q_o (STB/month)
0.5	18,578.3
1.5	15,386.3
2.4	13.090.6
3.5	11441.4
4.4	9946.3
5.5	7932.6
6.3	7516.6
7.5	7046.2
8.5	7046.2
9.5	5680.5
10.5	5100.4
11.5	4579.5
12.5	4111.8

Table E4.4b Data for an A-13 Well

p_i = 5790 psia
p_{wf} = 800 psia
B_{oi} = 1.36
μ_{oi} = 0.46
r_w = 0.25 ft
r_e = 1490 ft (160-acre spacing)
k = 0.392 md
h = 121 ft
ϕ = 0.101
c_{ti} = 2.73 × 10⁻⁶ psi⁻¹
s = −3.85 (r_{wa} = 11.75)
Midperforation depth = 9300 ft

SOLUTION

Two graphical methods are used to identify the pattern of rate decline. These methods are:

1. log–log type curve matching of declining rate on the depletion stem of the type curve
2. a plot of q versus t on semilog paper

Figure E4.4a is a log–log plot of the production data from table E4.4a. The plot matches very well on any depletion stem of figure 4.5, indicating exponential decline.

 Figure E4.4b is a semilog plot of the same data. The plot gives a straight line that corresponds to equation (4.27). The intercept and slope of the curve determine the constants q_{oi} and D where

EXAMPLE 4.4 continued

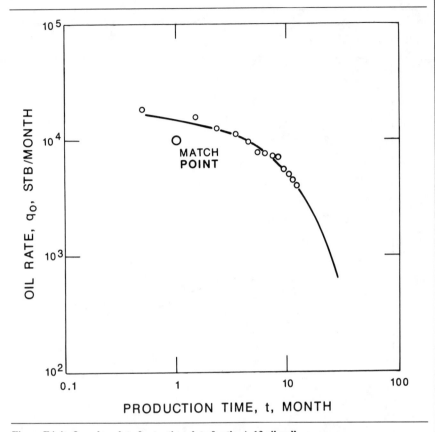

Figure E4.4a Log–log plot of rate–time data for the A-13 oil well.

$q_{oi} = 16,500\,\text{STB/month}$,

$$D = -\frac{\ln(4100/16,500)}{12.5} = 0.114\,\text{month}^{-1}$$

In the absence of production records, the parameters in equation (4.27) can also be estimated from reservoir data obtained from the buildup test. Using equation (4.29),

$$q_{oi} = \frac{0.392(121)(5790 - 800)}{141.2(0.46)(1.36)[\ln(1490/11.75) - 0.5]} = 617/\text{STB/D}$$

$$= 18,767\,\text{STB/month}.$$

and from equation (4.30),

EXAMPLE 4.4 continued

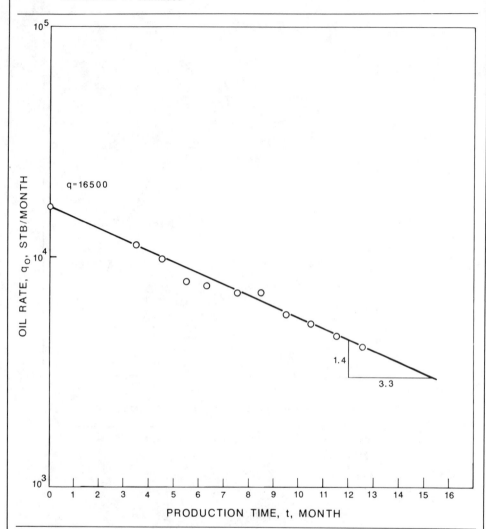

Figure E4.4b Semilog plot of rate–time data for the A-13 oil well.

$$D = \frac{2(0.000264)(0.392)}{0.101(0.46)(2.73 \times 10^{-6})(1490^2 - 11.75^2)[\ln(1490/11.75) - 0.5]}$$

$$= 8.46 \times 10^{-5}\,\text{hour}^{-1} = 0.12\,\text{month}^{-1}.$$

The decline parameters q_{oi} and D can also be obtained from the match point of the logarithmic plot of figure E4.4a on the depletion decline type curve in figure 4.6. As indicated in figure E4.4a, the match point is:

EXAMPLE 4.4 continued

$t = 10$ months, $\qquad t_{Dd} = 1.22$;

$q = 1000\,\text{STB/month},\qquad q_{Dd} = 0.054.$

Using the match point in equations (4.32a) and (4.33a), gives

$$q_{oi} = (q/q_{Dd})_{\text{match}} = \frac{1000}{0.054} = 18{,}518\,\text{STB/month},$$

$$D = \left(\frac{t_{Dd}}{t}\right)_{\text{match}} = \frac{1.22}{10} = 0.122\,\text{month}^{-1}.$$

As stated earlier, not all wells exhibit exponential decline during depletion. In many cases, a more gradual hyperbolic decline is observed where the rate–time performance is better than that estimated from the analytical solution. Hyperbolic decline results from natural and artificial driving energies that slow down pressure depletion compared with the depletion caused by pure expansion of a "slightly compressible" oil. Hyperbolic decline is exhibited if the reservoir drive mechanism is solution-gas drive, gas-cap expansion, or water drive. It is also exhibited when the natural drive mechanism is supplemented by water or gas injection. In any case, the presence of these driving energies implies that total compressibility increases and recovery is improved compared with a pure oil expansion drive mechanism.

When plotted on semilog paper (log rate versus linear time), data showing hyperbolic decline tends to curve upward, as shown in figure E4.5b. On the same plot, exponential decline is represented by a straight line with slope

$$D = -\frac{\ln[q_o(t^*)/q_{oi}]}{t^*} = -2.302\,\frac{\log[q_o(t^*)/q_{oi}]}{t^*},$$

where t^*, $q_o(t^*)$ is any rate–time point on the semilog straight line, and an intercept of

$$q_{oi} = q_o(t = 0).$$

Arps's equation for hyperbolic decline, equation (4.26), can also be expressed in terms of dimensionless variables and the coefficients of the analytical decline equation (eq. [4.2.3]) to give

$$q_{Dd} = \frac{A}{(1 + bBt_D)^{1/b}}. \tag{4.31}$$

To plot equation (4.31) as a single type curve that exhibits exponential, harmonic, and hyperbolic declines, Fetkovich defined new dimensionless unit variables q_{Dd} and t_{Dd}, where

$$q_{Dd} = q_o/q_{oi} \tag{4.32a}$$

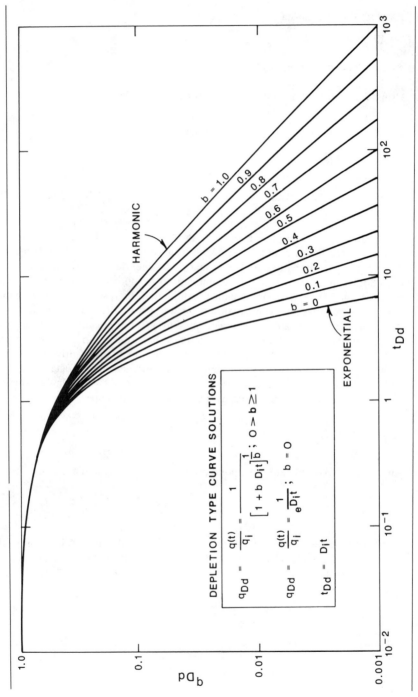

Figure 4.6 Depletion decline type curve, based on Arps's empirical equations. Reprinted by permission of the SPE-AIME from Fetkovich 1980, fig. 1. © 1980 SPE-AIME.

or

$$q_{Dd} = q_D/A, \qquad (4.32b)$$

and

$$t_{Dd} = Dt \qquad (4.33a)$$

or

$$t_{Dd} = Bt_D, \qquad (4.33b)$$

where A and B are as expressed by equations (4.24) and (4.25).

In terms of unit variables, Arps's exponential decline equation becomes

$$q_{Dd} = e^{-t_{Dd}} \qquad (4.34)$$

and the hyperbolic decline equation becomes

$$q_{Dd} = \frac{1}{(1 + bt_{Dd})^{1/b}}. \qquad (4.35)$$

Fetkovich plotted these equations as a type curve with unit dimensionless variables, as shown in figure 4.6 for $b = 0$ to 1 in increments of 0.1.

Using figure 4.6, type-curve matching can determine q_{oi}, D, and the decline exponent b for a given well from available production records. The matching technique is simpler than the alternative methods suggested by Arps. It is also more accurate, particularly if rate–time data show scatter. Although statistical best-fit methods can be used with Arps's equations, we caution against their general application. They are susceptible to misuse, particularly with regard to force-fitting infinite-acting data to Arps's *depletion* equations. Example 4.5 illustrates type-curve matching with the depletion decline type curve, using Arps's hyperbolic field data.

EXAMPLE 4.5 APPLICATION OF THE DEPLETION TYPE CURVE FOR MATCHING FIELD DATA USING ARPS'S HYPERBOLIC DECLINE EXAMPLE

An Arps No. 13 oilwell is showing hyperbolic decline. The constant-pressure rate data of the well is listed in table E4.5.

Tasks
1. Identify the decline exponent b, the coefficient D, and the initial depletion rate q_{oi}, using a match technique on the depletion type curve.
2. Plot the data on semilog paper and compare the results with the prediction that would result from assuming exponential decline.
3. Comment on the nature of the reservoir drive mechanism.

EXAMPLE 4.5 continued

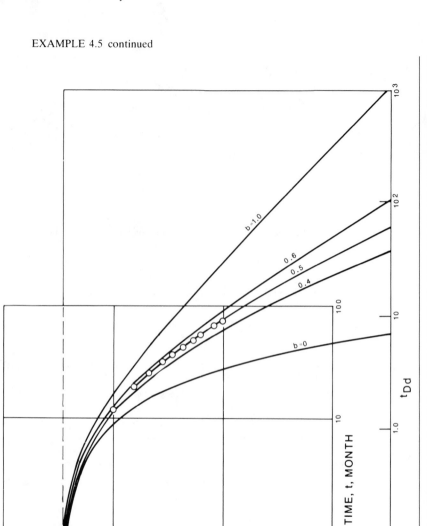

Figure E4.5a Match of the rate decline data on the hyperbolic decline curve for the Arps No. 13 oil well. Reprinted by permission of the SPE-AIME after Fetkovich 1980, fig. 10. © 1980 SPE-AIME.

EXAMPLE 4.5 continued

Table E4.5 Constant-Pressure Rate Decline Data for the Arps No. 13 Oil Well

t (months)	q_o (STB/month)
0.5	30,000
14	9000
19.3	6532
25.1	4621
31.1	3541
38.5	2862
44.9	2252
50.1	1869
55.7	1593
67.1	1158
74.7	1041

SOLUTION

Figure E4.5a is a log–log plot of the rate decline data in table E4.5 The plot matches the hyperbolic decline stem with $b = 0.5$ in figure 4.6. The following match point is selected:

$t = 100$ months, $t_{Dd} = 12$;

$q(t) = 1000$ STB/month, $q_{Dd} = 0.033$.

Using the match point and equation (4.33a) gives

$$D = \frac{12}{100} = 0.12 \, \text{month}^{-1}.$$

Using equation (4.32a) we obtain

$$q_i = \frac{1000}{0.033} = 30{,}303 \, \text{STB/month}.$$

A semilog plot of the decline data is given in figure E4.5b. For comparison the figure also includes an indication of exponential ($b = 0$) decline.

Exponential decline is more rapid than hyperbolic. For example, after 60 months the $b = 0.5$ hyperbolic decline predicts a rate of 1400 STB/month, whereas the exponential decline predicts a rate of 750 STB/month. A hyperbolic decline in this well implies that the reservoir drive energy is probably supported by an extraneous energy source such as an aquifer.

EXAMPLE 4.5 continued

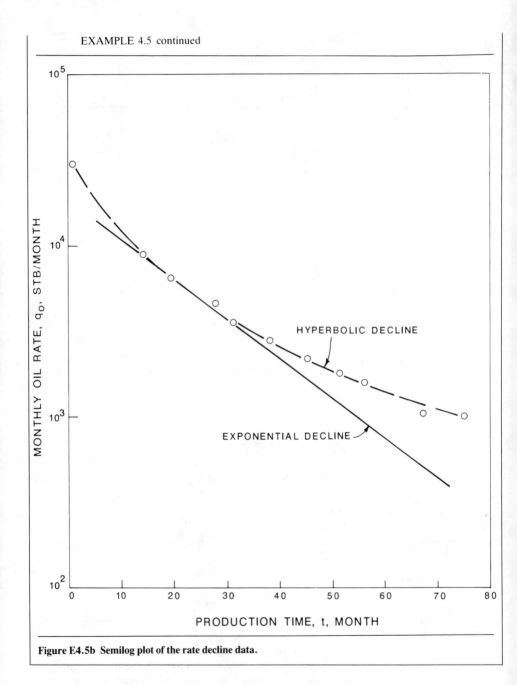

Figure E4.5b Semilog plot of the rate decline data.

Thus far in this chapter we have considered transient and depletion decline separately. Since the transition from infinite-acting to pseudosteady state is practically instantaneous, a natural extension of the decline type curve is to combine transient and depletion relations onto a single graph. Fetkovich (1980) presented such a combination type curve, shown in figure 4.7. He used the unit variables t_{Dd} and q_{Dd} to define the general type curve, which covers both transient and exponential declines. The figure is, in fact, a plot of the analytical solution in figure 4.5 using dimensionless unit variables. The result is that all the depletion stems of the analytical exponential solution (for different values of r_e/r_{wa}) collapse into a single curve. Also, in the "early" t_{Dd} region, stems marked $r_e/r_{wa} = 10$, 20, 50, etc., represent infinite-acting decline. At first glance, the display of these stems appears erroneous, since decline during the infinite-acting period does not depend on outer radius r_e. A careful observation, however, concludes that each stem actually represents a different segment of the single line transient infinite-acting q_D solution. To support the explanation, the construction of figure 4.7 is illustrated schematically in figure 4.8.

The $q_D(t_D)$ solution is shown in figure 4.8(a) for values of $r_e/r_{wa} = 10$ and 50. The transition from infinite-acting to pseudosteady-state flow is marked on the curve by an arrow for each value of r_e/r_{wa}. The curveature of the pseudosteady-state decline curves is identical for all values of r_e/r_{wa}. Fetkovich (1980) showed that a transformation of q_D and t_D to q_{Dd} and t_{Dd} will move the points marked by arrows onto a common point, thus forcing all depletion stems to overlay one another on a single curve. Figure 4.8(b) is the result of the units transformation, where the analytical exponential solution is expressed in terms of the unit variables $q_{Dd} = q_D/A$ and $t_{Dd} = Bt_D$. By substituting A and B from equation (4.24) and (4.25) in the unit variables these units are related to the ratio r_e/r_{wa} by the expressions

$$q_{Dd} = [\ln(r_e/r_{wa}) - 0.5]q_D, \tag{4.36}$$

$$t_{Dd} = \frac{2}{[(r_e/r_{wa})^2 - 1][\ln(r_e/r_{wa}) - 0.5]} t_D. \tag{4.37}$$

Figure 4.8(b) shows also that the transformation splits the single infinite-acting curve in figure 4.8(a) into two curves, each is labeled with the corresponding value of r_e/r_{wa}.

To further generalize the unit type curve Fetkovich (1980) included Arps's hyperbolic and harmonic curves in the depletion region, resulting in the general unit type curve shown in figure 4.9. Each r_e/r_{wa} stem represents some 2½ log cycles of infinite-acting decline period prior to the onset of pseudosteady-state decline (starting at $t_{Dd} = 0.3$). Note that apparent wellbore radius is used consistently in the definitions of dimensionless quantities, and therefore the type curves can be used for wells with positive or negative skin factor.

Application of the general unit type curve is best suited for analysis of rate–time data that exhibits both transient and depletion decline. A match to the unit type curve allows determination of reservoir parameters and prediction of future rate–time performance. The first step of the procedure is to read the value of r_e/r_{wa}

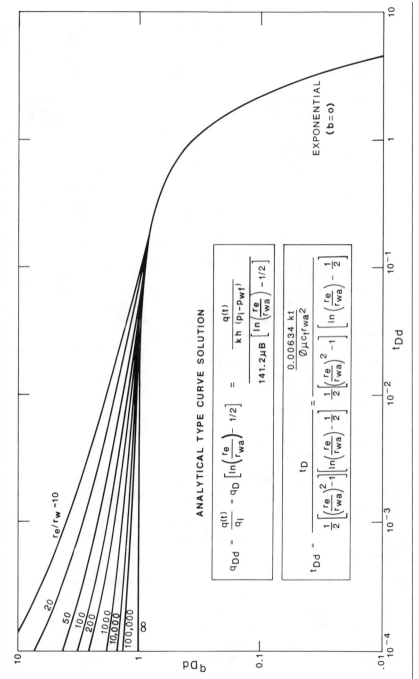

Figure 4.7 General unit type curve including transient decline and exponential depletion periods. Reprinted by permission of the SPE-AIME from Fetkovich 1980, fig. 3. © 1980 SPE-AIME.

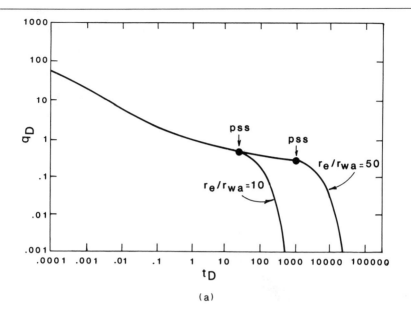

(a)

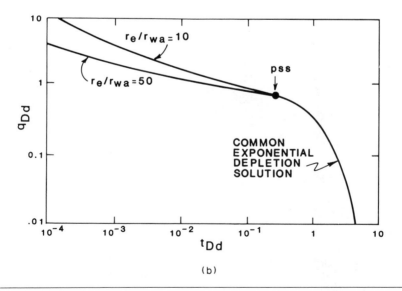

(b)

Figure 4.8 Graphical method for developing the unit type curve based on the analytical dimensionless-rate solution.

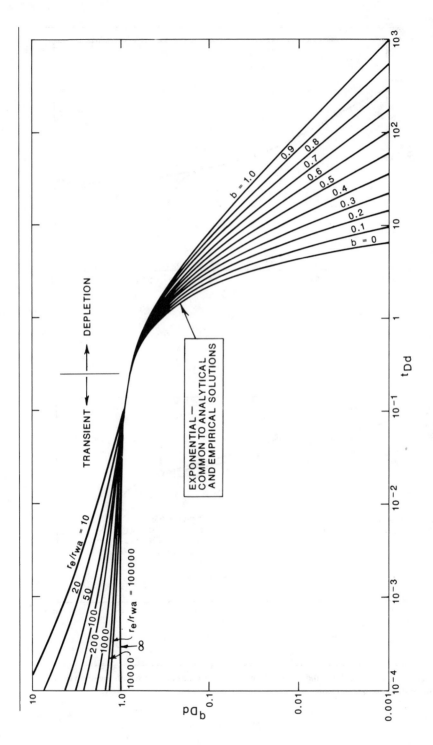

Figure 4.9 Complete rate solution plotted in terms of unit variables. Reprinted by permission of the SPE-AIME from Fetkovich 1980, fig. 4. © 1980 SPE-AIME.

from the transient ray match. If depletion decline is hyperbolic, then the value of b is determined by the depletion ray match. Further, the match point determines permeability k, skin s (or r_{wa}), and drainage radius r_e (i.e., initial oil in place). Permeability is calculated from

$$k = \frac{141.2\mu_i B[\ln(r_e/r_{wa}) - 0.5]}{h(p_i - p_{wf})}\left(\frac{q_o}{q_{Dd}}\right)_{match}, \tag{4.38}$$

using r_e/r_{wa} as obtained from the match.

The apparent wellbore radius is determined from the match point by

$$r_{wa}^{\,2} = \frac{0.00634k}{\phi\mu_i c_t(0.5)[(r_e/r_{wa})^2 - 1](\ln(r_e/r_{wa}) - 0.5)}\left[\frac{t(\text{days})}{t_{Dd}}\right]_{match}, \tag{4.39}$$

from which skin is determined:

$$s = -\ln(r_{wa}/r_w),$$

and drainage radius is calculated as

$$r_e = r_{wa}\left(\frac{r_e}{r_{wa}}\right)_{match}. \tag{4.40}$$

Knowing the drainage radius, in-place reserves drained by the well are calculated by the simple volumetric equation

$$N(\text{well}) = \frac{\pi r_e^2 h\phi(1 - S_w)}{5.615 B_{oi}}. \tag{4.41}$$

Equations (4.40) and (4.41) imply that the decline stem of the type curve is a manifestation of the reservoir size.

A certain difficulty in rate decline analysis stems from the erratic nature of monthly production rates. These fluctuations may reflect a variety of uncontrollable events, such as workovers, labor strikes, and pipeline shutdown. Type curve analysis may be used in such cases only if production data are smoothed to reflect average production rate over extended time intervals.

4.3   **WELL STIMULATION.** Most oil and gas wells are stimulated, either upon completion or later in their production life. The main objective of stimulation treatment is to increase production capacity. Productivity is improved by two methods (1) removing formation damage and increasing permeability in the vicinity of the wellbore, and (2) creating a conductive fracture extending from the wellbore into the reservoir, to increase the effective wellbore radius. The first method is called *matrix acidizing* and the second one is called *fracturing*.

Acidizing. Matrix acidizing is a chemical stimulation method in which acid removes damage and increases permeability near the wellbore. The acid acts by dissolving minerals that make up the original formation matrix, as well as pore-plugging materials that result from mud invasion or fines migration. Acid is injected into the formation at pressures considerably less than the formation fracturing pressure, resulting in radial flow into the formation. The acid enters the rock and flows through the natural pores and flow channels, reacting with the walls of the pores and the flow channels and enlarging them. It also reacts with clay particles attached to the walls of the pores and with invading fines and clay particles caught in narrow pore passages. The chemical reaction between the penetrating acid and the rock gradually slows down as the acid is spent, until finally the reaction is completed and additional radial penetration of the spent acid produces no additional reaction.

Acidizing is usually designed to create a front of reacting acid that will reach the estimated radius of formation damage. It is also designed so that the chemical reaction will restore the original undamaged formation permeability. It is not usually intended to affect a radius beyond the damaged zone.

In sandstone reservoirs treatment is usually performed with a mixture of hydrofluoric (HF) and hydrochloric (HCl) acids, typically 3% HF and 12% HCl. The acid reacts with quartz (silicon dioxide), silicates (encompassing feldspars and clay minerals present in the sandstone), and the carbonates that most often serve as cementing agents in sandstones. The acid reacts, to a great extent, with the plugging materials rather than with the rock matrix. Usually, injection of 50 to 250 gallons per foot of production interval is sufficient to remove damage near the wellbore.

In carbonate reservoirs (limestones and dolomites), HCl alone is used, in which case the rock itself reacts and dissolves, rather than the plugging materials that cause formation damage. The dissolved carbonate rock disperses plugging particles and enlarges the flow passages, thereby removing damage. Normally, a 15% by weight HCl acid is used. However, acid concentration may vary from 5% to 37%. The volume of HCl injected is usually limited to 50–250 gallons per foot, a volume sufficient in most cases to remove damage to a radius of 3–5 ft from the wellbore. Penetration of acid in carbonate rock is typically nonuniform, since the pore structure is formed by vugs and hairline fissures. The resulting channels created by acid are known as "wormholes." A summary of common rock–acid reactions in carbonates and sandstones is given in table 4.1.

Although a wide variety of carbonate textures and compositions are found in reservoir rocks, their reactions with hydrochloric acid are fast and simple, and the products are soluble in spent acid. Reactions of sandstone materials with hydrofluoric acid are more complicated. They are listed in table 4.1 according to four categories: rock matrix (silica and feldspars), clays, carbonates, and formation brines.

As indicated, certain sandstone–acid reactions may produce insoluble salts that tend to precipitate and plug flow channels. The fluosilicic acid (H_2SiF_6) produced by the reactions may subsequently react with ions of sodium (Na^+) and potassium (K^+) to produce insoluble salts. Furthermore, when the concentration of HF becomes very small, the fluosilicic acid can decompose yielding silicon tetrafluoride (SiF_4)

Table 4.1 Stoichiometry of Common Matrix-Acidizing Reactions.

I. STOICHIOMETRY OF MATRIX ACIDIZING REACTIONS

  A. HCl + Carbonate rock

    1. $2HCl + CaCO_3 \rightleftarrows CaCl_2 + H_2O + CO_2 \uparrow$
       |calcite|

    2. $4HCl + CaMg(CO_3)_2 \rightleftarrows CaCl_2 + MgCl_2 + 2H_2O + 2CO_2 \uparrow$
       |dolomite|

    3. $2HCl + MgCO_3 \rightleftarrows MgCl_2 + H_2O + CO_2 \uparrow$
       |dolomite|

    4. $2HCl + FeCO_3 \rightleftarrows FeCl_2 + H_2O + CO_2 \uparrow$
       |siderite|

  B. HF + sandstone matrix materials

    1. $SiO_2 + 4HF \rightleftarrows SiF_4 + 2H_2O$
      |quartz|
      $SiF_4 + 2HF \rightleftarrows H_2SiF_6$
              |fluosilicic|
              |acid|

    2. $NaAlSi_3O_3 + 22HF \rightleftarrows 3H_2SiF_6 + AlF_3 + NaF + 8H_2O$
      |feldspars|

  C. HF + sandstone clay materials

    1. $Na_4SiO_4 + 8HF \rightleftarrows SiF_4 + 4NaF + 4H_2O$
      $2HF + SiF_4 \rightleftarrows H_2SiF_6$
      $2NaF + SiF_4 \rightleftarrows Na_2SiF_6 \downarrow$

    2. $36HF + Al_2Si_4O_{10}(OH)_2 \rightleftarrows 4H_2SiF_6 + 2H_3AlF_6 + 12H_2O$
       |bentonite|

  D. HF + calcareous minerals

    1. $2HF + CaCO_3 \rightleftarrows CaF_2 \downarrow + H_2O + CO_2 \uparrow$
      |calcite|

  E. H_2SiF_6 + spent HF + formation brines

    1. $H_2SiF_6 + 2Na^+ \rightarrow Na_2SiF_6 \downarrow + 2H^+$
    2. $H_2SiF_6 + 2K^+ \rightarrow K_2SiF_6 \downarrow + 2H^+$
    3. $2HF + Ca^{++} \rightarrow CaF_2 \downarrow + 2H^+$

  F. decomposition of fluosilicic acid

    1. $H_2SiF_6 \rightarrow SiF_4 + 2HF$
      $SiF_4 + 4H_2O \rightarrow Si(OH)_4 \downarrow + 4HF$

II. MOLECULAR WEIGHTS AND SPECIFIC GRAVITIES OF REACTANT

Reactant	Molecular weight	Specific gravity
HCl	36.5	2.723
$CaCO_3$	100.0	3.037
$MgCO_3$	84.3	2.872
$CaMg(CO_3)_2$	184.3	2.152
$CaCl_2$	111.0	2.325
$MgCl_2$	95.3	1.000
H_2O	18.0	
CO_2	44.0	

Note: $\downarrow$ Indicates solid precipitation
     $\uparrow$ indicates gas liberation

which undergoes hydrolysis to yield precipitation of silicic acid [$Si(OH)_4$]. Salt precipitation occurs also when HF contacts calcium ions (Ca^{++}) producing insoluble calcium fluoride (CaF_2).

To minimize the damaging effect of precipitating salts, sandstone acidizing is commonly performed in three stages:

1. a *preflush*, usually by HCl, which displaces formation brines and removes carbonate materials
2. an HF–HCl mixture treatment to react with rock matrix and plugging materials
3. an *afterflush*, commonly by either HCl, ammonium chloride (NH_4Cl), or a "mutual solvent," that displaces the reaction product away from the wellbore and reduces the precipitation damage.

In certain cases where damage in sandstone reservoirs is due to migration of clay particles, acid may need to penetrate deep into the formation. Special chemicals are used to retard the HF acid reaction. For example, injection of fluoboric acid (HBF_4) slowly generates reactive HF as it is hydrolyzed in aqueous solution. Alternatively, a stage injection of NH_4F followed by HCl causes gradual generation of HF. In either case, HF is formed at a slow rate and the reaction can proceed deeper into the formation.

Generally, the strategy for planning matrix acid treatment is based on the following considerations:

1. Acid must react with specific rock matrix and plugging materials to yield soluble products.
2. Products resulting from primary acid–matrix reactions do not react between themselves or with formation materials to create insoluble precipitates.
3. The reaction rate should be controlled to yield a desirable acid penetration and favorable porosity and permeability distribution around the wellbore.

It is difficult to predict the pattern of acid reaction in the rock near the wellbore. Two laboratory experiments by Shaughnessy and Kunze (1981) on long Berea sandstone cores gave understanding of the permeability distribution around a treated well. Some of the results are given in figure 4.10. They illustrate two important points: (1) HF–HCl mixtures react only a limited distance into the formation, independent of the volume of acid injected; and (2) HF–HCl mixtures can cause precipitation of solids, and thus reduce permeability, if the spent acid (with low concentrations of HF) resides stagnant in the formation for a period of only several hours. In both experiments the Berea core was preflushed with HCl to remove calcite, thus increasing permeability from 60 md to 110 md.

The first experiment shows the limited extent of acid reaction for a sandstone. Following the HCl flush, 14 pore volumes (PV) of a 3% HF–10% HCl mixture was passed through the 30-in. core. A nonreactive brine was immediately backflowed to remove spent acid. The core was then cut into 2-in. sections and each was tested for brine and fresh-water permeability. The results are shown in figure 4.10(a). The experiment showed that permeability increases substantially immediately adjacent to the injection face (within the first 12 in.), even though large volumes of acid pass through the core.

403

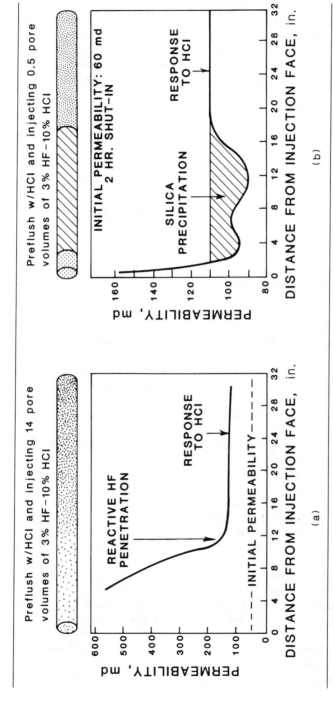

Figure 4.10 Permeability distribution in a Berea sandstone core treated with acid. Reprinted by permission of the SPE-AIME from Shaughnessy and Kunze 1981 figs. 5 and 9. © 1981 SPE-AIME.

In the second experiment with a companion Berea core, the initial HCl flush was followed by injection of one-half pore volume of a 3% HF–10% HCl mixture. The injected acid was then allowed to react within the core for two hours (without injection or flow from the core). A nonreactive brine was then backflowed to remove the spent acid. The core was cut into 2-in. sections and each was tested for brine and freshwater permeability. Figure 4.10(b) gives the results of the experiment.

Three distinct permeability zones were observed in the core:

1. Directly adjacent to the injection face there was a substantial gain in permeability due to the action of HCl and HF.
2. About 2 in. from the injection face permeability dropped abruptly. This is explained by a precipitation of silicate when the rock reacted slowly with a low concentration of spent HF.
3. About halfway into the core the permeability increases again to the level resulting from the HCl preflush, which implies that the HF–HCl mixture did not react beyond this point.

These test results indicate that permeability distribution resulting from acid treatment of a sandstone is a complex function of the acid mixture, injection rate, and time allowed to complete the reaction. In this particular example a two-hour period with spent acid stagnant in the formation had a negative effect. For a different combination of rock and acid, prolonged contact of spent acid may influence permeability differently. Although it is difficult to quantify the effects of the various factors governing acidizing treatment, general recommendations for treatment design have been established and practiced successfully by the industry Numerous publications such as those by Williams et al. (1979), Muecke (1982), and McLeod (1984) present practical recommendations for first treatment in fields where specific experience does not exist. The recommendations cover:

1. specification of treatment chemicals, their concentrations, and injection sequence
2. acid additives to inhibit corrosion, emulsion forming, and undesirable solids precipitation
3. injection rates, pressures, and volumes
4. methods to divert the acid into low-permeability intervals when stimulating long or heterogeneous pay zones.
5. additives to retard acid reaction and increase its penetration

In general, the first treatments in a field are "pilot" operations to establish field experience for planning and executing subsequent treatments.

To estimate the improvement of productivity due to acid treatment in terms of skin factor, flow efficiency, or apparent wellbore radius, it is necessary to estimate the permeability distribution near the wellbore after treatment. Long cores are not typically available for laboratory tests, and it is impossible to predict the post-acid permeability distribution near the wellbore. Two simple models used to relate permeability distribution to skin factor are illustrated in figure 4.11. The model in

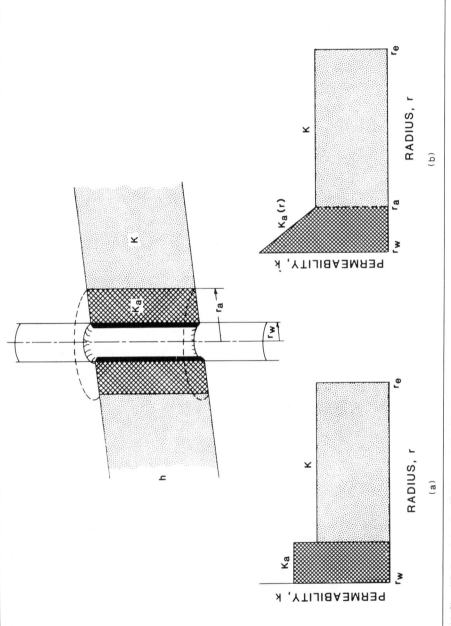

Figure 4.11 Simplified models of radial permeability distribution in the region affected by formation damage and matrix acidizing.

figure 4.11(a) relates skin factor s_a to radius r_a and permeability k_a of the affected zone, according to the relation

$$s_a = (k/k_a - 1)\ln(r_a/r_w). \tag{4.42}$$

The model in figure 4.11(b) gives

$$s_a = k \int_{r_w}^{r_a} \frac{dr}{rk_a(r)} - \ln(r_a/r_w), \tag{4.43}$$

where the permeability distribution function $k_a(r) = mr + b$ with slope $m = (k_{max} - k)/(r_a - r_w)$ and intercept $b = k_{max} - (k_{max} - k)/(r_a/r_w - 1)$. Maximum permeability k_{max} at the wellbore can be estimated from small core tests.

Standard acid response tests are performed on small core plugs in a high-pressure–high-temperature permeameter (HPTAP) of the type illustrated in figure 3.4. The apparatus is essentially a permeameter that can be programmed to perform a number of sequential flow tests with different liquids, including strong acids. A typical acid response test is illustrated in figure 4.12.

The flow sequence begins with a backflush of 3% NH_4Cl brine to rinse the core with minimal permeability impairment. The injection includes a preflush with brine and HCl, followed by an HF–HCl mixture, brine, fluoboric acid, and brine mixture. Finally, the core is backflushed with a nondamaging brine. The test sequence resembles the actual acidizing treatment planned for the well, and thus can give an indication of the expected permeability at the wellbore. The standard acid response test provides information for choosing a particular acid and additives for a particular formation. Test results, however, are actually more useful for comparing acid–additive treatments than for accurate prediction of near-wellbore permeability.

Various methods have been suggested to predict acidizing results. They are all based on essentially the same procedure: Simulate the acid reaction and calculate the resultant permeability increase. Prediction methods have been reported by Guin and Schechter (1971), Nierode and Williams (1971), McCune et al. (1975), Lund et al. (1976), Hill et al. (1981), Shaughnessy and Kunze (1981), and Hekin et al. (1982). These prediction models use highly idealized assumptions and thus lack the practical value needed for effective treatment selection.

The degree of treatment success may be established only by a post-acid well test or close monitoring of production history. The standard transient test for treatment evaluation is a pressure buildup, performed shortly after the acid job is completed. Test data are used to calculate post-acid skin (apparent wellbore radius), which can be compared with design skin. The effect of stimulation on rate decline can be predicted using the rate-decline type curves presented in previous sections and the apparent wellbore radius,

$$r_{wa} = r_w e^{-s}. \tag{2.34}$$

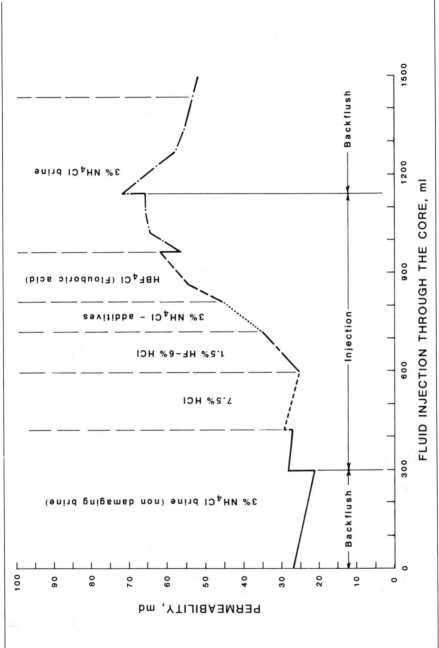

Figure 4.12 Acid response test on 1″ × 1″ plug of sandstone samples prepared from a well in the High Island 561 field, offshore Louisiana.

Fracturing. Fracturing is a well-stimulation method in which large conductive fractures are created in the formation around the wellbore, reaching far into the reservoir. Fractures are created by exerting a pressure in the wellbore exceeding the fracture initiation pressure of the formation. This pressure is applied from the surface by pumps that inject fluids at a rate exceeding that which can be injected into the rock matrix. When the formation can no longer accept the injected fluids at the high rate, new flow channels are formed. These new flow channels are the fractures. Fractures are initiated, propagated, and held open as long as injection proceeds. As injection ceases, the fracture tends to close again.

Two methods are used to keep the fracture open and conductive after injection stops:

1. *Propping the fracture.* Proppant materials are mixed at the surface with viscous fluids that carry and distribute the proppants as a slurry, depositing them in the fracture to hold the fracture open. This method is referred to as *hydraulic fracturing.*
2. *Acid etching along the fracture wall.* Acid is injected into the fracture following the inert "pad" fluid that creates the fracture. Acid etches the fracture walls to create irregular surfaces that keep the fracture partially open and conductive after injection stops and overburden pressure causes closure. This method is referred to as *acid fracturing.* The method is relevant only to carbonate reservoirs. Acid etching of fracture walls in sandstone formations is insufficient to provide high fracture conductivity.

Figure 4.13 is a schematic illustration of the two types of fracture. Figure 4.13(a) illustrates a hydraulic fracture, and figures 4.13(b) and 4.13(c) illustrate two types of acid fractures. The first acid fracture type (4.13[b]) is a conventional acid fracture. The second type (4.13[c]) is a fracture created by *viscous fingering,* a technique applied in soft carbonate rocks. To achieve viscous fingering, a low-viscosity acid is injected following injection of the high-viscosity, nonreactive pad fluid that creates the fracture. The reactive acid tends to penetrate as fingers through the viscous fluid. The result is a nonuniform fracture pattern of conductive channels.

The general arrangement of the equipment used for hydraulic fracturing is shown in figure 4.14. A truck-mounted pump injects fracturing fluid followed by a slurry of sand proppant and viscous carrying fluid. Slurries are mixed continuously in a truck-mounted blender.

Today it is generally believed that fracturing treatment results in a single fracture, oriented more or less in the vertical plane of the wellbore. This fracture propagates outward symmetrically in opposite directions from the wellbore. It is also believed that, in cases where a fracture job is carried out in a shallow formation, a horizontal (pancake) fracture may develop.

When a well is fractured, the effect on well performance is equivalent to an enlargement of the wellbore radius. In terms of constant-pressure rate behavior, stimulation yields an initial increase in rate (sometimes 10- or even 100-fold), followed by a rapid decline. The early increase in rate following stimulation is often referred to as *flush production.* The term *flush* implies a short-lived production, but in fact the behavior may last several years in low-permeability wells.

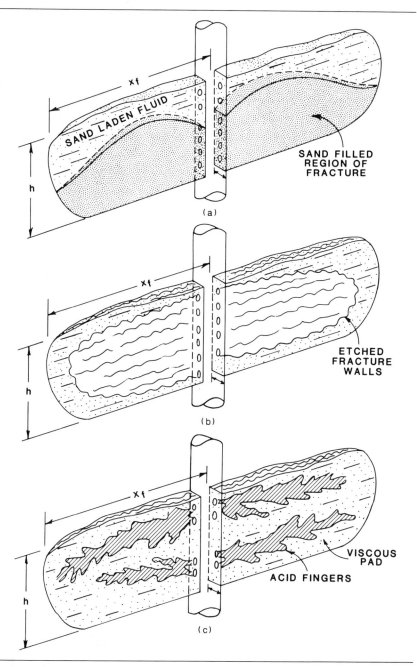

Figure 4.13 Vertically fractured wells.

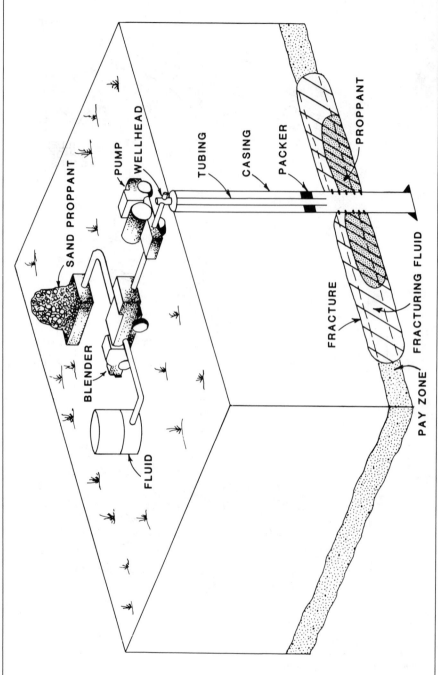

Figure 4.14 Arrangement of the system for fracturing. Reprinted by permission of the SPE-AIME, after Veatch, Jr., 1983, fig. 1, part 2. © 1983 SPE-AIME.

Once the post-fracture skin is determined, its effect on well productivity is best assessed by rate–time analysis. The profile of rate decline, rather than initial poststimulation rate (or a single value flow efficiency), reflects the true gain in production and the corresponding gain in net present value for the treated well. The behavior of a stimulated well can be analyzed using the radial flow model, where the fracture is quantified in terms of an equivalent wellbore radius. Two factors reflect the effect of stimulation on production: the *dimension* and the *flow conductivity* of the fracture. For mathematical treatment, vertical fractures are usually classified according to one of three models:

1. the infinite conductivity model, which assumes negligible pressure loss in the fracture;
2. the uniform flux model, which assumes a slight pressure gradient in the fracture, corresponding to an evenly distributed flux along the fracture face;
3. the finite conductivity model, which assumes constant and limited permeability in the fracture, resulting from proppant crushing, inefficient proppant distribution, or partial closure of an acid-etched fracture.

Schematic pressure distributions along the fracture are shown in figure 4.15 for each model.

Mathematical studies of the infinite conductivity and uniform flux models have established that the radial flow model can adequately describe production behavior if an apparent wellbore radius is used. For the infinite conductivity model,

$$r_{wa} = x_f/2, \tag{4.44}$$

and for the uniform flux model

$$r_{wa} = x_f/2.718, \tag{4.45}$$

where $2.718 = e = \ln(10)$.

The dashed line in the type curve of figure 4.5 illustrates a solution for the rate decline of an infinite-conductivity vertical fracture, expressed in terms of apparent wellbore radius $r_{wa} = x_f/2$. Deviation from the radial model is only found at very early times. In fact, data matching along the infinite-conductivity solution usually can also be fitted on the radial solution without much loss in accuracy. The depletion stems in figure 4.5 include ratios of r_e/r_{wa} down to 10. Other type curves, such as that published by Locke and Sawyer (1975), give solutions for vertical fracture ratios x_f/x_e less than 5 i.e., $r_e/r_{wa} < 10$, since $x_f/x_e = 0.5(r_{wa}/r_e)$.

The finite conductivity behavior of a fracture is quantified by a dimensionless fracture conductivity:

$$F_{cD} = \frac{k_f w}{k x_f}, \tag{4.46}$$

where

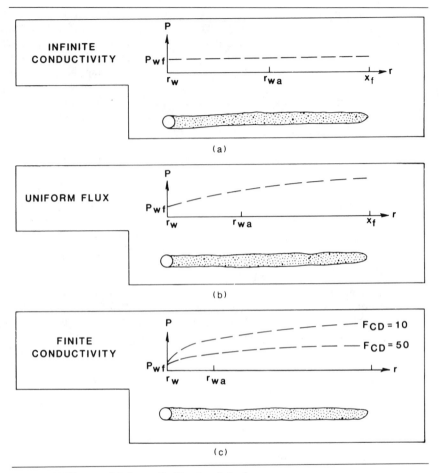

Figure 4.15 Three models for vertical fracture behavior.

k_f = fracture permeability (md),
w = fracture width (ft),
k = formation permeability (md),
x_f = vertical fracture half length (ft).

Several models–analytical, numerical, and electrolytic—estimate the composite effect of fracture length and fracture conductivity on a well's productivity. A list of 45 different models published since the late 1930s is given in a review by Cinco–Ley (1982). Layers of commercial proppant materials exhibit very high permeability as listed in table 3.5. Yet, in some cases fracture conductivity is low and the fracture length calculated from test data using the infinite conductivity assumption is overoptimistic. A limited fracture conductivity may result from:

1. incomplete placement of proppant in the fracture
2. improper proppant size distribution
3. improper proppant concentration in the fracture
4. large closure stresses, which cause crushing of proppant or proppant imbedment in the fracture wall.
5. plugging of the fracture by formation materials and fracturing fluid particles.

For an acid fracture, limited conductivity may result from:

1. improper placement of acid in the fracture
2. failure to control the acid reaction rate
3. homogeneous matrix with evenly etched fracture walls, which tend to close under pressure
4. soft formations with mechanical properties that allow ridges created by the acid reaction along the fracture walls to collapse under closure.

To facilitate discussion of fracture conductivity, table 4.2 gives characteristic values of the parameters in equation (4.46), illustrating the range of dimensionless fracture conductivities that can be expected. The effect of finite conductivity on production during the transient flow period has been studied using numerical reservoir simulators. Figure 4.16 gives a type curve expressing the infinite-acting dimensionless rate solution of a vertically fractured well producing at constant pressure. The figure covers dimensionless fracture conductivity ranging from 0.1 to 500; it was developed from data published by Agarwal et al. (1979). Dimensionless time in figure 4.16 is defined as

$$t_{Dxf} = \frac{0.000264kt}{\phi\mu_i c_{ti} x_f^2}. \tag{4.47}$$

The figure indicates that production rate increases with fracture conductivity. For very low fracture conductivities the performance approaches that of an unstimulated well.

Table 4.2 Characteristic Parameters Used in the Definition of Dimensionless Fracture Conductivity

Quantity	Value	Characteristic
k_f	10 D	Poor
	100 D	Good
	1000 D	Excellent
$k_f w^*$	100 md-ft	Poor
	1000 md-ft	Good
	10,000 md-ft	Excellent
F_{cD}	< 10	Poor
	10 – 50	Good
	> 50	Excellent

*An average fracture width of 0.01 ft (0.12 in. or 3 mm) is assumed.

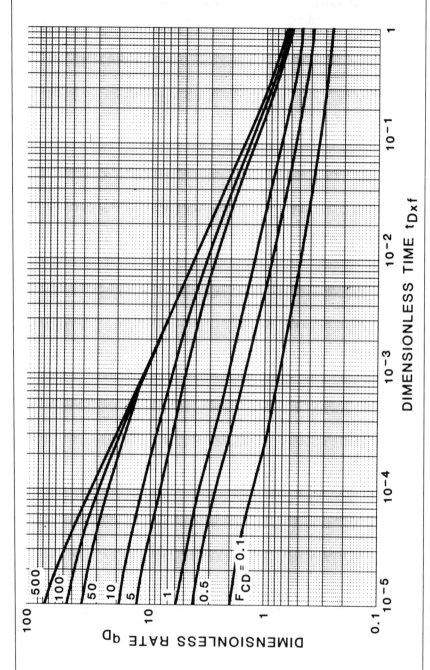

Figure 4.16 Infinite-acting dimensionless-rate solution for finite-conductivity vertically fractured wells. After Agarwal, et al. 1979.

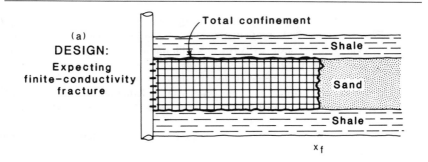

(a)
DESIGN:
Expecting
finite−conductivity
fracture

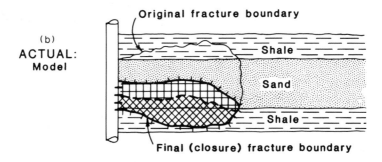

(b)
ACTUAL:
Model

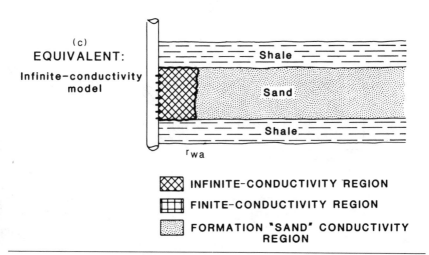

(c)
EQUIVALENT:
Infinite−conductivity
model

☒ INFINITE-CONDUCTIVITY REGION

▦ FINITE-CONDUCTIVITY REGION

▦ FORMATION "SAND" CONDUCTIVITY REGION

Figure 4.17 Unsuccessful fracture treatment, with proppant lost to a lower shale interval.

The type curve in figure 4.16 also shows that the performances of finite-conductivity fractures tend to converge at large times. For a well with $F_{cD} = 10$, $t_{Dxf} = 1$ marks the approximate time when a finite conductivity fracture behaves like an infinite conductivity fracture with the same fracture length. This implies that the well begins to behave as a radial well with an equivalent wellbore radius. Finite-conductivity behavior usually dies out before reaching pseudosteady state, and we can assume that most wells are adequately described by the infinite-conductivity or uniform-flux fracture models—i.e., by the radial solution using an apparent wellbore radius.

Often the result of fracture treatment is poorer than that expected by the design. Test data reveal the fact but do not reveal the reasons for the poor result. An example of an unsuccessful fracture job is shown in figure 4.17. The fracture extends vertically beyond the upper and lower formation boundaries into adjacent shale layers. Because of gravity, proppant tends to settle at the bottom of the fracture. When injection stops and treatment pressure starts to drop, horizontal stress due to the overburden pressure is exerted on the newly created fracture and

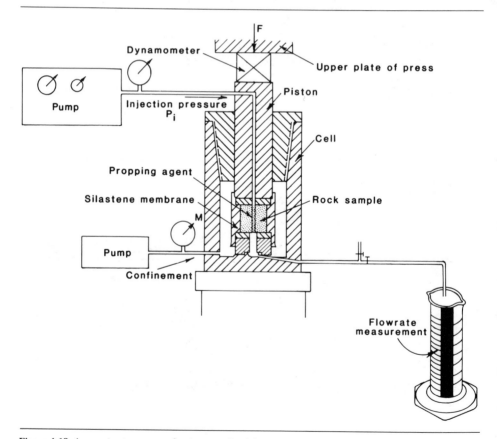

Figure 4.18 Apparatus to measure fracture conductivity.

the unpropped area tends to close. The result is an ineffective fracture with limited extension, reduced area to flow, and limited conductivity.

For fracture design purposes it is practical to perform a laboratory test to estimate fracture conductivity. The test apparatus is illustrated in figure 4.18. Two sections of the core plug are held in a special test cell. A proppant is sandwiched between the two sections. A combination of axial load and confining radial pressure simulates the overburden pressure that tends to close the fracture. Conductivity of the tested fracture is calculated from a flow experiment using kerosene. The practical value of such a test is to:

1. indicate the response of propping agents to fracture closing pressure
2. estimate fracture conductivity
3. study the effect of crushed proppants in hard formations
4. study the effect of proppant embedment along the surface of a fracture in soft rocks.

Crushing and embedment of proppants are illustrated schematically in figure 4.19.

Experimentally determined fracture conductivity does not usually reflect the actual behavior of a fractured well, because proppant distribution in the fracture is incomplete. To study the effect of fracture conductivity and fracture height on well performance we can use results presented by McGuire and Sikora (1960) and Tinsley et al. (1969). Figure 4.20 is a result of Tinsley's study. The figure plots steady-state flow efficiency, expressed as $[\ln(r_e/r_w)/\ln(r_e/r_{wa})]$, versus a fracture characterization parameter,

$$X = 0.593(h_f/h)(x_f/r_e)\ln(r_e/r_w)F_{cD},\qquad(4.48)$$

for several ratios of fracture half-length to drainage radius, x_f/r_e. Figure 4.20 applies for a fracture height h_f equal to formation thickness h—i.e., $h_f/h = 1$. Other curves, for $h_f/h = 0.25$ and 0.5, are given by Tinsley et al.

In figure 4.20 notice that $[\ln(r_e/r_w)/\ln(r_e/r_{wa})]$ tends to a constant at large values of X. This corresponds to the condition of an infinite conductivity fracture and can be quantified simply as $r_{wa} = x_f/2$. At small values of $X (X < 0.1)$, the ratio $[\ln(r_e/r_w)/\ln(r_e/r_{wa})]$ appears constant, approximately 1.7 for all values of x_f/x_e. This is misleading, since it is obvious that as X approaches zero the ratio should approach 1. The problem arises from Tinsley's choice of empirical equation to fit the electrolytic data for $X < 3$.

Tinsley's empirical equations for any h_f/h at $X > 0.1$ are for $0.1 < X < 3$:

$$\frac{\ln(r_e/r_w)}{\ln(r_e/r_{wa})} = (B/C)\{0.785[\tan(1.83\,x_f/r_e - 1.25) + 4.28] - (C)(D)\} + D\qquad(4.49)$$

and for $X > 3$:

$$\frac{\ln(r_e/r_w)}{\ln(r_e/r_{wa})} = \frac{F[\tan(Y+Z) - \tan(Z)] + 1}{C},\qquad(4.50)$$

where

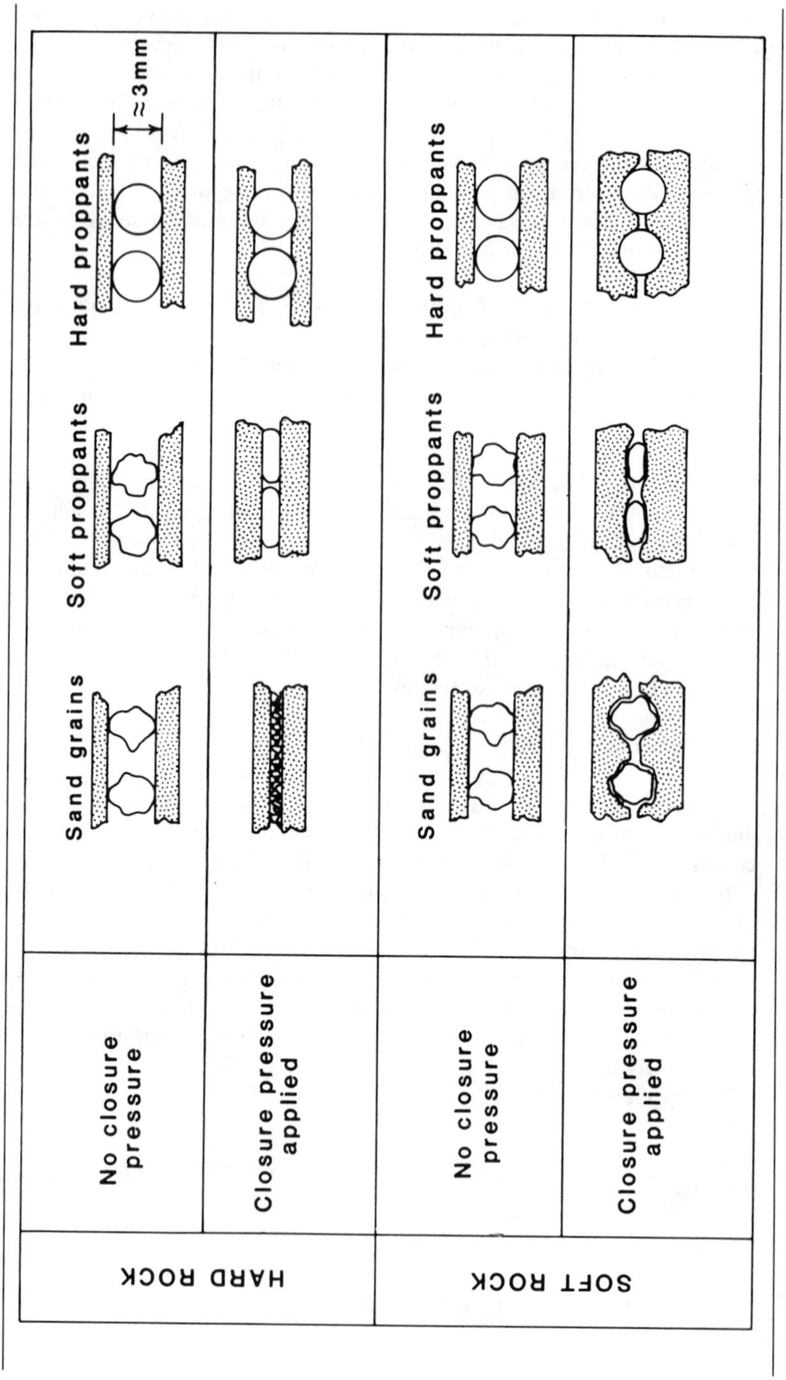

Figure 4.19 Response of propping agents to the fracture closing pressure.

$$B = \frac{3.334X - 0.334}{9.668},$$
$$C = 0.08(h/h_f) + 0.92,$$
$$D = 1 + 0.75(h_f/h),$$
$$F = 4.84/X^2 - 6.40/X + 2.38,$$
$$Y = (2.27 - 1.32/X)(x_f/r_e),$$
$$Z = 1.24/X^2 - 1.64/X - 0.84.$$

An important observation in figure 4.20 is related to the relative importance of fracture length and fracture conductivity. The figure indicates that for large X values, typical for low permeability reservoirs, fracture length dominates the productivity gain and the fracture exhibits infinite conductivity behavior even if the conductivity has a finite value. At low values of X, typical for medium permeability reservoirs, fracture conductivity, as well as fracture length governs productivity gain. The importance of the observation stems from the ability of the designer to

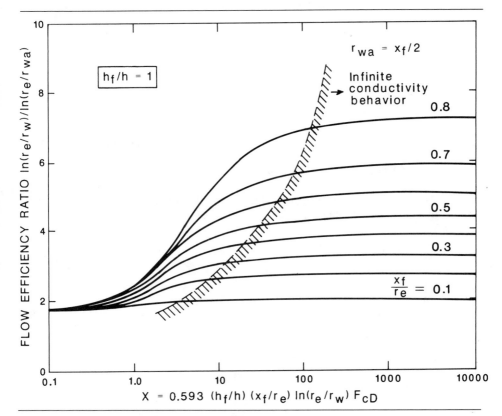

Figure 4.20 Increase of flow efficiency in a fractured well at steady-state production. Reprinted by permission of the SPE-AIME after Tinsley 1969, fig. 6. © 1969 SPE-AIME.

trade-off fracture conductivity for fracture length in designing and executing certain frac jobs.

The results by Tinsley et al. indicate that for productivity calculations a fracture with height h_f, half-length x_f, and conductivity F_{cD} can be modeled as a radial well with an apparent wellbore radius r_{wa}. Although they study steady-state conditions only, their results can also be applied to transient flow.

Example 4.6 illustrates the analysis of well performance for a well with a finite-conductivity fracture.

EXAMPLE 4.6 DECLINE BEHAVIOR OF THE KWB 2-2 OIL WELL AFTER FRACTURING

The well KWB 2-2 discussed in example 4.1 is considered a good candidate for hydraulic fracturing. To forecast the expected gain in revenue due to stimulation it is necessary to calculate rate decline of the stimulated well. Using fracture design calculations the service company proposes two fracture treatments. The estimated fracture half length and dimensionless fracture conductivity for treatment A are $x_f = 100$ ft and $F_{CD} = 200$, and for treatment B are $x_f = 250$ and $F_{CD} = 10$. It is assumed that in both cases the fracture height h_f equals formation thickness h.

SOLUTION

The first step is to calculate apparent wellbore radius, r_{wa}, corresponding to the expected treatment results.

Case A: The fracture parameter X is calculated from equation (4.48), which gives

$$X = 0.593(1.0)(100/744)[\ln(744/0.33)](200) = 123.$$

According to figure 4.20, the value of X falls in the region where r_{wa} can be quantified by an infinite conductivity fracture, i.e.,

$$r_{wa} = \frac{x_f}{2} = \frac{100}{2} = 50 \, \text{ft}.$$

Case B: The fracture parameter is

$$X = 0.593(1.0)(250/744)[\ln(744/0.33)](10) = 15.4,$$

and the relative fracture length is

$$\frac{x_f}{r_e} = \frac{250}{744} = 0.336.$$

Using these parameters in figure 4.20 gives a flow efficiency increase of

EXAMPLE 4.6 continued

$$\frac{\ln(r_e/r_w)}{\ln(r_e/r_{wa})} = 3.3.$$

Substituting well data and rearranging the ratio gives an apparent wellbore radius of

$$\ln r_{wa} = \ln 744 - \frac{\ln(744/0.33)}{3.3},$$

or

$$r_{wa} = 72\,\text{ft}.$$

Alternatively, equation (4.50) can be used instead of figure 4.20 to calculate the flow efficiency increase, where

$$B = \frac{3.334(15.4) - 0.334}{9.668} = 5.276,$$
$$C = 0.08 + 0.92 = 1.0,$$
$$F = 4.84/15.4 - 6.4/15.4 + 2.38 = 1.98,$$
$$Y = (2.27 - 1.32/15.4)0.336 = 0.734,$$
$$Z = 1.24/15.4^2 - 1.64/15.4 - 0.84 = -0.941,$$

and

$$\frac{\ln(r_e/r_w)}{\ln(r_e/r_{wa})} = \frac{1.98[\tan(0.734 - 0.941) - \tan(-0.941)] + 1}{1.0} = 3.30,$$

which is the same ratio as obtained from figure 4.20.

Production decline can then be calculated according to the procedure detailed later in example 4.7. Alternatively, it can be calculated by a program for the HP-41 programmable calculator, listed in Appendix B. The program computes rate decline and is used to solve this example. The program also computes cumulative production. The input data to the program are

$$q_D/q, \quad t_D/t, \quad \text{and} \quad r_e/r_{wa}.$$

Equation (4.2) calculates

$$\frac{q_D}{q} = \frac{141.2(0.2)(1.642)}{0.25(66)(2600 - 1200)} = 0.002,$$

and equation (4.3) calculates

$$\frac{t_D}{t_{days}} = \frac{0.00634(0.25)}{0.117(0.2)(30 \times 10^{-6})(r_{wa}^2)} = \frac{2258}{r_{wa}^2}.$$

EXAMPLE 4.6 continued

Thus, for case A

$$\frac{t_D}{t_{days}} = \frac{2258}{(50)^2} = 0.903$$

and

$$\frac{r_e}{r_{wa}} = \frac{744}{50} = 14.9,$$

and for case B

$$\frac{t_D}{t_{days}} = \frac{2258}{(72)^2} = 0.436$$

and

$$\frac{r_e}{r_{wa}} = \frac{744}{72} = 10.3.$$

**Table E4.6 Production Decline Forecast for the
KWB 2-2 Oil Well Calculated for Two Frac Treatments**

t (days)	$r_{wa} = 50$		$r_{wa} = 72$	
	q_o (STB/D)	N_p (STB)	q_o (STB/D)	N_p (STB)
1	506	811	644	1078
2	410	1262	512	1644
3	367	1648	451	2123
4	340	2000	415	2555
5	321	2330	389	2956
6	307	2644	370	3335
7	296	2945	355	3697
8	286	3235	343	4046
9	279	3518	333	4383
10	272	3793	324	4711
30	216	8542	251	10,276
60	188	14,552	210	17,119
90	166	19,855	178	22,925
120	148	24,558	152	27,865
150	131	28,728	129	32,068
180	116	32,424	110	35,643
210	103	35,702	93	38,685
240	91	38,609	79	41,273
270	81	41,187	68	43,475
300	72	43,472	58	45,348
330	64	45,498	49	46,941
360	56	47,295	42	48,297
365	55	47,574	41	48,503

EXAMPLE 4.6 continued

The computed results are given in table E4.6. Fracture treatment B ($r_{wa} = 72$) yields higher rates for the first 120 days, at which time the well has produced 3300 STB more than fracture treatment A ($r_{wa} = 50$). After 120 days, the "shorter" fracture (A) produces at higher rates than treatment B, and cumulative oil for both cases approaches the same value. After one year, treatment B ($r_{wa} = 72$) has produced only 930 STB more than treatment A ($r_{wa} = 50$). A "quick-look" economic analysis would indicate that the two treatments give approximately the same improvement in well performance.

In summary, *any stimulated condition obtained by acidizing or fracturing, can be interpreted as a radial well with an apparent wellbore radius.* The relation of fracture geometry to apparent wellbore radius was outlined in a previous section for different assumptions of fracture conductivity. We can quantify the result of stimulation treatment as a skin factor, where

$$s = -\ln(r_{wa}/r_w). \tag{4.21}$$

Skin factor should be used cautiously, however. A poststimulation negative skin does *not* imply that stimulation will yield a prolonged increase in production rate. On the contrary, a good rule of thumb is that the better the stimulation, the more rapidly the rate will decline with time.

Similar considerations apply to the use of flow efficiency for a stimulated well. Flow efficiency E_F should be expressed as the ratio of rate–time following stimulation to rate–time for zero skin:

$$E_F(t) = \frac{q_o(t) : \text{stimulation}}{q_o(t) : \text{zero skin}} \tag{4.51}$$

or

$$E_F(t) = \frac{q_D(t_D) : r_{wa} = r_w e^{-s}}{q_D(t_D) : r_{wa} = r_w}. \tag{4.52}$$

It is, therefore, wrong to express the success of a treatment in terms of a single constant flow efficiency calculated for the initial poststimulation production rate.

Figures 4.21 and 4.22 illustrate hypothetical rate–time profiles for a low-permeability oil well and a low-permeability gas well. Three profiles have been calculated for the oil and gas wells using skin factors of +5, 0, and −5. The calculation of oil rate decline in figure 4.21 is used as an example (example 4.7) later in the text. The figures indicate that rate declines gradually during the transient period for a well with zero or positive skin. For example, rate decline for $s = +5$ is 20% during the first 72 hours, and is 30% for $s = 0$. Unstimulated or damaged well rate–time behavior may be nearly constant until the onset of depletion, when decline is accelerated (this is more so for high-permeability formations).

For the stimulated case with $s = -5$, oil rate drops from 1377 STB/D after 2.4 hours to 424 STB/D after 72 hours, corresponding to a decline of 78% in three days. For the gas well, rate drops from 8343 Mscf/D after 2.4 hours to 1854 Mscf/D after 72 hours, also a 78% decline in three days. The time marking onset of depletion is not, however, dependent on skin. For the oil wells in figure 4.21, depletion starts after 165 days, independent of skin. For the gas wells in figure 4.22, depletion (i.e., pseudosteady state) does not commence for eight years (2860 days), independent of skin.

An abandonment rate of 2 STB/D has been chosen for the oil well. Two barrels per day represents the rate below which it is no longer economic to produce the well. Ultimate recovery is about 8.5% of initial oil in place (IOIP) for all three values of skin. The time required to produce the 8.5% IOIP is, however, dependent on skin: 8.4 years for $s = -5$, 19 years for $s = 0$, and 28 years for $s = +5$. Expressed in economic terms, 8.5% of IOIP recovered after 8.4 years has a much greater present value than 8.5% of IOIP recovered after 28 years. An economic analysis of rate–time data and treatment costs will determine which treatment can be justified, how long it takes to recover expenses (rate of return), and what additional present value can be recovered by different treatment designs.

For the gas well in figure 4.22, an abandonment rate of 50 Mscf/D has been chosen. The rate is determined by a minimum gas velocity required to lift and unload liquids—i.e., to avoid liquid loading. Well and reservoir data for the gas well are given in table 4.3. For all values of skin, abandonment rate is not reached

Table 4.3 Gas Well Data

p_i	= 5000 psia
k	= 0.01 md
ϕ	= 0.10
c_{ti}	= $200(10^{-6})$ 1/psi
B_{gi}	= $5.88(10^{-4})$ bbl/scf
r_w	= 0.354 ft
A	= 80 acres
r_e	= 1053 ft
g	= 0.7 (air = 1)
p_{wf}	= 1000 psia
h	= 111 ft
μ_{gi}	= 0.026 cp
S_w	= 0.55
T_R	= 160°F
G	= 5.28 MMM scf

Skin	% recovery at 40 year
−5	60
0	28
+5	18

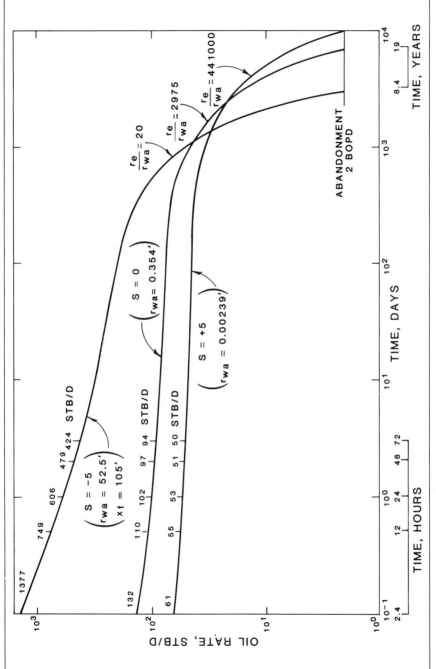

Figure 4.21 Effect of skin on rate–time behavior for a low-permeability oil well. Reprinted by permission of the author from Fetkovich 1982.

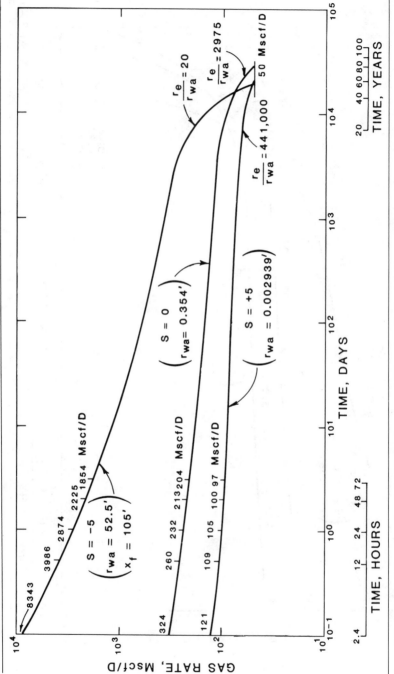

Figure 4.22 Effect of skin on rate–time behavior for a low-permeability gas well. Reprinted by permission of the author from Fetkovich 1982.

for more than 50 years (indicating that 80-acre spacing is too large). Using an *economic* life of 40 years, ultimate recovery is 60% of initial gas in place (IGIP) for $s = -5$, 28% IGIP for $s = 0$, and 18% IGIP for $s = +5$. Clearly, stimulation is required to produce reasonable gas reserves from this low-permeability well. Also, the well spacing should be reduced.

Example 4.7 shows the calculation procedure for the oil rate forecasts shown in figure 4.21. It is assumed that permeability has been determined by core analysis or well test interpretation. Drainage area is defined by well spacing, and other relevant properties are measured or estimated. The forecasting procedure is an excellent engineering tool for determining whether stimulation can be justified. Whether the objective fracture length considered in the forecast can be realized is usually uncertain. Design fracture lengths are typically overoptimistic and experience must be gained in a field to match well performance predictions to the fracture design criteria.

EXAMPLE 4.7 FORECASTING DECLINE BEHAVIOR FOR AN OIL WELL USING
RESERVOIR PROPERTIES AND THREE VALUES OF SKIN FACTOR

An M-80 oil well was completed without stimulation treatment. The initial well test indicates a skin factor of $+5$. Additional reservoir and test data are given in table E4.7a. To assess the effect of a planned fracture treatment, determine the production profile of the well with three values of skin factor: $+5$, 0, and -5. Also determine the productive life of the well until it reaches an abandonment rate of 2 STB/D.

SOLUTION

The effective wellbore radius corresponding to each of the skin factors is calculated using equation (2.34), and the results are listed in table E4.7b. In many cases, particularly in stimulated wells, the production profile with a given skin factor can be calculated using the type curve in figure 4.5. The following is a step-by-step procedure for establishing the rate profile for the case of $s = -5$.

Using equation (4.3), the real and dimensionless times are related by

$$t_D = \frac{0.00634 \times 0.2}{0.1 \times 0.3 \times 20 \times 20^{-6}} t \text{ (days)}$$

$$= 0.7656\, t.$$

The real and dimensionless rates are related by equation (4.2), which gives

$$q_D = \frac{141.2 \times 0.3 \times 1.2}{0.2 \times 50(3500 - 700)} q$$

$$= 550.8\, q_D.$$

EXAMPLE 4.7 continued

Table E.4.7a Well and Reservoir Data for the M-80 Oil Well

$p_{wf} = 700$ psia
$p_i = 3500$ psia
$k = 0.2$ md
$\phi = 0.1$
$c_t = 20 \times 10^{-6}$ psi^{-1}
$B_o = 1.2$
$r_w = 0.354$ ft
$r_e = 1053$ ft (80-acre spacing)
$h = 50$ ft
$\mu_o = 0.3$ cp
$S_w = 0.35$
$T_R = 150°F$
Initial oil in place (IOIP) $= 1.680 \times 10^6$ STB

Table E4.7b Effective Wellbore Radii and r_e/r_{wa} Values for $s = +5, 0, -5$

s	r_{wa} (ft)	r_e/r_{wa}
+5	0.0024	438,750
0	0.354	2,974
−5	52.54	20

The production profile is then established through the following steps:

1. List the times t to be considered.
2. Calculate t_D.
3. Determine the corresponding q_D from the type curve (fig. 4.5).
4. Calculate the corresponding q.

The results of this procedure for $s = -5$ are listed in table E4.7c and plotted in figure 4.21. Note that the $q_D - t_D$ data in table E4.6c are obtained from the radial solution in figure 4.5. When using the fractured well solution (the dashed curve in fig. 4.5), the predicted rate for the first day will be larger but will converge rapidly to the rates predicted by the radial solution.

A similar procedure can be used for the other two skin cases. However, because the depletion stems, r_e/r_{wa}, are beyond the range given by the type curves in figure 4.5, the relationship q_D versus t_D must be calculated by using equations. For the depletion period the calculating procedure is as follows:

1. List the times t to be considered.
2. Calculate the corresponding t_D using equation (2.129).
3. Calculate the corresponding t_{Dd} using equation (4.33b).
4. Calculate the corresponding q_{Dd} using equation (4.34).
5. Calculate the corresponding rate q using equation (4.32b).

This procedure implies the following relationships for the case of $s = +5$:

EXAMPLE 4.7 continued

Table E4.7c Production Profile for the M-80 Oil Well Calculated with $s = -5$

t (days)	t_D	q_D	q_o (STB/D)
0.1	0.0766	2.5	1377
0.5	0.383	1.35	749
1	0.766	1.1	609
2	1.53	0.86	479
5	3.83	0.71	391
10	7.66	0.58	319
25	19.1	0.46	253
50	38.3	0.41	226
100	76.6	0.365	201
250	191.4	0.275	151
500	382.8	0.182	100
1000	765.6	0.078	43
2000	1531	0.0146	8
2500	1914	0.0061	3.4
3000	2297	0.0028	1.5

$$t_D = 366 \times 10^6 t \ (\text{days}),$$

$$t_{Dd} = \frac{2}{[(438{,}750)^2 - 1]} \times \frac{1}{(\ln 438{,}750 - 0.5)} t_D$$

$$= 8.3 \times 10^{-13} t_D,$$

$$q_{Dd} = e^{-t_{Dd}},$$

$$q_D = \frac{1}{(\ln 438{,}750 - 0.5)} q_{Dd} = 0.08 q_{Dd},$$

$$q = 550.8 q_D.$$

Note that equation (4.34) is valid only for the depletion period, which starts at t_{pss}, calculated by

$$t_{pss} = 379 \frac{0.1 \times 0.3 \times 20 \times 10^{-6} \times \pi \times 1053^2}{0.2} = 3960 \text{ hours}$$

$$= 165 \text{ days.}$$

Considering transient production, the t_D corresponding to the end of transient flow for $s = +5$ is beyond the range of figure 4.5. Equation (4.12) is used instead of the figure.

For transient rate decline, the q_D versus t_D relationship is calculated directly from

EXAMPLE 4.7 continued

Table E4.7d Transient and Depletion Periods for the M-80 Oil Well Calculated with $s = +5$

t (days)	t_D	t_{Dd}	q_D	q_{Dd}	q (STB/D)
0.1	36×10^6		109×10^{-3}		60
1	366×10^6		97×10^{-3}		53.4
5	183×10^7		90×10^{-3}		49.6
10	366×10^7		87×10^{-3}		48
50	183×10^8		81×10^{-3}		44.6
100	366×10^8		79×10^{-3}.		43.5
150	549×10^8		78×10^{-3}		43
250*	915×10^8	759×10^{-4}	74×10^{-3}	927×10^{-3}	40.85
500	183×10^9	151×10^{-3}	68×10^{-3}	859×10^{-3}	37.88
1000	366×10^9	303×10^{-3}	59×10^{-3}	738×10^{-3}	32.54
2000	732×10^9	607×10^{-3}	43×10^{-3}	544×10^{-3}	24.01
3000	109×10^{10}	904×10^{-3}	32×10^{-3}	405×10^{-3}	17.84
5000	183×10^{10}	1.52	17×10^{-3}	218×10^{-3}	9.6
10,000	366×10^{10}	3.03	3.8×10^{-3}	48×10^{-3}	2.11

*Onset of pseudosteady state (depletion).

Table E4.7e Productive Life and Ultimate Recovery of the M-80 Oil Well Calculated with $s = +5, 0, -5$

Skin	Life (years)	% recovery (to 2 STB/D)
+5	28	8.42
0	19	8.44
−5	8.4	8.65

equations (4.11), (4.12), and (4.13) and then used for calculating q versus t. Results for the transient and depletion periods are calculated for $s = +5$, and are listed in table E4.7d, and plotted in figure 4.21. The productive life of the well until it reaches the abandonment rate of 2 STB/D is indicated on the curve and listed in table E4.6e. The cumulative production of the well was calculated using a programmable calculator program listed in Appendix B. The result is not included here, but the recovery percent at abandonment is listed in table E4.7e.

The use of type curves in figure 4.5 to forecast rate decline after stimulation is illustrated in example 4.8. When poststimulation production data of a stimulated well are available, the data can be matched to figure 4.5 or one of the other type curves given in sections 4.1 and 4.2. Such an analysis can be as effective for quantifying the success of stimulation as a pressure buildup test, without the cost and lost production of testing. Accurate rate–time analysis usually requires (1) production against a constant wellhead pressure, (2) daily rate measurements, and

(3) corrections for shut-in periods, changes in backpressure, and gradual decrease in backpressure (using the methods of reinitialization, superposition, and normalization). A reliable type-curve match can determine permeability, skin, or apparent wellbore radius, and drainage area (if the depletion stem has been reached).

EXAMPLE 4.8 ANALYSIS OF A WELL WITH INFINITE-CONDUCTIVITY FRACTURE

Thompson (1981) gives data for several tight gas wells which are used to illustrate the application of constant-pressure decline type curves. Thompson analyzes Well A in detail. Reservoir and well data for the Thompson A gas well are given in table E4.8a. A fracture half-length of 1030 ft with dimensionless conductivity of 500 is reported.

Calculate a rate–time forecast for the well assuming infinite-conductivity fracture. Compare the results with those reported by Thompson (fig. E4.8a) and discuss the differences.

SOLUTION

Dimensionless time for the well is calculated assuming the fracture has infinite conductivity. The apparent wellbore radius is

$$r_{wa} = x_f/2$$

$$= 1030/2$$

$$= 515 \, \text{ft},$$

giving dimensionless time of

$$t_D = \frac{0.00634k}{\phi \mu_{gi} c_{ti} r_{wa}^2} t \ (\text{days})$$

$$= \frac{0.00634(0.04)}{0.08(0.0143)(5.2 \times 10^{-4})(515)^2} t \ (\text{days})$$

$$= 0.00161 \, t \ (\text{days}).$$

Since initial pressure is 1175 psia, pressure-squared can be used to define dimensionless rate as

$$q_D = \frac{T \mu_{gi} Z_i}{0.703kh(p_i^2 - p_{wf}^2)} q_g \ (\text{scf/D})$$

EXAMPLE 4.8 continued

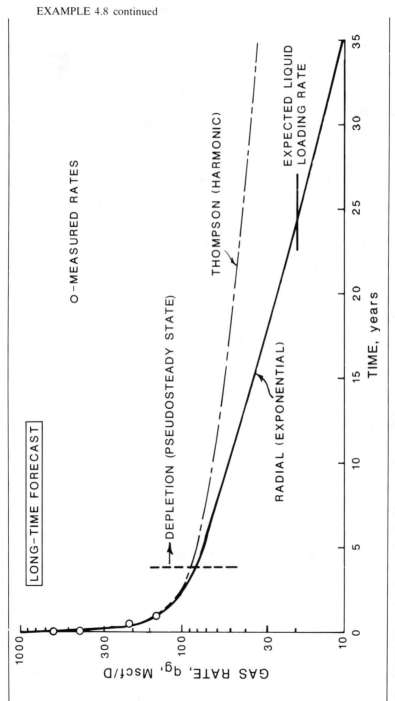

Figure E4.8a Long-time forecast for the Thompson A gas well.

EXAMPLE 4.8 continued

Table E4.8a Reservoir and Well Data for the Thompson A Gas Well

LOCATION	
State	New Mexico
County	San Juan
Geologic basin	San Juan
Formation	Mesaverde
Average depth	5626 ft
RESERVOIR DATA	
Initial reservoir pressure p_i	1175 psia
Bottomhole flowing pressure p_{wf}	600 psia
Reservoir temperature T	173 °F
Formation pay thickness h	29 ft
Formation permeability k	0.04 md
Formation porosity, ϕ	0.08 fraction
Initial gas viscosity μ_{g_i}	0.0143 cp
System compressibility c_{ti}	$0.0 \times 10^{-4}\,\text{psi}^{-1}$
Fracture half-length x_f	1030 ft
Dimensionless fracture capacity F_{cD}	500
Well drainage area	320 acres
Drainage radius r_e	2290 ft
Initial gas compressibility factor Z	0.87

$$= \frac{(173 + 460)(0.0143)(0.87)}{0.703(0.04)(29)(1175^2 - 600)^2} q_g$$

$$= 9.46 \times (10^{-6}) q_g.$$

Since a highly conductive fracture is indicated for the well, the infinite conductivity fracture solution (the dashed line in fig. 4.5) can be used. Furthermore, the infinite conductivity fracture solution approaches the plain radial solution at t_D values of 4 to 5.

Thereafter, the radial solution can be used instead. For the Thompson A well the two curves yield similar results after approximately 2480 days.

To determine the depletion stem on the type curve, drainage radius is calculated from the reported spacing of 320 acres, giving $r_e = 2106$ ft. The ratio r_e/r_{wa} is, then,

$$r_e/r_{wa} = 2106/515$$

$$= 4.1.$$

A depletion stem for $r_e/r_{wa} = 4$ is not shown in figure 4.5. The forecast, therefore, will apply the type curve for the transient period and the exponential decline equation for depletion. The time to pseudosteady state (depletion) must be estimated from equation (2.132), $t_{Dpss} = 0.1\pi(r_e/r_{wa})^2$, giving

$$t_{Dpss} = 0.1\pi(4.1)^2$$

$$= 5.3.$$

EXAMPLE 4.8 continued

**Table E4.8b Production Forecast for the Thompson A Gas Well
Using Infinite Conductivity and Plain Radial Solution as Compared
with Thompson's Predictions and Actual Field Production**

Time			Rate		q_g (Mscf/D)			
(days)	(years)	t_D	q_D	Infinite conductivity	Radial	Thompson	Actual field
5	0.014	0.00805	8.80	930	716	900	
15	0.041	0.0242	5.20	550	434	525	624
30	0.082	0.0483	3.75	396	321	378	428
183	0.5	0.295	1.70	180	157	175	211
365	1	0.588	1.30	137	123	135	144
730	2	1.18	1.01	107	99	160	
1460	4	2.35	0.81	78	78	(84)*	
2190	6	3.52	0.65	69	69	(75)*	
2920	8	4.70	0.57	61	61	(69)*	
3650	10	5.88	0.50	53	53	(64)*	
5475	15	8.81	0.36	38	38	(53)*	
7300	20	11.8	0.26	27**	27**	(46)*	
9125	25	14.7	0.18	19	19	(41)*	
10,950	30	17.6	0.13	14	14	(36)*	
12,775	35	20.6	0.095	10	10	(33)*	

Notes
*Values calculated assuming $q_D = 1/p_D$, which is not correct for pseudosteady state. Rates are therefore too high and should not be used.
**Minimum gas rate required to lift liquids is about 25 Mscf/D. Rate forecast beyond this point is highly questionable.

In fact, this relation only applies to larger ratios of r_e/r_{wa}. A more accurate estimate of $t_{Dpss} = 2.0$ is calculated by the program in Appendix B. Depletion decline is therefore assumed to start at $t_D = 2$ or $t_{pss} = 1250$ days (3.4 years).

The first rate forecast in table E4.8b lists the rate data obtained from the infinite conductivity solution (dashed line in fig. 4.5) for times up to 1250 days. Thereafter, rates are calculated using the radial solution for depletion. This is done manually by using equation (4.34). It may, however, be calculated by using the program in Appendix B.

The second rate forecast in table E4.8b uses the radial solution for early times (solid line in fig. 4.5). The result is a more pessimistic decline during the first three years.

The third rate forecast is given by Thompson (1981). During the first three years of transient decline, the $F_{cD} = 500$ type curve used by Thompson (fig. E4.8b) gives very similar results to the infinite conductivity type curve in figure 4.5. This is, of course, expected, for such a high fracture conductivity. The forecast beyond three years is calculated by Thompson using the assumption that $q_D = 1/p_D$. There is a *fundamental* error in using $q_D = 1/p_D$ for pseudosteady state. (The reason given for making the assumption is that a type curve was not available for q_D in the region of

EXAMPLE 4.8 continued

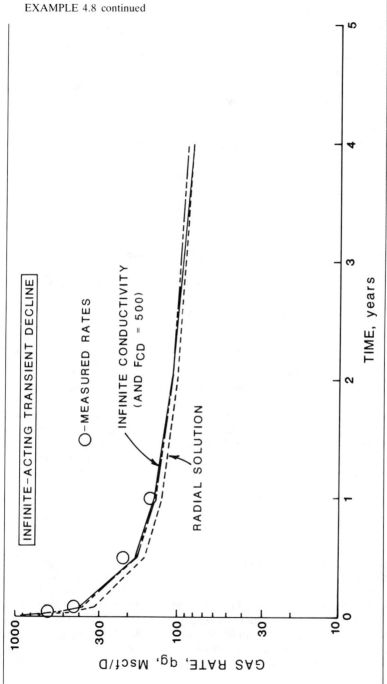

Figure E4.8b Infinite acting transient decline for the Thompson A gas well.

EXAMPLE 4.8 continued

pseudosteady state flow. In fact, Locke and Sawyer [1975] had published such a type curve for infinite conductivity fractures.) The erroneous calculation is based on the observation that $1/p_D$ closely approximates q_D during infinite-acting flow. However, it is easily shown that the same does *not* apply for pseudosteady-state conditions. If used, the method results in over optimistic harmonic decline (p_D is a linear function of t_D during pseudosteady state), instead of exponential decline as expected from the analytical solution. Furthermore, Thompson's forecast is probably overoptimistic in relation to the production life of the well. It concludes a 35-year production forecast, whereas the well will probably experience liquid loading and thus flow problems after about 20 years, when rate approaches 25 Mscf/D. Forecasting an additional 15 years gives an additional 100 MMscf (using the radial decline analysis). Thus 20% of the ultimate recovery cannot probably be realized.

In a publication reviewing the state of the art of hydraulic fracturing, Veatch (1983) lists the three main steps in designing a fracture treatment:

1. Estimate the rate–time forecast for several fracture geometries and fracture conductivities.
2. Determine the details of fracture treatment and cost to achieve each fracture condition.
3. Select a fracture treatment that maximizes the economic returns.

The procedure is illustrated in figure 4.23, adapted from Veatch's discussion.

The fracture planning procedure illustrated in figure 4.23 utilizes two calculation programs, one for well performance the other for fracture design. For a given well, the well performance program calculates the rate decline and cumulative production for various fracture conditions. It also calculates revenue from the well in terms of net present value. The fracture design model specifies treatment parameters needed to achieve the specific fracture conditions assumed in the well performance design and calculates the cost of treatment for each fracture condition. Combining revenues calculated by the first program with the cost from the second program gives the net profit expected from each fracture size. It also points out the most profitable fracture condition for a particular well.

4.4   **SPECIAL METHODS IN DECLINE TYPE CURVE ANALYSIS.** The previous three sections applied rate–time type curves to analyze rate decline in wells producing against a constant bottomhole flowing pressure. The rate–time analysis can be further expanded to include (1) a well that has experienced an abrupt change in backpressure, (2) a well with continuously changing bottomhole flowing pressure, and (3) a well that has been stimulated after a period of prestimulation production. Three type-curve manipulation techniques are used to facilitate the rate decline analysis for these three cases, namely superposition, rate–pressure normalization, and reinitialization.

437

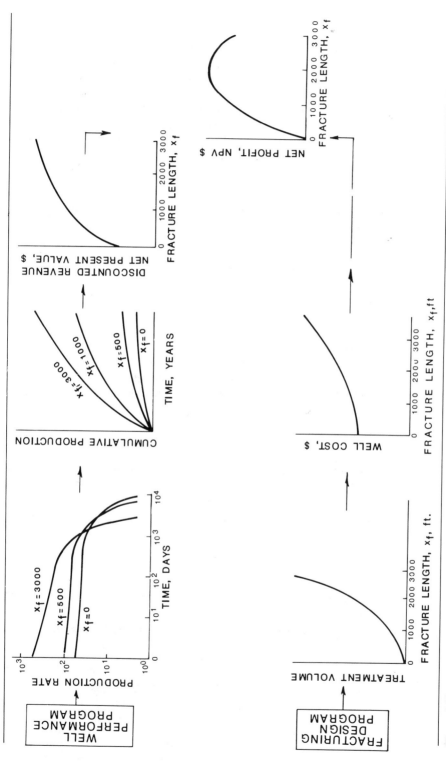

Figure 4.23 Considerations to optimize a fracture stimulation treatment. Reprinted by permission of the SPE-AIME after Veatch, Jr., 1983, fig. 1, part 1. © 1983 SPE-AIME.

Abrupt Backpressure Change. A reduction in wellhead backpressure can be used to increase production rate. It is often considered at a late stage of primary production to prolong the period of natural flow. Reduction of wellhead pressure at a late stage of recovery is usually associated with reduction of separator pressure, which establishes the need for installation of a pump or compressor downstream the separator to boost the transfer of oil and gas. Increased pumping and compression capacity requires large investment and has considerable operational and economic consequences. It is therefore desirable to predict the long-term production gain by a pressure reduction before such a decision is made.

A single abrupt change in backpressure can be treated by the method of *superposition*. For an abrupt change in wellhead pressure at time t_1 the superposition principle implies that rate decline is the algebraic sum of two decline trends. Fetkovich (1980) has given several examples for calculating the effect of a change in backpressure using type curves and superposition.

First, the rate decline established from initial backpressure is extrapolated to times beyond the backpressure change at time t_1, as if no change had occurred. In equation form, the extrapolation is written

$$q_{o1}(t) = \frac{kh(p_i - p_{wf1})}{141.2\mu_o B_o} q_D(t_D).$$

(4.53)

A second rate decline is initiated at time t_1, caused by the change in backpressure from p_{wf1} to p_{wf2}. The dimensionless time related to this decline is $t_D - t_{D1}$, where t_D is dimensionless time since initial production began and t_{D1} is the dimensionless time corresponding to t_1. In equation form, the new rate decline is given by

$$q_{o2}(t) = \frac{kh(p_{wf1} - p_{wf2})}{141.2\mu_o B_o} q_D(t_D - t_{D1}), \qquad t_D > t_{D1}.$$

(4.54)

The resulting expression for total rate, $q_o(t)$, at $t > t_1$ is the sum of q_{o1} and q_{o2}, or

$$q_o(t) = \frac{kh(p_i - p_{wf1})}{141.2\mu_o B_o} q_D(t_D) + \frac{kh(p_{wf1} - p_{wf2})}{141.2\mu_o B_o} q_D(t_D - t_{D1}).$$

(4.55)

It is convenient to rearrange equation (4.55) as

$$q_o(t) = \frac{kh(p_i - p_{wf1})}{141.2\mu_o B_o} \left[q_D(t_D) + \left(\frac{p_{wf1} - p_{wf2}}{p_i - p_{wf1}} \right) q_D(t_D - t_{D1}) \right].$$

(4.56)

By analogy to the oilwell solution, a single superposition for low-pressure gas wells is written

$$q_g = \frac{0.703kh(p_i^2 - p_{wf1}^2)}{T\mu_{gi} Z_i} \left[q_D(t_D) + \left(\frac{p_{wf1}^2 - p_{wf2}^2}{p_i^2 - p_{wf1}^2} \right) q_D(t_D - t_{D1}) \right].$$

(4.57)

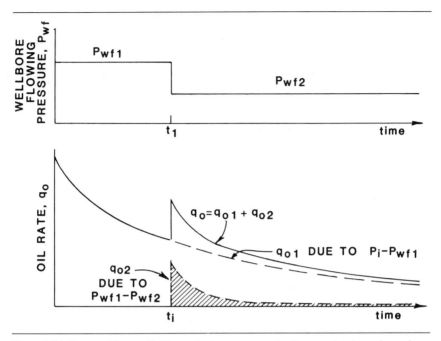

Figure 4.24 Superposition applied to constant-pressure production experiencing a change in backpressure.

More generally, using pseudopressure, which is valid for all pressure ranges in gas wells, superposition is written

$$q_g = \frac{0.703kh[m(p_i) - m(p_{wf1})]}{T} \times \left\{ q_D(t_D) + \left[\frac{m(p_{wf1}) - m(p_{wf2})}{m(p_i) - m(p_{wf1})} \right] q_D(t_D - t_{D1}) \right\}. \tag{4.58}$$

Figure 4.24 illustrates graphically the principle of superposition applied to a single change in backpressure. The figure indicates the pressure condition at a wellbore prior to and following the sudden change in backpressure; the solid line shows the expected rate profile. Up to time t_1, the rate decline is a result of the original pressure drawdown $(p_i - p_{wf1})$. Beyond t_1 the actual rate is the superposition of two trends, the extrapolation of the initial trend, indicated by a dashed line, and a rate profile starting at time t_1 due to a drawdown $(p_{wf1} - p_{wf2})$, which is also indicated by a dashed line.

Example 4.9 illustrates the method of superposition used to predict the effect of backpressure reduction on the production profile and thus on the economics of a gas well producing into a high-pressure pipeline. Referring to equations (4.56–4.58), it can be concluded that the result of a backpressure change can be substantial for highly undersaturated oil and high-pressure gas wells but may be nominal for low-pressure gas and solution-gas oil wells. The reason is that the pressure function p^2 for low-pressure gas and saturated oil wells tends to reduce the second term in the superposition.

EXAMPLE 4.9 RATE DECLINE FOLLOWING ABRUPT CHANGE IN BACKPRESSURE

After 155 hours of natural flow, well M-4x (example 4.2) is put on gas lift to reduce wellbore flowing pressure to 1800 psia.

Forecast the production profile for the first 100 hours following the scheduled change of flowing bottomhole pressure.

SOLUTION

The rate decline after gas-lift startup is calculated from equation (4.56) as

$$q_o = \frac{52(30)(3360 - 2660)}{141.2(2.3)(1.1)} \left[q_D(t_D) + \frac{(2660 - 1800)}{(3360 - 2660)} q_D(t_D - t_{D1}) \right],$$

or

$$q_o = 3056.8[q_D(t_D) + 1.23 q_D(t_D - t_{D1})]$$

$$= 3056.8 q_D(t_D) + 3755.4 q_D(t_D - t_{D1})].$$

The relationship for $q_D(t_D)$ and $q_D(t_D - t_{D1})$ can be calculated manually as done in example 4.7, or by the program in Appendix B, as done in examples 4.7 and 4.8. Either way, the necessary well data for calculations are obtained from the match point of example 4.2, which yields

$$\frac{t_D}{t_{hours}} = 6.5, \text{ or } \frac{t_D}{t_{days}} = 156$$

and

$$\frac{q_D}{q} = \frac{0.033}{100} = 3.3 \times 10^{-4}.$$

In addition, we calculate

$$\frac{r_e}{r_{wa}} = \frac{3000}{35} = 86$$

EXAMPLE 4.9 continued

Table E4.9 Production Profile of the M-4x Oil Well with Abrupt Change in Backpressure

t (hours)	t (days)	t_D	$t_D - t_{D1}$	$q_D(t_D)$	$q_D(t_D - t_{D1})$	q_o (STB/D)
12	0.5	78		0.359		1097
24	1.0	156		0.329		1005
36	1.5	234		0.304		929
48	2.0	312		0.291		889
60	2.5	390		0.283		865
72	3.0	468		0.276		843
84	3.5	546		0.270		825
96	4.0	624		0.266		813
108	4.5	702		0.262		800
120	5.0	780		0.259		791
132	5.5	858		0.256		782
144	6.0	936		0.253		773
155	6.46	1014		0.251		767
156*	6.5	1014		0.251		767
168	7.0	1092	78	0.249	0.359	2109
180	7.5	1170	156	0.247	0.329	1990
192	8.0	1248	234	0.245	0.304	1890
204	8.5	1326	312	0.243	0.291	1835
216	9.0	1404	390	0.241	0.283	1799
228	9.5	1428	468	0.239	0.276	1767
240	10	1560	546	0.238	0.270	1741
252	10.5	1638	624	0.237	0.266	1723

*Abrupt change in backpressure.

and

$$t_{D1} = 6.5(156) = 1014,$$

considering the fact that gas-lift startup requires one hour and thus starts after 156 hours. Table E4.9 lists the computed rates before and after the backpressure change. As usually expected in undersaturated oil wells, backpressure change has considerable effect on production rate.

Normalization. During transient production, flowing bottomhole pressure may vary simultaneously with production rate. If the pressure varies in a smooth manner, rate decline can be treated with a constant-pressure type curve if the rate used in the curve is normalized by pressure drop according to the relationship

$$q_n(t) = \frac{q_o(t)}{p_i - p_{wf}(t)}.$$ (4.59)

For gas wells rate is normalized by $(p_i^2 - p_{wf}^2)$, or by $[m(p_i) - m(p_{wf})]$, depending on conditions of pressure.

Normalization is based on the observation that a plot of normalized rate $q_n(t)$ versus production time matches the dimensionless rate–time type curve. The rate normalization technique has been used for analyzing pressure-transient behavior since it was first suggested by Gladfelter, Tracy, and Wilsey (1955). The validity of this approach was confirmed by Ramey (1965) and by Winestock and Colpitts (1965). Additional substantiation of the method is given by Fetkovich et al. (1984) who illustrate the match of data from Cullender's (1955) well No. 3 to the rate-decline type curve.

Strictly speaking, normalization should only be used during the infinite-acting period. Fortunately, this does not create a problem, since simultaneous pressure and rate decline usually stabilizes to a constant-pressure condition before pseudosteady state is reached. Example 4.10 applies the method of normalization to gaswell data given in Cullender's paper (1955) on isochronal testing.

EXAMPLE 4.10 NORMALIZATION APPLIED TO CULLENDER'S (1955) DATA FOR GAS WELL NO. 3

The Cullender gas well No. 3 reported in example 2.20 has been repeatedly tested during a period of nine years. The tests were isochronal tests, and test data are reported in table E4.10. The well is in the Hugoton field, Texas, where all wells were initially acid fracced.

To illustrate the concept of normalization, plot the normalized test rates versus test time and try to match the plot on the constant-pressure type curve in figure 4.5.

SOLUTION

In example 2.20, the backpressure exponent observed during a multirate test is $n = 0.95$. Thus, to normalize the rate, column 6 is calculated and added to table E4.10, listing $q/(p_R^2 - p_{wf}^2)^n$.

A plot of the test time t from column 1 versus the normalized rate in column 6 gives the graph in figure E4.10 (Fetkovich). The curve is then further matched on the type curve in figure 4.5, obtaining the match point

$$t_D = 3.2, \qquad t = 10 \text{ hours};$$

$$q_D = 1.1, \qquad q_g/(\Delta p^2)^n = 0.1\frac{\text{MscfD}}{\text{psia}^{1.9}} \times 1000\frac{\text{scf}}{\text{Mscf}}$$

$$= 100\frac{\text{scf/D}}{\text{psia}^{1.9}}$$

The permeability is calculated from the match point as

EXAMPLE 4.10 continued

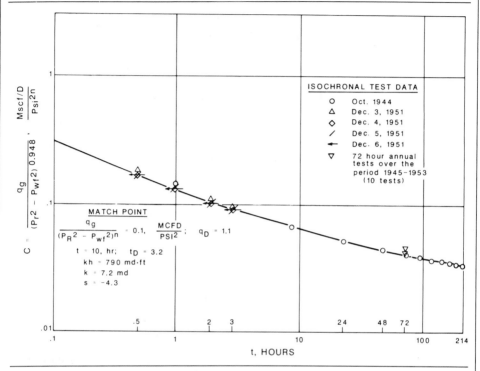

Figure E4.10 Plot of normalized production rate versus time for the Cullender No. 3 gas well. Reprinted by permission of the SPE-AIME from Fetkovich et al. 1984, fig. 15. © 1984 SPE-AIME.

$$kh = \frac{(T\mu Z)_i}{0.703}\left[\frac{q/(\Delta p^2)^n}{q_D}\right]_M$$

$$= \frac{550(0.012)(0.925)}{0.703}\left(\frac{100}{1.1}\right)$$

$$= 790\,\text{md-ft},$$

$$k = kh/h = \frac{790}{110} = 7.2\,\text{md},$$

and the skin factor is calculated from

$$r_{wa} = \left[\frac{0.000264k}{\phi\mu c_t}\left(\frac{t}{t_D}\right)_m\right]^{0.5}$$

$$= \left[\frac{0.000264 \times 7.2}{(0.071)(0.12)(0.0016)}\left(\frac{10}{3.2}\right)\right]^{0.5} = 20.8\,\text{ft},$$

EXAMPLE 4.10 continued

Table E4.10 Test Data for the Cullender No. 3 Gas Well

1	2	3	4	5	6
Test time (hrs)	Test ref.	p_R (psia)	p_{wf} (psia)	q_g (MMscf/D)	$\dfrac{q_g}{(p_R^2 - p_{wf}^2)^{0.95}}$
0.5	12-3-51	352.4	344.7	0.983	2.81×10^{-4}
0.5	12-4-51	352.3	329.5	2.631	2.73×10^{-4}
0.5	12-5-51	351.0	318.7	3.654	2.67×10^{-4}
0.5	12-6-51	349.5	305.4	4.782	2.59×10^{-4}
1	10-11-44	441.6	431.7	1.229	2.24×10^{-4}
1	12-03-51	352.4	342.4	0.977	2.19×10^{-4}
1	12-04-51	352.3	322.9	2.588	2.13×10^{-4}
1	12-05-51	351.0	309.5	3.565	2.10×10^{-4}
1	12-06-51	349.5	293.6	4.625	2.06×10^{-4}
2	12-3-51	352.4	339.4	0.970	1.70×10^{-4}
2	12-4-51	352.3	315.4	2.533	1.70×10^{-4}
2	12-5-51	351.0	298.6	3.453	1.66×10^{-4}
2	12-6-51	349.5	279.6	4.438	$1.65, \times 10^{-4}$
3	12-3-51	352.4	337.6	0.983	1.53×10^{-4}
3	12-4-51	352.3	310	2.500	1.49×10^{-4}
3	12-5-51	351.0	291.4	3.390	1.48×10^{-4}
3	12-6-51	349.5	270.5	4.318	1.46×10^{-4}
9	10-11-44	441.6	420.7	1.229	1.11×10^{-4}
24	10-11-44	441.6	414.7	1.187	0.852×10^{-4}
72	7-7-53	336.1	292.4	1.164	0.706×10^{-4}
120	16-11-44	441.6	404.3	1.163	0.619×10^{-4}
214	10-11-44	441.6	401.4	1.156	0.575×10^{-4}

which gives

$$s = -\ln(r_{wa}/r_w) = -\ln(20.8/0.292) = -4.3.$$

Permeability and skin factor can also be calculated by using equation (2.75) developed in chapter 2 for the constant C in the backpressure equation

$$kh = \frac{\left\{ D^{1-n} \dfrac{[q_g/(\Delta p^2)^n]_M}{q_{DM}^{2n-1}} \right\}^{1/n} T\mu_{gi} Z_i}{0.703}$$

Substituting D, calculated in example 2.20 as 6.9×10^{-8} 1/scf/D,

$$kh = \frac{\{[6.9(10^{-8})]^{0.05}[(100/(1.1)^{0.95}]\}^{1/0.95}(550)(0.012)(0.925)}{0.703}$$

$$= 425 \, \text{md-ft},$$

EXAMPLE 4.10 continued

resulting in $k = 3.9$ md, $r_{wa} = 15.4$ ft, and $s = -4.0$.

The discrepancy between permeability and skin calculated above is partly due to the inaccuracy in estimated D (from equation [2.65]) and partly from the approximate nature of the backpressure constant being written in terms of D. Even for this example where $n = 0.95 \approx 1$, the two methods yield different estimates of k (7.2 and 3.9 md) and, to a lesser extent, skin (-4.3 and -4.0). It is important when using calculated values of k and s (or r_{wa}) to choose the flow equation consistent with the constants used to evaluate k and s. For example, the backpressure constant C for IPR calculations using $k = 7.2$ and $s = -4.3$ is given by equation (2.67), while constant C for IPR calculations using $k = 3.9$ and $s = -4.0$ is given by equation (2.75); in both cases, the backpressure equation (1.33) is used with $n = 0.95$.

Normalization cannot be used when flowing pressure changes stepwise. In such cases it is necessary to apply the principle of superposition:

$$q(t) = \frac{kh}{141.2\mu_o B_o} \sum_{j=1}^{n} (p_i - p_{wfj}) q_D(t_{Dn} - t_{Dj-1}), \tag{4.60}$$

where $t_{Do} = 0$. It is important to recognize, however, that flowing pressure must be expressed as a series of constant-pressure increments for equation (4.60) to apply.

Reinitialization of Poststimulation Production. The behavior of a well that is stimulated or restimulated after a previous period of production can be divided into two distinct periods, prestimulation and poststimulation. Time is reinitialized to zero at the beginning of each period, and strictly speaking superposition is not used. In the case of constant-pressure production, declining rates in both periods can be matched, with certain adjustments, to the same rate-decline type curve.

During the prestimulation period, rate decline is controlled by initial well and reservoir parameters and can be analyzed according to the methods and type curves discussed in sections 4.1–4.3. Performing a stimulation treatment at time t_1 abruptly increases the apparent wellbore radius and therefore changes the rate-decline pattern. In most low-permeability reservoirs the prestimulation flowing wellbore pressure does not change after stimulation, and the ratio q_o/q_D determined from the prestimulation type-curve match remains unchanged after

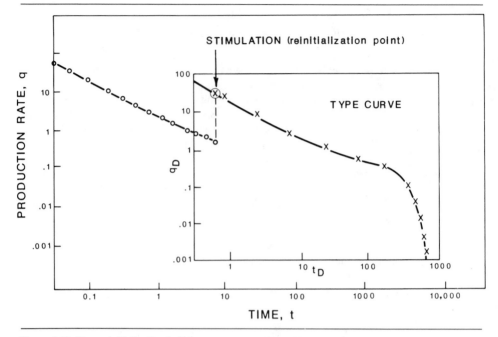

Figure 4.25 Time reinitialization technique.

stimulation. Values of t_D and r_e/r_{wa}, on the other hand, must be modified to represent the new wellbore condition r_{wa}.

Time is reinitialized to zero following stimulation. The relation between dimensionless and real time is changed according to the apparent wellbore radius achieved by stimulation. Figure 4.25 illustrates the procedure for reinitialization of production time to match rate–time data following stimulation. The time reinitialization technique may be used to plan stimulation or restimulation treatments. It can also be used to evaluate the results of stimulation treatment by comparing poststimulation data with the rate–time forecast.

4.5   FIELD PRODUCTION STRATEGY: COMPOSITE WELL PERFORMANCE. The deliverability of oil and gas wells deteriorates as depletion proceeds. The primary cause is declining reservoir pressure and increased resistance to flow. The general effect of depletion on inflow performance is illustrated in figure 4.26 as a pressure–rate–time diagram. The actual performance of a field during depletion depends mainly on the reservoir drive mechanism and the manner in which the field is developed. The usual trends are (1) decreases of wellhead pressure, (2) decline of oil and gas rates, (3) increase of gas–liquid ratio, and (4) increase of water fraction. Declining wellhead pressure is often associated with constant production rate. Wellhead pressure is continuously reduced by an operator who wants to maintain

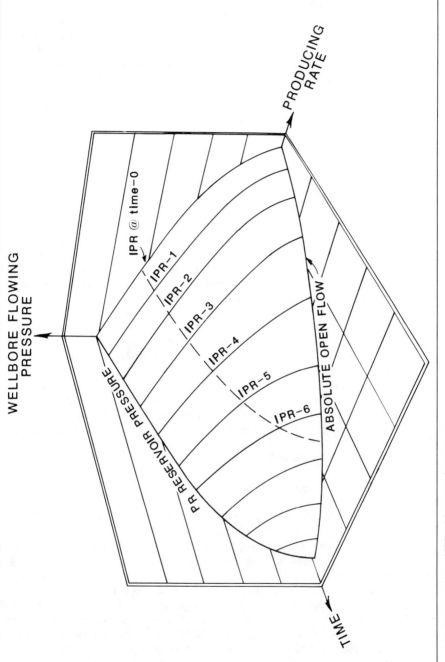

Figure 4.26 Deterioration of IPR with reservoir recovery.

constant rate in spite of declining reservoir pressure. Declining rates are associated with a constant wellhead pressure, usually controlled by the separator pressure or regulated by transportation line requirements. Increasing gas–liquid ratio and water fraction as dictated by the reservoir drive mechanism causes an increase in resistance to flow for the main producing phase. This, in turn, results in rate and pressure decline, and increasing loads on the separators and water-removal facilities.

Forecasting production performance is essential for technical planning and economic evaluation of alternative development strategies. Offshore fields usually cannot be developed unless sufficient delineation wells are drilled, a platform is built, field processing facilities are installed, and pipelines or tanker loading facilities are constructed. Offshore development requires large initial investments, which can be justified only if sufficient reserves are available and production level can be maintained for an extended period of time. Major offshore fields are typically produced at a relatively constant field rate. This is particularly the case for offshore gas fields where the gas purchaser requires a certain field deliverability over an extended period, often ten to twenty years. To explain the economical arguments for planning and controlling a particular production schedule, figure 4.27 illustrates the production, cost, and net cash-flow profile of a marginal offshore oil field. The production profile reflects a particular field development schedule where, one by one, wells are drilled, completed, and put on production. The result is a stepwise buildup of production level, indicating that simultaneous drilling and production are taking place on the same platform. The buildup period is followed by a period of constant oil production. The figure also indicates that, despite a constant oil rate, gas production may rise rapidly when reservoir pressure drops below the bubble point. In some oil reservoirs, gas revenues represent a significant fraction of total revenues (20% to 50%). In recent years the value of gas has gradually increased to become a key factor in economic planning.

In relation to associated gas production, the differential in value per unit energy between oil and gas is rapidly diminishing. Average energy values of gas and oil are

Gas: 1 Mscf = 1.1 million BTU,

Oil: 1 STB = 5.6 million BTU.

If gas can be sold at $4 per Mscf and oil at $25 per barrel, the price per million BTU is $3.6 for gas and $4.5 for oil. In terms of conservation, recovery must be calculated in terms of energy and not merely barrels of oil. If gas prices continue to increase and oil prices decrease or stabilize, the energy value of gas may soon exceed that of oil.

The duration of a scheduled oil or gas plateau depends mostly on sales contracts, production equipment, and regulatory control. Rules of thumb used in the Norwegian North Sea are annual plateau rates equalling 5% of the initial recoverable gas reserves for gas fields and 10% of the recoverable oil reserves for oil fields. The production decline shown in figure 4.27(a) occurs when the wells can no longer sustain the plateau rate with a wellhead pressure sufficient to process and transport the oil and gas. How rapidly rate declines is determined by depletion and the flow characteristics of reservoir fluids.

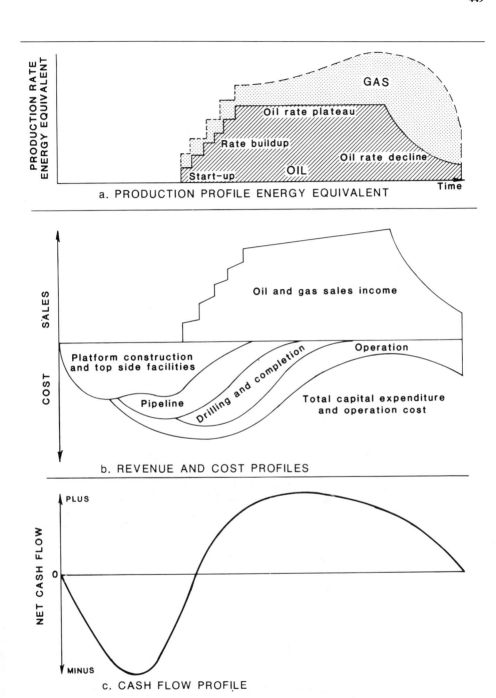

Figure 4.27 Production and economic forecast for a marginal offshore oil field.

The revenue profile for oil and gas sales is illustrated in figure 4.27(b). Actual revenue depends not only on the production profile, but on the prices of oil and gas. Forecasting price trends is more uncertain than determining the production profiles. Economists usually forecast prices assuming a linear price increase or, in the case of gas, according to the expected price development set out by the gas sales contract. It is imperative to calculate the economics of offshore projects using several price development scenarios, including the most pessimistic, when prices fall.

Figure 4.27(b) also indicates the cost of developing and operating the field. Total costs include (1) the platform and topside facilities, (2) pipeline construction or lease, (3) drilling and completion, and (4) operation and overhead. The cost of field development in the proximity of existing pipeline gathering systems and process facilities can be significantly lower than if those facilities must be designed and built. Access to existing facilities is therefore a major factor in the development of marginal fields. In the Northern North Sea, the possibility of sharing facilities by several neighboring fields is perhaps the single most important factor governing the commerciality of even large fields.

Figure 4.27(c) gives the cash-flow profile after deduction of taxes and royalties. Cash flow can be converted to any of several profit indicators that determine the economics of a given offshore project or set its rank among several projects competing for the same financial resources.

It is obvious from figure 4.27 that the crux of an economic analysis for an offshore field is development of a realistic production profile. It is particularly important to establish the length of the production plateau. The technical and economic reasoning for an extended rate plateau is also valid for onshore fields located far from a competitive market. Similar to offshore fields, a substantial initial investment is required for building an infrastructure before production begins. Long-term sales contracts and expensive transportation networks enforce, in such cases, production considerations not usually applicable to "conventional" onshore fields. Most onshore fields can be developed gradually, where each well is put on production after completion. Production restrictions are usually limited to government-imposed regulations that seek to enforce an equitable depletion of the natural resources. Onshore gas fields may be restricted in production by seasonal and economic fluctuations in demand. Typically this results in variations of wellhead condition and irregular rate–time behavior.

A simple procedure for estimating how long a well can produce at a constant rate is illustrated in figure 4.28. The method assumes that transient production is relatively short-lived and depletion is the main cause of decreasing wellbore flowing pressure. The first step in figure 4.28 is to determine the IPR at several times during depletion, as defined by cumulative oil production N_p. At the desired plateau rate, one enters the IPR at each stage of depletion and finds the corresponding flowing wellbore pressure. Then the gradient curves corresponding to the plateau rate and producing GLR, $R(N_p)$ are chosen. Each curve is entered with the bottomhole flowing pressure $p_{wf}(N_p)$, and a corresponding wellhead flowing pressure $p_{wh}(N_p)$ is determined by moving up the gradient curve a distance equal to well depth. The wellhead flowing pressures are plotted versus cumulative oil production and the curve is extrapolated to the point when p_{wh} equals the minimum allowable wellhead flowing pressure, $p_{wh\,min}$.

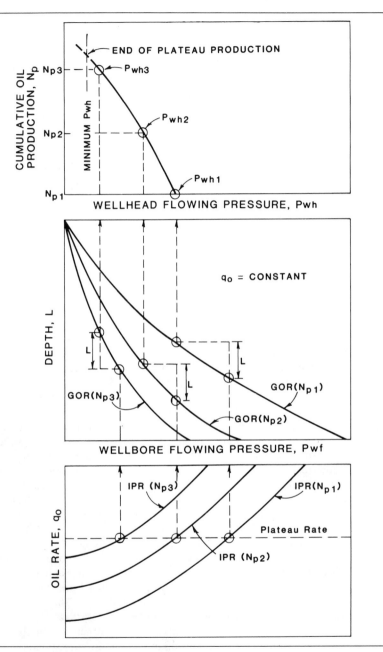

Figure 4.28 Simplified procedure for determining the duration of plateau production before reaching minimum wellhead pressure.

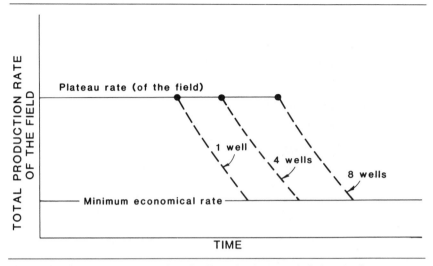

Figure 4.29 Effect of increased number of wells on the plateau period of production.

Cumulative production is converted to time by dividing by the field rate, where field rate equals average well rate q_o times the number of wells N_w. It is worth noting that the procedure in figure 4.28 requires data from material balance calculations to determine the deteriorating IPRs. Example 4.11 to come later in the text provides an instance of the procedure shown in Figure 4.28.

The length of the field plateau rate depends on the number of producing wells. More wells result in a longer plateau as shown in figure 4.29. When more wells produce the field plateau, each well produces a smaller fraction of the total rate. Consequently, each well produces with a smaller pressure drawdown, which is reflected in a higher wellhead pressure. This results in a longer plateau period before reaching the minimum allowable wellhead pressure. The extended plateau will not necessarily be proportional to the number of wells, but the relation is strong. Similar reasoning can be used to consider the effect of stimulation treatments on the length of the rate plateau. That is, stimulation prolongs the plateau.

Plateau production ends when wellhead pressure reaches the minimum allowable wellhead pressure. This marks the onset of a new production period, which is dominated by the constant pressure condition. If material balance calculations are available, the declining rate at a constant wellhead pressure can be determined according to the procedure illustrated in figure 4.30. The IPR curves and tubing performance relationship curves (TPR) for several stages of depletion are placed on the same figure. All TPR curves are constructed with the same wellhead pressure. The intersection points of an IPR and its corresponding TPR determine expected flowing bottomhole pressure and natural flow rate at each stage of depletion. The rates are plotted versus cumulative production. Time is expressed by

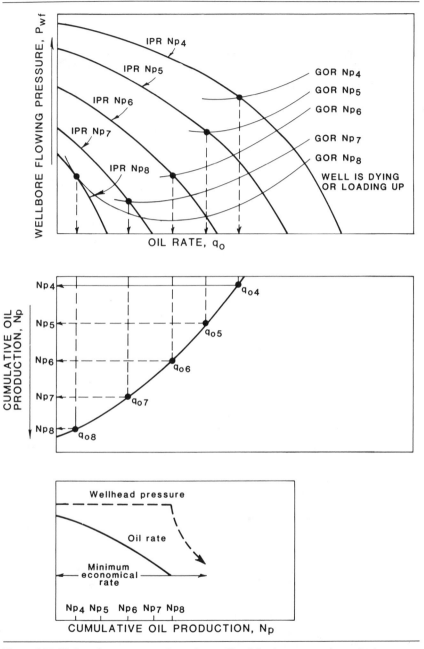

Figure 4.30 Well performance procedure when wellhead flowing pressure is constant.

$$t = \int_0^{N_p} dN_p/q, \tag{4.61}$$

which can be solved graphically by plotting $1/q_o$ versus N_p and finding the area under the curve between two values of N_p. Example 4.11 illustrates calculation of production plateau length and rate decline at a constant wellhead pressure.

EXAMPLE 4.11 DEPLETION CHARACTERISTICS OF AN OFFSHORE OIL WELL

A semisubmersible floating production vessel, Transnor 68, is planned for producing the small Ina oil field, located adjacent to the major Agulia field. The Ina field consists of eight subsea completed satellite wells connected by flexible flowlines and production risers to the production vessel. The appraisal well, Ina No. 4, was selected to represent the characteristics of a typical Ina well. A reservoir study using material balance calculations, relative permeability, and PVT data established the depletion characteristics of the field. The results of the study are given in table E4.11a.

A multirate test of Ina No. 4 established that the IPR of the well is

$$q/q_{max} = \left[1 - \left(\frac{p_{wf}}{p_R} \right)^2 \right]^{0.9},$$

where

$p_R \quad = 4000\,\text{psia},$

$q_{max} = 480\,\text{STB/D}.$

Additional well data are given in table E4.11b.

The study requires investigation of the production profile for two production schedules:

Table E4.11a Reservoir Characteristics of the Ina Field

Cumulative production N_p (STB)	Average pressure p_R (psia)	Pressure function $\left(\frac{k_{ro}}{\mu_o B_o} \right)_{p_R}$	Production gas–oil ratio R (scf/STB)
0	4000	0.2234	600
100,000	3520	0.147	1000
200,000	3100	0.1117	1600
300,000	2800	0.0714	2500
400,000	2500	0.0446	5000
500,000	2300	0.0440	2500

EXAMPLE 4.11 continued

Table E4.11b Well Data for a Typical Ina Well

Casing OD	7 in.
Tubing	2⅞ in. × 8000 ft
Midperforations	8000 ft

Case 1: The well is producing "wide open" without a choke against a constant separator pressure of 175 psia. It was calculated that the well will produce with a constant wellhead pressure of 200 psia. The rate will decline with reservoir depletion until a rate of $q = 200$ STB/D is reached. Then, production will be enhanced by gas lift.

Case 2: The wells will be regulated to produce at a plateau rate of 200 STB/D (each well) until the wellhead pressure reaches a minimum of 200 psia.

Prepare the production profile of the well for each case and estimate the cumulative production and time at which artificial lift will be initiated.

SOLUTION

The first step is to establish future IPRs. For each depletion stage there is a new absolute open flow, calculated from equation (2.102). For example, for $N_p = 100,000$ bbl the maximum rate is

$$(q_{max})_2 = (q_{max})_1 \left[\frac{(k_{ro}/\mu_o B_o)_2}{(k_{ro}/\mu_o B_o)_1} \times \frac{(p_R)_2}{(p_R)_1} \right]^n$$

$$= 480 \left(\frac{0.1474}{0.2234} \times \frac{3500}{4000} \right)^{0.9}$$

$$= 292.8 \, \text{STB/D}.$$

Furthermore, assuming the exponent n does not change with depletion, the new IPR equation is and with the new q_{max} it becomes:

$$q_o = 292.8 \left[1 - \left(\frac{p_{wf}}{3500} \right)^2 \right]^{0.9}$$

Then the IPR curve is plotted using the IPR equation.

Table E4.11c gives q_{max} and several points on the IPR curve for each depletion stage from $N_p = 0$ to $N_p = 500,000$ STB. Results are also shown in figure E4.11. In case 1, gradient curves for 2⅞" tubing with $p_{wh} = 200$ psia and tubing length of 8000 ft are used to determine the tubing performance curve (TPR). For each depletion stage the gradient curves are selected by the appropriate GOR.

The procedure is done manually and the results are listed in table E4.11d and

EXAMPLE 4.11 continued

Table E4.11c IPRs for Ina Oil Wells at Various Depletion Stages

p_R (psia)		4000		3500		3100		2800		2500		2300
$q_{o\max}$ (STB/D)		480		293		205		125		74		68
	p_{wf} (psia)	q_o (STB/D)	p_{wf}	q_o	p_{wf}	q_o	p_{wf}	q_o	p_{wf}	q_o	p_{wf}	q_o
	0	480	0	293	0	250	0	125	0	74	0	68
	1000	453	750	280	750	194	500	121	500	71	500	65
	2000	371	1500	244	1500	161	1000	110	1000	63	1000	56
	3000	228	2250	181	2250	104	1500	92	1500	49	1500	41
	4000	0	3000	89	3000	17	2000	46	2000	29	2000	19
			3500	0	3100	0	2500	30	2500	0	2300	0
							2800	0				

Table E4.11d Tubing Intake Performance at Various Depletion Stages (Tubing 2⅞″ × 8000 ft and $p_{wh} = 200$ psia)

N_p (STB)	0	100,000	200,000	300,000	400,000
GOR (scf/STB)	600	1000	1600	2500	5000
q_o (STB/D)		Tubing intake pressure p (psia)			
50	2100	1740	1400	1050	680
100	1810	1550	1180	840	630
200	1680	1400	1020	729	630
400	1600	1300	1000	690	740
600	1580	1450	1000	750	1000

plotted in figure E4.11. The intersection of IPR and TRP at each depletion stage gives the natural flow rate at that depletion stage. The natural flow rates read from the graph are listed in table E4.11e.

Linear interpolation between $N_p = 100,000$ STB and $N_p = 200,000$ STB yields $N_p = 170,590$ STB as the point when the minimum economical rate, $q = 200$ STB/D is reached.

The time elapsed to that point is given by

$$t = \sum \frac{\Delta N_p}{q_{\text{average}}} = \frac{100,000}{0.5(406 + 248)} + \frac{70,590}{0.5(248 + 200)} = 621 \text{ days} = 1.7 \text{ years.}$$

457

EXAMPLE 4.11 continued

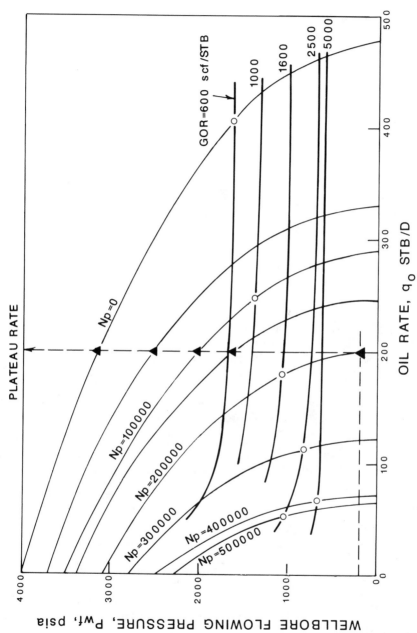

Figure E4.11 Graphical procedure to determine the decline of natural flow rate during constant wellhead production.

EXAMPLE 4.11 continued

Table E4.11e Flow Rates at Constant Wellhead Pressure

N_p (STB)	q_o (STB/D)
0	406
100,000	248
200,000	180
300,000	113
400,000	·67
500,000	54

Table E4.11f Wellhead Decline at Plateau Rate

N_p (STB)	p_{wf} (psia)	p_{wh} (psia)
0	3150	1060
57,500	2500	720
100,000	2025	620
137,500	1625	410
172,500	825	70

Considering case 2, a constant rate of 200 STB/D is represented by a vertical line through $q = 200$ STB/D in figure E4.11. The point where the line intersects the IPR determines p_{wf} at each stage of depletion. The p_{wf} can be used as an intake pressure to the gradient curve of $q = 200$ STB/D, yielding wellhead pressure p_{wh}. The readings of p_{wf} and p_{wh} are listed in table E4.11f.

Using linear interpolation between the last two points in table E4.11f, we obtain that the wellhead pressure declines to 200 psia when

$$N_p = 137500 + \frac{(410 - 200)(172,500 - 137,500)}{(410 - 70)} = 159,118 \, \text{STB}.$$

The time to reach this stage is

$$t = \frac{Np}{q} = \frac{159,188}{200} = 795 \text{ days} = 2.2 \text{ years}.$$

It is important to recognize that each well in a field can maintain its "share" of the plateau rate for a certain length of time. Field decline is somewhat gradual at the beginning, as the weak producers first reach the minimum wellhead condition, but becomes rapid when the best producers reach the minimum wellhead pressure condition.

From rate–pressure considerations as illustrated in figure 4.30, rate decline may continue as long as the tubing performance curve and corresponding IPR curve have an intersection point. When the two curves no longer intercept but are merely

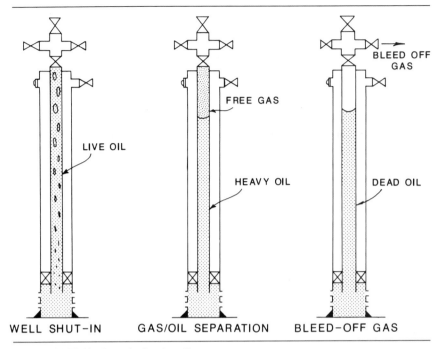

Figure 4.31 Fluid column in shut-in well.

tangent to each other, the well has reached an unstable flow condition and may cease flowing at any instant. General experience shows that the unstable natural flow condition may continue for long periods, though with a reduction in total production. A small disturbance that moves flow conditions away from the tangent point may kill the well.

A short shut-in is usually enough to disturb an unstable flow equilibrium and kill the well. Figure 4.31 illustrates what takes place in the tubing following shut-in.

Initially there is a distribution of gas throughout the oil column in the tubing. After some time, gas separates to the top of the tubing. When the well opens again, gas bleeds off and the remaining oil may have a sufficiently large gradient to keep the well shut in. The well can be brought back into production by unloading the "dead" liquids and reducing the hydrostatic head in the tubing. Unloading is usually performed by wireline swabbing or kick-off methods, which inject or circulate into the tubing a light fluid such as diesel oil, natural gas, or nitrogen. Several methods for unloading a well are illustrated in figure 4.32.

Most operators initiate artificial lift before naturally flowing wells approach the unstable flow stage. Others try to postpone investment in artificial lift by using various kinds of "poor boy" measures to maintain natural flow. This may include bypassing existing production manifolds, isolating weak wells in a special low-pressure production system, and avoiding the testing of weak wells. Eventually, the

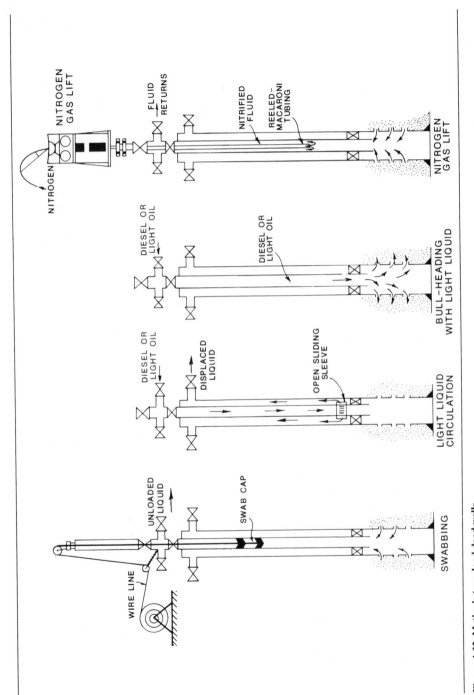

Figure 4.32 Methods to unload dead wells.

expense of keeping weak wells flowing may exceed the cost of introducing artificial lift and the operator will be forced to abandon natural flow production.

The methods outlined in this section use the reservoir material balance, IPR, and TPR to calculate production profiles. In some cases the profile can be calculated using only dimensionless pressure and rate solutions. The pseudosteady-state type curve may combine with simple tubing performance models to forecast production conditions during depletion. When the gas–liquid ratio and water cut change substantially, the effect of multiphase flow must be accounted for in reservoir and tubing performance, and the dimensionless pressure–time methods may no longer be valid.

Whichever technique is used to forecast rate decline, the forecast should not be extrapolated indefinitely using rate–pressure analysis without considering additional governing factors that can terminate production:

1. Gas and high-GOR wells tend to load up with liquid and cease flowing as gas rate declines to a minimum critical value.
2. In wells producing by artificial lift, lifting costs may become prohibitive when total liquid production is continuously increased to maintain a desired oil rate.

The problem of liquid loading in gas wells and high-GOR oil wells is of great concern in many fields. The source of the problem is that reservoir gas entering the well and flowing to the surface is associated with formation water, reservoir oil, or condensate. At high gas rates, the associated liquid is continuously carried over to the surface by the gas and liquid loading is not a problem. As gas rate declines, gas velocity decreases to a limit where it can no longer carry the liquids to the surface, and liquid starts to accumulate at the bottom of the well.

A liquid-loaded well starts to produce irregularly, with significant fluctuation as liquid is unloaded in batches and transported to the surface in slugs. Eventually, gas rate declines to a level where not enough energy is available to unload the well even in batches, and the well dies. The literature suggests two methods of forecasting well loading. One method is based on calculating a critical unloading gas velocity, below which there is no continuous unloading. The other method uses specially developed wet-gas gradient curves to account for liquid loading. Details and discussions of the two methods appear in several publications, including Duggan (1961), Turner et al. (1969), and Lea (1982).

Forecasting a production profile may become more complicated when in addition to natural depletion it is affected by other factors. The most pronounced are:

1. reservoir pressure maintenance by water or gas injection
2. water flooding
3. enhanced oil recovery techniques
4. artificial lift
5. extension of the field by step-out and in-fill wells
6. well problems such as plugging, paraffin and scale deposits, casing collapse, and formation plugging
7. well stimulation
8. production allocation or other regulatory restrictions

9. natural catastrophes that damage the field and production facilities
10. production downtime due to routine and major workovers

Stimulation treatment, water flood, and enhanced oil recovery may create peaks in field production, but they typically fall off quickly in a manner similar to rate decline during primary recovery. Figure 4.33 shows an example of a production profile for an onshore field (fig. 42 by Fetkovich et al., 1984) influenced by water flooding. A large-scale water injection scheme had started after 13 years of primary recovery. The water injection rate was about eight times higher than the oil production rate. Six months after initiating injection, water broke through in the producing wells and the water–oil ratio started to increase. The injection slowed down the oil rate decline and helped to stabilize production at an approximately constant level. It is uncommon to predict the secondary recovery effect indicated by the example at the initial planning phase of field development. Water or gas flooding initiated at an early stage to maintain reservoir pressure must, however, be considered when preparing a rate forecast. Unfortunately, uncertainties introduced by water flooding and gas injection greatly reduce the integrity of a forecast.

The schedule of adding new wells and the schedule of introducing artificial lift to flowing wells also affects the production profile. A result of these effects is illustrated by the production profile in figure 4.34. The Sholom Aleichem field in figure 4.34 is located in Stephens and Carter Counties, southern Oklahoma. According to the figure, field rate started declining before the field had been completely developed. The production profile shown is a result of adding more wells, deterioration of the natural flow performance of individual wells, and the gradual introduction of artificial lift started in 1974. It is probably the most typical production characteristic of onshore oil fields. It is considerably more complicated when compared with examples of naturally flowing fields presented in this chapter. Similar methods, however, may analyze the production characteristics of the field and individual wells.

It is interesting to note that completely unrestricted production is uncommon for oil fields in the United States. For example, Texas has enforced a limiting gas–oil ratio of 2000 scf/STB for oil wells since 1933. It is not unusual for high-shrinkage and volatile oil wells to reach the 2000 GOR only shortly after depletion begins. Production allowables are also commonplace in the U.S.

During the oil-rate plateau, gas rate will have the same form as the producing gas–oil ratio curve $R(N_p)$. The gas rate equation is simply

$$q_g(N_p) = q_o R(N_p). \tag{4.62}$$

When oil rate begins to decline, gas rate normally declines accordingly, even though GOR continues to increase. The gas equation is written

$$q_g(N_p) = q_o(N_p) R(N_p). \tag{4.63}$$

The $q_g(N_p)$ relation can also be expressed as $q_g(t)$ by converting cumulative oil to time. A typical gas-rate profile for a solution gas-drive reservoir is shown in figure 4.35. Figure 4.36 illustrates gas performance for a North Sea oil reservoir producing

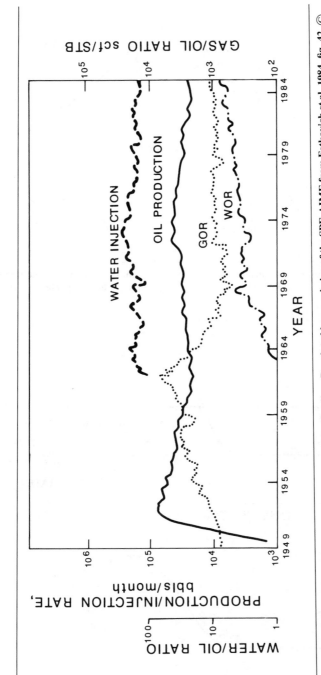

Figure 4.33 Field example of production response to water flooding. Reprinted by permission of the SPE-AIME from Fetkovich et al. 1984, fig. 42. © 1984 SPE-AIME.

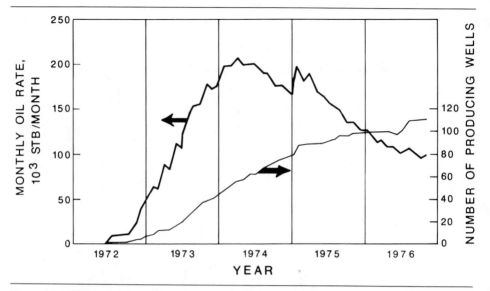

Figure 4.34 Field production and drilling activity for the Sholom Aleichem field in southern Oklahoma. Reprinted by permission of the SPE-AIME from Clark and Wall 1978, fig. 3. © 1978 SPE-AIME.

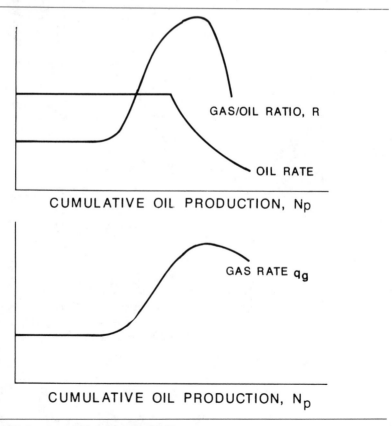

Figure 4.35 Gas rate calculation for an oil field.

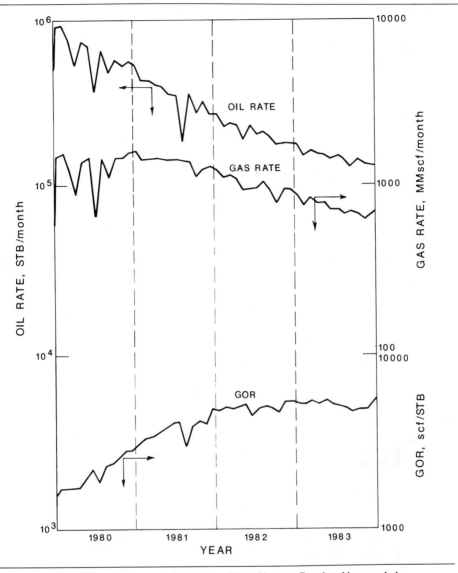

Figure 4.36 Production performance of Edda field, offshore Norway. Reprinted by permission of the SPE-AIME from Fetkovich et al. 1984, fig. 34. © 1984 SPE-AIME.

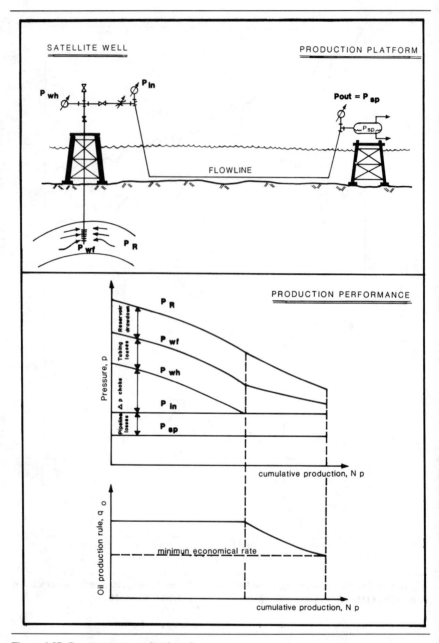

Figure 4.37 Constant rate production plan.

against a constant wellhead pressure. The Edda field in figure 4.36 is a satellite to the main Ekofisk field and produces to the central processing and transfer facilities of Ekofisk. The large capacity of the central facilities permits producing the field "wide open," without a rate plateau. Without the use of Ekofisk facilities, the Edda field would require an extra investment for handling facilities. Such an investment could be economically justified only if the facilities are sized to operate near their maximum capacity for a prolonged time, a condition that implies a constant production rate.

A very useful display of pressure-rate-time behavior for field planning purposes is given in figure 4.37. It shows an offshore installation where a well on a satellite platform is producing through a flow-line to the separator on the main production platform. While producing at a constant rate, the reservoir pressure is gradually declining, demanding a corresponding reduction of wellbore and wellhead pressures. The display shows the effect of the IPR, tubing size, choke opening, flowline size and separator pressure on the length of the production plateau. In the case of offshore fields, figure 4.37 is probably the most comprehensive display of results of a complete well performance analysis.

To complete this section, it is important to realize that production forecasting can be very subjective. That is, two engineers, given the same basic data, will not necessarily predict the same production profile. In fact, forecasts are often made for a specific purpose and may be biased to suit this purpose. For instance, a company deciding whether to develop a marginal offshore discovery may tend to present a conservative forecast to arrange better tax considerations from the government. On the other hand, a company borrowing money for development of oil and gas properties tends to present the most favorable forecast possible. It is probably correct to say that any production forecast is dependent to some extent on the purpose of its application.

4.6   **SUMMARY.** This chapter adds the time dimension to analysis of well performance. Up to this point all discussions were based on "snapshot" performance, where the pressure–rate relationship of a producing well is related to a particular state of depletion. Expanding the snapshot IPRs into a series of performance relations as a function of time allows development of a production profile. Two categories of production profiles are addressed; constant pressure, and constant rate. Constant-pressure production implies a continuous drop of production rate. Constant rate implies a continuous drop in the flowing bottomhole and wellhead pressures. Constant-rate production is typical of fields where production level is limited by one of the following constraints:

1. limited capacity of the surface processing and handling facilities
2. local reservoir problems, such as gas and water coning
3. sales and delivery contracts that specify fixed delivery levels
4. regulatory constraints and production allowables.

Without constraints as well may produce "wide open," at or near its maximum flow capacity, implying production at a constant flowing pressure governed by the separator or flowline backpressure. Constant-pressure production is also typical of wells that initially produced at plateaus they can no longer sustain at existing wellhead conditions.

Two distinct flow periods are observed in wells: transient and pseudosteady state. The transient period is characterized by a rapid change of flow conditions in the well. It starts with production start-up and continues until the rate–pressure disturbance triggered at the wellbore propagates and reaches the boundaries of the drainage region. When outer boundaries are reached by the pressure disturbance and the entire reservoir starts to contribute to production, conditions at the well tend to stabilize, and the transient period smoothly changes to a pseudosteady state. Pseudosteady state is, therefore, associated with depletion and the two terms are used interchangeably in the book. Medium- to high-permeability reservoirs exhibit short transient periods that have small effects on the production of wells. In low-permeability reservoirs, on the other hand, the transient period can be long and may dominate the production for months and even years.

For the particular case of constant-pressure production the rate decline can be analyzed by a set of type curves, which plot the rate versus time in a dimensionless form. The type curves reflect a combination of analytical and empirical solutions to the problem of constant-pressure rate decline. The curves cover both the transient and depletion periods and are valid for both stimulated and unstimulated wells. Type curves can be used to extrapolate production data and thus to generate rate forecasts. In addition, the possibility of matching production data to type curves allows calculation of formation permeability, skin factor, and the radius of drainage for a given well.

An analysis of constant-pressure rate decline is of particular interest for stimulated wells. The impact of stimulation on production is equivalent to an enlargement of wellbore radius. Therefore, stimulated wells can be analyzed by radial-solution type curves using an effective wellbore radius in the expression for dimensionless time. The result of stimulation is higher initial (poststimulation) production followed by a rapid rate decline. Thus the assessment of a treatment should be based on the new rate *profile* rather than on the initial poststimulation rate. In cases of constant-rate production stimulation causes an upward shift of the wellhead pressure profile and thus, prolongs the plateau period. In either case, the rate and pressure profiles can be predicted by type curves.

Special mathematical methods—namely superposition, normalization, and reinitialization—allow application of the constant-pressure type curves to cases when pressure varies either abruptly or gradually. These methods are useful for forecasting the effect of stimulations or changes of wellhead pressure taking place at times after the initial start-up.

Production profiles may also be calculated by methods that combine reservoir depletion characteristics with variations of the inflow performance relationship and vertical flow performance. The methods are rather simple but require input data from material balance and vertical flow calculations that in many cases are not available. Whichever method is used for obtaining a production profile, the result is needed and used for economic and technical planning of oil and gas fields. A production profile is also necessary to extrapolate production conditions of a flowing well to the point when natural flow ceases, and to project how the well will react to the introduction of artificial lift. Artificial lift is then the subject of the following chapter.

5   FUNDAMENTALS OF ARTIFICIAL LIFT

When reservoir pressure is insufficient to sustain the flow of oil to the surface at adequate rates, natural flow must be aided by *artificial lift*. This chapter extends concepts and methods used in the engineering of flowing wells to the design and analysis of artificially lifted wells. Two basic forms of artificial lift are discussed: continuous gas lift and bottomhole pumping. Both methods supplement the natural drive energy of the reservoir and increase the flow by reducing backpressure at the wellbore caused by flowing fluids in the tubing.

The rate–pressure relationship of a well is used for investigating the need to introduce artificial lift, selecting the most suitable lift system, and determining its size and capacity. Three artificial lift systems are discussed in this chapter: positive displacement pumps, dynamic displacement pumps, and continuous gas lift. The discussion emphasizes the rate–pressure characteristics of each system and explains how it is used to

1. identify candidates for artificial lift: Which wells presently or some time in the future will produce more economically with artificial lift?
2. determine the most suitable artificial lift method to match the particular conditions of a well and of a field
3. size the equipment and design the details of the lift system

This chapter presents methods and considerations to perform these tasks.

5.1   METHODS OF ARTIFICIAL LIFT. There are two basic forms of continuous artificial lift: downhole pumping and gas lift. Downhole pumping is accomplished by operating a pump at the bottom of the well. Gas lift is accomplished by injecting gas into the lower part of the production tubing. Downhole pumps boost the transfer of liquid from the bottomhole to the wellhead, eliminating backpressure caused by the fluids flowing in the tubing. Injection of gas into the production string aerates the flowing fluid, reducing the pressure gradient and lowering backpressure at the formation.

For both lift methods, the production rate is increased by reducing wellbore flowing pressure. In principle, both methods achieve the same result as lowering wellhead pressure or increasing tubing size in naturally flowing wells, but, because artificial lift consumes significant amounts of generated energy, it is introduced only after all adjustments in a natural flow system are exhausted.

Figure 5.1 illustrates pressure conditions in a well producing with two forms of artificial lift. Most artificial lift sizing calculations stem from this figure. The IPR curve relates the wellbore flowing pressure p_{wf} to flow rate at the surface. The pressure traverse curve at a given wellhead pressure determines the tubing intake backpressure p_{in} at a particular flow rate. Stable production can only exist if these two pressures, p_{wf} and p_{in}, are equal.

In the pumping well, the pump provides the pressure difference $p_{in} - p_{wf}$ needed

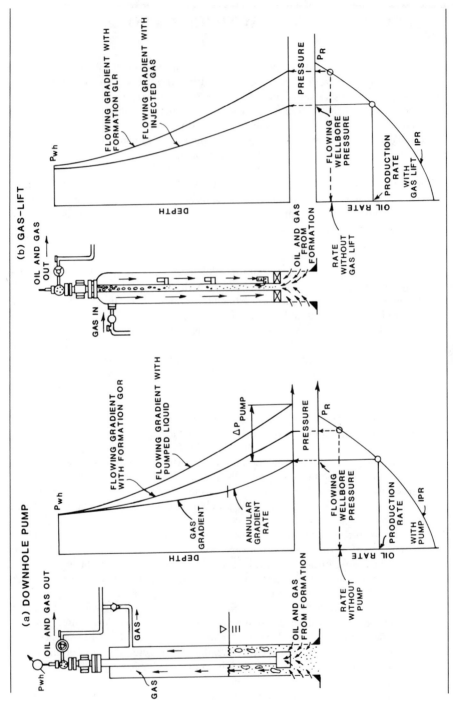

Figure 5.1 Pressure conditions in wells producing with the aid of downhole pump or gas lift.

to overcome tubing backpressure and sustain stable flow. In the gas-lift well, gas injected into the tubing reduces the flowing pressure gradient to a level where $p_{in} = p_{wf}$ as needed for stable flow in the well.

The effect and approach to handling bottomhole-free gas are different for the two artificial methods. In pumping wells, free gas is intentionally segregated from the liquid before fluid enters the pump, being vented to the surface through the tubing/casing annulus. In gas-lift wells the annulus is sealed by a production packer and free gas is forced to mix and flow upward with the well fluid; in fact, the free gas assists artificial lift and reduces the requirement for injected gas. Eliminating free gas in pumps is a fundamental requirement for efficient pumping. Inversely, forcing free gas into the production string in gas-lift wells is important for efficient operation and reduced energy consumption.

Figure 5.1 indicates the limit on production rate achieved by each lifting method. Downhole pumps may withdraw reservoir fluid at rates approaching the absolute open flow. In gas lift, on the other hand, backpressure exerted by the flowing fluid column limits the reduction of wellbore flowing pressure and thus limits production to a rate significantly less than the absolute open flow. In fact, bottomhole flowing pressure cannot be lowered below wellhead pressure by means of gas lift. An important observation in the pressure diagram is that there exists a relationship between the wellbore flowing pressure, the liquid level in the annulus, and the casinghead backpressure. This relationship plays a significant role in determining the pump setting depth and its allowable pumping rate.

In review, the pressure and flow conditions illustrated in figure 5.1 are the keys to designing artificial lift systems. The pressure diagram establishes the size and operating conditions of the lift system needed to produce a well at a given rate or a given wellbore flowing pressure. This then provides the basis for selecting equipment and performing a detailed mechanical design of the system. Excluded from the discussion are wells with low productivity and low reservoir pressure that require *batch* lift instead of *continuous lift*. Batch lift includes intermittent gas lift, plunger lift, and chamber lift.

5.2   OILWELL PUMPING

5.2.1   **Calculating Pumping Requirements.** Essentially, pumps raise the pressure in a liquid by transforming mechanical work into potential energy, that is, pressure. Liquid enters the pump at a given pressure, called *suction pressure*, and leaves it at a higher pressure, called *discharge pressure*. By *pump pressure* we usually refer to the difference between the discharge and the suction pressures. Pump pressure corresponds to the gain in potential energy of the liquid. This gain represents only a fraction of the total work used to drive a pump. The efficiency of a pump depends on how efficiently it can transform the driving forces into fluid potential energy.

Pumps are generally classified according to the physical principle used to transform driving forces into pressure. Figure 5.2 illustrates the main classes of conventional pumps: positive-displacement and dynamic-displacement pumps. Positive-displacement pumps develop pressure by moving a piston or cam to reduce the volume of a compression chamber. This compression raises the pressure of

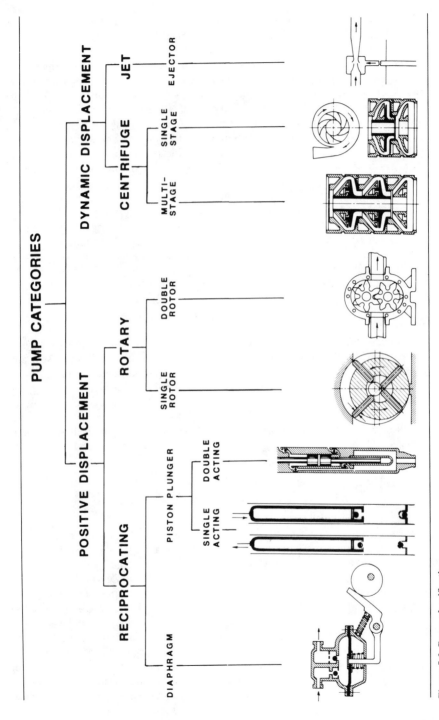

Figure 5.2 Pump classification.

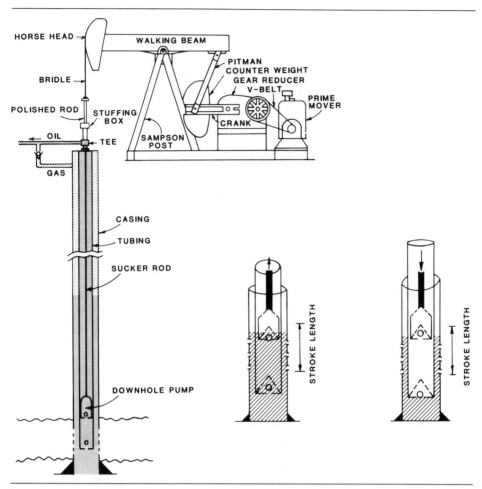

Figure 5.3 Sucker rod pump.

liquid in the chamber. Dynamic-displacement pumps develop pressure by a sequence of accelerations and decelerations of the pumped liquid. Dynamic energy is required to accelerate the liquid and to build up required levels of kinetic energy, then the liquid is decelerated and kinetic energy is transformed into potential energy. This energy transformation results in pump pressure. Both classes of pumps are used in oilwell pumping. Each class includes two types of pumps:

POSITIVE-DISPLACEMENT PUMPS:

1. *Sucker rod pump* (fig. 5.3)—a positive-displacement pump that compresses liquid by the reciprocating motion of a piston. The piston is actuated by a string of

sucker rods that extend from the bottomhole pump to the pumping unit at the surface.

2. *Reciprocating hydraulic pump* (fig. 5.4)— a positive-displacement pump with a reciprocating piston. The piston is actuated by a reciprocating hydraulic motor coupled and assembled with the pump. The downhole motor is driven by a power fluid injected at high pressure from the surface.

DYNAMIC-DISPLACEMENT PUMPS:

1. *Centrifugal submersible pump* (fig. 5.5)—a dynamic-displacement, multistage centrifugal turbine pump coupled by a short shaft to a downhole electrical motor. The motor is supplied with electrical power by a cable extending to the surface.

2. *Jet pump* (fig. 5.6)—an ejector-type dynamic-displacement pump operated by a stream of high-pressure power fluid that converges into a jet in the nozzle of the pump. Downstream from the nozzle, the high-velocity, low-pressure jet is mixed with the well's fluid. The stream of the mixture is then expanded in a diffuser, and as the flow velocity drops pressure is built up.

The fundamental difference in the pumping performance of positive and dynamic-displacement pumps stems from a fundamental difference in the rate–pressure relationships of the pumps. In positive-displacement pumps the pump rate is independent of pump pressure. Pump rate can be changed only by varying the displacement motion in the pump, for example, by varying piston diameter, stroke, or speed. This characteristic implies that with a steady pump motion, the discharge pressure does not significantly affect pump rate. In fact, if such a pump is not protected by a pressure-relief valve or overload cut-out, pump discharge pressure may build up without significant rate decline until the pump breaks down mechanically.

For dynamic-displacement pumps, the pump rate depends on pump pressure. The rate is low at high pressures and high at low pressures. In fact, it is possible to choke or even shut in a turbine pump without damage, using a backpressure throttle valve. The rate–pressure relationship of a dynamic-displacement pump is called the *pump characteristic*. It is usually made available by the pump manufacturer, based on tests performed at laboratory conditions.

In general, oilwell pumps can operate only if they are submerged in liquid. This is because they need a certain positive pressure at the suction side to operate efficiently. Usually, pump manufacturers specify the minimum required suction pressure, expressed in terms of a column of fresh water, and referred to as net positive suction head (NPSH). The required NPSH for a given pump is a function of pump rate and liquid properties. For oilwell pumps, NPSH requirements are simplified to a few rules of thumb which satisfactorily determine minimum suction pressure for normal applications. These rules of thumb are listed in table 5.1.

Sizing an oilwell pump comprises two primary duties:

1. determining the pumping requirements in the well
2. selecting a pump to fulfill the pumping requirements

475

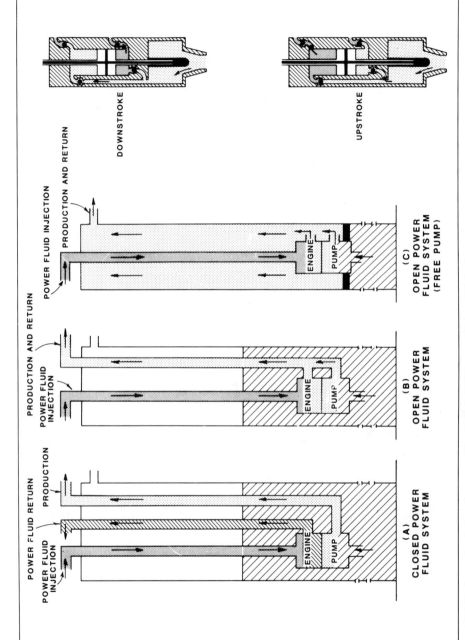

Figure 5.4 Reciprocating hydraulic pump. After Coberly 1961 by permission of Kobe, Inc.

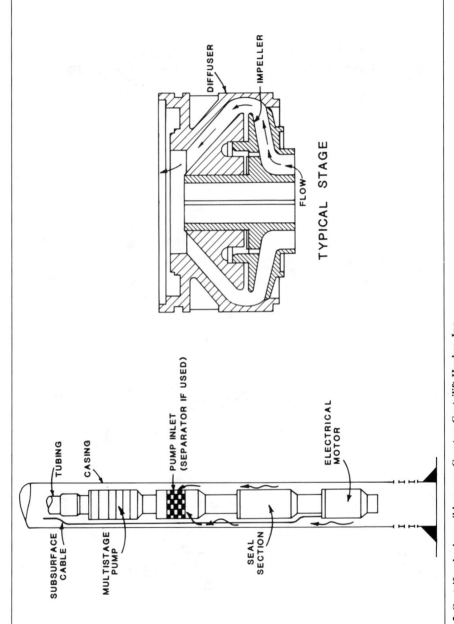

Figure 5.5 Centrifugal submersible pump. Courtesy Centrilift-Hughes, Inc.

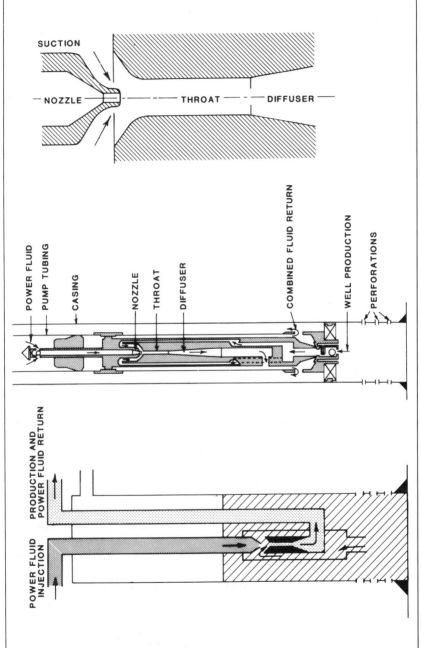

Figure 5.6 Jet pump. After Petrie et al. 1983 by permission of Gulf Publishing Company.

**Table 5.1 Minimum Required Suction Pressure
and Liquid Level above Pump in Oilwell Pumping**

1. ROD PUMPS	
1.1 Small oil rate (less than 10 STB/D)	Fluid level at pump intake
1.2 High rate	Fluid level 75 ft above pump intake
2. CENTRIFUGAL PUMP	150–300 psia
3. RECIPROCATING HYDRAULIC PUMPS	50 psia
4. JET PUMP	
4.1 Pumping depth less than 5000 ft	500 psia
4.2 Pumping depth = 10,000 ft	1000 psia
4.3 Pumping depth > 10,000 ft	1500 psia

The pumping requirement is merely the pumping pressure needed to maintain a desired wellbore flowing pressure or a desired production rate. It is determined by combining

1. the well's inflow performance (IPR)
2. the maximum permissible pressure drawdown in the well, or the maximum allowable production rate, and
3. the wellhead pressure and the pressure traverse in the production string.

A procedure for establishing the required pumping pressure for four different cases is illustrated in figure 5.7. Depending on whether the limitation is maximum drawdown or maximum rate, the IPR determines wellbore flowing pressure p_{wf} corresponding to a given rate, or inversely, the rate corresponding to a given p_{wf}.

Calculating the pressure traverse in the casing, starting with wellbore flowing pressure at midperforations to the pump determines the flowing pressure at the pump suction. Calculating, the pressure traverse in the tubing from the wellhead pressure at the surface and down to the pump determines the needed pump discharge pressure. The calculated difference between suction and discharge pressures is the required pump pressure. Two extreme pumping conditions are considered in figure 5.7. Figure 5.7(a), (b) illustrates cases where the pump rate is much lower than the absolute open flow. This situation typically occurs when an operator uses undersized pump equipment already existing in inventory. Undersized pump equipment is usually operated at maximum equipment capacity. The other extreme case is a well pumping near its maximum well capacity, as in figure 5.7(c), (d). It is, then, the inflow performance that limits the possible production rate and not the lift system. A general observation in figure 5.7 is that the permissible pumping rate increases with pump setting depth. In fact, maximum rates are possible when the pump is set below the perforations, allowing a minimum backpressure at the wellbore and efficient gas separation.

Example 5.1 illustrates a procedure to establish pump requirements. Similar casing fluid gradients below and above the pump were assumed in example 5.1. In reality there are different pressure gradients in the flowing fluid below the pump

479

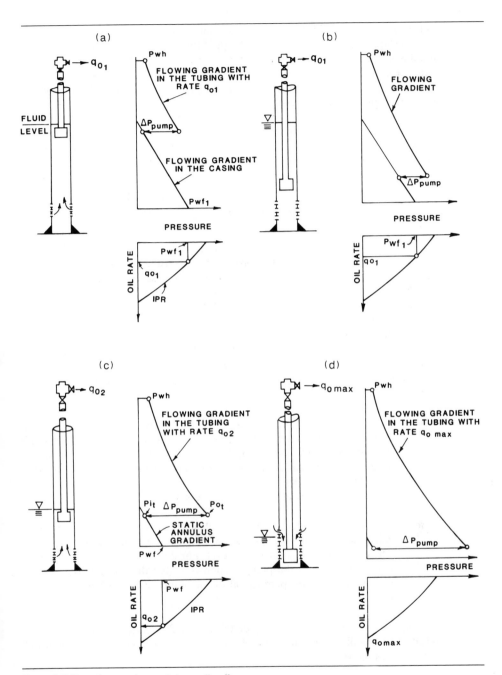

Figure 5.7 Pumping requirements in an oil well.

and the stationary fluid in the tubing/casing annulus above it. Free gas segregated from the liquid at the pump inlet migrates up through the static liquid column in the annulus and is vented from the casing at the surface. The migrating gas bubbles form a gaseous liquid column in the annulus with a hydrostatic pressure gradient significantly lower than that of a gas-free liquid column. Several methods for calculating the average pressure gradient in the annulus liquid columns are presented by Gilbert (see McCoy 1978; ERCB 1978; McCoy et al. 1985). Ignoring the difference between gaseous and gas-free columns as is done in example 5.1 does not usually affect the validity of design calculations. It may, however, have a considerable effect on interpreting test data in pumping wells.

EXAMPLE 5.1 CONSIDERATIONS AND PROCEDURES TO ESTABLISH PUMPING REQUIREMENTS

The B3-30 oil well in the Belayim field is producing water-free oil from the highly porous and permeable zone of the upper Rudeis sandstone formation. At present, the natural flow rate of the well is 420 STB/D. A reservoir study investigating possibilities for increasing the peak production of the field includes a recommendation to increase the rate of B3-30 by installing a bottomhole pump. Designing a pumping system in the well is somewhat complicated, considering the depth of the pay zone and the relatively high pumping rate required. A variety of pumping arrangements were considered, including a large beam pumping unit, a reciprocating hydraulic pump, and a centrifugal submersible pump. To assess the feasibility of the pumping alternatives it is necessary to investigate two pump installation alternatives:

Case A: The pump is installed at or just below the perforations, as illustrated in figure E5.1a. The deep installation allows a pumping rate near the well's absolute open flow potential. It is assumed that with an effective gas separator all free gas at the pump suction is separated and vented through the annulus to a surface vapor recovery system. The vapor recovery system collects gas at atmospheric pressure.

Case B: The pump is installed at 6000 ft, as illustrated in figure E5.1b. Experience gained in the field suggests that the pump will operate satisfactorily only when it is submerged in 100 ft of oil. For design purposes, it is assumed that all free gas at the pump suction is vented through the annulus and recombined with the pumped oil stream at the surface, downstream to the wellhead.

The separator is located at the tank battery, some 2.5 miles away from the well, resulting in a wellhead backpressure of 200 psia for both cases. Reservoir and well data are as follows:

Reservoir pressure p_R 2800 psia
Production GOR   600 scf/STB

EXAMPLE 5.1 continued

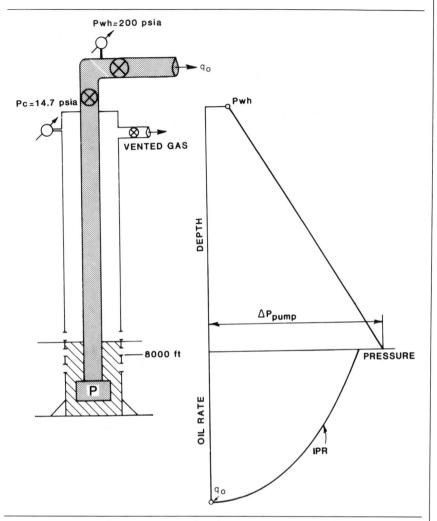

Figure E5.1a Pump installation arrangement and corresponding pumping diagram for pump installed at or just below the perforations.

EXAMPLE 5.1 continued

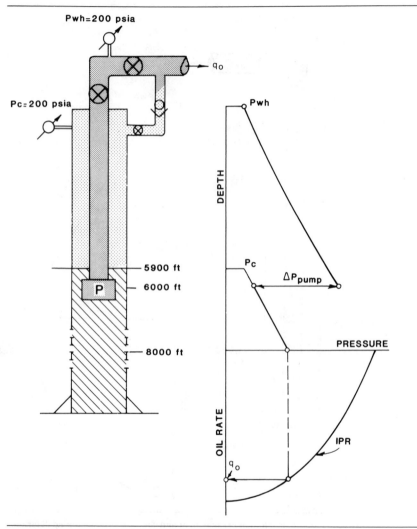

Figure E5.1b Pump installation arrangement and corresponding pumping diagram for pump installed at 6000 ft.

EXAMPLE 5.1 continued

Stock tank oil gravity	28 API
Gas gravity	0.7 (air = 1.0)
Water faction	0.5 %
Bubble-point pressure	3480 psia
Reservoir temperature	160 °F
Midperforation depth	8000 ft
Tubing size	3.5 in.
Casing size	7 in.

A recent multirate test established that the IPR of the well is

$$q_o = 600[1 - (p_{wf}/p_R)^2]^{0.8}$$

The following assumptions are made to simplify the study:

1. All free gas at the pump intake is vented through the annulus (in both cases).
2. The hydrostatic pressure of the gas column in the annulus can be neglected.
3. The average gravity of the oil column in the annulus is approximated by the gravity of the stock-tank oil.
4. The average pressure gradient of the two-phase fluid flowing between the perforations and the pump is 0.381 psi/ft. The gradient was obtained by wireline runs of a pressure gauge into the casing below the tubing shoe.
5. At the calculated pump suction pressure in case B (238 psia) the correlations given in chapter 1 for solution gas–oil ratio and formation-volume factor yield: $B_o = 1.072$ bbl/STB, $R_s = 38$ scf/STB.
6. The set of gradient curves in appendix A is valid and may represent the pressure traverse in the tubing above the pump.

The validity of the IPR and gradient curves should be substantiated by calculating the natural flow rate and comparing it with measured rate.

SOLUTION

A method for calculating the natural flow rate is given in chapter 1. As explained in chapter 1 the natural flow of the flowing well with 8000 ft of 3.5-in. tubing is obtained from the intersection of the IPR and the TPR curves in a rate–pressure plot, given in figure E5.1c. The points on the IPR curve (table 5.1a) are calculated from the IPR equation, and the points on the TPR curve (table 5.1b) are determined from the gradient curves for 3.5-in. tubing. At the intersection point the flow rate is 438 STB/D. This is a good check of the measured rate, 420 STB/D.

Pumping Diagram for Case A
A schematic plot of the pumping diagram is given in figure E5.1a. Since the absolute open flow rate, 600 STB/D, is produced with near-zero bottomhole pressure, all gas initially dissolved in the reservoir oil is liberated and vented through the annulus. A zero GLR curve may, therefore, represent the pressure

EXAMPLE 5.1 continued

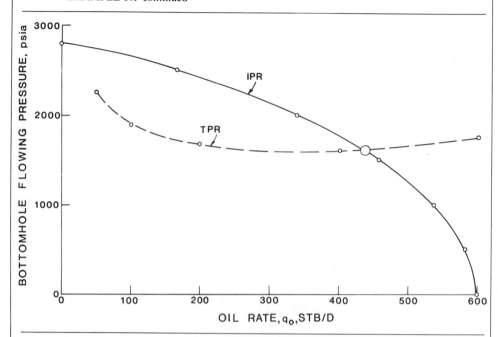

Figure E5.1c Natural flow rate for the B3-30 oil well.

Table E5.1a Inflow Performance Relationship for the B3-30 Oil Well

p_{wf} (psia)	q_o (STB/D)
0	600
500	584.6
1000	538.0
1500	457.7
2000	339.0
2500	167.4
2800	0

Table E5.1b Tubing Performance Relationship for the B3-30 Oil Well with 3½-in. Tubing

q_o (STB/D)	p_{wf} (psia)
50	2250
100	1900
200	1700
400	1610
600	1760

EXAMPLE 5.1 continued

traverse of the oil flowing in the tubing above the pump. For 600 STB/D flowing in 3.5-in. tubing, the gradient curve in figure A-10 (appendix A) is a straight line with a slope of $(dp/dh)_1 = 0.42$ psi/ft. The required pump discharge pressure is then calculated from the pressure traverse in the tubing:

$$p_{discharge} = p_{wh} + (dp/dh)_1 \Delta h$$

$$= 200 + 0.42 \times (8000)$$

$$= 3560 \text{ psia.}$$

The discharge pressure is enough to complete the diagram as the pump suction pressure is near zero and for calculating purposes, the pump is considered to be located at midperforation depth. An observation regarding the operating condition of the pump is that the liquid flow rate in the pump approaches the stock-tank rate.

Pumping Diagram for Case B

A schematic plot of the pumping diagram is given in figure E5.1b. The required fluid level in the annulus is 100 ft above the pump, i.e., at a depth of 5900 ft. The flowing bottomhole pressure is the sum of casing head pressure, hydrostatic, pressure of the annulus gas column, and the hydrostatic pressure of the annulus liquid column. Neglecting the effect of gas column, we calculate:

$$p_{wf} = p_{ch} + (dp/dh)_2 \Delta h$$

$$= 200 + 0.384(8000 - 5900)$$

$$= 1006 \text{ psia,}$$

where $(dp/dh)_2 = 0.384$ psi/ft is the gradient of a static column of 28° API oil in the annulus, as listed in the conversion table in appendix C and casing head pressure p_{ch} is 200 psia. With $p_{wf} = 1006$ psia and a flowing gradient of 0.381 psi/ft below the pump, the calculated pump suction pressure is

$$p_{suction} = 1006 - 0.381(8000 - 6000)$$

$$= 244 \text{ psia.}$$

From the IPR equation, production rate at $p_{wf} = 1006$ psia is 537 STB/D. Using the gradient curve for 600 STB/D, the gradient of $(dp/dh)_1 = 0.42$ psi/ft is valid in the tubing above the pump. Pump discharge pressure is then

$$p_{discharge} = p_{wh} + (dp/dh)_1 \times 6000$$

$$= 200 + 0.42 \times 6000$$

$$= 2720 \text{ psia}$$

EXAMPLE 5.1 continued

The required pressure difference in the pump is

$\Delta p_{pump} = p_{discharge} - p_{suction}$

$= 2720 - 244$

$= 2476\,psi.$

The insitu liquid rate displaced by the pump is

$q_o B_o = 537(1.072)$

$= 575\,bbl/D.$

The pumping requirements in example 5.1 are calculated for a well at a particular stage of reservoir depletion. These requirements may change continuously with depletion associated with considerable changes is reservoir conditions including reservoir pressure decline, deteriorating IPR, and variation in gas–oil ratio. Furthermore, pumping wells in water-flooded reservoirs experience declines in oil productivity with increasing water–oil cut. As a result, it is necessary to pump more liquid to maintain a constant oil rate. Long-term changes in reservoir and pumping conditions govern the period that a given pump size may economically pump a well before it should be replaced by a different-size pump or even by a different pump type.

Ideally, we should install artificial lift equipment that can efficiently produce a well during its entire life. Practically, it is difficult to fulfill this requirement. Nelly (1981), in a panel discussion at the 1981 SPE Fall meeting, offered the following comments about artificial lift design:

Two approaches have frequently been taken in the past, both of which, in my opinion, are extreme and wrong. In some cases we predict long-term reservoir performance and install artificial lift equipment that can handle the well over its entire life. This frequently led to the installation of oversized equipment in the anticipation of ultimately producing large quantities of water. As a result, the equipment may have operated at poor efficiency due to underloading over a significant portion of its total life. The other extreme is to design for what the well is producing today and not worry about tomorrow. This can lead to change after change in the type of lift equipment installed in the hole. We may operate efficiently short term but spend large amounts of capital dollars in changing equipment. The design engineer must consider both long-term and short-term aspects. Our aim is to maximize the overlife efficiency of the operation. This may or may not anticipate a lift system change in the future.

A compromise between existing and long-term needs as advocated by the citation, is the most common approach for sizing an artificial lift system. There are, however, many cases where due to various arguments as "extreme" approach is regarded as the most suitable.

5.2.2   Considerations in Sizing Positive-Displacement Pumps. It was noted previously that the pump rate of a positive displacement pump is independent of pump pressure. The rate is fixed by volumetric displacement of the pump. While pump pressure does not affect rate, it affects the pump driving forces and energy consumption. This characteristic has two implications for pumping oil wells:

1. The pressure traverse of the flowing fluid in the tubing, and therefore the wellhead pressure, does not affect pump rate. Neither does the wellbore flowing pressure, as long as it does not drop below a certain minimum needed for satisfactory pump operation. The result is that pump rate does not change if reservoir or surface pressure changes.
2. Pump rate is controlled directly by the speed of its drive. There is a linear relationship between displacement motion (i.e., the speed of the drive) and pump rate.

The two types of positive-displacement pump used in oil wells are sucker rod pumps and reciprocating hydraulic pumps. The typical rod pump is a single-acting cylinder–piston mechanism. It displaces liquid during only half of the pump cycle, while the other half-cycle is used to fill the compression chamber with liquid. Figure 5.8 illustrates a rod pump and explains its pumping cycle. The rod pump consists of a stationary "barrel" and a reciprocating "plunger". In conventional pumps the barrel is threaded to or inserted inside the tubing and the plunger is attached to the rod string. The pump has two check valves, usually a single-ball and seat type. The stationary suction valve is at the bottom of the barrel and is called a *standing valve*. The discharge valve moves with the plunger and is therefore called a *traveling valve*.

The pump cycle consists of two strokes: charging and discharging. Pump charging occurs during the upstroke of the plunger and discharge occurs during the downstroke. During the charging stroke, the plunger moves upward, displacing fluid above it. At the same time the pump barrel below the plunger is filled with new liquid. During the discharge stroke the plunger moves downward with the traveling valve open, allowing liquid in the barrel to bypass the plunger and move into the tubing. The upward liquid displacement occurs during the upstroke. The traveling valve then acts as a check valve to retain the displaced liquid above the plunger as the plunger moves upward. During the downstroke the traveling valve opens, allowing liquid from below the plunger to pass by. At the same time, the standing valve acts as a check valve to retain the fluid in the pump barrel.

The complete pumping system, including the surface driving unit, is illustrated in figure 5.3. The pump is driven by either an electrical motor or an internal combustion engine, referred to as the *prime mover*. The rotation movement of the prime mover is transmitted through a belt drive to a reduction gear box and further to a *crank and pitman mechanism*, which converts steady rotary driving motion into cyclic motion. The cyclic motion is transmitted to a lever unit called the *walking beam*. The beam transforms the cyclic motion into a vertical reciprocating motion and transmits it to the downhole pump by a string of threaded sucker rods. At the top of the wellhead there is a seal unit called the *stuffing box*. The stuffing box seals around the rod at the top of the tubing while allowing the reciprocating motion of

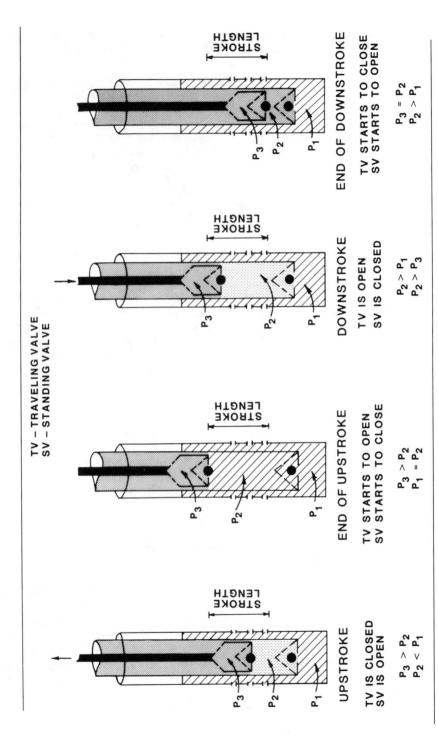

Figure 5.8 Pumping cycle in rod pumps.

the string. The top sucker rod reciprocating across the stuffing box has a smooth surface, and is thus called the *polished rod*. The polished rod is suspended from the edge of the walking beam (horse head) by a flexible bridle made of steel wires. The geometry of the horse head is arranged so that the polished rod is always centered in the stuffing box despite offsetting lateral motion associated with the reciprocating vertical motion of the horse head. In review, the entire system serves the objective of converting rotary prime-mover motion into reciprocating downhole pump motion.

The daily pumping rate of a rod pump is the product of liquid displaced during one pumping cycle and the number of cycles per day. In equation form it is expressed as

$$q = 0.1484 N E_v A_p S_p \qquad (5.1)$$

where

q = pumping rate (bbl/D),
N = pump speed (strokes/min [SPM]),
A_p = plunger area (in.^{2}),
S_p = effective plunger stroke (in.),
E_v = volumetric efficiency.

The volumetric efficiency reflects small leakage between the plunger and the barrel of the pump and is defined as

$$E_v = \frac{\text{actual pumping rate}}{\text{pump displacement rate}}. \qquad (5.2)$$

The primary reason for leakage is that it is difficult to maintain a perfect seal between two moving metal surfaces (Stearns 1943). Even so, the small leakage provides a necessary lubrication to the sealing surface between the plunger and the barrel. Volumetric efficiency is usually in the range of 0.7 to 0.8. Obviously, if leakage becomes severe due to bad sealing, the pump's efficiency decreases rapidly.

The designer may achieve a desired pump rate from several combinations of A_p, S_p, and N. It is also possible to change the combination if the pump is already installed. The adjustments are not complicated but do require some resources and efforts. Changing pump size requires pulling the pump out of the well with a service rig and running a new pump. Changing the pump stroke requires a change in the geometry of the surface beam unit. This is done by a maintenance crew assisted by a crane or other lifting equipment. Changing pump speed is the simplest task. It is done by changing sheaves in the V-belt drive between the prime mover and the reduction gearbox.

Most rod pumping equipment in the world is manufactured and purchased according to API (American Petroleum Institute) standards published by the API committee on production equipment (Moody 1961). API spec. 11AX (1979) provides dimensions of subsurface pumps with bore sizes for use in 2⅜-, 2⅞-, and 3½-in. tubing. API spec. 11B (1982) provides dimensions of sucker rods, and API std. 11E (1982) covers dimensions, design, and rating of beam-type pumping units.

Plunger sizes (pump bores) covered by the API vary from 1¼ to 2¾ in. The maximum API plunger size for a given tubing size is listed in table 5.2. The maximum stroke depends on the size of the surface pumping unit. API specifies pumping units of increasing size with maximum strokes from 16 in. to 300 in. For a given unit it is possible to change stroke length by adjusting the position of the pin that connects the crank and the pitman.

The effective stroke of a downhole pump S_p may be substantially different (less) from surface stroke. This results from the elasticity of the tubing and the rod string, both subjected to alternating pumping load. During the upstroke the rod string is loaded by the displaced fluid and therefore tends to stretch. During downstroke (when the traveling valve opens) liquid load is relieved from the rod string, and the string recoils. Tubing is loaded in an inverse sequence. During the upstroke it is relieved from the load of the fluid and recoils. During downstroke it is loaded by the column of fluid and stretches. The alternating stretch and recoil of rod and tubing affect the relative movement of the plunger in the barrel and thus the effective stroke of the pump. It is difficult to predict effective plunger stroke by simple analytical methods because of the complex dynamic loading of rods during the pumping cycle. Figure 5.9 illustrates effective plunger stroke compared with surface stroke for a particular pump assembly, as calculated by an analog simulator. The effective pump stroke in figure 5.9 is considerably smaller than the surface stroke. In most applications it is in the range of 40% to 90% of the surface stroke. It may, however, approach surface stroke if the system is properly designed and tuned. Details on the mechanical design applied to achieve maximum pump displacement are beyond the scope of this book.

The speed N is varied by changing the surface driving speed. There is no limit on the slowest speed, though it is difficult to operate below 6 SPM with conventional motors. The maximum pumping speed, on the other hand, is limited by two factors. The first is the minimum time needed to permit satisfactory liquid filling of the pump during upstroke. Usually the filling time does not present a practical limit

Table 5.2 Maximum Pump Size for Given Tubing Size

Pump type	Tubing size (in.)			
	1.900	2⅜	2⅞	3½
Tubing one piece, thin-wall barrel (TW)	1½	1¾	2¼	2¾
Tubing one-piece, heavy-wall barrel (TH)	1½	1¾	2¼	2¾
Tubing liner barrel (TL)		1¾	1¼	2¾
Rod one-piece, thin-wall barrel (RW)	1¼	1½	2	2½
Rod one-piece, heavy-wall barrel (RH)	1⅟₁₆	1¼	1¾	2¼
Rod liner barrel (RL)		1¼	1¾	2¼

Courtesy Kobe, Inc. 1961

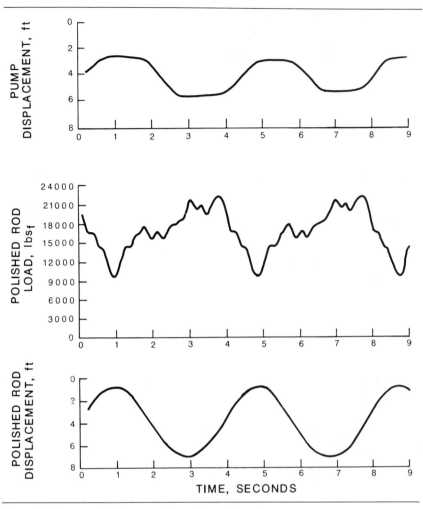

Figure 5.9 Forces and displacements in a rod pumping system.

unless the oil is viscous and the suction pressure is low. The second factor is the need to avoid resonance by reciprocating at a frequency different from the natural frequency of the rod string. Most wells are pumped at speeds of from 6 to 20 SPM. Three issues dominate the planning of a sucker rod pumping system:

1. matching pumping system capacity to the deliverability of the well to avoid "pump-off" conditions
2. ensuring mechanical compatibility between the various components of the system
3. minimizing lifting cost by minimizing the initial investment and maintaining low operating cost

Starting a pump in a shut-in well initiates a transient period when the annulus liquid is gradually unloaded and the fluid level drops. The unloading ends and fluid level stabilizes when the well's inflow rate equals the pump displacement rate. The new equilibrium is, in fact, the state described by the pumping requirement diagram in figure 5.7.

If the pump displacement rate is large in relation to the well's inflow capacity, the unloading will continue and fluid level will drop until pump submergence is insufficient to fill the pump during the upstroke. A partially filled pump results in a condition usually referred to as *pump-off*. During the downstroke in a partially filled pump, the traveling valve opens only after the plunger strikes the liquid surface, thereby creating a hammerlike impact called *fluid pound*. Fluid pound may cause mechanical damage to the pump, rod string, and, in certain cases, surface equipment. In addition, incomplete liquid fillup and suction of gas from the annulus into the pump reduces the volumetric efficiency and creates undesirable loads on the driving motor and unnecessary power consumption. Excess pump capacity may result from overestimation of the well's capacity. It may, however, develop in the well as a result of reservoir depletion. In either case, pump displacement should be reduced to avoid pump-off conditions. Reduction of pump displacement may often require a costly change in pumping equipment. Many operators prefer to cope with excess pump capacity by operating the pump intermittently. The early practice was to manually stop and start the pumping operation, but this has since evolved into standardized automatic pumping control. Usually automatic controllers are merely time clocks (percentage timers), stopping and starting the pump at predetermined time intervals. Rod pumps may also be protected from pump-off conditions or may operate intermittently by a combination of pump-off detectors and automatic controllers. Westerman (1977) describes five techniques to detect and control pump-off conditions using

1. fluid-level detectors
2. flow/no-flow detectors
3. vibration and fluid-pound detectors
4. electrical-motor-current sensing
5. rod-loading sensing

Rod pumping systems are comprised of a prime mover, reduction gearbox beam pumping unit, rod string, and downhole pump. To ensure trouble-free operation, loads developed on individual components in the systems should be below the maximum permissible level.

To assist in selecting and sizing pumping equipment, the API RP 11L (1977) recommends equipment for a given set of lift conditions. The so-called API method has been developed by an electric analog simulator (Griffin 1968) that incorporates all of the important system variables. Data produced by the simulator was used to construct a set of design charts correlating dimensionless pump speed and dimensionless rod stretch with dimensionless plunger stroke and dimensionless crank torque. The charts were used to develop recommendations (API Bull. 11L3, 1970) for selecting combinations of rod string, pump size, pump stroke, and pumping speed that may produce satisfactorily at a variety of rates (from 100 to 1500 STB/D) from a given depth (from 2000 to 12,000 ft).

Mathematical models simulating pumping systems yield proprietary design methods compatible with the API method (Gibbs 1963; 1982). Operators of rod pumping systems often prefer to purchase design and analysis services from the proprietors of these methods to supplement the publically available API method. There is no general rule as to what combination of pumping component systems will yield the lowest initial investment. Other considerations such as standardization, versatility, and availability may override the decision. It is generally observed, however, that for given pumping conditions, larger pump size, longer stroke, and lower pump speed yields lower polished rod horsepower (Tait and Hamilton 1984). Polished rod horsepower combined with drive-motor efficiency (Patton 1963; Skinner 1984) provide an indication on pump operating cost.

The other type of positive-displacement pump is a hydraulic-driven reciprocating pump, as illustrated in figure 5.4. A power fluid is injected from the surface at high pressure and actuates a subsurface reciprocating motor. At least two fluid paths are needed in a well producing by hydraulic pumping—one for the injected power fluid and one for the produced fluid. Figure 5.4 illustrates three arrangements of flow path, one arrangement with separate paths upward for the exhausted power fluid and the produced fluid, and two arrangements that commingle the upward paths. The piston of the motor is connected to the piston of the pump by a short connecting rod. The pump reciprocates, together with the piston of the motor. The exhausted power fluid from the motor returns to the surface either through a special return tube or as a mixture with the produced fluid through the production string. The pump is double-acting—i.e., it displaces fluid during the upstroke and the downstroke. The pumping cycle is illustrated in figure 5.4. During the upstroke, liquid in the upper chamber is compressed and displaced out of the chamber as new well fluid fills the lower chamber. During downstroke the pumping action is in the lower chamber and the upper chamber is filled with liquid. Each chamber has two valves, a suction valve and a discharge valve. The valves open and close alternatively to facilitate the double pumping action. If the pump-motor assembly is fastened to the bottom of the tubing, the pump is called a *fixed pump*. If the tubing string is first installed with a special *seat nipple* at the bottom, and then the pump lowered to seat in the nipple, it is called a *free-pump* installation and the pump can be retrieved to the surface by merely reversing the power fluid flow.

A variety of downhole and surface equipment is available from hydraulic pumps suppliers. Bleakley (1978) presents an excellent review of the available equipment, and more detailed information is available from supplier's publications.

The pumping rate is controlled by two parameters: the injection rate of the power fluid and the ratio of pump-to-motor piston size. These two factors are related to production rate by

$$q = q_{PF} \times \frac{A_{\text{pump}}}{A_{\text{motor}}}, \qquad (5.3)$$

where

q = rate of production (B/D),
q_{PF} = rate of injection power fluid (B/D),

A_{motor} = motor piston area (in.^{2}),
A_{pump} = pump piston area (in.^{2}).

Commercial pumps are available with several pump and motor sizes. Pump piston size varies from $^{13}/_{16}$ in. to $2\frac{3}{8}$ in. Motor piston size varies from 1 in. to 2 in. The ratio of pump-to-motor size varies from 0.55 to 1.55. Pump speed ranges from 50 to 100 strokes per minute. The only practical limit on the maximum rate of a pump (for a given size) is the time needed to fill the pump chambers. This depends on the effective viscosity of produced fluids and on submergence pressure. Recommendations for the maximum permissible rate are given by pump manufacturers and listed in their catalogs. Unlike rod pumps, it is easy to vary the rate of a hydraulic pump by controlling the injection rate of power fluid with control valves at the surface.

GAS EFFECT ON POSITIVE-DISPLACEMENT PUMPS. Calculations of pump rate should also consider the effect of free gas on the volumetric efficiency. Gas interference in the pumping process is a general problem. Free gas is undesirable in all types of pumps, but particularly in positive-displacement pumps, where free gas reduces effective pump displacement by:

1. delaying the opening of the suction (standing) valve at the start of the suction stroke and thereby causing incomplete filling of the compression chamber with liquid (due to the presence of free gas)
2. delaying the opening of the discharge (or traveling) valve at the start of the compression stroke (due to the compressibility of the gas in the chamber)

Figure 5.10 illustrates the effect of free gas on the effective stroke of a rod pump as originally described by Schmoe (1958). If gas occupies a portion of the pumping chamber, the traveling valve will not open immediately at the start of the downstroke. Its opening is delayed until the plunger has compressed the gas in the pump to a pressure equal to the hydrostatic fluid pressure in the tubing above the pump. Thus, gas occupying the space EC is compressed to the volume ED before pressure rises to the level required to open the traveling valve.

The standing valve does not open at the start of the upstroke. Its opening is delayed until the free gas expands and the pressure inside the pump is reduced to the producing bottomhole pressure at the pump setting depth. Only the space AE of the pump is then filled with liquid. The overall result is that pump volumetric efficiency, expressed as the ratio of the net displacement (AE) to total displacement (AC) is reduced considerably. Extremely low efficiency is commonly referred as "gas locking."

Clegg (1963) investigated pump volumetric efficiency under various bottomhole production conditions. To account for the shrinkage of reservoir oil (more than 1 bbl must be pumped to obtain 1 STB), he expressed the net pumping rate in terms of stock tank production and defined the overall pump efficiency as

$$E_{VT} = \frac{\text{stock tank liquid rate}}{\text{pump displacement rate}} . \qquad (5.4)$$

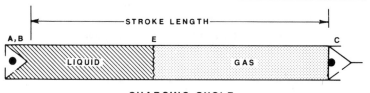

CHARGING CYCLE
PUMP SHOWN AT TOP OF STROKE

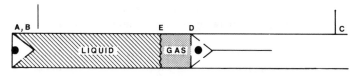

COMPRESSION CYCLE
PUMP SHOWN AT INSTANT JUST BEFORE
TRAVELING VALVE OPENS

END OF COMPRESSION CYCLE

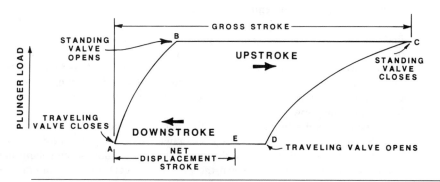

Figure 5.10 The effect of free gas on the effective stroke of a rod pump.

Note that overall volumetric efficiency E_{VT} reflects both the volumetric pump efficiency $E_{V(p)}$ and the shrinkage of produced oil, given by the formation volume factor $B_{o(p)}$. For water-free production, equation (5.4) becomes

$$E_{VT} = \frac{E_V(p)}{B_o(p)}. \tag{5.5}$$

Clegg's observations are summarized in figure 5.11. Overall pump efficiency is highly dependent on the relationship of suction to bubble-point pressures, and on the efficiency of free-gas separation at the pump intake. For suction pressures above the bubble point, both slippage (E_V), and formation-volume factor increase with pressure, and their ratio (E_{VT}) remains essentially constant. Below the bubble point, pump efficiency depends on the degree of free-gas separation. In the absence of a downhole separator, some separation occurs and gas is vented through the annulus, but some gas is carried over by the liquid and enters the pump. At pressures close to the bubble point, gas bubbles are small and easily entrained and carried by the fluid. At lower suction pressure, gas bubbles are larger and easy to separate, allowing improved pump efficiency. From figure 5.11 it is seen that a particular suction pressure range with low efficiency should be avoided by controlling pump rate and pump setting depth. Usually pump efficiencies are very erratic, difficult to predict, and must be determined by trial and error. Clegg observed that "if the pump is set too low, the pump intake pressure will be high, gas separation will be poor, and efficiencies may be low. If the pump is set too high, the gas separation may be good; however, the well will soon pump off and the overall efficiency will again be low."

Several measures were proven effective to minimize the detrimental gas effect. These include:

1. installing a bottomhole gas separator
2. maintaining high compression ratio in the pump
3. minimizing the idle volume in the compression chamber
4. selecting a suitable setting depth
5. avoiding long-stroke pumps
6. allowing unrestricted venting of annulus gas

Figure 5.11 indicates the gain in pumping efficiency obtained by adding a bottomhole separator. Efficiency increase from 20% to 80% can be achieved. Several gas separators, often referred to as gas anchors, are described by Schmoe (1958) and Clegg (1963). They are recommended in all pumping applications except those that have a suction pressure near or above the bubble point, or those having extremely low gas–oil ratios.

The compression ratio of a reciprocating pump, defined as the ratio of the ideal to gross volume of the compression chamber, is perhaps the most important consideration in pumping gassy wells. Idle volume is the undisplaced volume in the pump, due to a clearance between the piston (plunger) and the bottom of the cylinder (standing valve) at the end of the compression stroke. Idle volume in gaseous wells implies that a certain amount of free gas is not swept by the piston. This gas

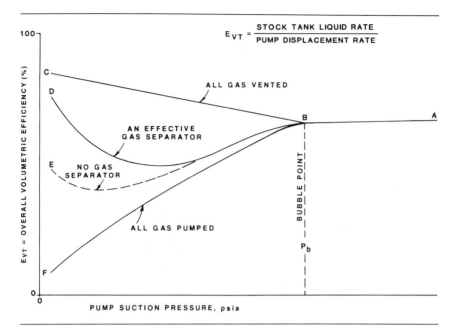

$$E_{VT} = \frac{\text{STOCK TANK LIQUID RATE}}{\text{PUMP DISPLACEMENT RATE}}$$

Figure 5.11 The combined effect of gas and formation-volume factor on the volumetric behavior of a rod pump. After Clegg 1963 by permission of American Petroleum Institute.

expands, delaying the opening of the suction valve (standing valve), and causes low liquid fillage and, thus, low volumetric efficiency. In sucker rod pumps an idle volume is a result of the clearance made to accommodate the cages of the standing and traveling valves. Improper spacing of the plunger in the pump barrel is another major cause for the large clearance or idle volume. Close spacing and small-clearance valve cages are essential for good operation in gaseous wells. Hydraulic pumps do not need to be spaced. They are constructed with a very small clearance, and thus develop very high compression ratios. Though they can handle a certain amount of free gas, mechanical problems may develop in the presence of excess gas. Another recommendation for reciprocating pumps in gassy wells is to avoid long strokes. Long strokes cause more free gas to enter the pump and promote gas evolvement during the fillage of the pump.

Pump setting depth in gassy wells is also related to the efficiency of gas separation. Installing the pump some 30 ft to 100 ft below the perforations, enhances separation of free gas. If such an installation is not possible, the pump should be installed high enough above the perforations to avoid the turbulent flow region near the perforations.

5.2.3   Considerations in Sizing Dynamic-Displacement Pumps. At the beginning of section 5.2 it was stated that the rate of a dynamic-displacement pump depends on pump pressure. Furthermore, each pump has a particular rate–pressure relationship. This fact has two implications in relation to oilwell pumping:

1. Changes in either reservoir pressure or surface backpressure affect pump rate.
2. Pumping rate can be predicted only if pressure conditions in the well and the IPR are known.

The most common dynamic-displacement pump is the submersible centrifugal pump, a multistage turbine pump driven by a downhole electrical motor. Each stage in the pump is a small turbine, consisting of a rotating impeller and a stationary diffuser. The liquid enters the impeller, where it is accelerated and gains velocity and kinetic energy. From the impeller it is discharged to the diffuser, where it decelerates. The kinetic energy of the decelerated liquid is transformed into potential energy, which corresponds to a pressure increase. In a multistage pump, the stages are arranged in series. That is, many stages are assembled together as a "pancake," where the discharge end of a stage is the suction to its adjacent overlying stage. The total pressure developed across the pump is very nearly the sum of the pressures from the individual stages, as if they were operated individually. Further description of the pump, its mechanical and electrical components, and the related well completions appear in many publications (Coltharp 1984; Allis and Capps 1984; Kilvington and Gallivan 1984; Williamson 1984), as well as in supplier manuals.

The characteristics of centrifugal pumps are reported in a standard form as a graph displaying curves of pumping head, pumping power, and pump efficiency versus the pump rate. Figure 5.12 is a typical pump characteristic curve for a submersible centrifugal pump. The characteristics of a pump are measured and reported for a constant driving speed. The standard test liquid is fresh water, with specific gravity of 1.0 and viscosity of 1 cp. In multistage oilwell pumps the reported performance is, in most cases, related to a stack of 100 stages.

Pumping head is the discharge pressure, expressed as a column of the pumped liquid:

$$h = \frac{\Delta p}{\rho} \times \frac{g_c}{g},\qquad(5.6)$$

where ρ is density, g is gravitational acceleration, and g_c, is a constant (32.2 in the English unit system and 1.0 in the metric system). In field units equation (5.6) is

$$h = \frac{144}{\rho}\Delta p = \frac{\Delta p}{0.433\gamma},\qquad(5.7)$$

where h is given in ft, Δp in psi, γ = specific gravity, (water = 1), and ρ = density in lb/ft^3.

The discharge pressure developed in a centrifugal pump increases with increasing liquid density. When expressed in terms of head, however, a given centrifugal pump develops the same head with various fluids having different densities. As a result, a single rate–head relationship developed with water is valid for other liquids

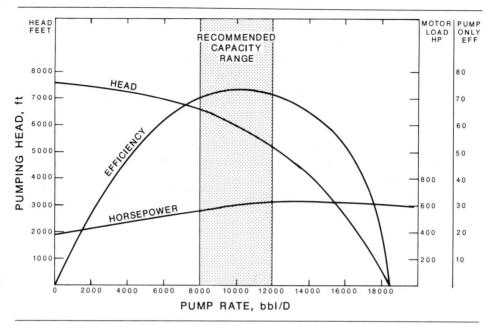

Figure 5.12 Pump characteristic chart of submersible centrifugal pump. Courtesy TRW Energy Products Group.

with different densities. Adjustments in the curve are needed only when the viscosity of the pumped fluid varies significantly from water viscosity.

Pumping power is defined as the time–rate of pumping work. It is related to pumping rate and pressure by

$$\text{power} = \frac{\text{work}}{\text{time}} = q\Delta p. \tag{5.8}$$

The customary unit of power for combustion engines is horsepower (HP) and for electrical motors is the kilowatt (kw). The two power units are related by

$$1\,\text{HP} = 0.746\,\text{kw}.$$

Pumping power is often referred to as *hydraulic power*. It is less than the *mechanical power* consumed by driving the pump. The relation between hydraulic power and mechanical power is defined as pump efficiency:

$$E = \frac{\text{hydraulic power}}{\text{mechanical power}}. \tag{5.9}$$

Pump efficiency indicates the efficiency of converting mechanical power into a product of rate and pressure. Efficiency is a complex function of a pump's mechanical structure, and it is obtained by laboratory testing of a pump prototype. Pump efficiency E is an entirely different concept from the volumetric efficiency E_V for positive-displacement pumps; volumetric efficiency is related to pump displacement, whereas pump efficiency is related to pump power. In dynamic-displacement pumps the volumetric efficiency is meaningless and displaced volumes are expressed by the pump characteristic curve.

The characteristic curves for turbine pumps are reported at constant driving speed:

3500 RPM with 60 Hertz AC electrical supply (typical in USA)
2915 RPM with 50 Hertz AC electrical supply (typical in Europe)

In most pumping applications the electrical power supply to the driving motor has a constant frequency and thus the pump is operated at constant speed. The constant-speed characteristic curve therefore provides all the necessary information on pump pressure and power requirements.

Determining the actual pressure–rate–power relationship from the water-related pump characteristic curve requires the following procedure:

1. Correct the reported pumping head for actual liquid viscosity if substantially different than 1 cp.
2. Convert pump head to pump pressure:

$$\Delta p \text{ (psi)} = h_{water} \text{ (ft) } 0.433\gamma. \tag{5.10}$$

3. Correct the power requirements for the density and viscosity of the liquid (if different from water). Pump power increases linearly with increasing specific gravity and thus,

$$P = P_{water} \times \gamma, \tag{5.11}$$

where γ is the specific gravity of the pumped liquid (water $= 1.0$), and P is pumping power.

The adverse effects of viscosity on pump performance include reduction of pump head and efficiency, and a corresponding increase in power consumption. There is no trivial method to predict the performance of a pump with high-viscosity liquid (>1 cp). Usually, the characteristic curve is used together with viscosity corrections established experimentally and reported by the manufacturer for each pump type. An example of the viscosity correction procedure is given later in the text.

Another factor that controls the range of pump rate and pressure for turbine pumps is the axial force across the impeller. Differential pressure and hydrodynamic forces across the impeller in each stage create forces acting in the axial direction. If the impeller in a given pump type is free to move axially along the pump drive shaft, the axial load is transferred from the impeller to the stator through friction pads. If the pump design is such that the impeller is fixed on the shaft, axial loads are transmitted through the shaft to a thrust bearing. In either case, the design of the pump attempts to minimize development of thrust loads by a variety of balancing arrangements.

Impellers are normally designed for axial balance at rates corresponding to peak pump efficiency. At this rate the axial momentum applied to impellers by the pumped liquid is equal to the downward force applied by the pressure difference across the impeller and thrust wear is minimal. Pump manufacturers therefore recommend pump operation within 25% ($\pm$12.5%) of the peak efficiency. The recommended operating range is indicated on the pump characteristic chart and is considered an important criterion when selecting a pump.

Sizing turbine pumps is also affected by the presence of free gas. Free gas entering a centrifugal pump reduces pump performance. First it reduces the net liquid volume through the pump, and second it reduces the average density of the pumped liquid, thereby resulting in lower discharge pressure. The gradual decline in pump performance with increasing quantities of free gas continues to a certain limit. Beyond this limit pump performance becomes erratic and deteriorates abruptly.

After reviewing the factors that influence pump performance, we proceed with the procedure of sizing and selecting a pump for a given well. The first task in pump selection is to determine the required pumping conditions. Pump depth is usually selected above the perforations so that well fluids passing the electrical motor will provide a necessary cooling to the motor housing. There are no special requirements for the distance between the pump and the perforations except for the argument that the deeper the pump the larger the allowable pressure drawdown and the higher the possible rate. An exception is in gaseous wells, where it is an advantage to place the pump above the turbulent area immediately near the perforations. Additional setting depth options can be considered if a sufficient rat hole (free hole below the perforations) exists in the well. The pump can then be installed below the perforations, thereby maximizing allowable drawdown and production. Figure 5.13(a) illustrates a pump set below the perforations equipped with a skirt or shroud to force fluid flow along the motor for cooling purposes.

In any installation, pump setting depth should allow for a suction pressure of at least 150 psia. This implies that the pump should be submerged in a liquid column of approximately 350 ft. Without sufficient submergence, pump performance deteriorates.

Once the setting depth is determined, the next step is to determine the required pressure and rate of the pump. The pumping diagram in figure 5.7 illustrates the relationship between pump size, pressure, rate, and depth conditions. For a particular well the diagram is established using

1. pump setting depth
2. well IPR
3. desired pump suction pressure (if other than the lowest allowable)
4. wellhead pressure
5. pressure traverse in the tubing

Once pumping conditions are established, pump selection is merely a search for a compatible pump size listed in manufacturers' catalogs.

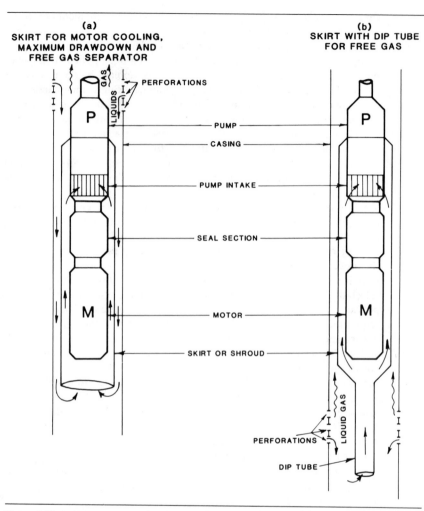

(a)
SKIRT FOR MOTOR COOLING,
MAXIMUM DRAWDOWN AND
FREE GAS SEPARATOR

(b)
SKIRT WITH DIP TUBE
FOR FREE GAS

PERFORATIONS

PUMP

CASING

PUMP INTAKE

SEAL SECTION

MOTOR

SKIRT OR SHROUD

PERFORATIONS

DIP TUBE

LIQUID GAS

P

M

P

M

Figure 5.13 Arrangements (a) to install centrifugal pump below the perforations or (b) to provide dip tube extended below the perforations. Courtesy Centrilift-Hughes, Inc.

The following is a step-by-step procedure for selecting a centrifugal pump from manufacturers' characteristic sheets. The procedure starts after the pumping diagram has been established and the pumping rate and pressure have been calculated.

1. Select the pump diameter. The most economical pump is normally the largest-diameter pump the casing will accommodate. Data on casing–pump compatibility is specified in pump catalogs.
2. Select a pump that has a peak efficiency near the desired production rate of the well and obtain its performance (characteristic) curve.

3. Read the pump head at the desired rate from the performance curve. When the curve is related to 100 stages divide the reading by 100 to determine the average head per single stage (remember, the performance is usually given per 100 stages).
4. Calculate the pressure that corresponds to the head of a single stage.
5. Divide the total required pump pressure by the calculated pressure of a single stage to determine the number of stages needed. The type and the calculated number of single stages are usually sufficient to specify a pump.

Once the pump is selected for a particular well, the motor, power cable, switch board, and transformer are selected according to the power requirements of the pump.

This procedure is valid for conventional pump applications. There are, however, three distinct cases of pump selection:

1. Conventional wells—pumping in wells with low gas–liquid ratio.
2. Viscous fluids wells—pumping viscous oil (low API gravity) or oil–water emulsions
3. Gaseous wells—pumping in wells with high GLR

The 5-step procedure for selecting and sizing pumps in low GLR, low viscosity wells is illustrated in examples 5.2 and 5.3.

EXAMPLE 5.2 SIZING OF CENTRIFUGAL PUMP FOR SHALLOW-WATER WELL

A water well, Madelein Dulce No. 3, is planned as a water source for the water-injection project in the Sidri oil field. The water source is a shallow aquifer in a limestone formation with 10% average porosity and 1–6 darcy permeability. The well is located 7 miles east of the oil field and will transfer water to the waterflooding plant through a 6-in. flowline. It is common to use large-volume centrifugal submersible pumps in water source wells. Because most of the submersible pumps in the oil field were supplied by a single supplier, Reda, the same supplier is considered for the water-well pump.

Additional well data are given in table E5.2. Select a pump that will produce the well at a rate of 10,000 bbl/D and boost the water against 500 psia flowline backpressure.

Table E5.2 Well Data for the Madelein Dulce No. 3 Water Well

Reservoir pressure	400 psia
Perforation depth	1000 ft
Productivity index (constant) J	100 bbl/D/psi
Constant wellhead pressure (pipeline inlet pressure)	500 psia
Tubing size	4.5 in. × 1000 ft
Hydrostatic water gradient	0.433 psi/ft
Flow friction losses (at 10 000 bbl/D)	0.024 psi/ft

EXAMPLE 5.2 continued

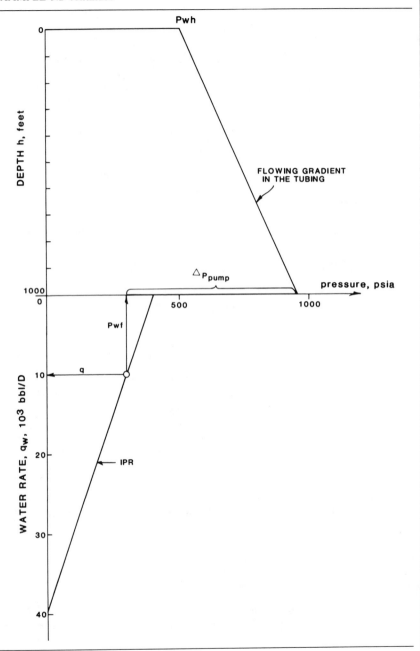

Figure E5.2 Pumping diagram for the Madelein Dulce No. 3 water well.

EXAMPLE 5.2 continued

SOLUTION

According to the manufacturer's catalog, having a casing size of 9⅝ in. allows installation of a Reda pump series 650 (or equivalent pump size from another manufacturer). Within the 650 series, a particular pump type the IN10000 (fig. 5.12) will operate near peak efficiency with 10,000 bbl/D.

The required discharge pressure of the pump is calculated from the pressure traverse in the tubing, as

$$p_{discharge} = p_{wh} + h[(dp/dh)_h + (dp/dh)_f]$$

$$= 500 + 1000(0.433 + 0.024)$$

$$= 957 \, psia,$$

where $(dp/dh)_h$ is the hydrostatic pressure gradient and $(dp/dh)_f$ is the flow friction pressure gradient in the tubing.

The suction pressure is approximately p_{wf}, and thus may be calculated from the IPR as

$$p_{suction} = p_{wf} = p_R - \frac{q}{J}$$

$$= 400 - \frac{10,000}{100}$$

$$= 300 \, psia.$$

The calculated suction and discharge pressures were used to plot the pumping diagram in figure. E5.2.

Recalling the pump performance is given in terms of head, the required pumping head when pumping water is calculated from the pumping pressure by equation (5.10) as

$$\Delta h = \frac{2.31}{1.0}(957 - 300)$$

$$= 1517 \, ft.$$

At a rate of 10,000 bbl/D the pump characteristic curve reads a pumping head of 6000 ft per 100 stages, or 60 ft/stage. The total number of stages needed is then $1517/60 = 25.3 \approx 26$.

EXAMPLE 5.3 SIZING OF CENTRIFUGAL PUMP FOR A HIGH-WATER-FRACTION, LOW-GLR WELL

The Ardmore No. 24 oil well is producing with a high water cut from a water-

EXAMPLE 5.3 continued

Table E5.3 Well Data for the Ardmore No. 24 Oil Well

Midperforation depth	5200 ft
Pump setting depth	5000 ft
Production casing	7 in. (ID × 6.276 in.)
Tubing (before pump replacement)	2.875 in. (ID = 2.44 in.)
Constant wellhead pressure	100 psia
Constant casing head pressure	100 psia
Produced water specific gravity γ_w	1.00
Produced oil API gravity	28 API ($\gamma = 0.886$)
Production GOR	100 scf/STB
Surface water cut	90%
Reservoir pressure p_R	1600 psia
Surface water viscosity	1.2 cp (0.0008 lb/ft-s)

flooded reservoir. Well data are listed in table E5.3. A waterflood expansion program is being pursued in the field by drilling additional injection wells and converting existing producing wells into injectors to complete the flood pattern. In response to the program, the Ardmore 24 oil well has experienced a significant increase in reservoir pressure and wellbore flowing pressure. To handle the possible increased liquid withdrawal, it was decided to replace the sucker rod pump with a high-rate centrifugal pump.

To determine the productivity of the well at a high production rate, a variable-speed test pump has been installed temporarily in the well and the well was tested for 7 days. The data collected during the test establishes that the IPR is essentially a linear pressure–rate function and can be expressed as

$$q_L = 1.538(p_R - p_{wf}).$$

To allow maximum withdrawal, the permanent pump will be installed just above the perforations at 5000 ft. To maintain a minimum suction pressure of 300 psia at the pump depth and estimating 100 psi pressure loss between the pump suction and midperforations, bottomhole flowing pressure cannot be lower than 400 psia. Additional assumptions are made for pump-size calculations:

1. The effect of free gas and oil shrinkage can be ignored.
2. No emulsion is formed.

Perform the first two design steps:

Step 1: Select the type of pump that will pump the well down to $p_{wf} = 400$ psia (corresponding to fluid level approximately 800 ft above perforations).

Step 2: Calculate the number of pump stages.

EXAMPLE 5.3 continued

SOLUTION

Step 1: Using a p_{wf} of 400 psia in the IPR equation calculates a production rate of 1845 bbl/D. From manufacturers' catalogs, the Centrilift-Y-62B is the largest pump inside 7 in. casing that will pump efficiently at 2000 bbl/D. The pump performance curve is given in figure E5.3. At a pump rate of 1845 bbl/D the pumping head read from the characteristic curve is 45 ft/stage.

Step 2
The total required pumping pressure is

$$\Delta p_{\text{pump}} = p_{\text{discharge}} - p_{\text{suction}}, \tag{E5.1}$$

where

$$p_{\text{discharge}} = p_{wh} + \rho(g/144g_c)h_1 + \Delta p_{f_1}, \tag{E5.2}$$

$$p_{\text{suction}} = p_{wf} - \rho(g/144g_c)(h_2 - h_1) - \Delta p_{f_2}, \tag{E5.3}$$

and

p_{wh}	= wellhead pressure (psia),
p_{wf}	= flowing bottomhole pressure at midperforations (psia),
h_1	= pump setting depth (ft),
h_2	= midperforations depth (ft),
ρ	= fluid density (lb/ft^3),
$\rho(g/144g_c)h$	= hydrostatic pressure of column h (psia),
Δp_{f_1}	= flow friction pressure losses above the pump (psi),
Δp_{f_2}	= flow friction pressure losses below the pump (psi).

In most pipe flow engineering calculations, the friction pressure loss for single-phase flow is calculated by Moody's correlation (Moody 1944)

$$\Delta p_f = \frac{fLv^2\rho}{2g_c d}, \tag{E5.4}$$

where the parameters and units are:

Parameters	*English Units*
d = internal line diameter	ft
v = velocity	ft/sec
ρ = density	lb/ft^3
μ = viscosity	lb/ft-sec
p = pressure	lb/ft^2
g_c = factor	32.2
L = length of line	ft
f = Moody friction factor	—

EXAMPLE 5.3 continued

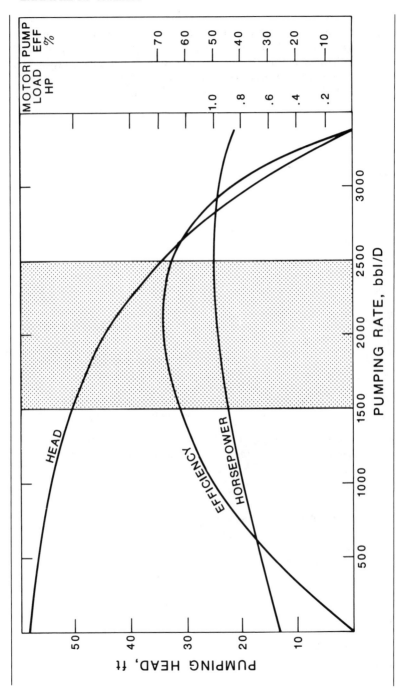

Figure E5..3   One-stage performance curve, for the Centrilift Y-62B pump. Courtesy Centrilift-Hughes, Inc.

EXAMPLE 5.3 continued

The average pipe flow velocity, in equation (E5.4) calculated in field units, is

$$v = \frac{0.012q}{d_i^2},$$
(E5.5)

where

v = average liquid velocity (ft/s),
q = flow rate (bbl/D),
d_i = pipe inside diameter (in.).

The friction factor is obtained from Moody's diagram or can be calculated with the following equations:

$$f = \frac{64}{Re}, \qquad Re \leqslant 2200,$$
(E5.6)

$$f = \left[-1.8 \log \left(\frac{6.9}{Re} + \frac{\varepsilon/d}{3.7} \right)^{1.11} \right]^{-2}, \qquad Re > 2200,$$
(E5.7)

where ε/d is the relative roughness of pipe and assumes the value of 0.008 for casing and 0.003 for tubing; and Reynolds number Re, in any consistent unit set, is

$$Re = \frac{\rho v d}{\mu}.$$
(E5.8)

For pipe flow calculations the viscosity of liquid is converted from centipoise to engineering units, using the conversion

$1\,cp = 0.001\,kg/m\text{-}s = 0.001\,N\text{-}s/m^2 = 0.000672\,lb/ft\text{-}sec.$

Considering the high water fraction with no emulsion forming, the apparent viscosity of the mixture may be approximated by water viscosity. The apparent density of the mixture is calculated as

$\rho_{mixture} = 0.9\,\rho_{water} + 0.1\,\rho_{oil}$

$= 0.9 \times 62.4 + 0.1 \times 0.886 \times 62.4$

$= 61.69\,lb/ft^3,$

where 0.886 is the specific gravity of 28°API oil and 62.4 lb/ft³ is water density produced.

The old 2⅞-in. tubing string appears to be too small for the new rate. The need to replace it can be verified by calculating the pump discharge pressure needed to produce 1845 STB/D. Substituting well data in equation (E5.8, E5.7, E5.5, E5.4, E5.2) gives

EXAMPLE 5.3 continued

$$v_1 = \frac{0.012 \times 1845}{2.44^2}$$

$$= 3.718 \, \text{ft/s},$$

$$Re_1 = \frac{61.69 \times 3.718 \times 2.44}{12 \times 1.2 \times 0.000672}$$

$$= 57.84 \times 10^3,$$

$$f_1 = \left[-1.8 \log \left(\frac{6.9}{57.84 \times 10^3} + \frac{0.003}{3.7}^{1.11} \right) \right]^{-2}$$

$$= 0.0272,$$

$$\Delta p_{f_1} = \frac{0.0272 \times 5000 \times (3.718)^2 \times 61.69 \times 12}{2 \times 32.2 \times 2.44}$$

$$= 8975 \, \text{psi},$$

$$p_{\text{discharge}} = 100 + (61.69/144)500 + 8975$$

$$= 11,216 \, \text{psia}.$$

The calculated discharge pressure governed primarily by the friction-loss component is obviously too high, so a larger tubing should be used. Generally, for a flow rate of 1845 bbl/D, 3½- or 4½-in. tubing is more appropriate. Selecting a 4½-in. 12.60-lb/ft tubing with an average inside diameter of 3.958 in., the discharge pressure is recalculated:

$$v_1 = \frac{0.012 \times 1845}{(3.958)^2}$$

$$= 1.33 \, \text{ft/s},$$

$$Re_1 = \frac{61.69 \times 1.33 \times 3.958}{12 \times 1.2 \times 0.000672}$$

$$= 34.59 \times 10^3,$$

$$f_1 = \left[-1.8 \log \left(\frac{6.9}{34.59 \times 10^3} + \frac{0.003}{3.7}^{1.11} \right) \right]^{-2}$$

$$= 0.0279,$$

$$\Delta p_{f_1} = \frac{0.0279 \times 5000 \times (1.33)^2 \times 61.69 \times 12}{2 \times 32.2 \times 3.958}$$

EXAMPLE 5.3 continued

$$= 700\,\text{psia.}$$

$$p_{\text{discharge}} = 100 \times (61.69/144)5000 + 700$$

$$= 2941\,\text{psia.}$$

A similar procedure is used to calculate suction pressure:

$$v_2 = \frac{0.012 \times 1845}{(6.276)^2}$$

$$= 0.562\,\text{ft/s,}$$

$$Re_2 = \frac{61.69 \times 0.562 \times 6.276}{12 \times 1.2 \times 0.000672}$$

$$= 22.7 \times 10^3,$$

$$f_2 = \left[-1.8\log\left(\frac{6.9}{22.7 \times 10^3} + \frac{0.008}{3.7}\right)^{1.11} \right]^{-2}$$

$$= 0.0375,$$

$$\Delta p_{f_2} = \frac{0.0375 \times 200 \times (0.562)^2 \times 61.69 \times 12}{2 \times 32.2 \times 6.276}$$

$$= 4.38\,\text{psi.}$$

Substituting this value in equation (E5.3) gives

$$p_{\text{suction}} = 400 - (61.69/144)200 - 4.38 = 309\,\text{psia.}$$

The required pumping pressure is then

$$\Delta p_{\text{pump}} = p_{\text{discharge}} - p_{\text{suction}}$$

$$= 2941 - 309$$

$$= 2632\,\text{psia.}$$

Converting the pressure to pumping head

$$\Delta H = \frac{\Delta p_{\text{pump}}}{0.433 \times \gamma}$$

$$= \frac{2632.2}{0.433 \times 0.989}$$

EXAMPLE 5.3 continued

$$= 6146.5\,\text{ft},$$

and recalling the pumping head per stage, the required number of pump stages is

$$\text{stages} = \frac{\Delta H}{(\Delta H \text{ per stage})}$$

$$= \frac{6146.5}{45} = 131.$$

In wells producing viscous fluids, viscosity corrections should be made to adjust pump performance curves. The American Hydraulic Institute has published viscosity correction factors for pumps of conventional hydraulic design (fig. 5.14). Note that viscosity in the correction curve is given in Saybolt Universal Units (SSU) or kinematic viscosity units, centistokes. Neither of these units is used in petroleum production. For conversion to customary field units, centistokes is related to centipoises by

$$\text{centistokes} = \frac{\text{centipoises}}{\text{specific gravity}}.$$

Viscosity can be obtained from laboratory tests of well fluid samples. If viscosity test data are not available, it is possible to use a general correlation such as Beal (1946), Chew and Connally (1959), or Beggs and Robinson (1975).

Some oils have the tendency to form emulsions with produced brines. Emulsion viscosity is difficult to estimate. If experimental data are lacking, it is possible to predict emulsion viscosity from the chart in figure 5.15 (Woelflin, 1942). Example 5.4 illustrates pump selection for a well requiring special considerations for viscosity.

EXAMPLE 5.4 VISCOSITY CORRECTION FOR THE CHARACTERISTICS OF A PUMP

A pumping diagram was prepared to determine the pumping conditions in Fearans well No. 1. The well produces low gravity, moderate viscosity oil from zones 3 and 5 in the Fearan west reservoir. The following pumping conditions were determined:

Pump rate	1900 bbl/D
Pump head	6000 ft
Oil gravity at pump suction	22 API ($\gamma = 0.92$)
Oil viscosity at suction temp (120°F)	80 cp

Select a certrifugal pump to fulfill the pumping requirements.

EXAMPLE 5.4 continued

SOLUTION

Pump selection is made after pump data are translated to an equivalent water pumping condition. This is done using correction factors C_q, C_h, and C_E from figure 5.14. The correction factors relate water to viscous liquid according to the following equations:

$$q_o = C_q \times q_w, \tag{E5.9}$$

$$\Delta h_o = C_h \times \Delta h_w, \tag{E5.10}$$

$$E_o = C_E \times E_w, \tag{E5.11}$$

$$P_o = \frac{q_o \Delta h_o \gamma_o}{3960 \times E_o}, \tag{E5.12}$$

where

q = rate (GPM [gallons per minute]),
Δh = pumping head (ft),
P = pump power (HP),
E = pump efficiency (%),
C_q = rate correction factor,
C_h = head correction factor,
C_E = efficiency correction factor,
γ = gravity (water = 1.0),

and where the subscript o indicates oil or viscous fluid and w indicates fresh water.
To use figure 5.14 the pumping rate is expressed in gallons per minute:

$$1900(\text{bbl/D}) \times 42(\text{gal/bbl}) \times \frac{1}{1440} (\text{D/min}) = 55.5 \text{ GPM}.$$

In addition, the oil viscosity given as dynamic viscosity, in centiposes (cp), has to be converted to kinematic viscosity, in centistokes (cSt) used in figure 5.14. Dividing 1 cp by density in grams per cubic centimeter gives 1 cSt, a conversion that may be approximated (though dimensionally incorrect) by

$$\text{centistokes} = \frac{\text{centipoises}}{\text{specific gravity}}, \tag{E5.13}$$

which gives

$$\frac{80}{0.92} = 87 \text{ centistokes}.$$

EXAMPLE 5.4 continued

Furthermore, considering the relatively low head range covered by figure 5.14, pump selection will be done first on the basis of 100 ft head, and then the number of stages and power requirement will be multiplied by 60.

Entering figure 5.14 with 55.5 GPM, moving up to intersect 100 ft pumping head, then continuing horizontally to the 88-centistoke line and upward to the intersection with correction factors, we read $C_q = 0.82$, $C_h = 1.0$, $C_E = 0.58$. For the purpose of using the characteristic curve, the pump has to deliver a water equivalent of

$q_w = 55.5/0.82$

$= 67.7\,\text{GPM}$

$= 2317\,\text{bbl/D}$

at a pump head (per 100 feet)

$\Delta h_w = 100/1.0$

$= 100\,\text{ft.}$

From the manufacturer's data sheet, a pump type MEGO I-70 has peak efficiency of 0.81 at 70 GPM water pumping. With viscous oil the efficiency is reduced to

$E_o = 0.81 \times 0.58$

$= 0.47$

and the power per 100-ft head is increased to

$P_o = \dfrac{q_o \times \Delta h_o \times \gamma_o}{3960 \times E_o}$

$= \dfrac{55.5 \times 100 \times 0.85}{3960 \times 0.47}$

$= 2.54\,\text{HP.}$

For a 6000-ft pumping head, the power requirement is

$2.54 \times 60 = 152.4\,\text{HP.}$

In review, the high viscosity in this example increases significantly the pump's power requirement, but has no effect on the pumping head or number of pumping stages.

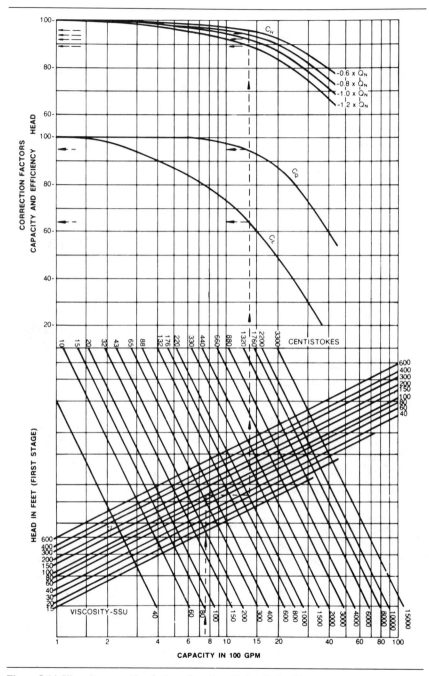

Figure 5.14 Viscosity correction factors. Courtesy Hydraulic Institute.

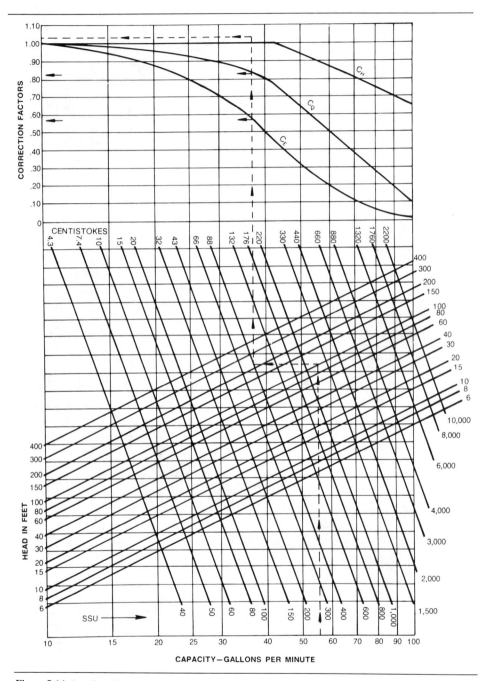

Figure 5.14 (continued)

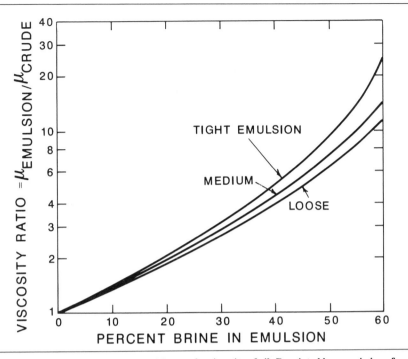

Figure 5.15 The effect of water emulsion on the viscosity of oil. Reprinted by permission of American Petroleum Institute from Woelflin, 1942, fig. 3.

Free gas may enter the pump in gaseous wells and impair the performance of the pump. Gas affects the performance of each stage in three ways:

1. It increases the total fluid displaced and thereby reduces net liquid displaced.
2. It reduces the average density of the pumped fluid and thereby reduces pump discharge pressure.
3. It increases the compressibility of the pumped fluid, causing significant density increase between the suction and the discharge.

As gaseous fluid passes from stage to stage, free gas is compressed, its volume decreases, its density increases, and a certain amount of gas is dissolved in the liquid. As a result, the average mixture density changes considerably, suggesting that head and pressure calculations should be made on a stage-by-stage basis. Furthermore, a considerable density change between the suction and the discharge in a multistage pump implies that certain stages may operate beyond the recommended range. If free gas cannot be effectively separated and vented through the annulus, a tapered pump assembly may reduce its detrimental effect (Swetnam and Sackash 1978). Large stages are used at the bottom of the pump to compress gas, and smaller stages are used at the upper part of the pump to build up pressure.

The stages are selected such that operating conditions are within the recommended operating range. Flow diagrams illustrating the logic of sizing tapered pumps are given in example 5.5.

EXAMPLE 5.5 SIZING OF A PUMP FOR A GASEOUS WELL

Prepare a flow diagram illustrating the logic of a computer program or a manual procedure for calculating the number of pump stages needed to pump gaseous wells. Prepare the diagram for two cases:

Case A: The pump type is predetermined and all pumping stages are identical.

Case B: The pump consists of several stacks of different pumping stages. Each stack is made of the most efficient stage type for the in-situ conditions in the stack.

SOLUTION

The main program requires an input from several subroutines and data files that calculate or store the following:

1. pumping conditions: $p_{suction}$, $p_{discharge}$, Δp_{pump}, pumped liquid rate, and amount of free gas separated and vented through the annulus
2. fluid properties at pump conditions:
   B_g, R_s, γ_o, γ_g, B_o, $\gamma_{mixture}$
3. a data file with pump characteristic curves, Δh, P, and E versus q

The flow chart for case A is illustrated in figure E5.5. In case A, the total required pump pressure (Δp_T) is divided into an arbitrary numbers of equal pressure increments ($ITOT$), giving $\Delta p = \Delta p_T/(ITOT)$. The arithmetic average pressure in the first increment is used to calculate the in-situ fluid properties, the average mixture density, (ρ_{av}), and the in-situ total volumetric flow rate (q_T). The average density is then used to express the pressure increment in terms of head increment. Given the type of pumping stage and the information on its performance, allows one to calculate the pumping head $\Delta h_s(q_T)$ and pumping power $P_s(q_T)$ per stage and pump efficiency. Dividing the required pumping head by the head of each stage gives the number of stages required for the pertinent pressure increment. The number of required stages is calculated and recorded. The procedure is repeated by using the outlet pressure of the first increment as the input pressure of the second, repeatedly for all the remaining increments. The total number of pumping stages is then the sum of the stages calculated for each pressure increment. Case B is basically the same, except for having the freedom to select the most efficient (yet mechanically compatible) stage for each pressure increment.

EXAMPLE 5.5 continued

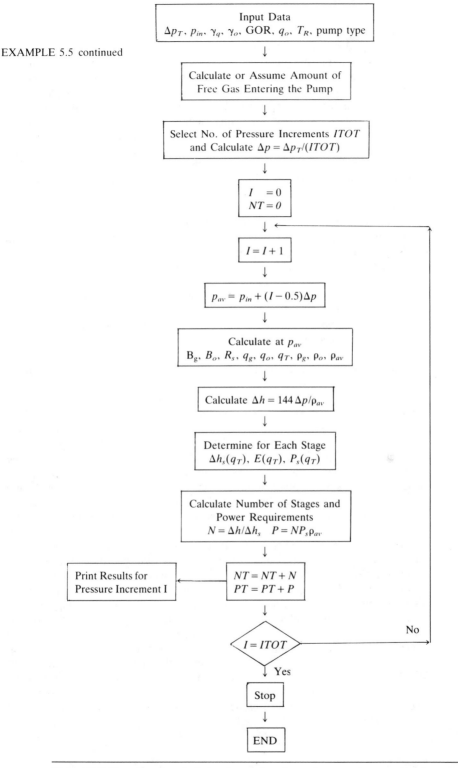

Figure E5.5 Flow chart for calculating the number of pumping stages in a centrifugal pump (all pumping stages are identical)

To reduce the amount of free gas, pumps are normally provided with a gas separator installed at the pump inlet. The separator enhances segregation of free gas and diverts separated gas to the annulus (Lea and Bearden 1982; Kobylinski et al. 1985). Two types of gas separators are currently available for centrifugal pumps. The cup type segregates free gas from liquid by an abrupt change in flow direction. The centrifugal type employs a rotating element powered by the pump shaft to create centrifugal force, which separates the light gas from the heavy liquid. In both cases, a change in flow direction applies centrifugal force, which enhances phase segregation. Separation of gas may be further improved by installing the pump below the perforations (fig. 5.13[a]), or by providing the pump with a dip tube or shroud arrangement (fig. 5.13[b]).

Modern gas separators are very efficient and if properly sized are capable of avoiding deterioration of pump performance in gaseous wells. A criterion for separation efficiency is based on results published by Lea and Bearden (1982) who investigated the effect of gaseous fluids on submersible pump performance. They concluded that if free-gas volume entering the pump exceeds 10% by total volume, pump performance becomes erratic and starts to deteriorate. The tolerable free-gas percentage increases with increasing suction pressure.

Pump selection is based on a steady-state IPR. Steady-state deliverability is reached after a short transient period when the well is unloaded as the pump produces liquid accumulated in the annulus after a shut-in. When the pump is started, the initial suction pressure is high, corresponding to static fluid level. The suction pressure drops as pumping and unloading proceed, until a steady working point and a stable suction pressure are reached. At the steady working point, the pumping rate matches the deliverability of the well and the fluid level is stabilized. Unlike in the case of a positive displacement pump, the rate of unloading a well by centrifugal pumping is not constant. As the liquid level in the annulus drops, the required pump pressure increases and the pumping rate decreases. If the well productivity is overestimated, or the pump is oversized, the fluid level will continue to drop until the well is pumped off as the annulus fluid level approaches the pump setting depth. If a well is pumped off, then the pump does not transfer enough fluid to allow proper cooling and lubricating. The result is usually a damaged pump. To protect the pump the electrical control system is capable of sensing the sharp drop in motor current associated with pump-off, and the pump is shut down automatically. One possibility to reduce pump capacity and avoid pump-off is to increase wellhead pressure using the choke. Increasing backpressure, however, increases energy consumption, reduces pump efficiency, and may cause excessive thrust wearout. The simplest method to continue production without replacing an oversized pump is to utilize a special timer arrangement that restarts the pump after a period sufficient to build up the liquid level in the annulus. This shut-down and startup may then continue in a cyclic manner. Cyclic operation, however, is undesirable in electrical pumps (Neely and Patterson 1984). Restarting a pump results in a large current surge that can damage the motor and its cable. Recent developments allow reduced starting voltage or "soft" start, and these have managed to reduce the detrimental effect of cycling. Oversized pumps with a capacity of 25–30% above well capacity may then operate satisfactorily applying cyclic operation.

In some cases, rapid changes in reservoir conditions and well deliverability may require frequent changes of pump size, and therefore pumps with variable-speed controllers have become increasingly popular. The effect of speed variations on pumping head is illustrated in figure 5.16. The figure shows increasing pump rate and head for increasing pump speed (RPM). In fact, the trends indicated by the figure reflect relationships existing for all centrifugal pumps, usually referred to as pump affinity laws.

Pump affinity laws relate the rate, head, power, and efficiency of a centrifugal pump to the impeller speed:

for rate

$$\frac{q_1}{q_2} = \frac{N_1}{N_2} = \frac{f_1}{f_2},$$
(5.12)

where

q = rate (BPD),
N = speed (RPM),
f = frequency (Hertz);

for head

$$\frac{h_1}{h_2} = \left(\frac{N_1}{N_2}\right)^2 = \left(\frac{f_1}{f_2}\right)^2,$$
(5.13)

for power

$$\frac{\text{HP}_1}{\text{HP}_2} = \left(\frac{N_1}{N_2}\right)^3 = \left(\frac{f_1}{f_2}\right)^3,$$
(5.14)

and for efficiency

$$E_{N_2} = E_{N_1}(q_2),$$
(5.15)

meaning the new efficiency, E_{N_2}, is obtained by entering the corrected rate, q_2, to the original characteristic curve (for 50 Hertz).

Efficiency and recommended pump operating range are related, since the pump operates best with minimum axial thrust at the point of peak efficiency. Figure 5.16 indicates that the point of peak efficiency moves to the left with speed reduction. It indicates also that the recommended operating range is wide for the high-speed range and narrow at low speeds.

Variable speed can be achieved by installing a variable-frequency drive (VFD) unit in place of the standard motor controller at the surface. It has the ability to convert fixed-voltage, fixed-frequency power input into variable-frequency power output with the voltage-to-frequency ratio essentially constant. A VFD unit allows smooth pump speed control over a relatively wide range. The variable-speed

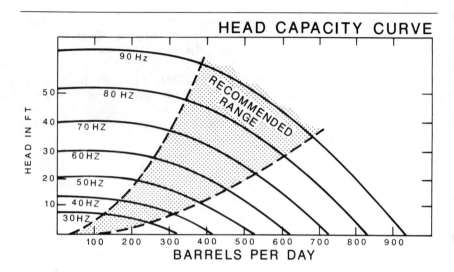

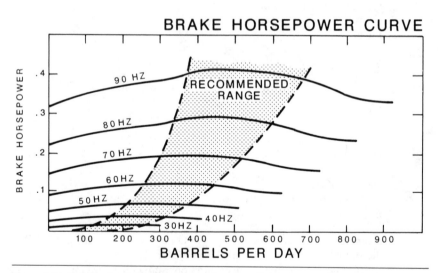

Figure 5.16 Pumping head changes with varying pumping speed. Courtesy Centrilift-Hughes, Inc.

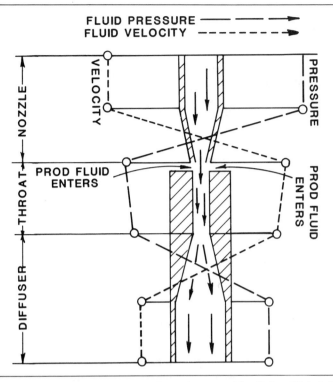

FLUID PRESSURE ——— —— ⟶
FLUID VELOCITY ———————▶

Figure 5.17 **Pressure and velocity traverse along a jet pump. After Bell and Spisak 1973. Reprinted by permission of the SPE-AIME from Bell and Spisak 1973, fig. 1. © 1973 SPE-AIME.**

controller allows great flexibility in adjusting pump rate to the deliverability of the well. Automatic control can be arranged, so that pump speed is changed in response to measurements of fluid level in the annulus. The control system includes a downhole pressure transducer to measure suction pressure and transmit the information to the surface frequency controller. The controller adjusts the frequency to maintain a preset suction pressure. Setting the controller to the minimum allowable suction pressure results in maximum drawdown and maximum possible production rate. If well deliverability changes, the rate will change correspondingly, maintaining suction pressure essentially constant.

Pumping wells in waterflooded fields is perhaps the most common application of variable-speed pumps (Kelley 1980; Barnes and Tinker 1985). Adding injection wells to the field or increasing water injection rate may vary significantly the deliverability of producing wells, allowing increased fluid withdrawals. Using variable-speed pumps allows increased pumping rate without pulling and replacing existing downhole equipment. Variable-speed pumps are also used for testing high-rate wells to determine their deliverability. Multirate tests using temporarily installed VFD pumps provide the information needed to size a fixed-speed pump.

The variable-speed pump has two drawbacks:

1. The price is almost double that of a constant-speed pump.
2. It exhibits decreasing efficiency and significant variations in power demand as frequency varies.

These result in a cautious approach by operators when considering alternative artificial-lift solutions.

Sizing variable-speed pumps for a well with varying deliverability is essentially a search for a pump that will produce maximum rates for a large range of well conditions. Example 5.6 illustrates the sizing calculations for variable-speed pumps.

Another dynamic-displacement pump is the jet pump, shown in figure 5.6. It is not widely used but has certain interesting features. Its greatest advantage is the lack of any moving parts. The buildup of pump pressure is achieved by converting the kinetic energy of the power fluid into potential energy for lifting the reservoir and power fluids. The conversion of kinetic to potential energy in the pump corresponds to the profile of fluid velocity and pressure along the pump, as illustrated in figure 5.17. The increasing velocity at the nozzle corresponds to decreasing pressure of the power fluid. Decreasing mixture velocity in the diffuser corresponds to pressure buildup.

EXAMPLE 5.6 VARIABLE-SPEED PUMP WITH CONSTANT SUCTION-PRESSURE CONTROL

Production decline calculations for the Ina oil field (example 4.11) forecast rapid rate decline reaching the minimum economical rate within less than 2 years. The results emphasize a need to consider a pressure maintenance program at an early production stage and/or introduction of artificial lift. Presently, gas lift is the only artificial lift method being operated successfully in subsea completed wells (such as the satellite wells in the Ina field).

Centrifugal submersible pumps were not installed in subsea wells due to the limited capacity of the existing subsea electrical connector to transmit the high power required to operate the pump. The operator, however, is inclined to consider an experimental installation with an electrical pump in one well (Ina No. 4) to test the performance on newly developed connectors and to verify the capability of pumping subsea completed wells. Considering the depletion characteristics of the well, investigated in example 4.11, the well appears to be a good candidate for an electrically driven centrifugal pump with closed-loop speed control. The controller will vary the speed of the pump and thus, the pump rate so that the bottomhole flowing pressure is held constant, $p_{wf} = 500$ psia, to avoid pump-off.

Size the pump and calculate the operating conditions according to the following sequence:

1. Determine the expected variations in pump rate and pump head with depletion.
2. Select a pump size that can operate efficiently and can, as much as possible, adjust for changes in the well by varying the speed.

EXAMPLE 5.6 continued

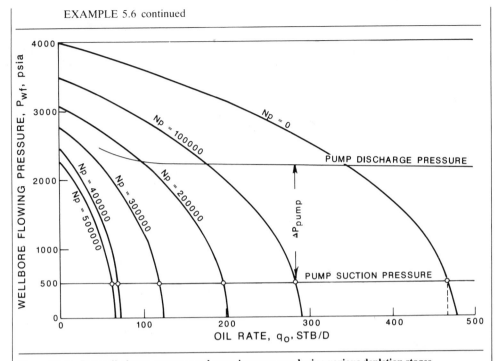

Figure E5.6a Pump discharge pressure and pumping pressure during various depletion stages.

3. Calculate the variations of frequency, efficiency, and power requirement that occur with depletion.
4. Estimate how long the variable-speed pump can operate before it should be retrieved and changed due to over or under capacity.

Well and reservoir data are given in example 4.11. Additional well data are given in table E5.6a. The study assumes that all free gas at the suction of the pump is separated and vented through the annulus. The calculated amount of solution gas at 500 psia suction pressure is $R_s = 200$ scf/STB.

SOLUTION

The natural flow conditions of the Ina No. 4 well were established in example 4.11, where future IPR curves were calculated and plotted. The IPR curves are plotted again in figure E5.6a. A horizontal line at $p_{wf} = 500$ psia intersects the IPRs at rates corresponding to a constant suction pressure. The range of rate varies from $q = 468$ STB/D at $N_p = 0$ bbls to $q = 62$ STB/D at $N_p = 500,000$ bbls.

According to manufacturers' catalogs, a variable-speed pump that operates within the determined rate range is the Centrilift-B-11W model. The characteristic curve of the pump at a 60-Hz electricity frequency is given in figure E5.6b. The

EXAMPLE 5.6 continued

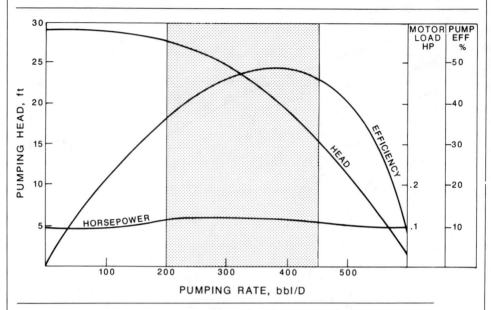

Figure E5.6b One-stage performance curve for the Centrilift-B-11W pump. Courtesy Centrilift-Hughes, Inc.

Table E5.6a Well and Production Data for the Ina No. 4 Oil Well

Tubing	2.875 in. × 8000 ft
Casing	7 in.
Well depth	8000 ft (IPR reference depth)
Wellhead pressure	200 psia, constant for the production life of the well
Pump installation depth	just above perforations (approx. 8000 ft)
Solution gas–oil ratio at 500 psia	200 scf/STB
Formation volume factor at 500 psia	1.2
Oil gravity at pump suction	0.8

Table E5.6b Pumping Head Requirements with Various Production Rates

q_o (STB/D)	q_p (bbl/D)	$p_{discharge}$ (psia)	Δp_{pump} (psi)	Δh_{pump} (ft)
50	60	2980	1985	5730
100	120	2240	1740	5023
200	240	2240	1740	4792
400	480	2080	1660	4972
468	561	2080	1660	

EXAMPLE 5.6 continued

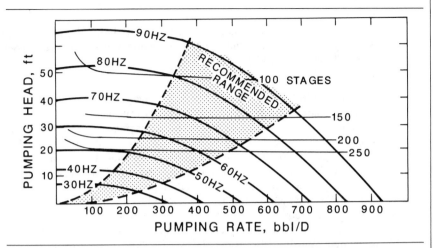

Figure E5.6c One-stage performance and pumping requirements with different stage assemblies (pump type B-11W).

characteristics with variable speed are given in figure 5.13. The following is a step-by-step procedure for sizing the pump.

Step 1
Prepare a table of $p_{\text{discharge}}$ versus production rate. The considered rates are the ones obtained with $p_{wf} = 500$ psia at various depletion stages. The discharge pressure is obtained from the gradient curves using $p_{wh} = 200$ psia and GLR = 200 scf/STB. The results are listed in table E5.6b and plotted in figure E5.6a. The stock-tank oil rate is converted to the pump suction condition by $q_p = q_o B_o$, where $B_o = 1.2$ bbl/STB at 500 psia and well temperature. The corrected rate is also listed in table E5.6b. A constant pump suction pressure (500 psia) governed by the automatic control implies that the pump differential pressure is

$$\Delta p_{\text{pump}} = p_{\text{discharge}} - 500.$$

Using equation (5.7), the differential pressure determines the required pump head

$$\Delta h_{\text{pump}} = \Delta p_{\text{pump}}/(0.433 \times 0.8).$$

Table E5.6c Operating Conditions for a 200-Stage Pump

N_p (bbl)	q_o (STB/D)	q_p (bbl/D)	f (Hz)	P (HP)	E (%)
0	468	561.6	74	46	25
100,000	284	340.8	60	24	48
200,000	196	235.2	58	20	40

EXAMPLE 5.6 continued

Step 2

Four assemblies of pump stages are considered: 100, 150, 200, and 250 stages. Relating the required pumping head to the number of stages in each assembly, the required pumping head per stage is

$\Delta h_{stage} = \Delta h_{pump}/$number of stages.

Recalling table 5.6b, the required pumping head, and thus the required head per stage, is related to a series of rates. This is translated to a family of curves of pumping rate versus required pumping head per stage for the four considered pump assemblies. These curves can be plotted together with the pump characteristic curve in figure E5.6c. The result is a plot that combines the available pumping head per stage versus rate (pump characteristic curve) with the required pumping head per stage versus rate. Each intersection point between the curves indicates a condition where the rate and head developed by a single pumping stage equals the rate and head required to maintain 500 psia suction pressure. Note that the rate of the required head curve reflects the inflow performance of the well, as it is calculated from the IPRs using 500 psia wellbore flowing pressure. As reservoir depletion proceeds, the IPR deteriorates and the rate declines, the speed of the pump should vary accordingly. It is possible to select a pump assembly that will cover the widest range of rate decline without exceeding the pump operation range. From figure E5.6c, a 100-stage pump can operate initially with high frequency and cover the range from 561 to 340 bbl/D. Below 340 bbl/D, further rate adjustment is impossible and the pump has to be replaced by a pump with more stages (i.e., 200 stages). Another possibility is to start with a 150-stage pump, which can be used from an initial rate of 561 bbl/D to 270 bbl/D and then be replaced by a 200-stage pump. A 200-stage pump operates at its upper allowable limit pumping 561 bbl/D but otherwise covers the widest range.

Frequency variation of the selected pump can be read directly from figure E5.6c. The corresponding variations in pump efficiency and power requirement are obtained by direct reading from figure E5.6b. For the case of a 200-stage pump the values are listed in table E5.6c. The table indicates that the well will produce 200,000 STB before it is necessary to change the pump.

Similar to all other dynamic-displacement pumps, the jet pump has a characteristic curve that expresses the relationship between production rate, power-fluid rate, power-fluid pressure, discharge pressure, and pump efficiency. Characteristic curves are given in manufacturers' catalogs. A universal characteristic curve, generalized for various nozzle/throat geometries, has been prepared and presented by Petrie, Wilson, and Smart (1983). The curve and its application for pump sizing are beyond the scope of this book.

5.3   **GAS LIFT.** In section 5.1 it was mentioned that gas-lift production is achieved by continuous injection of gas at the bottom of the production string. The injected gas is mixed with produced fluid, decreases the flowing gradient in the production string, and thus lowers the bottomhole flowing pressure.

Figure 5.18 is a typical layout of a well and the surface facilities in a field producing by continuous gas lift. It shows gas-compression and gas-distribution

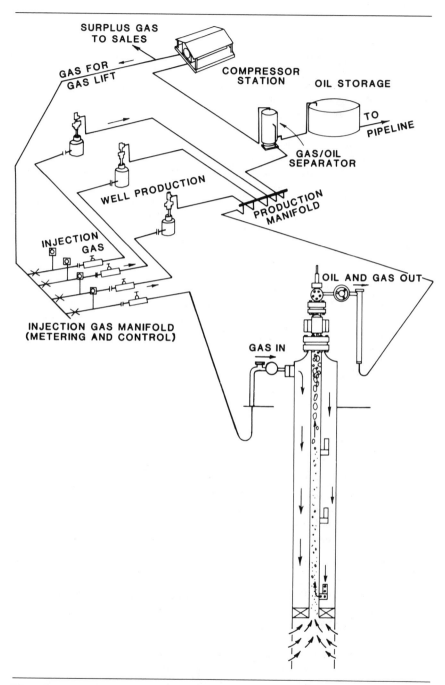

Figure 5.18 A gas-lift system. Courtesy American Petroleum Institute.

facilities at the surface and a typical injection arrangement at the bottom of the well. Similar gas-lift installations with fixed central-compression facilities have been used for oil production since the early 1920s. Chapter 1 in volume 77 of the *Transactions of the American Institute of Mining and Metallurgical Engineers* (AIME) is dedicated entirely to the description of gas-lift installations operated at the end of the 1920s in oil fields in Texas, Gulf coast region, Oklahoma, Kansas, and California. Other publications in the same period (Lake 1927) established the basic engineering considerations that are presently used, with certain improvements, to design modern gas-lift systems. The basic objective of gas-lift design, as stated by McWilliams in the discussion of Lake's paper, is to "equip our wells in such a manner as to compress a minimum amount of gas to produce a maximum amount of oil." Lake (1927) noted that oil production by gas lift can be controlled by changing gas volumes, injection depth, wellhead pressure, and tubing size.

The effect of gas injection on production rate is best illustrated by the pressure–depth–rate diagram in figure 5.19. The diagram referred to as a gas-lift diagram, relates IPR of the well, gas-injection depth, gas-injection rate, surface-injection pressure, and production rate. It is a snapshot of steady-state conditions established in the well after it has been unloaded and inflow has been stabilized.

The diagram in figure 5.19 is relevant to conventional gas-lift arrangements where gas is compressed into the casing at the surface and flows from the annulus into the tubing through a single gas-injection valve close to the bottom of the well. The conventional injection valve is merely an orifice to restrict and control the passage of gas from the casing to tubing. As the diagram indicates, wellbore flowing pressure is determined by the pressure traverse in the tubing above and below the injection point. Assuming linear pressure traverse below and above the injection point, the wellbore flowing pressure can be expressed as

$$p_{wf} = p_{wh} + G_{av}D_{ov} + G_{bv}(D_f - D_{ov}), \tag{5.16}$$

where

D_{ov} = depth of injection valve (ft),
D_f = depth of formation, midperforation, (ft),
G_{av} = average pressure gradient above injection point, a function of the gas rate injected (psi/ft),
G_{bv} = average pressure gradient of flowing formation fluid below the point of injection (psi/ft).

Two parameters in equation (5.16)—the injection depth and the flowing pressure gradient above the injection point—may be varied independently by the designer in a given well. The ability to control the bottomhole flowing pressure and production rate in a gas-lift well thus amounts to the ability to control the depth of injection and the flowing pressure gradient.

Though a deep injection point implies efficient gas lift, the injection point may be selected at any depth up to a maximum determined, primarily, by the maximum possible surface-injection pressure. For a given surface-injection pressure, there is a depth where the casing pressure equals flowing tubing pressure. This point is referred to as the *pressure balance point*. To account for pressure drop across the

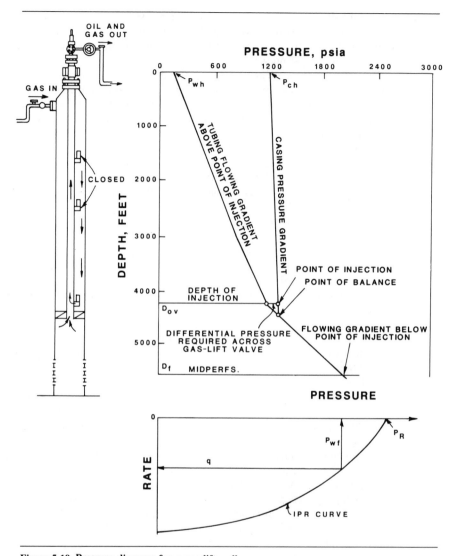

Figure 5.19 Pressure diagram for a gas-lift well.

injection valve it is located a short distance above the balance point, so that the pressure drop across the valve plus the casing pressure are equal to the tubing pressure at that depth. The size of the orifice in the injection valve is selected to give a 50- to 200 psi pressure drop.

The second independent variable in the diagram, the flowing gradient in the tubing, is controlled by the gas-injection rate. Increasing injection rate increases the gas–liquid ratio in the tubing, and up to a certain limit, decreases the flowing gradient. Beyond this limit, the flowing pressure gradient is increased by larger gas–liquid ratios.

Expressing the interrelations between the variables governing gas-lift production as a gas-lift diagram is essential to all methods used to design and control gas-lift performance. Whether displayed graphically, or expressed as a set of equations, the following elements are the essence of gas-lift engineering:

1. reservoir inflow performance (IPR)
2. approximate flowing gradient in the production tubing below the injection point
3. surface-gas-injection pressure
4. gas gradient in the casing
5. amount of injected gas
6. approximate flowing gradient in the production tubing above the injection point.

A procedure to construct a gas-lift diagram is demonstrated in examples 5.7 and 5.8, following a presentation of certain considerations and simplifying assumptions used in the procedure.

Surface-injection pressure depends on the gas compressor rating. It is usually in the range of 700–1100 psia; together with injection rate, it determines the pressure traverse in the casing/tubing annulus. Unless the gas rate is very high, or the casing/tubing annulus is small, gas density governs the pressure gradient in the annulus.

The pressure traverse can be calculated using conventional pipe flow calculations where the annular cross section area is translated to an apparent (effective) radial pipe cross section. Annular restrictions due to external upset tubing connections or tubing couplings (collars) can be practically ignored in the calculations. For quick design calculations, the friction component is usually ignored and the gas pressure gradient in the casing is approximated by the weight of a static gas column. For further simplification the gradient is assumed constant, giving a linear pressure traverse. The surface and downhole pressures can be related by a simple equation suggested by Gilbert (1954):

$$p_{downhole} = p_{surface}(1 + H/40,000), \tag{5.17}$$

where

p = casing/tubing annulus pressure (psia),
H = the distance from the surface to the gas-lift valve (ft).

If the injection point is unspecified, the casing pressure traverse may be extended until it intersects the pressure gradient in the tubing below the injection point, thereby establishing the pressure balance point. The flowing gradient below the injection point can be calculated from multiphase flow correlations or estimated from gradient curves, if available, for flow of the given reservoir fluid at the particular rate assumed in the diagram. Similarly, the flowing gradient above the injection point can be calculated from correlations or estimated from a gradient curve using the gas–liquid ratio in a mixture of reservoir fluid plus the injection gas. Example 5.7 illustrates the first part of the procedure for constructing a gas-lift diagram where production rate by gas lift is related to injectiond depth.

EXAMPLE 5.7 ESTIMATING WELLBORE FLOWING PRESSURE AND CONTINUOUS PRODUCTION RATE WITH A GIVEN INJECTION DEPTH

A gas-lift study is performed for the wells of the Carinia oil field, which produces from the Namorado sandstone formation in the Campus Basin. An appraisal well S-5 is representative of the wells in the field for gas-lift design purposes. The relevant well data are given in table E5.7a. Estimate the continuous production rate from a single well when injecting gas at 900 psia surface pressure and the injection valve is just above the perforations. Calculate the injection depth required to produce the well at a rate of 200 STB/D. The estimated pressure drop in the gas-injection valve, Δp_v, is 100 psi. For design purposes, gas pressure in the annulus is represented by a straight line of equation (5.17) from the surface to 8000 ft.

SOLUTION

The tasks in this example are concerned with pressure conditions in the annulus and in the tubing below the gas-injection point. When injecting at 8000 ft, the flowing bottomhole pressure equals approximately the flowing pressure in the tubing at the injection point. It is, therefore, related to the annulus pressure by

$$p_{wf} = p_{annulus} - \Delta p_{valve},$$

which can be further expressed in terms of surface-injection pressure and pressure of gas column, calculating

$$p_{wf} = 900 \left(1 + \frac{8000}{40000} \right) - 100$$

$$= 980 \, \text{psia}.$$

The production rate is then calculated from the IPR as

$$q = 0.2(p_R - p_{wf})$$

EXAMPLE 5.7 continued

Table 5.7a Well Data for an S-5 Appraisal Well

Formation	Namorado
Formation pressure (at 8000 ft)	2650 psia
Midperforations	8000 ft
Wellhead pressure	200 psia
Tubing	8000 ft × 3.5 in.
Formation gas–liquid ratio	600 scf/STB
Water fraction	0%
Well IPR	$q = 0.2(2650 - p_{wf})$

$$= 0.2(2650 - 980)$$

$$= 334\,\text{STB/D}.$$

To produce the well at a rate of 200 STB/D the required bottomhole pressure, calculated from the IPR, is

$$p_{wf} = 2650 - 200/0.2$$

$$= 1650\,\text{psia}.$$

Expressing the tubing pressure at the injection point in terms of p_{wf} and tubing flowing gradient, and the annulus pressure in terms of annulus gas pressure gives

$$900(1 + D_{ov}/40{,}000) - 100$$

$$= 1650 - 0.39(8000 - D_{ov}), \text{ where } G_{bv} = 0.39 \text{ psi/ft}.$$

Solving for D_{ov}, the injection depth is

$$D_{ov} = \frac{900 - 100 + 0.39 \times 8000 - 1650}{0.3675} = 6449\,\text{ft}.$$

The tubing pressure at the injection point is then

$$1650 - 0.39(8000 - 6449) = 1045\,\text{psia}$$

It is important to realize that pressure conditions in the annulus and in the tubing below the injection point are not sufficient to confirm the feasibility of gas-lift production. It is also necessary to verify the conditions in the tubing above the injection point, as shown in example 5.8.

The production rate calculated in example 5.7 was based only on the flow conditions at and below the injection point. It is obvious, however, that to sustain the calculated production rate it is necessary to maintain a particular pressure

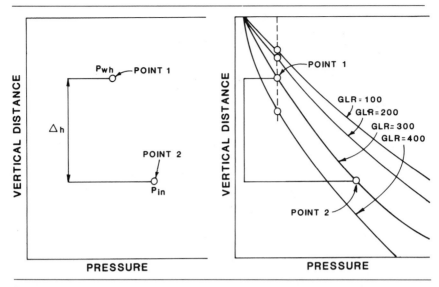

Figure 5.20 Matching of pressure conditions above the injection point to a gradient curve.

traverse above the injection point. This pressure traverse corresponds to a particular gradient curve that matches two points on the pressure traverse: the wellhead pressure and the tubing pressure at the injection depth. Figure 5.20 illustrates a quick manual procedure for matching pressure conditions in the tubing above the injection point to a gradient curve. The matched gradient curve determines the required gas–oil ratio in the tubing. Knowing the reservoir GOR and the required tubing GOR allows calculation of the gas needed for injection. Example 5.8 illustrates the matching procedure to identify a gradient curve and the calculation of the required gas-injection rate. In fact, matching the gradient curve in example 5.8 completes the procedure for constructing the gas-lift diagram, started in example 5.7.

EXAMPLE 5.8 GAS-INJECTION RATE TO MAINTAIN A PARTICULAR PRODUCTION RATE

Complete the pressure diagram for the S-5 well (example 5.7) and determine the amount of injected gas needed to produce the well at a rate of 200 STB/D.

Estimate the per-well power requirement for compression with a compressor suction pressure of 65 psia. A quick estimation of compression power requirements can be obtained from the relation

$$P = 2.23 \times 10^{-4} q_g [(p_2/p_1)^{0.2} - 1],$$

where

EXAMPLE 5.8 continued

P = power (HP),
q_g = gas rate (scf/D),
p_1 = compressor inlet pressure (psia),
p_2 = compressor output pressure (psia).

SOLUTION

The production conditions calculated in example 5.7 determine a particular pressure drop in the tubing between the gas injection point and the wellhead. The pressure drop implies a particular gradient curve with a particular gas–liquid ratio. The gradient curve and the corresponding gas–liquid ratio can be identified by matching a gradient curve to the two known pressure points in the tubing:

1. wellhead $h = 0$, $p = 200$ psia
2. injection point $h = 6449$ ft, $p = 1045$ psia

The gradient curve of GLR = 1000 scf/STB matches the two points. The injection gas–liquid ratio is then calculated as the difference between the obtained flowing GLR and the formation GLR, that is, $1000 - 600 = 400$ scf/STB. The gas injection rate q_g is then

$$q_g = (1000 - 600)q_o$$

$$= 400(200)$$

$$= 80 \times 10^3 \, \text{scf/D}.$$

The required compressor power per well is estimated as

$$P = 2.23 \times 10^{-4}(80 \times 10^3)[(900/65)^{0.2} - 1]$$

$$= 12.34 \, \text{HP}.$$

The state of equilibrium described by the gas-lift diagram is not a stable one. If, for any reason, the pressure in the tubing across the valve drops momentarily, more gas will be injected into the tubing, causing the tubing pressure to drop even further. It may be stabilized, however, by controlling the surface injection rate. Constant surface injection rate implies a drop of casing pressure if injection rate across the gas injection valve increases. This, in turn, tends to reduce pressure drop across the valve and thus decreases injection rate. Another control capability is included in certain types of injection valve that automatically reduce injection rate in response to tubing pressure drop.

The gas-lift diagram can be used to study the functional relationship between variables in design and operation of a gas-lift system. For example, in figure 5.21 it is used to investigate the possibility of increasing production by increasing the

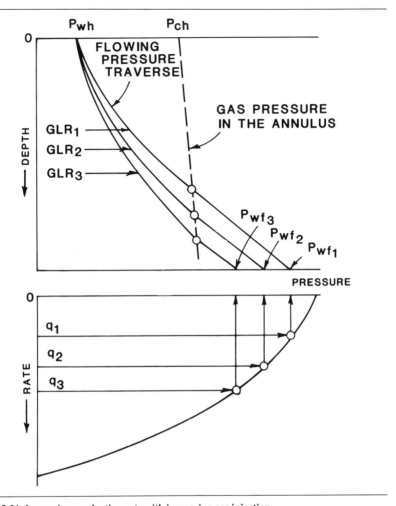

Figure 5.21 Increasing production rate with increasing gas injection.

gas-injection rate. As demonstrated in the figure, wellbore flowing pressure drops and production rate increases as more gas is injected. It illustrates also that a higher gas-injection rate allows injection at a deeper point without increasing injection pressure or changing the pressure traverse in the annulus.

Figure 5.22 investigates the change in injection depth and gas-injection rate needed to maintain a constant production rate as the reservoir depletes and the IPR deteriorates. The figure explains the advantage of controlling both the injection depth and the amount of injected gas. Controlling these two factors by proper selection and spacing of continuous gas-life valves, production rate can be adjusted as needed during the life of a well.

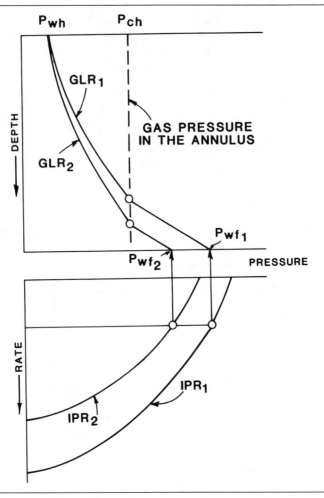

Figure 5.22 Control of production rate during reservoir depletion.

The basic assumption applied in figures 5.21 and 5.22 is that a higher gas–liquid ratio in the tubing results in a smaller pressure gradient. This assumption is correct only up to a limiting GLR. From the set of gradient curves in Appendix A, it can be seen that the pressure gradient decreases with increasing GLR, to a certain limit. Increasing GLR above this limit causes an increase in gradient. The minimum gradient curve signifies minimum flowing bottomhole pressure and maximum production rate. Increasing gas-injection rate, therefore, may increase the production rate to a maximum level beyond which increasing gas rate results in decreasing production rate. Poettmann and Carpenter (1952) and Bertuzzi et al. (1953) discussed this behavior and its application to the design of efficient gas-lift systems. Bertuzzi et al. translated this behavior to a curve relating injection rate to production rate. The curve, referred to as the gas-lift performance curve, has become the standard expression of gas-lift deliverability.

A step-by-step procedure to construct the gas-lift performance curve is illustrated in figure 5.23. Figure 5.23(a) illustrates the general trends observed in gradient curves as GLR varies. This trend implies that at a given rate and constant wellhead pressure, the tubing intake pressure varies with GLR. A plot of tubing intake pressure, given in figure 5.23(b), indicates that for each flow rate in a given tubing size there is a particular GLR that yields minimum tubing intake pressure. We refer to this GLR as *favorable GLR*. A plot of favorable GLR versus the corresponding rates in a given tubing size is given in figure 5.23(c). Favorable GLR decreases as oil rate increases. The favorable GLR is seldom equal to reservoir GLR, and it may be achieved only by adding gas to the tubing. The amount of gas required to achieve a favorable GLR is indicated also in figure 5.23(c).

Figure 5.23(d) is a plot of the locus of all minimum tubing intake pressures versus their corresponding flow rates. As mentioned before, a minimum tubing intake pressure at a given flow rate is obtained with the favorable GLR. The locus line divides the plane of the graph into two regions. The region below the line is where intake pressure is less than the minimum pressure required to sustain flow, and thus flow in the tubing cannot exist. No matter how much gas is injected, the tubing intake pressure cannot sink below the minimum indicated by this line. The region above the line is where all possible flow situations in the tubing occur, with or without gas injection. In fact, the intersection between the IPR of the well and the locus of the minimum intake pressures (fig. 5.23[d]) gives the point of maximum liquid rate possible from the particular well. Figure 5.23(e) illustrates the significance of this intersection point in terms of a tubing performance curve. It shows that tubing performance curves for any GLR higher or lower than the preferable GLR will intersect the IPR at a lower liquid rate.

For the particular well plotted figure 5.23(d), formation GLR is lower than the favorable ratio, and therefore injection of gas increases the production. On the other hand, in wells where formation GLR is higher than the favorable GLR there is no gain in production by gas lift.

Oil rate versus favorable GLR is shown in figure 5.23(f). Calculating the injection GLR as the difference between the favorable and formation GLRs and further computing the corresponding injection rate yields the plot of the gas-lift performance curve you will see in figure 5.25. Example 5.9 illustrates the procedure to construct the gas-lift performance curve and to determine maximum liquid rate possible by gas lift.

The procedure in example 5.9 is valid for reservoir conditions existing at a particular stage of depletion. Similar calculations can be made for any stage of depletion later in the life of the well. Figure 5.24 adds the time dimension and illustrates the decline of the maximum rate at each stage of depletion. As shown in figure 5.24(a), the favorable GLR for a given liquid rate is independent of reservoir behavior. Therefore, in spite of depletion, the locus of favorable GLRs in figure 5.24(b) does not change. On the other hand, IPRs shown in figure 5.24(b) deteriorate with depletion and therefore intersect the locus at progressively decreasing rates. The result is a decreasing maximum liquid rate, which is plotted

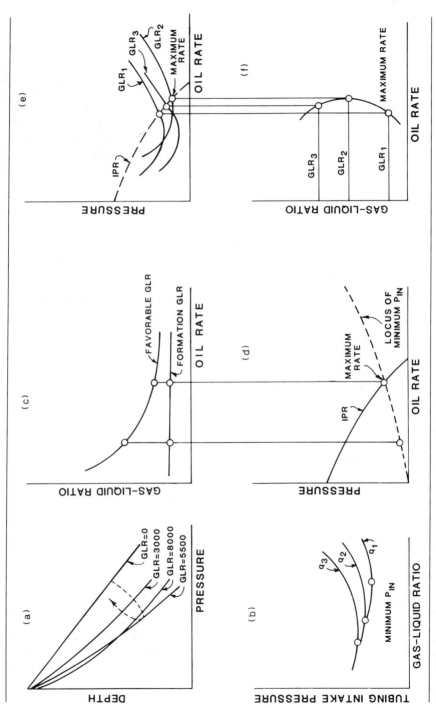

Figure 5.23 A step-by-step procedure to construct the gas-lift performance curve.

541

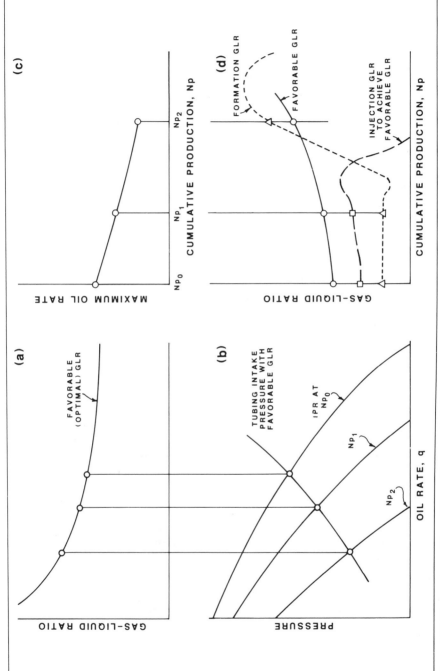

Figure 5.24 Changes in gas-lift conditions with reservoir depletion.

versus cumulative production in figure 5.24(c). The injection rate required to maintain maximum liquid rate as the reservoir depletes is the difference between the favorable GLR and formation GLR. Summarizing the time behavior of a gas-lift system, figure 5.24(d) plots the changes of reservoir GLR, favorable GLR, and gas injection GLR needed to produce the maximum liquid rate, versus cumulative production at each stage in the well's life. Figure 5.24(d) indicates that, for solution gas-drive reservoirs, the needed gas-injection GLR increases at early stages but drops rapidly as reservoir GLR increases. Example 5.10 illustrates the procedure to determine depletion effect on gas-lift performance.

EXAMPLE 5.9 CALCULATING MAXIMUM POSSIBLE PRODUCTION RATE BY GAS LIFT

Gas lift is one of the artificial lift options considered for the Lagoa Seca field. Data for a typical well in the field are listed in table E5.9a.

Two cases of gas-lift production are investigated:

Case 1: An unlimited amount of injection gas is available to produce the well at or near its maximum production rate.

Case 2: A limited amount of injection gas, 180 Mscf/D, is allocated to each well.

Investigate the performance of a well producing under each case.

SOLUTION

Case 1
The gas–liquid ratios that yield minimum pressure loss in $2\frac{7}{8}$-in. tubing (favorable GLR) are listed in table E5.9b and plotted versus rate in figure E5.9. With 65-psia wellhead pressure the minimum tubing intake pressure at 5000 ft is determined from the favorable gradient curve and listed also in table E5.9b. Plotting p_{in} from table E5.9b versus q in figure E5.9 gives the locus of minimum intake pressures. The straight-line IPR of the well is also plotted in figure E5.9. The intersection of IPR with the locus of $(p_{in})_{min}$ gives maximum flow rate from this well by means of gas lift. Reading from the graph, maximum rate is $q_{max} = 260$ STB/D. The favorable GLR corresponding to this maximum rate is indicated on figure E5.9: GLR = 3750 scf/STB. The required injection rate is calculated as

$$(q_g)_{inj} = (GLR - R_s)q$$

$$= (3750 - 400)260$$

$$= 871 \times 10^3 \text{ scf/D}$$

$$= 871 \text{ Mscf/D}$$

EXAMPLE 5.9 continued

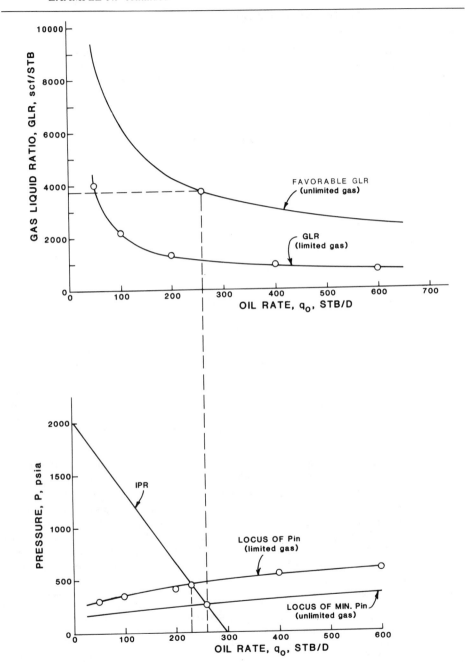

Figure E5.9 Gas-lift performance for a Lagoa Seca well.

EXAMPLE 5.9 continued

Table E5.9a Well Data for a Typical Lagoa Seca Well

Reservoir pressure	2000 psia
Wellhead pressure	65 psia
Reservoir solution gas–oil ratio	400 scf/STB
Tubing	2⅞-in. × 5000 ft
IPR	$q = 0.15(2000 - p_{wf})$

Table E5.9b Tubing Intake Pressure with Favorable GLR

q (STB/D)	Favorable GLR (scf/STB)	p_{in} (psia)
50	8800	180
100	6300	210
200	4300	250
400	3250	300
600	2400	380

Table E5.9c Tubing Intake Pressure with Limited Gas-Injection Rate

Rate (STB/D)	Injection GLR (scf/STB)	Total GLR (scf/STB)	p_{in} (psia)
50	3600	4000	280
100	1800	2200	350
200	900	1300	400
400	550	950	550
600	300	700	600

Case 2

The GLRs obtained by injecting 180 Mscf/D in addition to 400 scf/STB of reservoir oil are calculated and listed in table E5.9c. Given 65 psia wellhead pressure, the tubing intake pressure with a flowing GLR is obtained from the gradient curves and listed versus rate in table E5.9c. The p_{in} values are plotted versus q and form the intake pressure curve in figure E5.9. The intersection of this curve with IPR defines the flowing conditions for 180 Mscf/D gas injection. The intersection is at a rate of 230 STB/D. An interesting observation is that the calculated gas injection rate in case 1 is 3.5 times higher than in case 2, whereas the production rate is only 10% higher.

EXAMPLE 5.10 CHANGES IN GAS LIFT AND GAS-INJECTION REQUIREMENTS WITH RESERVOIR DEPLETION

A gas-lift production system is perhaps the only practical possibility to accelerate production of the Ina field (example 4.11). The first two tasks of a study to evaluate the performance of a gas-lift system are:

EXAMPLE 5.10 continued

1. Determine the maximum possible flow rates with gas lift and the favorable GLR to achieve these rates at each depletion stage.
2. Calculate the amount of gas needed for injection to achieve the maximum production rate.

The study assumes that gas is injected at the bottom of the tubing (8000 ft). All other well and reservoir data are specified in example 4.11.

SOLUTION

The IPR of Ina No. 4 was developed and plotted in figure E4.11. For this study, it is reproduced in figure E5.10a. For a given rate, the minimum possible intake pressure for the tubing is obtained from the favorable GLR line in the gradient curve. The favorable GLRs are listed in table E5.10a and plotted versus rate in figure E5.10b. For a given wellhead pressure, $p_{wh} = 200$ psia, the minimum intake pressure is read from the favorable gradient curves and listed in table E5.10a. The locus of minimum intake pressures is also plotted in figure E5.10a. The intersection points with IPR curves indicate maximum rates with gas lift. These maximum rates are given, versus cumulative production, in table E5.10b. The corresponding favorable GLRs are obtained from figure E5.10b and listed in table E5.10b. The required injection rate to achieve maximum production rate is calculated as

$$q_{inj} = (GLR_{favorable} - GLR_{reservoir})q_o.$$

The calculated results are listed in table E5.10b.

Table E5.10a Minimum Intake Pressure for Ina No. 4

q_o (STB/D)	Favorable GLR (scf/STB)	p_{intake} (psia)
50	8800	450
100	6300	530
200	4300	640
400	3250	760

Table E5.10b Maximum Gas-Lift Rates and the Corresponding Injection Rate

N_p (bbl)	q_{max} (STB/D)	Favorable GLR (scf/STB)	q_{inj} (MMscf/D)
0	460	2900	1.058
100,000	279	3750	0.766
200,000	194	4300	0.524
300,000	118	5750	0.384
400,000	70	7500	0.175
500,000	63	7850	0.337

EXAMPLE 5.10 continued

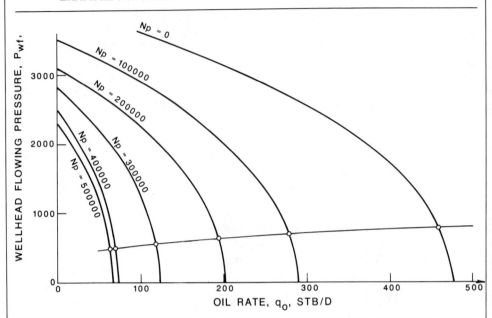

Figure E5.10a Maximum possible gas-lift production for the Ina No. 4 oil well.

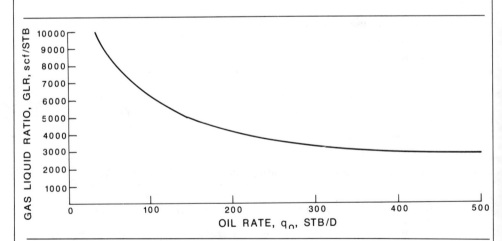

Figure E5.10b Flow rate versus gas–liquid ratio for the tubing of Ina No. 4

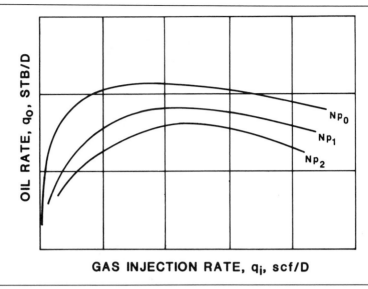

Figure 5.25 Typical oil rate versus gas-injection rate for a gas-lift well at various depletion stages.

Changes in reservoir conditions with depletion imply that the gas-lift characteristic curve also changes. In fact, for each depletion stage there is a different curve given together with a family of performance curves, as illustrated in figure 5.25. For any given stage of depletion, the oil rate curve increases rapidly with increasing GLR at the low GLR range, and then tends to level off before reaching the maximum oil rate. The particular shape of a gas-lift performance curve indicates that, beyond a certain point, substantial increase in gas injection is required to achieve relatively small increases in oil rate. In other words, very little production is gained by increasing gas injection beyond the maximum rate point.

The high cost of the gas compression and separation equipment needed to separate large gas quantities suggests that the maximum oil rate is not necessarily the most economical one (Simmons 1972; Redden et al. 1974). Translating produced oil and injected gas into monetary quantities using produced oil (and gas) revenues and the cost of gas injection, the operator may express the gas-lift performance curve in terms of revenue versus expenses, and obtain the curve illustrated in figure 5.26. The curve is continuous and smooth. It assumes gradual increase of injection cost. Such an assumption is only valid when a compression system has the capacity to increase injection with only incremental increases in cost. If increasing injection rate is achieved by upgrading the capacity of an existing compression system, the upgrading cost is reflected as a discontinuity and sometimes even a change of trend in the curve.

Various criteria have been proposed for using cost–revenue analysis to select the "optimal" operating conditions of a gas-lift system. They generally refer to one of two cases:

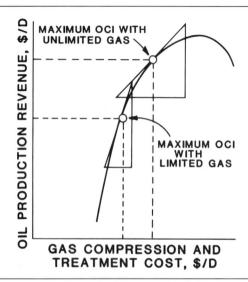

Figure 5.26 Production revenue versus gas-injection expenses in a gas-lift well. Reprinted by permission of the SPE-AIME from Redden et al. 1974, fig. 2. © 1974 SPE-AIME.

1. an individual well or field with an unlimited supply of injection gas
2. a group of wells with limited gas supply to be distributed among individual wells

For the case of unlimited gas supply Simmons (1972) and Redden et al. (1974) suggest that for a given depletion stage the most profitable rate occurs at a unit slope on the curve in figure 5.26. This point represents the situation when the incremental revenue gain from increasing oil rate is equal to the incremental increase in gas-injection expenses. This point is referred to as *maximum daily operating cash income* (maximum OCI). Up to this point, increasing gas injection yields a gain in profit. At the maximum OCI, incremental gain in profit is zero. Beyond this point the incremental gain becomes negative and the total profit starts to diminish. Figure 5.26 illustrates the maximum OCI at a particular stage of depletion. Similar procedures can calculate the maximum OCI for a series of future depletion stages. Maintaining maximum OCI during the life of a field requires a continuous increase in injection rate and progressively less total profit. This is not necessarily the most economical production schedule. Only a detailed economic analysis, including cost, revenue, and initial investment, can calculate a gas injection schedule that maximizes the operator's economic returns.

Often a gas-lift study is carried out when a compression system of given capacity is already installed. In such cases the designer needs to prepare a program for distributing the available gas among individual wells. In some gas-lift systems the available compressed gas is less than the rate needed to produce all the wells at their most economical rates. A new criterion should therefore be established to determine the most profitable gas allocation.

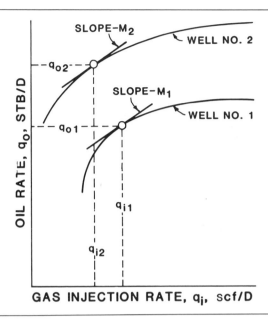

Figure 5.27 Gas allocation between wells for maximum production with limited gas-injection rate. Reprinted by permission of the SPE-AIME from Clegg 1982, fig. 2. © 1982 SPE-AIME.

The simplest approach for allocating available gas in such cases is to maximize the total daily oil rate achievable from the field with the available gas injection rate. Kleyweg et al. (1983) present a program for optimizing the gas-lift system in the Claymore field, summarizing their allocation approach by "*Once performance curves have been obtained for each well on the platform gas-lift optimization can be achieved. Two methods are possible:*

1. Analytical method, where each curve is represented by a polynomial, and then applying a linear-programming technique to calculate true optimised distribution of the available lift-gas.
2. Step-by-step method, where all wells are supplied with enough gas to kick them off and from then on the performance curves are scanned to find the curve with the maximum slope. The gas-lift rate to the corresponding well is then increased by one step and so on until all the available gas is distributed."

Figure 5.27 illustrates the application of the maximum rate approach for the simple case of a two-well system. Injection gas is plotted against produced oil rate for each individual well. A procedure formulated by Clegg (1982) suggests that maximum total production from the two wells is the sum of the rates q_{o1} and q_{o2}, where the two performance curves have equal slope $m_1 = m_2$ and the total available injection gas equals $q_{i1} + q_{i2}$. For fields with only a few wells the procedure in figure 5.27 can be performed manually by trial and error. Large fields with many wells may need computerized procedures.

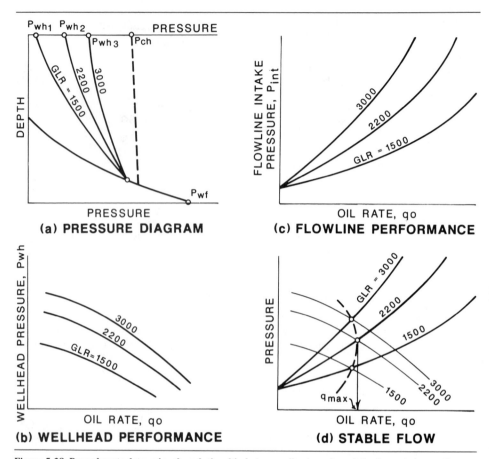

Figure 5.28 Procedure to determine the relationship between oil rate and gas-injection rate in a well affected by flowline performance.

All the discussions so far assume constant wellhead pressure. This assumption is usually valid when the wells are near the separator and producing against a constant separator pressure. In cases when the wells are away from the separator, wellhead pressure varies due to pressure loss along the flowline. The procedure to establish the relationship of oil rate to gas-injection rate in such cases is illustrated schematically in figure 5.28.

The gas-lift diagram in figure 5.28(a) illustrates GLR changes corresponding to changes in wellhead pressure p_{wh} when oil rate and injection point are held constant. The relationship p_{wh} versus GLR can be similarly developed with other rates; the result is illustrated in figures 5.28(b). The flowline performance curve is plotted in figure 5.28(c) as flowline intake pressure p_{in} versus flow rate. Recognizing that flowline intake pressure and wellhead pressure are essentially the same, figures 5.28(b) and (c) may be combined as in figure 5.28(d), where the intersection points of the curves with similar GLRs indicate stabilized flow conditions for the well–flowline system.

The procedure in figure 5.28 resembles a procedure presented in chapter 1 for naturally flowing wells. The only difference is the controllable gas–liquid ratio in gas-lift wells. In fact, the entire treatment of continuous gas lift is an extension of techniques and procedures developed earlier for naturally flowing wells. Continous gas injection is a major, but not the only aspect of gas-lift technology. A great deal of effort is required to design efficient startup and unloading of wells. Techniques for unloading gas-lift wells are not covered in this book.

The analysis, thus far, has concentrated on calculating the maximum possible oil rate by a continuous gas-lift method and the corresponding gas injection quantities. This information is important because it allows the determination of production limits, and thus the viability of gas lift as a potential artificial lift method in a given field. In the following, an extension is discussed of the analysis needed to relate the main parameters controlling the operation of a gas-lift well to its performance. This extension will allow a detailed design of gas-lift wells. It will also prepare the background for applying computerized procedures for gas-lift design and analysis.

The base case for the following discussion is where gas is injected through the annulus and the well produces through the tubing, as illustrated in figure 5.29. The discussion, however, is valid also for the arrangement where the gas is injected through the tubing and the production occurs through the annulus.

The flow equilibrium concept introduced in section 1.7 for naturally flowing wells is also valid, with few modifications, for continuous gas-lift wells. Figure 5.29 summarizes the idea and the application of this concept for gas lift.

Figure 5.29a indicates that fluids enter the production tubing from two separate flow paths. One path is flowing reservoir oil and gas from the perforations upwards, and another path discharges compressed gas from the annulus into the tubing through a gas injection valve. Thus, a node in the tubing in front of the entry point is, in fact, a join point of three flow paths: the reservoir, the discharged gas, and the tubing. The corresponding pressure versus rate relationships for the three paths are the IPR expressing reservoir inflow, the TPR expressing flow through the tubing correspondingly, and the Discharge Performance Relationship (DPR) expressing the discharge through the gas-lift valve.

The IPR and TPR have been extensively discussed in chapter 1. The DPR will be discussed later in this section. At this point it is sufficient to note that the DPR is the relationship between the flow rate of the injection gas discharged into the tubing, q_{ginj}, and the gas stream pressure, p_{vt}, downstream of the discharge point.

Two basic fluid mechanics principles can be stated for the considered node: the continuity of flow and the conservation of mass. The continuity principle implies that the flowing pressure in the node is equal in all the joining streams. The conservation of mass principle, when expressed in terms of flow volume, implies that the algebraic sum of the oil flow rates and the algebraic sum of the gas flow rates entering and leaving the node are zero. Mathematically, these conditions give three equations which are sufficient to solve for the oil production rate, the gas injection rate, and the gas injection pressure. These equations are referred to as *flow equilibrium equations*.

Substituting the IPR, TPR, and DPR into the three equilibrium equations and solving simultaneously for the production rate, injection rate, and injection pressure

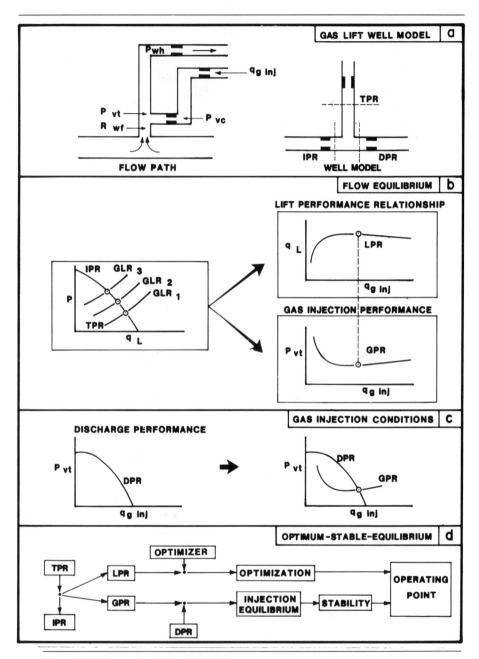

Figure 5.29 Flow analysis in gas-lift wells.

of interest is a rather straightforward mathematical exercise (three equations with three unknowns). Graphically, the three equations are solved in two steps. First, two equations are solved simultaneously assuming one unknown of the three is a parameter. The result is a curve representing the locus of all the solution points satisfying the first two equations. Then, the obtained locus is solved simultaneously with the third equation giving the particular solution that satisfies all three equations.

Figure 5.29b illustrates the first step of the solution where the IPR and the TPR are solved graphically assuming a variety of gas injection rates (variety of GLRs in the tubing). The obtained result is in the form of either one of two loci. The first one is called the Lift Performance Relationship (LPR), and the second one is the Gas-lift Performance Relationship (GPR).

The LPR curve expresses the relationship between the liquid production rate, q_L, and the gas injection rate, q_{ginj}. The curve was introduced earlier in this section in connection with gas-lift optimization analysis. The GPR, on the other hand, expresses the relationship between the gas injection rate and the pressure in the tubing in front of the gas injection valve, p_{vt}. The GPR is introduced here for the first time (in this text), and it will be used for sizing a downhole gas injection orifice and to determine the well's operation conditions.

Note the typical shapes of the LPR and the GPR. For the LPR, with increasing gas injection rate, the liquid rate increases rapidly in the beginning and then flattens gradually until it reaches a peak, beyond which the liquid rate starts decreasing gradually. Correspondingly, the pressure of the GPR decreases rapidly and then flattens gradually until a minimum is reached. Beyond it, the pressure starts increasing gradually.

The trend of the production rate versus gas injection rate exhibited by the LPR made the curve a key instrument in gas-lift optimization analysis since it was originally observed by Bertuzzi et al., (1953). Unfortunately, the other role of the LPR and GPR to provide an input to the second stage of the solution of equilibrium equations was never fully recognized and thoroughly explored.

To complete the process of solving the equilibrium equations, the GPR obtained in the first stage is solved together with the DPR as illustrated in figure 5.29c. This determines the particular gas injection rate, and the particular pressure in the tubing in front of the gas injection orifice that satisfy all the equilibrium conditions. The corresponding liquid production rate can be obtained from the IPR of LPR.

The significance of completing the solution of the three equilibrium equations is indicated in figure 5.29d. The explanation of this figure requires further discussion.

By definition, the DPR is the relationship between the gas flow rate and the downstream pressure in an orifice that operates with a constant upstream pressure, p_{vc}. The characteristics of the DPR are shown in figure 5.30. Figure 5.30a illustrates the effect of annulus pressure, p_{vc}, on the DPR of a given orifice. Figure 5.30b illustrates a situation where three different orifices operating with different upstream pressures inject the same rate with the same downstream pressure. Figure 5.30c illustrates three different orifices operating with a common annulus pressure. Finally, figure 5.30d illustrates the DPR of a widely used valve with a built-in throttling mechanism that reduces the orifice as flow rate increases. This is in contrast to the conventional orifice valve which is essentially a fixed size orifice.

Considering the shape of the GPR and the DPR, their simultaneous solution may

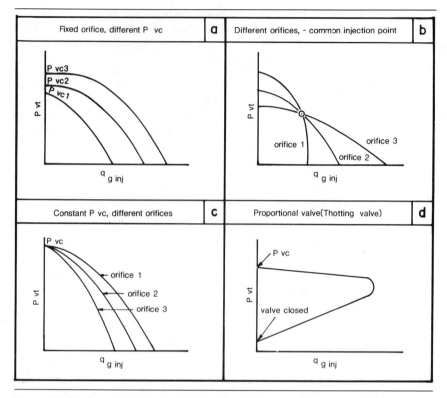

Figure 5.30 Discharge Performance Relationship, DPR.

yield two points. Applying the same reasoning as in the multiple solution case in flowing wells (section 1.7), one of the solutions here represents an unstable state.

As in natural flow, the stability can be determined by checking the relative trend of the upstream and downstream pressure-rate relationships. More specifically for the gas-lift case, it can be determined by checking the relative trend of the DPR (available pressure) and the GPR (required pressure).

Figure 5.31 illustrates a case where a particular injection rate can be achieved by two different orifices. The small orifice operating with a high injection pressure yields stable production, while the larger orifice operating with considerably lower annulus pressure yields unstable flow equilibrium. The reasoning for the instability was discussed in section 1.7 and will not be repeated here. Rather, the consequences of instability will be discussed.

From Figure 5.31 it is obvious that a combination of the size of the downhole orifice, as well as the orifice's upstream pressure, governs the stability of the designed state of operation. As indicated in the figure, a high injection pressure with a small size orifice yields a stable production point that lies to the left-hand side of the GPR.

In many gas-lift wells, operating with a large orifice size and large or unrestricted gas supply, the stable operating point lies to the right-hand side of the peak of the

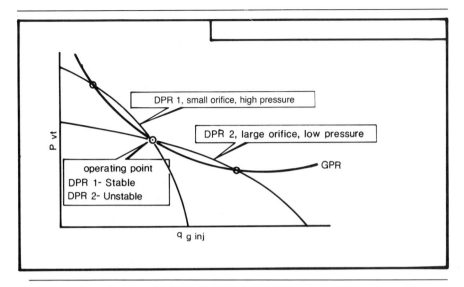

Figure 5.31 Stability analysis of a gas injection point.

LPR curve (Figure 5.29b). Such an operation is very inefficient, as the same amount of oil can be produced with much less gas if the operating point could be stabilized to the left-hand side of the peak.

Truly, operators of wells producing with continuous gas lift are, in certain cases, facing difficulties in regulating and maintaining the production rate or the gas injection rate at a desired level (Kleyweg et al., 1983). In many cases, stable liquid production rates are achieved only by injecting gas at considerably higher rates than originally planned. Otherwise, the production and injection can be stabilized only by replacing the downhole orifice with a smaller one which, in turn, requires higher injection pressure.

Operators are very reluctant to replace a downhole orifice in an attempt to stabilize the production of a gas-lift well. Rather, they are tempted to adjust the surface gas injection choke first. Throttling the injection gas at the inlet to the annulus, however, can lead to another undesirable phenomenon, namely the *annulus heading*. It is a severe pressure and rate oscillation that may occur if the size of the surface orifice is too small in relation to the size of the downhole one.

The reason for the heading phenomenon is the time lag between the discharge from and refill of gas to the annulus. In a steady state flow, the rate of surface injection into the annulus equals the rate of gas discharged from the annulus into the tubing, and the pressure is steady. When a sudden decrease in the tubing pressure promotes an excessive discharge of gas at the downhole orifice, the pressure at the bottom of the annulus will drop. Due to the compressibility of the gas and the large volume of the annulus, there will be a delay in affecting the pressure at the top of the annulus. Only after the pressure at the top of the annulus starts to drop, will the excessive pressure difference across the surface choke increase the gas injection rate.

If the surface orifice is small, the gas supply to the annulus cannot compensate fast enough for the high discharge rate. Thus, the pressure at the bottom of the annulus will continue to drop. Drop of annulus pressure will start to reduce the discharge rate into the tubing. Once again, the surface choke will be late to respond and will continue supplying excessive gas. This in turn will result in a build-up of annulus pressure. Under certain conditions, the described heading cycle will be repeated resulting in periodic alternation of production and injection rates. In extreme situations, the well may even die and flow alternately, similar to the behavior of wells producing with *intermittent gas lift*.

Though this section addresses only steady state aspects of continuous gas-lift production, the heading phenomena was brought up here to emphasize the importance of a proper sizing of the downhole orifice. It strongly supports the conclusion that a proper orifice sizing should account for the stability, as well as for an optimal relationship between production and injection rates. A design process combining these two design considerations is illustrated in figure 5.29d.

Another useful tool for designing continuous gas-lift wells is the *equilibrium curve* illustrated in figure 5.32. It has been used for many years by Shell Oil Company but received wider acceptance only after it was published in the API Gas-Lift Book (API, 1984). The curve displays the relationship between the downhole injection depth and the corresponding pressure downstream of the downhole orifice. It is, in fact, a locus of points obtained by constructing a set of gas-lift diagrams, each for a different production rate. As explained at the beginning of a section, a gas-lift diagram determines the injection depth and the corresponding downhole injection pressure for a considered production rate (Figure 5.32a). In the considered set, all the diagrams and thus all the points of the locus (Figure 5.32b) are for the same well (the same IPR) and are constructed with the same wellhead pressure and for the same gas injection rate.

In addition to the downhole injection pressure, a gas-lift diagram relates the injection depth to a particular production rate and a particular surface injection pressure (Figure 5.32c). Thus, each point on the locus of the injection depth versus injection pressure points corresponds uniquely to a production rate and a surface injection pressure.

The main use of the curve is in designing the start-up and the unloading of gas-lift wells, a transient process beyond the scope of this book. Regarding steady state operations, the curve is very useful as a basis for selecting a continuous injection depth in gas-lift well design.

Though, by definition, the curve is a locus of solutions obtained by preparing a set of gas-lift diagrams, there is a shorter procedure to develop it that does not require the actual construction of a set of gas-lift diagrams. This procedure is illustrated in figure 5.33. It is based on the fact that the sought locus of injection points is related to the locus of solution points obtained by solving a set of IPR curves at various nodes along the tubing, with a set of TPR curves at the corresponding nodes. The special feature about this procedure is that the considered nodes represent the gas injection points. Therefore, the GLR of the TPR curves in figure 5.33 is the sum of the formation GLR and the injection GLR. Each intersection point thus represents the equilibrium conditions at a corresponding gas injection point. As depth is a parameter in the plot of the locus of the equilibrium conditions at the various nodes, it is very easy to transfer the rate versus pressure locus into a depth versus pressure locus, namely the equilibrium curve.

557

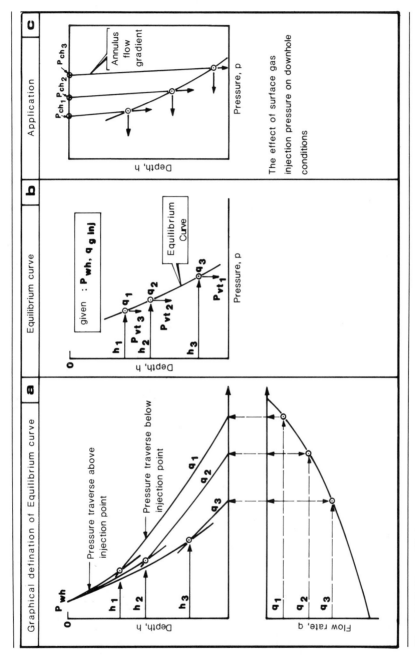

Figure 5.32 The equilibrium curve.

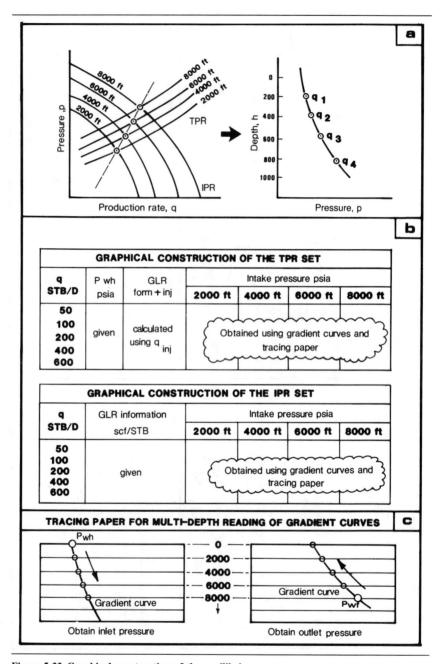

Figure 5.33 Graphical construction of the equilibrium curve.

Using a sheet of tracing paper together with a set of gradient curves can speed up the construction of the equilibrium curve by the described method. A tracing paper marked with the set of horizontal lines representing the various depths under consideration allows multiple reading of pressures along the gradient curve. A step by step procedure is illustrated in figures 5.33b and 5.33c. It consists of the following steps:

TPR
1. Draw on tracing paper a set of parallel horizontal lines spaced according to the depth scale of the available gradient curves.
2. Calculate the GLR above the gas injection point and identify the corresponding gradient curve.
3. Mark the point of the wellhead pressure on the relevant gradient curve. Start, for example with the gradient curve of the lowest rate (50 STB/D).
4. Overlay the tracing paper on the gradient curve such that the zero depth line of the tracing paper intersects the gradient curve at the point marked in step 2.
5. Read from the gradient curves the pressures at the intersection points with the depth curves of the tracing paper. These are the intake pressures at the considered depth. List the intake pressures in the upper table in figure 5.33b.
6. Repeat the same procedure with the gradient curves of other rates (100, 200, 400, 600, STB/D) and complete the upper table in figure 5.33b.
7. Plot the data listed in the upper table in figure 5.33b as a set of TPR curves for various depths.

IPR
1. Draw on tracing paper a set of parallel horizontal lines spaced according to the depth scale of the available gradient curves.
2. Plot the IPR of the well at mid-perforation depth.
3. Determine from the TPR the p_{wf} corresponding to the rate of the lowest rate gradient curve (50 STB/D).
4. Determine the gradient curve with the formation GLR and mark on it the p_{wf} pressure point.
5. Overlay the tracing paper on the gradient curve such that the mid-perforation depth line of the tracing paper intersects the gradient curve at the point marked in step 5.
6. Read the pressures at the points of intersection with the depth lines of the tracing paper and list the data in the lower table in figure 5.33b.
7. Repeat the same procedure with the other rate gradient curves and complete the lower table in figure 5.33b.
8. Plot the data listed in the table as a set of IPR curves.

As explained earlier, the intersection points of the TPRs and the IPRs of the same depth are essentially the pressure and rate of the points of the equilibrium curve. Listing these points and then plotting them as pressure versus depth gives the equilibrium curve.

5.4   SELECTION OF AN ARTIFICIAL-LIFT METHOD. The three primary factors governing selection of artificial-lift methods are:

1. production rate
2. downhole flowing pressure
3. gas–liquid ratio

There are also secondary factors, such as

1. oil viscosity and gravity
2. gas–liquid ratio
3. depth, rate, and wellbore size
4. well deviation angle
5. sand and solids production
6. scales and paraffin deposits
7. corrosive nature of oil and gas
8. completion from offshore platform or subsea completion

Generally, rod pumps are only applicable for relatively low-rate wells, usually less than 600 STB/D. Rates up to 5000 STB/D may be produced by hydraulic pumps. Higher rates can only be produced by turbine pumps or gas lift.

The most pronounced limitation on the range of applicability is downhole flowing pressure. Continuous gas lift cannot lower wellbore flowing pressure below a certain limit, determined by the wellhead pressure and minimum flowing gradient in the tubing. Therefore, gas lift can only be used in wells that produce economically at relatively high wellbore flowing pressures. To emphasize this argument, example 5.11 illustrates a case with a need to lower the bottomhole flowing pressure below the possible range of gas lift.

EXAMPLE 5.11 PERFORMANCE OF A WELL PRODUCING WITH ARTIFICIAL LIFT

The production rate profile and corresponding pressures in the TR-1 well in the Trestakk oil field are given in figure E5.11. What kind of information about the field and the well is obtained by a quick look at the figure?

EXAMPLE 5.11 continued

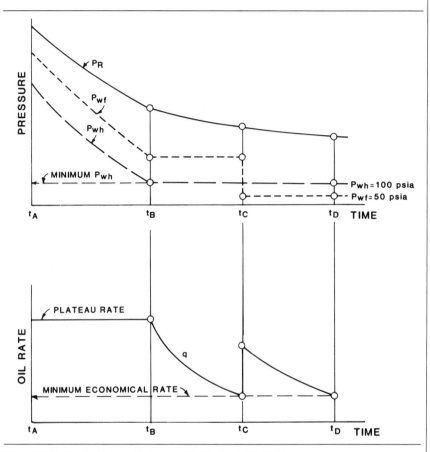

Figure E5.11 **Production profile for a well in the Trestakk oil field.**

SOLUTION

According to the figure, the field produces at a plateau oil rate until time t_B, when declining wellhead pressure p_{wh}, reaches a minimum. From t_B to t_C the field produces at a constant pressure with declining rate. When the rate reaches the minimum economic level, at time t_C, artificial lift is introduced. Artificial lift lowers bottomhole flowing pressure below the wellhead pressure. This can occur only with a downhole pump.

There is usually a wide range of overlap in the rate and GLR conditions acceptable for production by various lift systems. In fact, most wells can produce satisfactorily by one of several lift methods. The actual selection is, therefore, a result of weighing additional considerations such as field location, operational experience, capital and operational expenditures, and mechanical status of the wells. The location of a field—onshore versus offshore—and the spacing of the wells are often the overriding criteria. For example, sucker rod pumping is not usually suitable for offshore installations. Fields with wide well spacing are not good candidates for gas lift or hydraulic pumping, since they require centralized gas compression and power fluid pumping facilities.

Personal preference and the operational experience of the individual or the team selecting the system is an important argument. There is a tendency to select a familiar system. In many cases more suitable systems are rejected simply because the operator has no experience with them.

Cost is an important consideration. The cost of artificial lift consists of initial installation cost and cost of operation. It is difficult to establish a list that ranks installation and operation costs of the various lift systems. Costs can be estimated for a particular field only after sizing the equipment and preparing a general field layout. In general, operational costs are sharply influenced by compressed gas availability and the cost of electrical power.

The mechanical condition of wells is another important consideration. It refers to the following factors:

1. depth of the well
2. wellbore configuration—deviation, casing size, and perforation interval
3. sand and solids production
4. corrosive fluids
5. well temperature
6. buildup of paraffin and scale deposits

Mechanical conditions often impose severe constraints, particularly in wells completed initially for natural flow without foreseeing the need for introducing artificial lift.

To conclude the discussion on selecting a lift system, table 5.3 summarizes several relevant reservoir, well, and operating conditions and lists their compatibility with different artificial lift methods.

The table adopts many arguments originally authored by S. G. Gibbs and published by Brown (1982). Other arguments, reflecting the experience of major operating companies were presented by Neely et al. (1981).

Table 5.3 Features of Various Artificial Lift Methods

ROD PUMPS	
Positive features	*Negative features*
Reliable—long time between failures.	Crooked holes present friction problem.
Relatively simple—rugged mechanical system.	High solids production is troublesome.
Possible to vary rate and easy to match well capacity.	Gassy wells usually lower volumetric efficiency.
Units easily changed to other wells with minimum cost.	Depth limited, primarily due to rod capability.

Table 5.3 (continued)

ROD PUMPS	
Positive features	*Negative features*
Efficient, simple, and easy for field people to operate.	Obtrusive in urban locations.
Applicable to slim holes and multiple completions.	Heavy and bulky in offshore operations.
Can pump a well down to very low pressure.	Susceptible to paraffin problems.
Easy to determine pumping problems.	Tubing cannot be internally coated for corrosion protection.
Can lift high-temperature and viscous oils.	H_2S limits depth at which a large-volume pump can be set.
Can use gas or electricity as power source.	Limitation of downhole pump design in small-diameter casing.
Corrosion and scale treatments easy to perform.	
Applicable to pump-off control if electrified.	
Available in different sizes.	

HYDRAULIC RECIPROCATING PUMPS	
Positive features	*Negative features*
Can pump large volumes from great depth.	Large power oil storage.
Crooked holes present minimal problems.	Relatively high failure rate.
Unobtrusive in urban locations.	Repaired by specially trained mechanics.
Power source can be remotely located.	High solids production is troublesome.
Easy to vary rate and match to well capacity.	Operating costs are sometimes higher.
Can use gas or electricity as power source.	Usually susceptible to gas interference—usually not vented
Downhole pumps can be circulated out in free systems.	Vented installations are more expensive because of extra tubing required.
Can pump a well down to fairly low pressure.	Treating for scale below packer is difficult.
Applicable to multiple completions.	Difficult to obtain valid well tests in low-volume wells.
Applicable offshore.	Requires two strings of tubing for some installations.
Closed system will combat corrosion.	Problems in treating power water where used.
Easy to pump in cycles by time clock.	Safety problem for high-surface-pressure power oil.

Table 5.3 (continued)

ELECTRIC SUBMERSIBLE PUMPS	
Positive features	*Negative features*
Can lift extremely high volumes.	High failure rate—short time between failures.
Unobtrusive in urban locations.	Long downtime for repairs—requires tubing retrieval
Simple to operate.	Not applicable to multiple completions.
Easy to install downhole pressure sensor for telemetering pressure to surface via cable.	Only applicable with electrical power.
Crooked holes present no problem.	High voltages (1000 V) are necessary.
Applicable offshore.	Impractical in shallow, low-volume wells.
Corrosion and scale treatment easy to perform.	Difficult to match to well capacity.
Availability in different sizes.	Expensive to change equipment to match declining well capability.
Lifting cost for high volumes generally very low.	Cable causes problems in handling tubulars.
	Cables deteriorate in high temperatures.
	System is depth limited (10,000 ft) due to cable cost and inability to install enough power downhole (depends on casing size).
	Gas and solids production are troublesome.
	Casing size is a limitation.
	Difficult for well problems analysis.

HYDRAULIC JET PUMPS	
Positive features	*Negative features*
Simple to vary rate.	Relatively inefficient lift method.
Retrievable without pulling tubing.	Requires at least 20% submergence to approach best lift efficiency.
Has no moving parts.	Design of system is more complex.
No problems in deviated or crooked holes.	Pump may cavitate under certain conditions.
Unobtrusive in urban locations.	Very sensitive to any change in backpressure.
Applicable offshore.	The producing of free gas through the pump causes reduction in ability to handle liquids.
Can use water as a power source.	Power-oil systems are fire hazard
Power fluid does not have to be so clean as for hydraulic piston pumping.	High-surface-power fluid pressures are required
Corrosion-scale-emulsion treatment easy to perform.	
Power source can be remotely located.	

Table 5.3 (continued)

GAS LIFT	
Positive features	*Negative features*
Can produce high rates from high-productivity wells.	High initial investment.
Flexible, easy to change rate.	Limited reservoir pressure drawdown.
Can handle large volume of solids with minor problems.	Lift gas is not always available.
Unobtrusive in urban locations.	Not efficient in lifting small fields or one-well leases.
Power source can be remotely located.	Difficult to lift emulsions and viscous crudes.
Easy to obtain downhole pressures and gradients.	Not efficient for small fields or one-well leases if compression equipment is required.
Lifting gassy wells is no problem.	Gas freezing and hydrate problems.
Sometimes serviceable with wireline unit.	Problems with dirty surface lines.
Crooked holes present no problem.	Some difficulty in analyzing properly without engineering supervision.
Corrosion is not usually as adverse.	Cannot effectively produce deep wells to abandonment.
Applicable offshore-platforms and subsea completions.	Casing must withstand lift pressure.
	Safety problem with high-pressure gas.

Courtesy S. G. Gibbs; modified by Brown (1982), tables 1 and 2.

5.5   **SUMMARY.** Two methods are used for continuous artificial lift; pumping and gas lift. Both methods enhance production rate by lowering the wellbore flowing pressure. A pump can produce the well at very low wellbore flowing pressures and thus approach the maximum open-flow potential of the well. Gas lift, on the other hand, is limited to a certain minimum wellbore flowing pressure. Therefore, the potential production rate may be considerably less for gas lift than for pump lift.

Several types of pumps are used in oil wells, in two categories: positive displacement and dynamic displacement. For a given pump speed, the positive-displacement pump displaces a fixed rate of liquid, independent of pressure. In dynamic-displacement pumps the liquid rate depends on pressure conditions at the inlet and the outlet of the pump. Each dynamic-displacement pump, therefore, has a particular pump pressure–rate relationship. This relationship is usually presented graphically as a pump characteristic curve.

Positive-displacement pumps are sized by volumetric rate. A properly sized pump allows maximum possible production from a well, often only slightly less than the absolute open flow. It is important, however, not to exceed the deliverability of the well. Pressure conditions do not affect pump rate. In relation to pressure, the only requirement of a positive-displacement pump is that a certain amount of positive pressure exists at the pump suction. For pumping oil wells, this pressure is usually expressed as a depth of pump submergence.

Dynamic-displacement pumps are affected by pressure conditions in the wellbore. Volumetric rate decreases as the differential pressure across the pump increases. Thus both suction and discharge pressures affect the production rate of a well. The most commonly used dynamic-displacement pump is the turbine centrifugal pump, driven by a downhole electrical motor. This pump may operate at constant speed or at variable speed. For variable-speed pumps, changes of wellbore conditions resulting from depletion and encroaching water may be compensated by changing pump speed. This allows a much wider range of operating conditions for a given-size pump and a longer period before the pump must be replaced by a different-size pump.

The gas-lift method is used only in wells that produce economically with relatively high flowing bottomhole pressures (typically high-productivity reservoirs). Gas lift requires few moving parts downhole and thus is suitable for wells producing sand or other solids. Two considerations play roles in planning an efficient gas-lift system: (1) Gas should be injected into the production string as deep as possible; and (2) there is an "optimal" amount of injected gas resulting in the most economical gas-lift operation. Sizing a gas-lift system amounts to calculating the relationship between (1) gas-injection rate and pressure, (2) depth of gas-injection valve, and (3) production rate. The relationship between these factors is presented graphically in a gas-lift diagram. The performance of gas lift in a given well is expressed by the gas-lift performance curve relating gas injection rate to oil production rate. Translating the two variables to cost and revenue allows determination of the operating conditions that yield the operator's best economical return.

APPENDIX A. GRADIENT CURVES

Reprinted by permission of American Petroleum Institute from Gilbert 1954, p. 143.

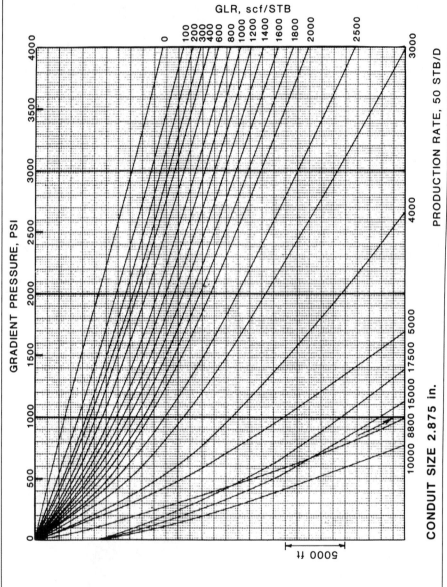

Figure A.1

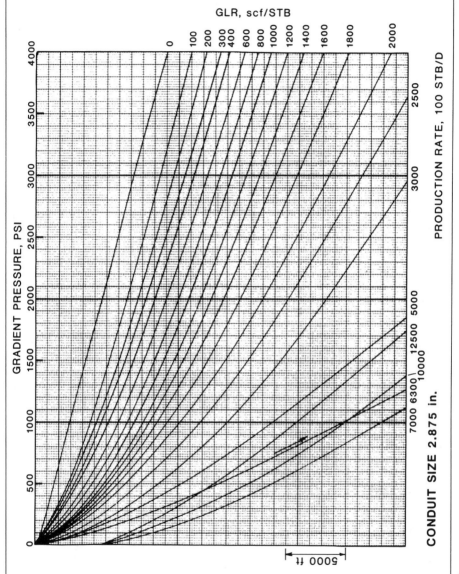

GLR, scf/STB

GRADIENT PRESSURE, PSI

PRODUCTION RATE, 100 STB/D

CONDUIT SIZE 2.875 in.

5000 ft

Figure A.2

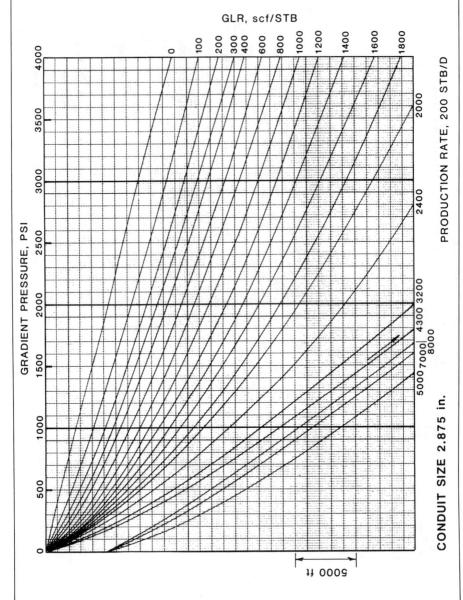

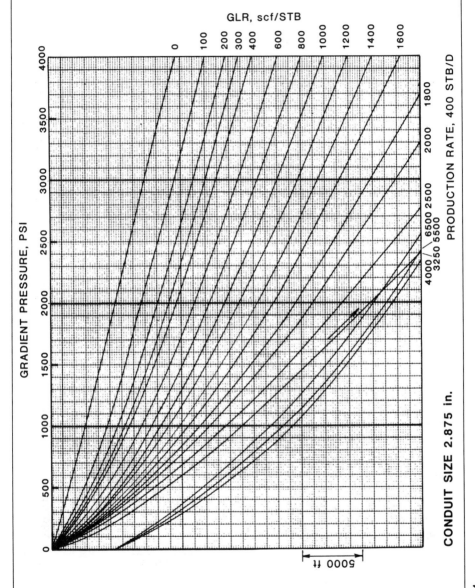

Figure A.4

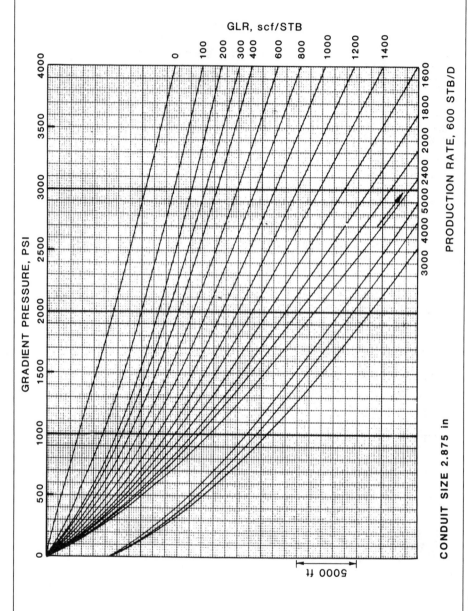

CONDUIT SIZE 2.875 in

Figure A.5

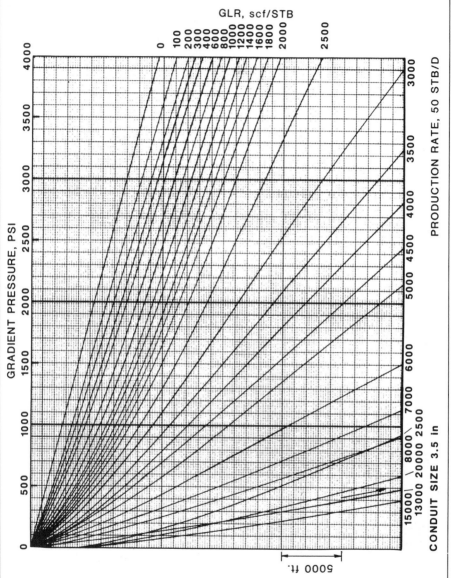

Figure A.6

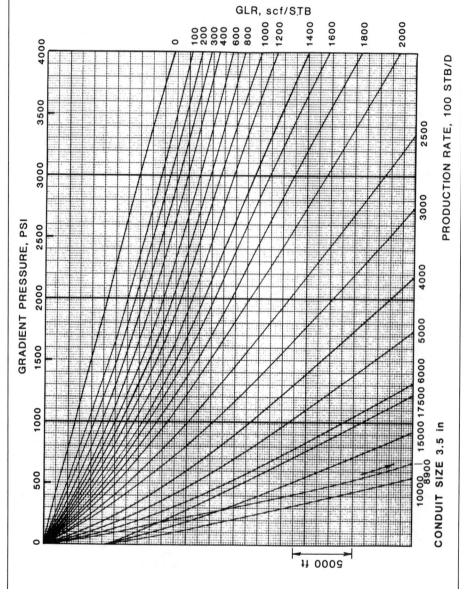

GLR, scf/STB

GRADIENT PRESSURE, PSI

PRODUCTION RATE, 100 STB/D

CONDUIT SIZE 3.5 in

5000 ft

Figure A.7

575

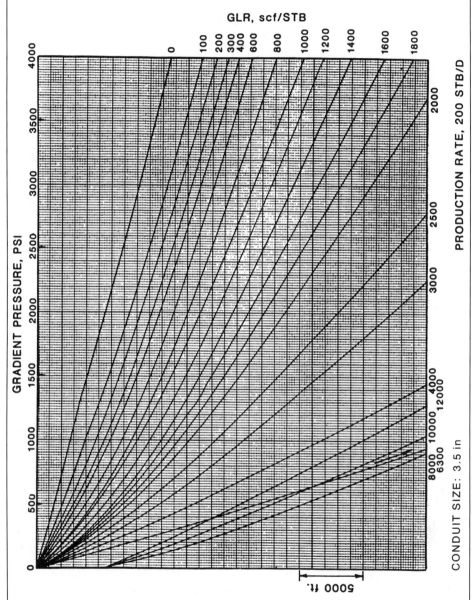

Figure A.8

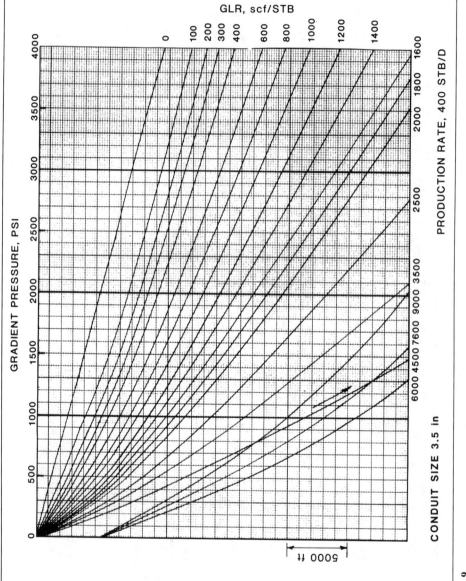

Figure A.9

577

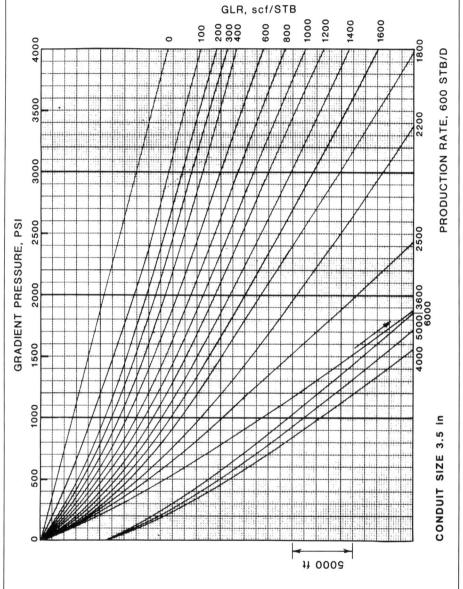

Figure A.10

APPENDIX B. TYPE CURVES AND RATE DECLINE PROGRAM

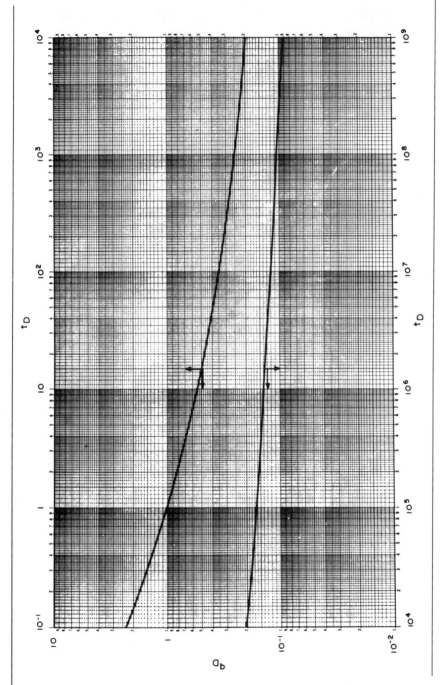

Figure B.1 Infinite-acting dimensionless-rate solution. Reprinted by permission of the SPE-AIME from Earlougher 1977, fig. 4.12, p. 5. © 1977 SPE-AIME. Data from Jacob and Lohman 1952.

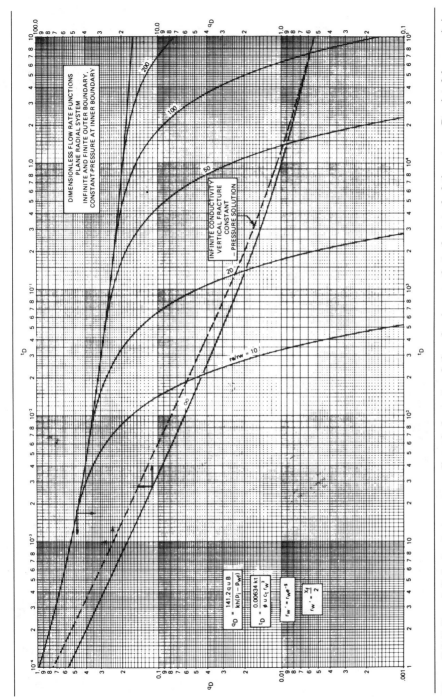

Figure B.2 Full analytical, constant-pressure, dimensionless-rate solution showing pseudosteady-state depletion stems. Reprinted by permission of the SPE-AIME from Fetkovich and Thrasher 1979, fig. 1, SPE paper 7928. © 1979 SPE-AIME.

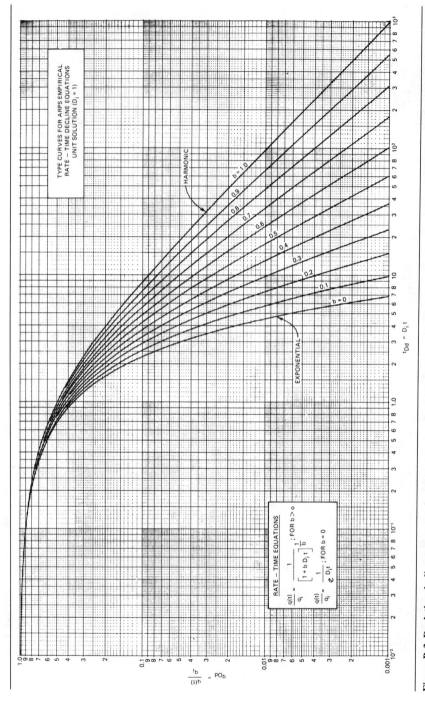

Figure B.3 Depletion decline type curve, based on Arps's empirical equations. Reprinted by permission of the SPE-AIME from Fetkovich 1980, fig. 1. © 1980 SPE-AIME.

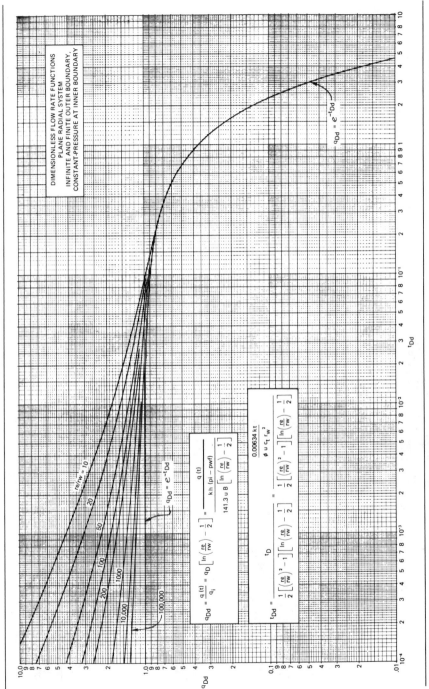

Figure B.4 General unit type curve including transient decline and exponential depletion periods. Reprinted by permission of the SPE-AIME from Fetkovich 1980, fig. 3. © 1980 SPE-AIME.

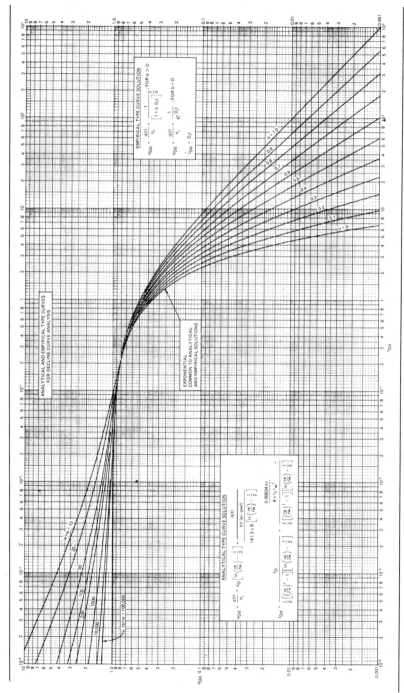

Figure B.5 Complete rate solution plotted in terms of unit variables. Reprinted by permission of the SPE-AIME from Fetkovich 1980, fig. 4. © 1980 SPE-AIME.

585

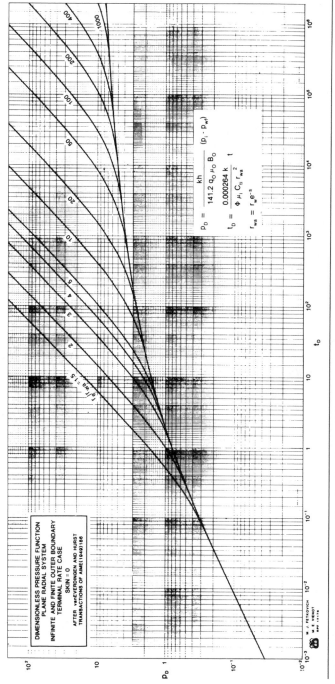

Figure B.6 Dimensionless pressure function for plane radial system, constant rate, infinite and finite outer boundary, and zero skin factor. Reprinted by permission of the SPE-AIME from Fetkovich and Vienot 1983, SPE paper 12179, fig. 8. © 1983 SPE-AIME.

DEC-CHW DECLINE PROGRAM: USER INSTRUCTIONS FOR HP-41C. The DEC-CHW decline program is given in three tables at the end of this appendix; Table B.1 gives an example run of the DEC-CHW decline program for example 4.7. Thereafter, Table B.2 lists contents of the 24 registers used by DEC-CHW. Table B.3 gives a complete listing of DEC-CHW with general comments.

General Comments. A printer must be used for proper execution of DEC-CHW. If a printer is not available, the code must be modified manually. Additional R/Ss must be input to halt output for inspection.

One of the most important restrictions assumed by DEC-CHW is that the time unit used in the rate q is the same as the unit for time t. That is, when q_D/q and t_D/t are calculated, the time unit used in q (e.g., days for STB/D) must be the same as the unit used for t in t_D/t.

Comments on Execution, Input, and Output. To execute the program, push (XEQ) (ALPHA) "DEC-CHW" (ALPHA). Input description follows the example run in table B.1

1. FIX?2.00. The number of digits to the right of the decimal. The present default value for Flx is given. A new value can be entered or R/S (without an entry) assumes the default.

2. ARPS b?0.00. Arps' decline exponent:

$b = 0$:exponential (analytic pss) decline
$0 < b < 1$: hyperbolic declines
$b = 1$: harmonic decline (seldom used)

$b > 1$: *never* use!

The present default value for b is shown. Enter a new value or push R/S (without entry) to keep the default. Note: For $b = 1$ to work, use $b = 0.999$.

3. RE/RWa?15.00. Dimensionless radius, r_e/r_{wa}. Any value greater than 2.00 is valid. The present default for RE/RWa is shown. Enter a new value or push R/S (without entry) to keep the default.

4. QD/Q?2.01E-3. Dimensionless rate constant, q_D/q. The present default is shown. Enter a new value or push R/S (without entry) to keep the default. If zero (0.0) is entered, it is assumed that input dimensionless variables will be unit variables q_{Dd}/q and t_{Dd}/t instead of q_D/q and t_D/t. This would be the case, for example, if data are matched to the type curve in figure 4.9. Steps 5 and 7 remain unchanged, but step 6 asks for t_{Dd}/t instead of t_D/t.

5. MCF/MO (ALPHA MODE). Unit for rate. Any unit is allowed as long as the time unit in the denominator (e.g., days in STB/D) is the same as the unit entered for time (step 7) and the unit is consistent with the value of q_D/q entered. To change the default unit MCF/MO, merely enter a new character string; there is no need to delete MCF/MO first. The ALPHA mode is automatically engaged, so do not push the ALPHA key before entering a new unit. Once the new string is entered (or the default unit is used), push R/S without leaving ALPHA mode.

6. TD/T?0.90. Dimensionless time constant, t_D/t. The present default for TD/T is shown. Enter a new value or push R/S (without entry) to keep the default.

7. MO (ALPHA MODE). Unit for time. The unit must corresond to the time unit entered for rate (step 5) and the definition of t_D/t. To change the default unit of MO (months), merely enter a new character string; no need to delete MCF/MO first. The ALPHA mode is automatically engaged, so do not push the ALPHA key before entering a new unit. Once the new string is entered (or the default unit is used), push R/S without leaving ALPHA mode.

8. TDd/T = 4.00E-3   QDd/Q = 4.19E-3. Calculated unit dimensionless constants. The input valves of t_D/t and q_D/q together with r_e/r_{wa} are used to calculate unit constants. Note that slightly different expressions for A and B (equations [4.24] and [4.25]) are used to give a more accurate representation of the $q_D(t_D)$ analytical solution for small r_e/r_{wa},

$$A = \frac{1}{[\ln(r_e/r_{wa}) - 0.75 + 0.736(r_e/r_{wa})^{-0.644}]},$$ (B.1)

$$B = \frac{2}{\{(r_e/r_{wa})^2[\ln(r_e/r_{wa}) - 0.75 + 0.66(r_e/r_{wa})^{-1}]\}}.$$ (B.2)

If unit dimensionless constants q_{Dd}/q and t_{Dd}/t are entered (steps 4 and 6), then values of q_D/q and t_D/t will be displayed instead.

9. TPSS = 40.35DAYS   TDPSS = 36.32. Calculated times to pseudosteady state (depletion). The first time has units specified by the user. The second time is dimensionless. The equation used for TDPSS is slightly different from that given in the text (equation [2.132]), to make the program more accurate for small values of r_e/r_{wa}:

$$t_{Dpss} = 0.177(r_e/r_{wa})^2 - 0.234(r_e/r_{wa}).$$ (B.3)

10. DT1?1.00DAYS. First time increment. The first time increment may be different from subsequent time increments in some situations. For example, an annual forecast is to be made starting in March. Here DT1 would equal $12 - 2 = 10$ months (full year less January and February), while DT (step 11) would equal 12 months for all subsequent years. The unit is that entered by the user (step 7). The present default for DT1 is displayed. Enter a new value or push R/S (without entry) to keep the default.

11. DT?1.00DAYS. Subsequent time increments (assumed constant). The unit is that entered by the user (step 7). The present default for DT is displayed. Enter a new value or push R/S (without entry) to keep the default.

12. END T?10.00DAYS. Time to terminate forecast. The unit is that input by the user (step 7). The present default for END T is shown. Enter a new value or push R/S (without entry) to keep the default. If zero (0.0) is entered for END T, it is assumed that the forecast will be terminated by a minimum rate instead of a maximum time. In this case, *END Q?* will be prompted, for the minimum rate, which should have the rate unit specified in step 5.

13. CUM1?0.00. Cumulative production prior to the start of the forecast. The unit should be the same as the volumetric unit used for rate (step 5); if rate is STB/D then CUM1 must be given in STBs and not thousands or millions of STBs. A typical situation, where cumulative production exists prior to the forecast, would be production following stimulation where reinitialization is used. The present default for CUM1 is displayed. Enter a new value or push R/S (without entry) to keep the default.

14. T = 1.00DAYS. Cumulative time.

15. Q = 505.92STB/D. Instantaneous rate at T(=1.00 days).

16. CUM = 811.67 (STB). Cumulative production from time zero (0.0) to T(=1.00 days), plus the value of CUM1 entered. CUM has the same volumetric unit as rate (e.g., STB if rate is given in STB/D). Cumulative production is calculated for T < TPSS using integration of the $q_D(t_D)$ functions given in equations (4.9) to (4.11) (analytical expressions are provided by Edwardson et al. 1962). Conversion from dimensionless cumulative production Q_D to real cumulative (N_p or G_p) is given by the simple relation

$$N_p(\text{or } G_p) = Q_D \times (t/t_D) \times (q/q_D).$$

Cumulative production for T > TPSS is calculated in a two-step procedure. First, dimensionless cumulative production at TPSS is calculated from integration of the expressions for $q_D(t_D)$ in equations (4.9) to (4.11). Incremental cumulative production from TPSS to T is calculated from analytical integration of PSS (equations [4.23] and [4.31]), which is then added to Q_{Dpss}. Given dimensionless cumulative production Q_D, actual cumulative production is found from the relation given above.

17. DCUM = 811.67 (STB). Cumulative production since the previous time (0.00 in this case). DCUM has the same volumetric unit as rate (e.g., STB if rate is given in STB/D). For T = 2.00 (days) in table B.1, CUM = 1,261.99 (STB) and DECUM = 450.32 (STB). During the second day of production the well produces 450.32 STB. The instantaneous rate at the end of the second day is $q = 410.46$ STB/D.

Table B.1 Example Run Using DEC-CHW Decline Program for Example 4.7

```
DECLINE
C.H. WHITSON

b=0.00
RE/RWa=15.00

QD/Q=2.01E-3
UNIT=STB/D

TD/T=0.90
UNIT=DAYS

TDd/T=4.00E-3
QDd/Q=4.19E-3

TSS=40.35DAYS
TDPSS=36.32

DT1=1.00DAYS
DT=1.00DAYS
END T=10.00DAYS
CUM1=0.00

T=1.00DAYS
Q=505.92STB/D
CUM=811.67
DCUM=811.67

T=2.00DAYS
Q=410.46STB/D
CUM=1,261.99
DCUM=450.32

T=3.00DAYS
Q=366.56STB/D
CUM=1,648.37
DCUM=386.39

T=4.00DAYS
Q=339.64STB/D
CUM=2,000.54
DCUM=352.17
```

(continued from left column)

```
T=5.00DAYS
Q=320.84STB/D
CUM=2,330.28
DCUM=329.73

T=6.00DAYS
Q=306.68STB/D
CUM=2,643.73
DCUM=313.45

T=7.00DAYS
Q=295.48STB/D
CUM=2,944.60
DCUM=300.87

T=8.00DAYS
Q=286.31STB/D
CUM=3,235.35
DCUM=290.75

T=9.00DAYS
Q=278.60STB/D
CUM=3,517.70
DCUM=282.35

T=10.00DAYS
Q=272.00STB/D
CUM=3,792.92
DCUM=275.22
```

Table B.2 Registers for DEC-CHW

No.	Variable	Comment
00	b	Arps' exponent
01	RE/RWa	Dimensionless radius
02	TD	Dimensionless time
03	TDPSS	Dimensionless time at PSS
04	QD	Dimensionless rate
05	A	Constant for unit dimensionless time
06	B	Constant for unit dimensionless rate
07	SQRT(TD)	
08	ln TD	
09	T	Time
10	QD/Q	Dimensionless rate constant
11	TD/T	Dimensionless time constant
12	QDd/Q	Unit dimensionless rate constant
13	TDd/T	Unit dimensionless time constant
14		not used
15	*MCF/MO*	Default rate unit
16	*MO*	Default time unit
17	DT1	First time increment
18	DT	Subsequent time increment
19	TEND	Time to terminate forecast
20	QEND	Minimum rate to terminate forecast
21	CUMD	Dimensionless cumulative production
22	CUMDPSS	CUMD at TDPSS
23	CUM1	Initial (before forecast) cumulative production
24	CUMLAST	Previous-time cumulative production

Table B.3 Program Listings

INITIALIZATION / INPUT

	01♦LBL "DEC-CHW"	50 GTO 01
	02 CLX	51 "QD/Q="
	03 STO 23	52 ARCL X
	04 ADV	53 AVIEW
	05 "DECLINE"	54 CLD
	06 SF 12	55 CLA
	07 AVIEW	56 ARCL 15
Rate Unit ?	08 CF 12	57 AON
	09 "C.H. WHITSON"	58 PROMPT
	10 AVIEW	59 AOFF
Fix Format	11 2	60 ASTO 15
	12 "FIX?"	61 CF 23
	13 ARCL X	62 CLA
	14 PROMPT	63 "UNIT="
	15 FIX IND X	64 ARCL 15
	16 SF 29	65 AVIEW
	17 CLA	66 CLD
	18 "MCF/MO"	67 RCL 05
	19 ASTO 15	68 /
	20 "MO"	69 STO 12
	21 ASTO 16	70 RCL 11
Arp's b Exponent	22 RCL 00	t_D/t ?
	23 "ARPS b?"	71 ADV
	24 ARCL X	72 "TD/T?"
	25 PROMPT	73 ARCL X
	26 STO 00	74 PROMPT
	27 "b="	75 STO 11
	28 ADV	76 "TD/T="
	29 ARCL X	77 ARCL X
	30 AVIEW	78 AVIEW
	31 CLD	79 CLD
r_e/r_{wa} ?	32 RCL 01	80 CLA
	33 "RE/RWa?"	81 ARCL 16
	34 ARCL X	Time Unit ? 82 AON
	35 PROMPT	83 PROMPT
	36 STO 01	84 AOFF
	37 "RE/RWa="	85 ASTO 16
	38 ARCL X	86 CLA
	39 AVIEW	87 "UNIT="
	40 CLD	88 ARCL 16
	41 CLX	89 AVIEW
	42 XEQ "AB"	90 CLD
q_D/q ?	43 ADV	91 RCL 06
	44 RCL 10	92 *
	45 "QD/Q?"	93 STO 13
	46 ARCL X	94 ADV
	47 PROMPT	95 "TDd/T="
	48 STO 10	96 ARCL X
	49 X=0?	97 AVIEW
		98 "QDd/Q="
		99 ARCL 12

Table B.3 (continued)

	100 AVIEW		150 /
	101 CLD		151 STO 11
	102 GTO 02		152 ADV
	103♦LBL 01		153 "TD/T="
q_{Dd}/q ?	104 RCL 12		154 ARCL X
	105 ADV		155 AVIEW
	106 "QDd/Q?"		156 "QD/Q="
	107 ARCL X		157 ARCL 10
	108 PROMPT		158 AVIEW
	109 STO 12	Time to PSS =	159 CLD
	110 "QDd/Q="		160♦LBL 02
	111 ARCL X		161 RCL 03
	112 AVIEW		162 STO 02
	113 CLD		163 RCL 11
	114 CLA		164 /
	115 ARCL 15		165 STO 09
Rate Unit ?	116 AON		166 ADV
	117 PROMPT		167 "TSS="
	118 AOFF		168 ARCL 09
	119 ASTO 15		169 ARCL 16
	120 CLA		170 AVIEW
	121 "UNIT="		171 "TDPSS="
	122 ARCL 15		172 ARCL 03
	123 AVIEW		173 AVIEW
	124 CLD		174 CLD
	125 RCL 05		175 XEQ "QDSUB"
	126 *		176 RCL 21
	127 STO 10		177 STO 22
	128 RCL 13		178♦LBL "2a"
t_{Dd}/t ?	129 ADV		179 CF 00
	130 "TDd/T?"	First	180 ADV
	131 ARCL X	Time Increment ?	181 RCL 17
	132 PROMPT		182 "DT1?"
	133 STO 13		183 ARCL 17
	134 "TDd/T="		184 ARCL 16
	135 ARCL X		185 PROMPT
	136 AVIEW		186 STO 09
	137 CLD		187 STO 17
	138 CLA		188 "DT1="
	139 ARCL 16		189 ARCL X
Time Unit ?	140 AON		190 ARCL 16
	141 PROMPT	Subsequent	191 AVIEW
	142 AOFF	Time Increments ?	192 RCL 18
	143 ASTO 16		193 "DT?"
	144 CLA		194 ARCL 18
	145 "UNIT="		195 ARCL 16
	146 ARCL 16		196 PROMPT
	147 AVIEW		197 STO 18
	148 CLD		198 "DT="
	149 RCL 06		199 ARCL X

Table B.3 (continued)

Label	Code
	200 ARCL 16
	201 AVIEW
End Time ?	202 RCL 19
	203 "END T?"
	204 ARCL 19
	205 ARCL 16
	206 PROMPT
	207 STO 19
	208 X=0?
	209 GTO 04
	210 "END T="
	211 ARCL X
	212 ARCL 16
	213 AVIEW
	214 CLD
	215 RCL 17
	216 RCL 18
	217 +
	218 X>Y?
	219 SF 00
	220 CLX
	221 STO 20
	222 GTO 05
	223♦LBL 04
Minimum Rate ?	224 RCL 20
	225 "END Q?"
	226 ARCL 20
	227 ARCL 15
	228 PROMPT
	229 STO 20
	230 "END Q="
	231 ARCL X
	232 ARCL 15
	233 AVIEW
	234 1 E20
	235 STO 19
Initial Cumulative ?	236♦LBL 05
	237 RCL 23
	238 "CUM1?"
	239 ARCL 23
	240 PROMPT
	241 STO 23
	242 STO 24
	243 "CUM1="
	244 ARCL X
BEGIN CALCULATIONS	245 AVIEW
	246 CLD
	247♦LBL 03
	248 ADV
	249 RCL 09

Label	Code
Time =	250 "T="
	251 ARCL X
	252 ARCL 16
	253 AVIEW
	254 CLD
	255 RCL 11
Calculate q_D	256 *
	257 STO 02
	258 XEQ "QDSUB"
	259 RCL 04
	260 RCL 10
	261 /
Rate =	262 STO 04
	263 "Q="
	264 ARCL X
	265 ARCL 15
	266 AVIEW
	267 CLD
	268 RCL 21
	269 RCL 10
	270 /
	271 RCL 11
	272 /
Cumulative =	273 RCL 23
	274 +
	275 "CUM="
	276 ARCL X
	277 AVIEW
	278 RCL 24
	279 X<>Y
Incremental Cumulative =	280 STO 24
	281 X<>Y
	282 -
	283 "DCUM="
	284 ARCL X
	285 AVIEW
	286 CLD
	287 RCL 04
	288 RCL 20
	289 X>Y?
	290 GTO "2a"
	291 FS? 00
	292 GTO "2a"
	293 RCL 18
	294 ST+ 09
	295 RCL 19
	296 RCL 09
	297 X<Y?
	298 GTO 03
	299 SF 00

Table B.3 (continued)

DIMENSIONLESS RATE SUBROUTINE	300 X<>Y		350 RCL 02
	301 STO 09		351 *
	302 GTO 03		352 RCL 07
	303♦LBL "QDSUB"		353 *
	304♦LBL 01		354 +
	305 RCL 02		355 *
	306 .001		356 STO 04
	307 X>Y?		357 RCL 07
	308 GTO d		358 .616599
	309 RCL 03		359 *
	310 X=0?		360 RCL 02
Infinite Acting	311 GTO a		361 .0413008
$0.01 < t_D < 200$	312 RCL 02		362 *
	313 X>Y?		363 +
	314 GTO c		364 1
	315♦LBL a		365 +
	316 RCL 02		366 1/X
	317 SQRT		367 1.12838
	318 STO 07		368 RCL 07
	319 X↑2		369 *
	320 LN		370 1.19328
	321 STO 08		371 RCL 02
	322 RCL 02		372 *
	323 200		373 +
	324 X<=Y?		374 .269872
	325 GTO b		375 RCL 02
	326 X<>Y		376 *
	327 35.5372		377 RCL 07
	328 *		378 *
	329 47.421		379 +
	330 RCL 07		380 .00855294
	331 *		381 RCL 02
	332 +		382 X↑2
	333 2.60967		383 *
	334 RCL 02	Infinite Acting	384 +
	335 *	$t_D \geq 200$	385 *
	336 RCL 07		386 STO 21
	337 *		387 RTN
	338 +		388♦LBL b
	339 1/X		389 RCL 02
	340 43.5537		390 2.02623
	341 RCL 07		391 *
	342 *		392 RCL 08
	343 26.7544		393 1
	344 +		394 -
	345 13.3813		395 *
	346 RCL 02		396 3.90086
	347 *		397 +
	348 +		398 RCL 02
	349 .492949		399 /

Table B.3 (continued)

	400 RCL 08	PSS (b=0) Dimensionless Cumulatives	450 RCL 05
	401 X↑2		451 *
	402 /		452 STO 04
	403 STO 04		453♦LBL "c1"
	404 RCL 02		454 RCL 00
	405 2.02566		455 X≠0?
	406 *		456 GTO "c2"
	407 4.29881		457 RCL 03
	408 -		458 RCL 06
	409 RCL 08		459 *
Infinite Acting	410 /		460 CHS
$t_D \leq 0.01$	411 STO 21		461 E↑X
	412 RTN		462 RCL 02
	413♦LBL d		463 RCL 06
	414 X<>Y		464 *
	415 PI		465 CHS
	416 *		466 E↑X
	417 1/X		467 -
	418 SQRT		468 RCL 05
	419 STO 04		469 *
	420 RCL 07		470 RCL 06
	421 2		471 /
	422 *		472 RCL 22
	423 PI	PSS (0<b<1) Dimensionless Cumulatives	473 +
	424 SQRT		474 STO 21
	425 /		475 RTN
Pseudosteady	426 STO 21		476♦LBL "c2"
State - Depletion	427 RTN		477 RCL 00
	428♦LBL c		478 RCL 06
b = 0	429 RCL 06		479 *
	430 RCL 02		480 RCL 03
	431 *		481 *
	432 CHS		482 1
	433 E↑X		483 +
	434 RCL 05		484 RCL 00
	435 *		485 1/X
	436 STO 04		486 CHS
	437 RCL 00		487 1
	438 X=0?		488 +
	439 GTO "c1"		489 STO 21
$0 < b \leq 1$	440 RCL 06		490 Y↑X
	441 *		491 RCL 00
	442 RCL 02		492 RCL 06
	443 *		493 *
	444 1		494 RCL 02
	445 +		495 *
	446 RCL 00		496 1
	447 1/X		497 +
	448 CHS		498 RCL 21
	449 Y↑X		499 Y↑X

Table B.3 (continued)

	500 -	550 X<>Y
	501 1	551 ENTER↑
	502 RCL 00	552 X↑2
	503 -	553 .177
	504 /	554 *
	505 RCL 05	555 X<>Y
	506 *	556 .234
	507 RCL 06	557 *
	508 /	558 -
	509 RCL 22	559 STO 03
	510 +	560 RTN
PSS Constants	511 STO 21	561◆LBL "ERR"
A and B	512 RTN	562 "RE/RW<2"
	513◆LBL "AB"	563 AVIEW
	514 1	564 "*TOO SMALL*"
	515 STO 05	565 AVIEW
	516 STO 06	566 STOP
	517 RCL 01	567 END
	518 X=0?	
	519 RTN	
	520 LN	
	521 .75	
	522 -	
	523 STO 06	
	524 .736	
	525 RCL 01	
	526 -.644	
	527 Y↑X	
	528 *	
	529 +	
	530 1/X	
	531 STO 05	
	532 RCL 06	
	533 .66	
	534 RCL 01	
	535 /	
	536 +	
	537 RCL 01	
	538 X↑2	
	539 *	
	540 1/X	
	541 2	
	542 *	
	543 STO 06	
	544 CLX	
	545 STO 03	
	546 RCL 01	
	547 2	
	548 X>Y?	
	549 GTO "ERR"	

Error:
$r_e/r_{wa} < 2$

APPENDIX C. UNIT STYSTEM
IN PETROLEUM ENGINEERING

C.1 **BACKGROUND.** For almost a century the petroleum industry in many parts of the world has primarily used a hybrid unit system referred to as the "oilfield" system. The customary oilfield system is derived primarily from the English engineering system, but it also applies several units that are inconsistent with the rest of the system. Some of the inconsistent units originated in the field of petroleum engineering, while others have been borrowed. Through longterm usage, these units have become familiar and useful even though their inconsistency makes engineering calculations more complicated.

Presently there is a gradual conversion to the metric-based SI system, which is gaining general acceptance, though, a significant segment of the petroleum industry remains deeply rooted in the customary field unit system. There is no doubt that the coherent and less ambiguous SI system is technically superior to any other unit system. Furthermore, adopting the SI system gives the opportunity to establish a single, worldwide set of units and terms that will enhance technical communication. Conversion to the SI system is not without problems though. Campbell and Campbell (1985) described some practical problems with changing to the SI system: "To some extent, an old familiar set of problems has been exchanged for some new, unfamiliar ones. The old comfortable units possess a meaning through long usage that must be acquired for new units . . . . Attempting to eliminate these (old) terms suddenly is difficult. It jeopardizes and delays acceptance."

The greatest factor delaying conversion is probably the reliance of petroleum engineers on references and literature published almost entirely in the customary oilfield system. The use of two unit systems, therefore will probably continue for many years, during which time the petroleum engineer must continue to apply them simultaneously and interchangeably. This appendix presents the customary oil field system and the SI system, which appears, with certain modifications, to have been accepted by the petroleum engineering community. It also explains the rules and practice of converting data and equations from one unit system to another.

Unit conversion in engineering calculations usually presents two classes of problems: converting the units of given quantities, and modifying the constants in equations according to the units of the variables. In most cases, converting units of a given quantity is done merely by multiplying or dividing by a conversion factor obtained from a conversion table. There are, however, cases where the conversion is more difficult, requiring a series of multiplications and divisions according to certain rules. The conversion rules and their practice are presented in the following sections, but first a short summary of the commonly used unit systems is given.

C.2   **UNIT SYSTEMS.** Dimension is a means to express the magnitude of a measurable quantity. For example, length, time, mass, area, viscosity, and permeability are measurable quantities and have *dimensions*. Dimensional systems used to quantify physical phenomena apply two types of dimensions. (1) The *primary dimensions* are those selected to set up arbitary scales of measure. (2) The *secondary dimensions* are dimensions that can be expressed in terms of the primary dimensions. In mechanics we customarily employ length, time, and mass as primary dimensions, while all the other quantities such as area, viscosity, pressure, and permeability are expressed by secondary dimensions.

The magnitudes of the various dimensions are expressed by means of units. While the units of primary dimensions are arbitrary, the units of the secondary dimensions are derived from the units of the primary dimensions. Examples of primary units are feet, inches, meters, or yards for length; seconds, minutes, hours, or days for time; pounds, grams, or kilograms for mass. Examples of secondary units are meters per second or miles per hour for *velocity*; square meters or square feet for *area*. Different dimensional systems often apply different scales and units for the same dimensions, yet the most significant difference between dimensional systems is not in the units employed but in the choice of primary dimensions.

For mechanical quantities, the SI system uses length (m), time (s), and mass (kg) as primary dimensions; all other quantities are secondary. It is therefore called an *MLT* (mass–length–time) system. The cgs system (centimeter–gram–second) is also an MLT system. The British–American engineering system uses four primary dimensions: length (feet), time (second), mass (pound mass, lb_m), and force (pound force, lb_f), and therefore it is an FMLT (force–mass–length–time) system. The obsolete metric technical system is also an FMLT (kg_f–kg_m–m–s) system.

The units of secondary quantities are expressed by a combination of primary units; for example, the units of force in the SI system are kg-m/s^2. In certain cases, the combination of primary units is rather complicated and cumbersome to work with. Rather than carrying lengthy expressions, it is often convenient to give names to complex combinations of secondary units. For example, the term newton (N) is used in place of kg-m/s^2. Similarly, the unit of energy is newton-meter (N-m), abbreviated joule (J). Another example is the unit for power, the watt, defined as one joule per second. The practice of using pseudonyms for units of secondary dimensions is common to all unit systems, but it is applied extensively in the SI system.

The fundamental difference between the SI and the English engineering system is the different selection of primary units. In the SI system the force has a secondary unit derived from primary units using Newton's second law, which states that force is proportional to mass times acceleration. In equation form the dimensions of force (F), are related to the dimensions of mass (M) and acceleration (L/T^2) by

$$F = kML/T^2, \tag{C.1}$$

where k is a proportionality constant. In the SI system the secondary unit of force, newton (N), is defined such that $k = 1\,N/kg \times m \times s^{-2}$, simplifying expressions involving force and force-derived quantities (pressure and energy).

In the English system both mass and force are primary units. Mass is quantified by pound mass (lb_m) and force is quantified by pound force (lb_f). The units of force are defined such that the numerical value for the mass of a body (in lb_m) and its weight (in lb_f) at sea level on earth are numerically identical, i.e., a 10-lb_m ball weighs exactly $10\,lb_f$ at sea level on the earth (the same ball weights $1.67\,lb_f$ on the moon!). The gravitational accelerations at sea level conditions ($32.173\,ft/s^2$), fixes then the factor in equation (C.1) giving

$$k = \frac{1(lb_f)}{1(lb_m)(32.173)(ft/s^2)}$$

It is customary to denote the reciprocal of k by g_c, giving for the English system

$$g_c = 32.173(ft/s^2)(lb_m/lb_f),$$

and for the SI system $g_c = 1.0\dfrac{kg\,m/s^2}{N}$.

Considering the mass and force units, Newton's second law should include the factor g_c, and is therefore written

$$F = \frac{1}{g_c}ML/T^2 \tag{C.2}$$

In the SI system, however, where $g_c = 1$ (by choice), the presence of g_c is usually hidden, and Newton's second law is written simply as $F = ML/T^2$. Engineers completing their entire education using solely the SI system (e.g., in Norway) are, therefore, unfamiliar with the constant g_c and often fail to recognize it in other unit systems. For example, in the obsolete metric technical system where g_c must be included, it assumes the value

$$g_c = 9.81(m/s^2)(kg_f/kg_m).$$

Proceeding with unit systems, Table C.1 gives the SI units, names (pseudonyms), and symbols for the quantities most often used in petroleum engineering. Table C.2 gives the corresponding information for the English engineering system.

As mentioned earlier, the customary oilfield unit system is a hybrid system gradually evolved in the petroleum industry. The primary units are as in the English engineering system, but unlike the engineering system the secondary units are not derived directly from the primary units. The field units most frequently used are

- length: feet (ft)
- pressure: $lb_f/in.^2$ (psi)

Table C.1 Mechanical Quantities in SI Units

	Quantity	Dimension	Unit	Alias	Symbol
Secondary	Length	L	meter		m
	Time	T	second		s
	Mass	M	kilogram		kg
	Velocity	L/T	m/s		
	Acceleration	L/T^2	m/s^2		
Primary	Frequency	1/T	1/s	hertz	Hz
	Force	ML/T^2	kg $\times$ m/s^2	newton	N
	Pressure	M/T^{2}L	kg/(s^2 $\times$ m) = N/m^2	pascal	Pa
	Energy	ML^2/T^2	kg $\times$ m^2/s^2 = N $\times$ m	joule	J
	Power	ML^2/T^3	kg $\times$ m^2/s^3 = J/s	watt	W

Table C.2 Mechanical Quantities in English Engineering Units

	Quantity	Dimension	Unit	Alias	Symbol
Secondary	Length	L	foot		ft
	Time	T	second		s
	Mass	M	pound-mass		lbm
	Force	F	pound-force		lbf
	Velocity	L/T	ft/s		
	Acceleration	L/T^2	ft/s^2		
Primary	Frequency	1/T	1/s	hertz	Hz
	Pressure	F/L^2	lb$_f$/ft^2		
	Energy	LF	ft $\times$ lb$_f$		
	Power	LF/T	ft $\times$ lb$_f$/s		

- volume: barrels (bbl) for liquid standard cubic feet (scf) for gas
- volumetric rate: stock tank barrels per day (STB/D) for oil, standard cubic feet per day (scf/D) for gas
- viscosity: centipoise (cp)
- permeability: millidarcy (md)
- time: hours or days, according to the application
- oil density: API gravity (°API), pounds per cubic foot (lb$_m$/ft^3)
- gas density: pounds per cubic foot (lb$_m$/ft^3)
- temperature: degrees Farenheit (°F), absolute temperature (°F + 459.67) degrees Rankine (°R).

In particular applications that require surface pumping data, as in drilling, cementing, and stimulation, volume is often expressed in gallons, flow rates in gallons per minute, and density in pounds per gallon.

The obvious inconsistency in the secondary units results in extensive use of conversion factors in equations and computations.

The conversion of oilfield units to SI or to "SPE Metric Unit Standard" can be made with the help of unit conversion tables included in most petroleum-related manuals and textbooks. There is, however, a certain difficulty in using the pure SI system where secondary units may have very high or low numerical values when applied in the range of practical engineering problems. To account for this difficulty, the SPE recommends the use of a few "SPE Metric Preferred Units" to substitute for or supplement the pure SI units. This recommendation again introduces a certain amount of inconsistency to the equations, yet the calculations are relatively compact and easy to manage. The main modifications of the pure SI system accepted by the SPE are listed in table C.3.

For fast reference, table C.4 adopted with certain changes from Campbell and Campbell (1985) gives a useful summary of basic conversion factors frequently applied in petroleum engineering calculations. Examples in the following sections apply this table for units conversion.

Table C.3 SPE Preferable Metric Units

Quantity	Symbol	SI	Preferred	Conversion
Flow rate	q	m^3/s	dm^3/s	$1\,dm^3/s = 10^3\,m^3/s$
Permeability	k	m^2	μm^2	$1\,\mu m^2 = 10^{-12}\,m^2$
Pressure	p	Pa	kPa	$1\,kPa = 1000\,Pa$
Time	t	s	h	$1\,h = 3600\,s$
Compressibility	c	1/Pa	1/kPa	$1/kPa = 0.001\,1/Pa$

Table C.4 Summary of Basic Conversion Factors

Length

$1\,m = 3.281\,ft = 39.37\,in. = 100\,cm = 1000\,mm$
$1\,ft = 0.305\,m = 12\,in. = 30.5\,cm = 3050\,mm$
1 statute mile $= 1.61\,km$, $1\,km = 0.621$ statute mile

Area

$1\,m^2 = 10,000\,cm^2 = 10.76\,ft^2 = 1549\,in.^2$
1 hectare $= 10,000\,m^2 = 2.47$ acres, 1 acre $= 0.405$ hectare
1 sq mile (section) $= 2.59\,km^2 = 259$ hectares $= 640$ acres
1 acre $= 43,560\,ft^2 = 0.405$ hectare $= 4050\,m^2$

Volume

$1\,m^3 = 35.32\,ft^3 = 6.29\,bbl = 1000$ liters $= 1000\,dm^3$
1 liter $= 1\,dm^3 = 0.001\,m^3 = 1000\,cm^3 = 0.035\,ft^3 = 61\,in.^3$
$1\,ft^3 = 0.0283\,m^3 = 28.3$ liters
$1\,bbl\,(API) = 0.159\,m^3 = 159$ liters $= 5.61\,ft^3$

Mass

$1\,kg = 2.205\,lb_m = 1000\,g$
$1\,lb_m = 0.454\,kg = 454\,g$
1 ton (metric) $= 1000\,kg = 2205\,lb_m$

Table C.4 (continued)

Density

$1\,kg/m^3 = 0.001\,g/cm^3 = 0.0624\,lb_m/ft^3$
$1\,lb_m/ft^3 = 0.01602\,g/cm^3$
$1\,g/cm^3 = 1000\,kg/m^3 = 62.4\,lb_m/ft^3 = 1.0\,kg/L$

Force

$1\,N = 0.225\,lb_f = 0.102\,kg_f$
$1\,kg_f = 9.81\,N = 2.205\,lb_f$
$1\,lb_f = 4.45\,N = 0.454\,kg_f$

Pressure

$1\,bar = 14.50\,psi = 0.987\,atm = 1.02\,kg_f/cm^2$
$\quad\quad = 100\,000\,N/m^2 = 10^5\,Pa = 100\,kPa$
$1\,psi = 6.89\,kPa$

Temperature

$°C = \tfrac{5}{9}(°F - 32),\ K = °C + 273$
$°F = 1.8°C + 32,\ °R = °F + 460$

Viscosity

(Dynamic)
$1\,cp = 10^{-3}\,Pa \times s = 0.037\,lb_m/(min\text{-}ft) = 6.72 \times 10^{-4}\,lb_m/(s\text{-}ft)$
$1\,Pa \times s = 10^3\,cp$
(Kinematic)
$1\,cSt = 1.0\,mm^2/s = 1.08 \times 10^{-5}\,ft^2/s$

Permeability

$1\,md = 9.86 \times 10^{-16}\,m^2 = 9.86 \times 10^{-4}\,\mu m^2 = 1.127 \times 10^{-3}\,\dfrac{(B/D)\,cp}{ft^2(psi/ft)}$
$1\,m^2 = 1.01325 \times 10^{15}\,md$
$1\,\mu m^2 = 1.01325 \times 10^3\,md = 1 \times 10^{-12}\,m^2$

Work and heat

$1\,kJ = 0.948\,Btu = 1000\,N\text{-}m = 0.239\,kcal$
$1\,kcal = 4.19\,kJ = 3.97\,Btu$
$1\,Btu = 1.055\,kJ = 0.252\,kcal$

Power

$1\,kW = 3600\,kJ/h = 860\,kcal/hr = 367\,100\,kg_f\text{-}m/h$
$\quad\quad = 3415\,Btu/hr = 2.66 \times 10^6\,(ft\text{-}lb_f)/hr = 1.341\,HP$
$1\,HP = 0.746\,kW = 641\,kcal/h = 2690\,kJ/h$
$\quad\quad = 2545\,Btu/hr = 1.98 \times 10^6\,(ft\text{-}lb_f)/hr$

Table C.4 (continued)

Special Units

API GRAVITY (OF OIL)
$$\gamma(\text{water} = 1) = \frac{141.5}{131.5 + °\text{API}}$$

API BARREL
1 API bbl = 42 U.S. gallons = 35 U. K. (Imperial) gallons
$= 5.61\,\text{ft}^3 = 0.159\,\text{m}^3 = 159\,\text{liters}$

LIQUID FLOWRATE
$1\,\text{bbl/D} = 1.84 \times 10^{-6}\,\text{m}^3/\text{s} = 0.159\,\text{m}^3/\text{D}$

GAS−OIL RATIO
$1\,\text{scf/STB} = 0.178\,\text{m}^3/\text{m}^3$

Note: Reprinted, by permission, from J. M. Campbell and R. A. Campbell: "Application of the SI Metric System: Part 2—The Basic Units," *J. Pet. Tech.* (Oct. 1985) table 3, P. 1805. © 1985 SPE-AIME.

C.3   **DIMENSIONAL EQUATIONS AND CONVERSION FACTORS.** As previously explained, it is often necessary to convert units in the process of making calculations. The conversion is carried out using conversion factors listed in tables. If the needed factor is listed, the conversion is straightforward. If, however, the needed factor is not listed, it can be developed using a combination of factors that are listed. It is possible, in fact, to develop any needed conversion factor using only conversion factors between primary units. The conversion procedure in such cases starts with the given unit, multiplying it by a series of dimensionless ratios that neither change the dimensions nor the physical quantity expressed by the original unit. The dimensionless ratios are selected such that the original unit is cancelled and substituted by the new desired unit. The procedure is best illustrated by example C.1.

EXAMPLE C.1

Perform the following conversions:

1. $2\,\text{ft} \rightarrow \text{in.}$
2. $30\,\text{km} \rightarrow \text{miles}$
3. $2200\,\text{ft/s} \rightarrow \text{miles/hr}$
4. $500\,\text{scf/STB} \rightarrow \text{m}^3/\text{m}^3$
5. $60\,\text{cp} \rightarrow \text{lb}_{\text{m}}/\text{min} \times \text{ft}$, from table C.4, $1\,\text{cp} = 10^{-3}\,\text{pa} \times \text{s}$
6. $200\,\text{bbl/D} \rightarrow \text{m}^3/\text{s}$
7. $70\,\text{md} \rightarrow \mu\text{m}^2$; from table C.4, $1\,\text{md} = 9.869923 \times 10^{-16}\,\text{m}^2$

EXAMPLE C.1 continued

SOLUTION

The given quantity is first written with its units and then multiplied by a series of dimensionless ratios that do not change the magnitude or the dimension but change its units. The multiplications and cancellations proceed until the desired units are finally achieved:

1. $\dfrac{2\,\text{ft}}{}\left|\dfrac{12\,\text{in.}}{\text{ft}}\right| = 2 \times 12\,\text{in.} = 24\,\text{in.}$

2. $\dfrac{30\,\text{km}}{}\left|\dfrac{\text{mile}}{1.61\,\text{km}}\right| = \dfrac{30}{1.61}\,\text{miles} = 18.63\,\text{miles}$

3. $\dfrac{2200\,\text{ft}}{\text{s}}\left|\dfrac{\text{mile}}{5280\,\text{ft}}\right|\dfrac{3600\,\text{s}}{\text{hr}} = \dfrac{2200 \times 3600}{5280}\dfrac{\text{miles}}{\text{hr}} = 1500\,\text{miles/hr}$

4. $\dfrac{500\,\text{scf}}{\text{STB}}\left|\dfrac{6.29\,\text{STB}}{1\,\text{m}^3}\right|\dfrac{\text{m}^3}{35.32\,\text{ft}^3} = \dfrac{500 \times 6.29\,\text{m}^3}{35.32\,\text{m}^3} = 89.0\,\text{m}^3/\text{m}^3$

5. $60\,\text{cp} = \dfrac{60\,\text{cp}}{}\left|\dfrac{10^{-3}\,\text{Pa} \times \text{s}}{\text{cp}}\right| = \dfrac{60 \times 10^{-3}}{}\left|\dfrac{\text{kg m} \times \text{s}}{\text{s}^2\text{m}^2}\right|$

$= \dfrac{60 \times 10^{-3}\,\text{kg}}{\text{m} \times \text{s}} = \dfrac{60 \times 10^{-3}\,\text{kg}}{\text{m} \times \text{s}}\left|\dfrac{2.205\,\text{lb}_\text{m}}{\text{kg}}\right| \cdot \left|\dfrac{\text{m}}{3.281\,\text{ft}}\right| \cdot \left|\dfrac{60\,\text{s}}{\text{min}}\right|$

$= \dfrac{60 \times 10^{-3} \times 2.205 \times 60}{3.281}\dfrac{\text{lb}_\text{m}}{\text{min} \times \text{ft}} = 2.42\dfrac{\text{lb}_\text{m}}{\text{min} \times \text{ft}}$

6. $200\dfrac{\text{bbl}}{\text{D}}\left|\dfrac{\text{D}}{24\,\text{hr}}\right|\dfrac{\text{hr}}{3600\,\text{S}}\left|\dfrac{\text{m}^3}{6.29\,\text{bbl}}\right| = \dfrac{200\,\text{m}^3}{24 \times 3600 \times 6.29\,\text{s}}$

$= 368 \times 10^{-6}\,\text{m}^3/\text{s}$

7. $70\,\text{md} = \dfrac{70\,\text{md}}{}\left|\dfrac{9.86 \times 10^{-16}\,\text{m}^2}{\text{md}}\right|\dfrac{\mu\text{m}^2}{(10^{-6}\text{m})^2}$

$= \underline{70 \times 9.86 \times 10^{-4}\,\mu\text{m}^2} = 0.069\,\mu\text{m}^2.$

Note that in the SI system, μm^2 means one micro-meter squared, and *not* one micro meter-squared.

C.4   **CONVERSION CONSTANTS IN EQUATIONS.** Often we wish to change the units of variables appearing in an equation. To preserve the functional relationship expressed by an equation, a unit conversion factor is introduced to the equation. We shall illustrate the conversion by a simple example to calculate mass flow rate of a liquid flowing in a pipe.

In SI units the mass flow rate equation is written as

$$\dot{m}\,(\text{kg/s}) = q\,(\text{m}^3/\text{s}) \times \rho(\text{kg/m}^3), \tag{C.3}$$

while in oil field units it is written as

$$\dot{m}\,(\text{lb}_m/\text{d}) = 5.6146q\,(\text{bbl/D}) \times \rho(\text{lb}_m/\text{ft}^3). \tag{C.4}$$

The unit factor 5.6146 in equation (C.2) will guarantee that the same mass flow rate will be calculated by the two equations.

The equation unit factor is obtained by multiplying each variable in the equation with a factor that will preserve the original numerical value in spite of changing the units of the substituted quantities. For example, if the original equation includes the mass variable expressed in lb_m, when converting to kg, the mass variable should be multiplied by 2.205 because the number of kg expressing a certain mass will be 2.205 times smaller than the number of lb_m expressing the same amount of mass. It can be, therefore, stated that changing units of variables in equation requires multiplying each variable by a dimensionless constant c, equals to the conversion factor from the new to the old unit. It, in fact, expresses the number of old units per one new unit. For example, if the mass variable m is changing units from lb_m to kg, then the variable m in the equation should be multiplied by

$$c = 2.205\,\text{lb}_m/1\,\text{kg} = 2.205\,\text{lb}_m/\text{kg},$$

If the units of a variable are complicated, it is possible to calculate c starting with one new unit and multiplying it by a series of dimensionless ratios that cancel the starting units and yield eventually the equivalent number of old units. Using the example of the variable m,

$$1\,|\,\text{kg}\,| = 1\,|\,\text{kg}\,|\left|\frac{2.205\,\text{lb}_m}{1\,\text{kg}}\right| = 2.205\,|\,\text{lb}_m\,|,$$

and the value of c is then

$$c = 2.205.$$

The change of units in equation (C.1) from SI to field units is obtained by calculating the constants c_1, c_2, and c_3, that change the units in equation (C.3), giving

$$c_1\dot{m}(\text{lb}_m/\text{d}) = c_2q\,(\text{bbl/D}) \times c_3\rho\,(\text{lb}_m/\text{ft}^3),$$

where

$$c_1 = 1 \left| \frac{\text{lb}_m}{D} \right| \times \left| \frac{1\,\text{kg}}{2.205\,\text{lb}_m} \right| \times \left| \frac{D}{86,400\,\text{s}} \right| = 5.249 \times 10^{-6},$$

$$c_2 = 1 \left| \frac{\text{bbl}}{D} \right| \times \left| \frac{\text{m}^3}{6.29\,\text{bbl}} \right| \times \left| \frac{D}{86,400\,\text{s}} \right| = 1.8401 \times 10^{-6},$$

$$c_3 = 1 \left| \frac{\text{lb}_m}{\text{ft}^3} \right| \times \left| \frac{\text{kg}}{2.205\,\text{lb}_m} \right| \times \left| \frac{35.32\,\text{ft}^3}{\text{m}^3} \right| = 16.0181,$$

or

$$c_1 = 5.249 \times 10^{-6} \frac{\text{kg/s}}{\text{lb}_m/D},$$

$$c_2 = 1.8401 \times 10^{-6} \frac{\text{m}^3/\text{s}}{\text{bbl}/D},$$

$$c_3 = 16.0181 \frac{\text{kg/m}^3}{\text{lb}_m/\text{ft}^3}.$$

Rearranging the constants c_1, c_2, and c_3 calculates a compound constant C:

$$C = \frac{c_2 c_3}{c_1} = 5.6146,$$

which appears in equation (C.4). Another example of the conversion procedure is given in example C.2.

EXAMPLE C.2

The radial flow equation, in the consistent SI system, is

$$q = \frac{2\pi k h \Delta p}{B\mu \ln(r_e/r_w)},$$

where the units are

$k\,(\text{m}^2)$,
$h\,(\text{m})$,
$\Delta p\,(\text{pa})$,
$\mu\,(\text{pa} \times \text{s})$,.
$B\,(\text{m}^3/\text{m}^3)$,
$q\,(\text{m}^3/\text{s})$.

EXAMPLE C.2 continued

Convert the equation to the customary field units system.

SOLUTION

In the consistent SI units

$$q\,(\text{m}^3/\text{s}) = \frac{2\pi k\,(\text{m}^2) \times h\,(\text{m}) \times \Delta p\,(\text{Pa})}{\mu\,(\text{Pa} \times \text{s}) \times B\,(\text{m}^3/\text{m}^3) \times \ln(r_e/r_w)}.$$

In the customary oilfield units

$$q\,(\text{bbl/D}) = C\,\frac{K\,(\text{md}) \times h\,(\text{ft}) \times \Delta p\,(\text{psi})}{\mu\,(\text{cp}) \times B\,(\text{bbl/bbl}) \times \ln(r_e/r_w)}.$$

To determine C, rewrite the given SI unit equation as

$$[c_6 \times q\,(\text{bbl/D})] = \frac{2\pi[c_1 \times k\,(\text{md})][c_2 \times h\,(\text{ft})][c_3 \times \Delta p\,(\text{psi})]}{[c_4 \times \mu\,(\text{cp})][c_5 \times B\,(\text{bbl/bbl})]\ln(r_e/r_w)}$$

where

$$c_1 = 9.86 \times 10^{-16}\,\frac{\text{m}^2}{\text{md}}$$

$$c_2 = 0.3048\,\frac{\text{m}}{\text{ft}}$$

$$c_3 = 6.89 \times 10^3\,\frac{\text{pa}}{\text{psi}}$$

$$c_4 = 10^{-3}\,\frac{\text{Pa} \times \text{s}}{\text{cp}}$$

$$c_5 = 1\,\frac{\text{m}^3/\text{m}^3}{\text{bbl/bbl}}$$

$$c_6 = 0.1589\,\frac{\text{m}^3}{\text{bbl}} \times \frac{\text{D}}{86,400\,\text{s}}$$

$$= 1.84 \times 10^{-6}\,\frac{\text{m}^3/\text{s}}{\text{bbl/D}}$$

The new constant is then

$$C = \frac{2\pi c_1 c_2 c_3}{c_4 c_5 c_6},$$

calculating

$$C = \frac{2\pi(9.86 \times 10^{-16})(0.3048)(6.89 \times 10^3)}{10^{-3}(1)(1.86 \times 10^{-6})}$$

EXAMPLE C.2 continued

$= 0.007079$

$= 1/141.3.$

The relationship between the density or gravity of well liquid (production or treatment liquid) and its hydrostatic pressure gradient is often used in well technology calculations. Assuming a homogeneous, incompressible liquid column, table C.5 lists these relationships, and table C.6 lists them as ready data in field units.

Table C.5 Customary Units to Express Density and Hydrostatic Pressure Gradient of Well Liquid

Well liquid lighter than water (at 60°F)	Well liquid heavier than water
$\gamma = \dfrac{141.5}{131.5 + °\text{API}}$	$\gamma = \rho\,(\text{lb/gal})/8.34$
$\rho\,(\text{lb/ft}^3) = \gamma \times 62.37$	$\rho\,(\text{lb/ft}^3) = \gamma \times 62.37$
$\rho\,(\text{kg/m}^3) = \gamma \times 1000$	$\rho\,(\text{kg/m}^3) = \gamma \times 1000$
$\dfrac{dp}{dh}\,(\text{psi/ft}) = \dfrac{1}{144} \times \rho\,(\text{lb/ft}^3) = 0.433 \times \gamma$	$\dfrac{dp}{dh}\,(\text{psi/ft}) = 0.052\rho\,(\text{lb/gal})$
$\dfrac{dp}{dh}(\text{Pa/m}) = 9.81 \times \gamma \times 1000$	$\dfrac{dp}{dh}\,(\text{Pa/m}) = 9.81 \left[\dfrac{\rho\,(\text{lb/gal})}{8.34} \right] \times 1000$

Table C.6 Hydrostatic Pressure Gradient of Liquids

API gravity	Fluid gradient (psi/ft)	Density (lb/gal)	Fluid gradient (psi/ft)	Density (lb/ft^3)
60	0.320	11.0	0.571	82.3
55	0.329	11.2	0.582	83.8
50	0.338	11.4	0.592	85.3
48	0.341	11.6	0.603	86.8
46	0.345	11.8	0.613	88.3
44	0.349	12.0	0.623	89.8
43	0.351	12.2	0.634	91.3
42 Diesel	0.354	12.4	0.644	92.8
41	0.355	12.6	0.655	94.3
40	0.357	12.8	0.665	95.7
39	0.359	13.0	0.675	97.2
38	0.362	13.2	0.686	98.7
37	0.364	13.4	0.696	100.2
36	0.366	13.6	0.706	101.7
35	0.368	13.8	0.717	103.2
34	0.370	14.0	0.727	104.7
33	0.373	14.2	0.738	106.2
32	0.375	14.4	0.748	107.7
31	0.377	14.6	0.758	109.2
30	0.379	14.8	0.769	110.7

Table C.6 Hydrostatic Pressure Gradient of Liquids

API gravity	Fluid gradient (psi/ft)		Density (lb/gal)	Fluid gradient (psi/ft)	Density (lb/ft³)
28	0.384		15.0	0.779	112.2
26	0.389		15.2	0.790	113.7
24	0.394		15.4	0.800	115.2
22	0.399		15.6	0.810	116.7
20	0.405		15.8	0.821	118.2
18	0.410		16.0	0.831	119.7
15	0.418		16.2	0.842	121.2
12	0.427		16.4	0.852	122.7
10 fresh water	0.433		16.6	0.862	124.2
			16.8	0.873	125.7
Density (lb/gal)	Fluid Gradient (psi/ft)	Density (lb/ft³)	17.0	0.883	127.2
			17.2	0.894	128.7
8.34 fresh water	0.433	62.4	17.4	0.904	130.2
8.4	0.436	62.8	17.6	0.914	131.6
8.6	0.447	64.3	17.8	0.925	133.1
8.8	0.457	65.8	18.0	0.935	134.6
9.0	0.468	67.3	18.2	0.945	136.1
9.2	0.478	68.8	18.4	0.956	137.6
9.4	0.488	70.3	18.6	0.966	139.1
9.6	0.499	71.8	18.8	0.977	140.6
9.8	0.509	73.3	19.0	0.987	142.1
10.0	0.519	74.8	19.2	0.997	143.6
10.2	0.530	76.3	19.4	1.008	145.1
10.4	0.540	77.8	19.6	1.018	146.6
10.6	0.551	79.3	19.8	1.028	148.1
10.8	0.561	80.8	20.0	1.039	149.6

REFERENCES

Agarwal, R. G., Carter, R. D., and Pollock, C. B.: "Evaluation and Prediction of Performance of Low Permeability Gas Wells Stimulated by Massive Hydraulic Fracturing," *J. Pet. Tech.* (March 1979) 362–372; *Trans.*, AIME, **267**.

Al-Hussainy, R., Ramey, H. J. Jr., and Crawford, P. B.: "The Flow of Real Gases through Porous Media." *J. Pet. Tech.* (May 1966) 624; *Trans.*, AIME (1966) **237**, 637–642.

Allen, T. O.: "Creative Task Force Attack on Profit Loss Due to Formation Damage," paper SPE 4658 presented at the SPE 48th Annual Meeting, Las Vegas, Sept. 30–Oct. 3, 1973.

Allis, D. H. and Capps, W. M.: "Submersible Pumping–Long Beach Unit of East Wilmington Field: A 17-year Review," *J. Pet. Tech.* (August 1984) 1321–1325.

API Bull. 11L3: "Sucker Rod Pumping System Design Book," first edition (May 1970).

API "Gas Lift": Book 6 of Vocational Training Series, Production Dept., American Petroleum Institute (1984).

API Manual 14 BM: "API User Manual for API 14B Subsurface Controlled Subsurface Safety Valve Sizing Computer Program" (1978).

API RP11L: "Recommended Practice for Design Calculations for Sucker Rod Pumping Systems (Conventional Units)," third edition (February 1977).

API RP42: "API Recommended Practices for Laboratory Testing of Surface Active Agents for Well Stimulation," second edition, American Petroleum Institute (Jan. 1977).

API RP43: "API Standard Procedure for Evaluation of Well Perforators," third edition, American Petroleum Institute (July 1983).

API Spec 11AX: "Specification for Subsurface Sucker Rod Pumps and Fittings," seventh edition (June 1979).

API Spec 11B: "Specification for Sucker Rods," nineteenth edition (May 1982).

API Std 11E: "Specification for Pumping Units," twelfth edition (January 1982).

Arps, J. J.: "Analysis of Decline Curves," *Trans.*, AIME (1945) **160**, 228–247.

Arthur, M. G.: "Fingering and Coning of Water and Gas in Homogeneous Oil Sands," *Trans.*, AIME (1944–45) 183–199.

Aymx, J. W., Bass, D. M. Jr., and Whiting, R. L.: *Petroleum Reservoir Engineering*, McGraw-Hill Book Co. Inc., New York City (1960) 520–523.

Barnes, P. F. and Tinker, G. E.: "Production Technology Experience in Michigan Waterfloods," *J. Pet. Tech.* (Aug. 1985) 1446–1458.

Barril, R. J. and Gay, L. G.: "Controlling Sand Production in High Rate Gas Wells," *World Oil* (Sept. 1983) 52–56.

Beal, C.: "The Viscosity of Air, Water, Natural Gas, Crude Oil and Its Associated Gases at Oil-Field Temperatures and Pressures," *Trans.*, AIME (1946) **165**, 94–115.

Beggs, H. D. and Brill, J. P.: "A Study of Two-Phase Flow in Inclined Pipes," *J. Pet. Tech.* (May 1973) 607–617; *Trans.*, AIME (1973) **255**.

Beggs, H. D. and Robinson, J. R.: "Estimating the Viscosity of Crude Oil Systems", *J. Pet. Tech.* (Sept. 1975) 1140–1141.

Bell, C. A. and Spisak, C. D. : "Unique Hydraulic Lift System," paper SPE 4539 presented at the SPE 48th Annual Meeting, Las Vegas Sept. 30–Oct. 3, 1973.

Bell, W. T.: "Author's Reply to Discussions of Perforating Underbalanced—Evolving Techniques." *J. Pet. Tech.* (June 1985) 1067–1068.

Bell, W. T.: "Perforating," Chapter 3 from "Production Operations Course 1—Well Completions," Buzarde, L. E., Jr., Kastor, R. L., Bell, W. T., and DePriester, C. L., Society of Petroleum Engineers, AIME (1972) 210–351.

Bell, W. T.: "Perforating Underbalanced—Evolving Techniques." *J. Pet. Tech.* (Oct. 1984) 1653–1662.

Bertness, T. A.: "Observations of Water Damage to Oil Productivity," *Drill. and Prod. Prac.*, API (1953) 287–291.

Bertuzzi, A. F., Welchon, J. K., and Poettman, F. H.: "Description and Analyses of an Efficient Continuous Flow Gas-Lift Installation," *J. Pet. Tech.* (Nov. 1953) 271–78; *Trans.*, AIME, **198**.

Bigelow, E. L.: "A Practical Approach to the Interpretation of Cement Bond Log." *J. Pet. Tech.* (July 1985) 1285–1294.

Blacker, L. K.: "An Analysis of Rate-Sensitive Skin in Oil Wells," paper SPE 11187 presented at the SPE 57th Annual Technical Conference and Exhibition, New Orleans, Sept. 26–29 1982.

Bleakley, W. B.: "Design Consideration in Choosing a Hydraulic Pumping System." *Pet. Eng. Int.* (July 1978) 22–30.

Bratli. R. K. and Risnes, R.: "Stability and Failure of Sand Arches." *Soc. Pet. Eng. J.* (April 1981) 236–248.

Brons, F. and Marting, V. E.: "The Effect of Restricted Fluid Entry on Well Productivity," *Trans.*, AIME (1961) **222**, 1972.

Brown, K. E.: *Gas Lift Theory and Practice*, The Petroleum Publishing Co., Tulsa, OK (1967).

Brown, K. E.: "Overview of Artificial Lift Systems," paper SPE 9979 presented at the SPE International Petroleum Symposium, Bejing, China, March 18–26, 1982.

Brown, K. E.: *The Technology of Artificial Lift Methods*, Penn-Well Books, Tulsa, OK (1984) **4**, 134.

Bruist, E. H.: "Better Performance of Gulf Coast Wells," paper SPE 4777 presented at the SPE Symposium on Formation Damage Control, New Orleans, Feb. 7–8, 1974.

Campbell, J. M. and Campbell, R. A.: "Application of the SI Metric System: Part 1—The Basic System," *J. Pet. Tech.* (Aug. 1985) 1415–1419.

Campbell, J. M. and Campbell, R. A.: "Application of the SI Metric System: Part 2—The Basic Units," *J. Pet. Tech.* (Oct. 1985) 1801–1805.

Campbell, J. M. and Farrar, G. L.: *Effective Communications for the Technical Man*, The Petroleum Publishing Co., Tulsa OK (1972).

Cardwell, W. T. and Parsons, R. L.: "Average Permeabilities of Heterogeneous Oil Sands," *Trans.*, AIME (1945) **160**, 34.

Centrilift–Hughes: *Electrical Submersible Pumps and Equipment*, Catalogue, Centrilift–Hughes, Inc., Claremore, OK (1983).

Centrilift–Hughes: *Submersible Pump Handbook*, third edition, Centrilift–Hughes Inc., Claremore, (1981).

Chew, J. and Conally, C. A. Jr.: "A Viscosity Correlation for Gas-Saturated Crude Oils," *Trans.*, AIME (1959) **216**, 23–25.

Cinco-Ley, H.: "Evaluation of Hydraulic Fracturing by Transient Pressure Analysis

Methods," paper SPE 10043 presented at the International Petroleum Symposium, Bejing, China, March 18–26, 1982.

Clark, N. E. and Wall, L. J.: "Development of Sycamore Limestone, Sholom Aleichem Field, Stephens and Carter Counties," *J. Pet. Tech.* (Jan. 1978) 35–42.

Clegg, J. D.: "Discussion of Economic Approach to Oil Production and Gas Allocation in Continuous Gas Lift," *J. Pet. Tech.* (Feb. 1982) 301–302.

Clegg, J. D.: "Understanding and Combating Gas Interference in Pumping Wells," *Drill. and Prod. Prac.*, API (1963).

Coberly, C. J.: "Selection of Screen Opening for Unconsolidated Sands," API Drilling and Production Practice, American Petroleum Institute (1937).

Coberly, C. J.: *Theory and Applications of Hydraulic Oil Well Pumps*, Kobe, Inc., Huntington Park, CA (1961).

Coberly, C. J. and Wagner, E. M.: "Some Considerations in the Selection and Installation of Gravel Pack for Oil Wells," Technical Publication NO. 960 of the Petroleum Division of AIME, Los Angeles Meeting, Oct. 1937 (also in Well Completions, Reprint Series, SPE, **5**.

Coltharp, E. B.: "Subsurface Electrical Centrifugal Pumps," *J. Pet. Tech.* (April 1984) 645–652.

Cooke, C. E. Jr.: "Conductivity of Fracture Proppants in Multiple Layers," *J. Pet. Tech.* (Sept. 1973) 1101–1107; *Trans.*, AIME **255**.

Cooke, C. E. Jr., Kluck, M. P., and Medrano, R.: "Field Measurements of Annular Pressure and Temperature during Primary Cementing," paper SPE 11206 presented at the SPE Annual Fall Meeting, New Orleans, Sept. 26–29, 1982.

Cornell, D. and Katz, D. L.: "Flow of Gases through Consolidated Porous Media," *Ind. and Eng. Chem.* (Oct. 1953) **45**, 2145.

Craft, B. C. and Hawkins, M. F. Jr.: *Applied Petroleum Reservoir Engineering*, Prentice-Hall Book Co., Inc., Englewood Cliffs, NJ (1959).

Cullender, M. H.: "The Isochronal Performance Method of Determining the Flow Characteristics of Gas Well," *Trans.*, AIME (1955) **204**, 137–142.

Culter, J. M. and Rees, W. A.: "A Study of Water Coning in the Oil Creek Reservoir, North Antioch Field, Oklahoma," paper SPE 2814 presented at the Second SPE Symposium on Numerical Simulation of Reservoir Performance, Dallas, Feb. 5–6, 1970.

Dietz, D. N.: "Determination of Average Reservoir Pressure From Build-Up Surveys," *J. Pet. Tech.* (Aug. 1965) 955–959; *Trans.*, AIME, **234**.

Duggan, J. O.: "Estimating Flow Rate Required to Keep Gas Well Unloaded," *J. Pet. Tech.* (Dec. 1961) 1173–1176.

Dykstra, H. and Parsons, R. L.: "The Prediction of Oil Recovery by Waterflood," *Secondary Recovery of Oil in the U.S.*, 2nd. ed., API (1950) **161**.

Eakin, J. L. and Miller, J. S.: "Removal of Water Blocks from Gas-Producing Formations," *Drill. and Prod. Prac.*, API (1965) 26–31.

Earlougher, R. C., Jr.: *Advances in Well Test Analysis*, Monograph Series, SPE, Dallas (1977) **5**.

Edwardson, M. J., Girner, H. M., Parkison, H. R., Williams, C. D. and Matthews, C. S.: "Calculation of Formation Temperature Disturbances Caused by Mud Circulation, 225, I-416"; *J. Pet. Tech.* (April 1962) **416**.

ERCB: "Calculating Subsurface Pressure via Fluid Level Recorders," Energy Resources Conservation Board, Calgary, Alberta, Canada (1978).

Evinger, H. H. and Muskat, M.: "Calculation of Theoretical Productivity Factor," *Trans.*, AIME (1942) **146**, 126–139.

Fancher, G. H., Lewis, J. A., and Barnes, K. B.: "Some Physical Characteristics of Oil Sands," *Bull.* 12, Pennsylvania State C., Minerals Industries Experiment Station, University Park, MD (1933).

Fertl, W. H., Pilkington, P. E., and Scott, J. B.: "A Look at Cement Bond Logs," *J. Pet.*

Tech. (June 1974) 607–17.

Fetkovich, M. J.: "Decline Curve Analysis and Type Curves," presentation to the Denver SPE Section, December 9, 1982.

Fetkovich, M. J.: "Decline Curve Analysis Using Type Curves," *J. Pet. Tech.* (June 1980) 1065–1077.

Fetkovich, M. J.: "The Isochronal Testing of Oil Wells," paper SPE 4529 presented at the SPE 48th Annal Meeting, Las Vegas, Sept. 30–Oct. 3, 1973.

Fetkovich, M. J.: "Multipoint Testing of Gas Wells," SPE Mid-Continental Section, Continuing Education Course, Well Testing Analysis, March 17, 1975.

Fetkovich, M. J. and Thrasher, T. S.: "Constant Well Pressure Testing and Analysis in Low Permeability Reservoirs," paper SPE 7928 presented at the SPE Regional Meeting, Denver, May 1979 (8½ × 11 copies of the slide presentation, along with a type curve, were distributed at the meeting).

Fetkovich, M. J. and Vienot, M. E.: "Shape Factor, C_A, Expressed as Skin, s_{CA}," *J. Pet. Tech.* (Feb. 1985) 321–322.

Fetkovich, M. J. and Vienot, M. E.: "Rate Normalization of Buildup Pressure Using Afterflow Data," paper SPE 12179 presented at the SPE 58th Annual Technical Conference and Exhibition, San Francisco, Oct. 5–8, 1983.

Fetkovich, M. J., Vienot, M. E., Bradley, M. D., and Kiesow, U. G.: "Decline Curve Analysis Using Type Curves—Case Histories," paper SPE 13169 presented at the SPE 59th Annual Technical Conference and Exhibition, Houston, Sept. 16–19, 1984.

Firoozabadi, A. and Katz, D. L.: "An Analysis of High-Velocity Gas Flow through Porous Media," *J. Pet. Tech.* (Feb. 1979) 211–216.

Fitzgerald, D. D., McGhee, B. F., and McGuire, J. A.: "Guidelines for 90% Accuracy in Zone Isolation Decisions," paper SPE 12141 presented at the SPE 58th Annual Technical Conference and Exhibition, San Francisco, Oct. 5–8, 1983.

Flanigan, M. J.: "Smaller Gravel and Coated Screens Enhance 50-Year-Old Field," *J. Pet. Tech.* (May 1980) 575–763.

Forchheimer, P.: "Hydraulik", thirth edition. Leipzig und Berlin Vorlag und Druck Von B. G. Teubner (1930) 54. (in German)

Forchheimer, P.: "Wasserbewegung durch Boden," Zeitz. Ver. Deutsch Ing., Berlin (1901) **45**, 1781–1788. (in German)

Fussell, D. D.: "Single-Well Performance Predictions for Gas Condensate Reservoirs," **255**, I-860; *J. Pet. Tech.* (July 1973) 860.

Geertsma, J.: "Estimating the Coefficient of Inertial Resistance in Fluid Flow through Porous Media," *Soc. Pet. Eng. J.* (Oct. 1974) 445–450.

Gibbs, S. G.: "Predicting the Behavior of Sucker-Rod Pumping Systems," *J. Pet. Tech.* (July 1963) 769–778.

Gibbs, S. G.: "A Review of Method for Design and Analysis of Rod Pumping Installations," *J. Pet. Tech.* (Dec. 1982) 2931–2939.

Gilbert, W. E.: "Flowing and Gas-Lift Well Performance," *Drill. and Prod. Prac.*, API (1954) 143.

Gladfelter, R. E., Tracy, G. W., and Wilsey, L. E.: "Selecting Wells Which Will Respond to Production-Stimulation Treatment," *Drill. and Prod. Prac.*, API (1955) 117–128.

Goeken, R. J.: "Report on the Methods and Results of Concentric-Tubing Workovers". *Drill. and Prod. Prac.*, API (1958) 7–18.

Gondouin, M. et al.: "An Attempt to Predict the Time Dependence of Well Deliverability in Gas Condensate Fields," 240, II-113; *SPEJ* (June 1967) 113.

Green, L. and Duwez, P.: "Fluid Flow through Porous Materials," *J. Appl. Mech.* (March 1951) **18**, 39.

Griffin, F. D.: "New API Design Calculations for Sucker-rod Pumping Systems," *Drill. and Prod. Prac.*, API (1968).

Grosmangin, M., Kokesh, F. P., and Majani, P.: "A Sonic Method for Analyzing the Quality of Cementation of Borehole Casing," *J. Pet. Tech.* (Feb. 1961) 165–171; *Trans.*, AIME, **222**.

Guin, J. A. and Schechter, R. S.: "Matrix Acidization with Highly Reactive Acids," *Soc. Pet. Eng. J.* (Sept. 1971) 390–398; *Trans.*, AIME, **251**.

Gurley, D. C., Copeland, C. T., and Hendrick, J. O.: "Design, Plan and Execute Gravel Pack Operations for Maximum Productivity." *J. Pet. Tech.* (Oct. 1977) 1259–1266.

Hall, C. D. and Harrisberger, W. H.: "Stability of Sand Arches: A Key to Sand Control," *J. Pet. Tech.* (July 1970) 821–829.

Hamby, T. W. and Richardson, E. A.: "Shell's Sand Consolidation Experience—Delta Division," *Drill. and Prod. Prac.*, API (1968) 207–211.

Harris, M. N.: "The Effect of Perforating on Well Productivity," *Trans.*, AIME (1966) **237**, 518.

Hekin, Y., Fogler, H. S., and McCune, C. C.: "The Radial Movement of Permeability Fronts and Multiple Reaction Zones in Porous Media," *J. Pet. Tech.* (Feb. 1982) 94–107.

Hill, A. D., Lindsay, D. M., Silberberg, I. H., and Schechter, R. S.: "Theoretical and Experimental Studies of Sandstone Acidizing," *Soc. Pet. Eng. J.* (Feb. 1981) 30–42.

Holden, W. W., Prihoda, C. H., and Hall, B. E.: "Successful Stimulation of Fordoche Field with a Retarded HF Acid," *J. Pet. Tech.* (Aug. 1981) 1485–1490.

Hong, K. C.: "Productivity of Perforated Completions in Formations With or Without Damage," *J. Pet. Tech.* (August 1975) 1027–1038.

Houpeurt, A.: "Etude Analogique de L'Ecoulement Radial Circulaire Transitore des Gas Dans les Millieux Poreux," *Revue de l'Institute Francais du Petrole et Annales des Combustibles Liquides* (1953) **VIII**, 4, 5, 6.

Howard, R. A. and Watson, M. S. Jr.: "Relative Productivity of Perforated Casing," Parts I and II, *Trans.*, AIME (1950) **189**, 179, 323.

Hurst, W.: "Establishment of the Skin Effect and Its Impediment to Fluid Flow into a Well Bore," *Pet. Eng.* (Oct. 1953) B-6–B-16.

Hydraulic Institute: *Hydraulic Institute Standards for centrifugal, Rotary, and Reciprocating Pumps*", thirteenth edition, Hydraulic Institute, Cleveland, OH (1975).

Jacob, C. E. and Lohman, S. W.: "Nonsteady Flow to a Well of Constant Drawdown in an Extensive Aquifer," *Trans.*, AGU (Aug. 1952) 559–569.

Jones, F. O. Jr. and Lummus, J. L.: "Fluid-Loss Reducer for Clear Water." *Drill. and Prod. Prac.*, API (1959) 17–23.

Jones, L. G. and Slusser, M. L.: "The Estimation of Productivity Loss caused by Perforations—Including Partial Completion and Formation Damage," paper SPE 4798 presented at the Second Midwest Oil and Gas Symposium of SPE–AIME, Indianapolis, March 28–29, 1974.

Jones, L. G. and Watts, J. W.: "Estimating Skin Effect in a Partially Completed Damaged Well," *J. Pet. Tech.* (Feb. 1971) 249–252; *Trans.*, AIME, **251**.

Katz, D.L., Cornell, D., Kobayashi, R., Poettmann, F. H., Vary, J. A., Elenbaas, J. R., and Weinaug, C. F.: *Handbook of Natural Gas Engineering*, McGraw-Hill Book Company, New York City (1959).

Kelley, R. S.: "Productivity Determination and Pump Resizing Using Variable-Speed Electric Submersible Pump," *J. Pet. Tech.* (Sept. 1980) 1503–1508.

Kelly, T. S.: "Discussions of Perforating Underbalanced—Evolving Techniques," *J. Pet. Tech.* (June 1985) 1065–1067.

Kilvington, L. J. and Gallivan, J. D.: "Beatrice Field: Electrical Submersible Pump and Reservoir Performance 1981–1983," *J. Pet. Tech.* (Nov. 1984) 1934–1948.

King, G. E. and Hollingsworth, F. H.: "Evaluation of Diverting Agent Effectiveness and Cleanup Characteristics Using a Dynamic Laboratory Model—High Permeability Case," paper SPE 8400 presented at the SPE 54th Annual Technical Conference and Exhibition, Las Vegas, Sept. 23–26, 1979.

Kleyweg, D., Tiemann, W. D., and Dalziel, S. G.: "Gaslift Optimization—Claymore Field," paper SPE 11885 presented in Offshore Europe 83 Conference, Aberdeen, Scotland, September 6–9, 1983.

Klotz, J. A., Krueger, R. F., and Pye, D. S.: "Effect of Perforation Damage on Well Productivity," *J. Pet. Tech.* (Nov. 1974).

Knapp, R. H., Planty, R., and Voiland, E. J.: "A Gravel Coating Aqueous Epoxy Emulsion System for Water-Based Consolidation Gravel Packing: Development and Application," *J. Pet. Tech.* (Nov. 197.) 1489–1496.

Kobylinski, L. S., Taylor, F. T., and Brienan, J. W.: "Development and Field Test Results of and Efficient Downhole Centrifugal Gas Separator," *J. Pet. Tech.* (July 1985) 1295–1304.

Krueger, R. F. and Vogel, L. C.: "Damage to Sandstone Cores by Particles from Drilling Fluids," *Drill. and Prod. Prac.*, API (1954) 158–171.

Krueger, R. F., Fischer, P. W., and Vogel, L. C.: "Effect of Pressure Drawdown on the Cleanup of Clay- or Silt-Blocked Sandstone," *J. Pet. Tech.* (March 1967) 397–403.

Lake, F. W.: "Relation of Air–gas Lift to Gas–Oil Ratios and Effect on Ultimate Production," *Trans.*, AIME 77 (1927) 173–188.

Lea, J. F.: "Avoid Premature Liquid Loading in Tight Gas Wells Using Prefrac and Postfrac Test Data," *Oil and Gas J.* (Sept. 20, 1982) 123–128.

Lea, J. F. and Bearden, J. L.: "Effect of Gaseous Fluids on Submersible Pump Performance," *J. Pet. Tech.* (Dec. 1982) 2922–2930.

Lea, J. F. and Bearden, J. L.: "Gas Separator Performance for Submersible Pump Operation," *J. Pet. Tech.* (June 1982) 1327–1333.

Locke C. D. and Sawyer, W. L.: "Constant Pressure Injection Test in a Fractured Reservoir—History Match Using Numerical Simulation and Type Curve Analysis," paper SPE 5594 presented at the SPE 50th Annual Technical Conference and Exhibition, Dallas, Sept. 28–Oct. 1, 1975.

Locke, S.: "An Advanced Method for Predicting the Productivity Ratio of a Perforated Well," *J. Pet. Tech.* (Dec. 1981) 2481–2488.

Lund. K., Fogler, H. S., and McCune, C. C.: "On Predicting the Flow and Reaction of HCl/HF Acid Mixtures in Porous Sandstone Cores," *Soc. Pet. Eng. J.* (Oct. 1976) 248–260; *Trans.*, AIME, **261**.

Maly, G. P.: "Close Attention to the Smallest Job details Vital for Minimizing Formation Damage," paper SPE 5702 presented at the SPE Symposium on Formation Damage Control, Houston, Jan. 29–30, 1976.

Maly, G. P. and Krueger, R. F.: "Improper Formation Sampling Leads to Improper Selection of Gravel Size," *J. Pet. Tech.* (Dec. 1971) 1403–1408.

Matthews, C. S. and Lefkovitz, H. S.: "Studies on Pressure Distribution in Bounded Reservoirs at Steady State," *Trans.*, AIME (1955) **204**, 182–189.

McCoy, J. N.: "Determining Producing Bottomhole Pressures in Wells Having Gaseous Columns," *J. Pet. Tech.* (Jan. 1978) 117–119.

McCoy, J.N., Podio, A. L., and Huddleston, K. L.: "Acoustic Producing Bottomhole Pressures," paper SPE 14254 presented at the SPE 60th Annual Technical Conference and Exhibition, Las Vegas, Sept. 22–25, 1985.

McCune, C. C., Fogler, J. S., Lund, K., Cunningham, J. R., and Ault, J. W.: "A Model for the Physical and Chemical Changes in Sandstone during Acidizing," paper SPE 5157 presented at the SPE 50th Annual Technical Conference and Exhibition, Dallas, Sept. 28–Oct. 1, 1975.

McDowell, I. M. and Muskat, M.: "The Effect on Well Productivity of Formation Penetration beyond Perforated Casing," *Trans.*, AIME (1950) **189**, 309, 323.

McGuire, W. J. and Sikora, V. J.: "The Effect of Vertical Fractures on Well Productivity," *Trans.*, AIME (1960) **219**, 401–403.

McLeod, H. O.: "Matrix Acidizing," *J. Pet. Tech.* (Dec. 1984) 2055–2060.

McLeod, H. O. Jr.: "The Effect of Perforating Conditions on Well Performance," *J. Pet.*

Tech. (Jan. 1983) 31–39.

Meyers, K. O., Skillman, H. L., and Herring, G. D.: "Control of Formation Damage at Prudhoe Bay, Alaska, by inhibitor Squeeze Treatment," *J. Pet. Tech.* (June 1985) 1019–34.

Millhone, R. S.: "Completion Fluids For Maxamizing Productivity—State of The Art," *J. Pet. Tech.* (Jan. 1983) 47–55.

Millikan, C. V. and Sidewell, C. V.: "Bottomhole Pressure in Oil Wells," *Trans.*, AIME (1931) **92**, 194–205.

Mondshine, I.: "Crystalline Salt Systems Proving Valuable in Drilling/Completing", *Oil and Gas J.* (Jan. 19, 1981) 79–82.

Moody, L. F.: "Friction Factors for Pipe Flow," *Trans.*, AIME (Nov. 1944) **66**, 671–684.

Moody, W. C.: "API Specifications for Subsurface Pumps and Fittings," *Drill. and Prod. Prac.*, API (1961) 128–134.

Muecke, T. W.: "Principles of Acid Stimulation," paper SPE 10038 presented at the SPE Technical Symposium, Bejing, China, March 18–26, 1982.

Mullins, L. D., Baldwin, W. F., and Berry, P. M.: "Surface Flowline Sand Detection," paper SPE 5152 presented at the Second Midwest Oil and Gas Symposium of the SPE, Indianapolis, March 28–29, 1974.

Mungan, N.: "Permeability Reduction through Changes in PH and Salinity," *J. Pet. Tech.* (Dec. 1965) 1449–1453.

Muskat, M.: "The Effect of Casing Perforations on Well Productivity," *Trans.*, AIME (1943) **151**, 175–187.

Muskat, M.: *The Flow of Homogeneous Fluids Through Porous Media*, first edition, McGraw-Hill Book Company, Inc., New York City. (1937); second edition, International Human Resources Development Corporation, Boston, MA (1982).

Muskat, M.: "Partially Penetrating Wells in Isotropic Formations; Potential Distribution," *Physics* (1932) **2**, 329.

Muskat, M: *Physical Principles of Oil Production*, first edition McGraw-Hill Book Company, Inc., New York City (1949); second edition International Human Resources Development Corporation, Boston, MA (1981).

Muskat, M. and Evinger, H. H.: "Calculations of Theoretical Productivity Factors," *Trans.*, AIME (1942) **149**, 126–139.

Neely, A. B. and Patterson, M. M.: "Soft Start of Submersible Pumped Oil Wells," *J. Pet. Tech.* (April 1984) 653–656.

Neely, B., Gibson, F., Clegg, J., Capps, B., and Wilson, P.: "Selection of Artificial Lift Method," paper SPE 10337 presented at the SPE 56th Annual Technical Conference and Exhibition, San Antonio, October 5–7, 1981.

Nierode, D. E. and Williams, B. B.: "Characteristics of Acid Reactions in Limestone Formations," *Soc. Pet. Eng. J.* (Dec. 1971) 406–418; *Trans.*, AIME **251.**

Nisle, R. G.: "The Effect of Partial Penetration on Pressure Build-Up in Oil Wells," *Trans.*, AIME (1958) **213**, 85.

Nowak, T. J. and Krueger, R. F.: " The Effect of Mud Filtrates and Mud Particles upon the Permeability of Cores," *Drill. and Prod. Prac.*, API (1951) 164–181.

Odeh, A. S.: "An Equation for Calculating Skin Factor Due to Restricted Entry," *J. Pet. Tech.* (June 1980) 964–965.

Odeh, A. S.: "Pseudosteady-State Flow Capacity of Oil Wells with Limited Entry and an Altered Zone around the Wellbore," *Soc. Pet. Eng. J.* (Aug 1977) 271–178; *Trans.*, AIME, **270.**

Odeh, A. S.: "Steady-State Flow Capacity of Wells with Limited Entry to Flow," *Trans.*, AIME (1968) **243**, 43.

O'Dell, H. G. and Miller, R. N.: "Successfully Cycling a Low-Permeability, High-Yield Gas Condensate Reservoir," *J. Pet. Tech.* (Jan. 1967), 41; discussion 47.

Pardue, G. H., Morris, R. L., Gollwitzer, L. H., and Moran, J. H.: "Cement Bond Log—A

Study of Cement and Casing Variables," *J. Pet. Tech.* (May 1963) 545–555; *Trans.*, AIME, **228.**

Patton, L.D.: "Comparative Energy Requirement of Oilfield Pumping Units—Conventional vs. Front-Mounted," *J. Pet. Tech.* (Jan 1965) 26–32.

Penberthy, W. L. Jr. and Cope, B. J.: "Design and Productivity of Gravel Packed Completions," paper SPE 8428 presented at the SPE Annual Fall Meeting, Las Vegas, Sept. 23–26, 1979.

Perry, J. H. Editor: *Chemical Engineers Handbook*, fourth edition, McCraw-Hill Book Company, Inc., New York City (1963).

Peters, F. W. and Stout, C. M.: "Clay Stabilization during Fracturing Treatments with Hydrolyzable Zirconium Salts," *J. Pet. Tech.* (Feb. 1977) 187–194.

Petrie, H. L., Wilson, P. M., and Smart, E. E.: "Jet Pumping Oil Wells," three-part series, *World Oil* (Nov., Dec. 1983, and Jan. 1984.) Part 1, 51–56; Part 2, 109–114; Part 3, 101–108.

Poettmann, F. H. and Carpenter, P. G.: "Multiphase Flow of Gas, Oil, and Water through Vertical Flow Strings with Application to the Design of Gas-Lift Installations". *Drill. and Prod. Prac.*, API (1952) 257–317.

Raghavan, R.: "Well Test Analysis: Well Producing by Solution-Gas Drive," *J. Pet. Tech.* (Aug. 1976) 196–208; *Trans.*, AIME, **261.**

Ramey, H. J. Jr.: "Non-Darcy Flow and Wellbore Storage Effects in Pressure Buildup and Drawdown of Gas Wells," *J. Pet. Tech.* (Feb. 1965) 223–233; *Trans.*, AIME, **234.**

Rawlins, E. L. and Schellhardt, M. A.: *Back-Pressure Data on Natural Gas Wells and Their Application to Production Practices*, U. S. Bureau of Mines Monograph 7 (1936).

Reda Pump Division: "Submergible Pumps for the Petroleum Industry". Catalogue, TRW (1983).

Redden, J. D., Sherman, T. A. G., and Blann, J. R.: "Optimizing Gas Lift Systems," SPE 5150 paper presented at the SPE 49th Annual Meeting, Houston, Oct. 6–9, 1974.

Richardson, E. A. and Hamby, T. W.: "Consolidation of Silty Sands with and Epoxy Resin Overflush Process," *J. Pet. Tech.* (Sept. 1970) 1103–1108.

Rike, J. L.: "A Small Coiled-tubing Workover Rig". *Drill. and Prod. Prac.*, API (1967) 57–65.

Risnes, R., Bratli, R. K., and Horsrud, P.: "Sand Arching—A Case Study," paper EUR 310 presented at the European Petroleum Conference, London, England, October 25–28, 1982.

Roemershauser, A. E. and Hawkins, M. F.: "The Effect of Slant Hole Drainhole and Lateral Hole Drilling on Well Productivity", *J. Pet. Tech.* (Feb. 1955) 11–14.

Ros, N. C. J.: "An Analysis of Critical Simultaneous Gas/Liquid Flow through a Restriction and Its Application to Flowmetering," *Appl. Sci. Res.* (1960) **9**, Section A, 374.

Rowland, D. A.: "Pressure Buildup and Drawdown Behavior in Undersaturated Reservoirs of Discontinuous Permeability". Ph. D. thesis, Stanford U., Stanford, CA (1969).

Sage, V. R.: "Reel Tubing Units are Growing with Nitrogen," *Oil and Gas J.* (Sept. 3, 1979) 103–105.

Saucier, R. J.: "Considerations in Gravel-Pack Design," *J. Pet. Tech.* (Feb. 1974) 205–212.

Saucier, R. J. and Lands, J. F.: "A Laboratory Study of Perforations in Stressed Formation Rocks", *J. Pet. Tech.* (September 1978) 1347–1353.

Saunders, L. W. and McKinzie, H. L.: "Performance Review of Phenolic-Resin Gravel Packing," paper SPE 8425 presented at the SPE 54th Annual Technical Conference and Exhibition, Las Vegas, Sept. 23–26, 1979.

Schlumberger Well Services: *The Essentials of Cement Evaluation*, Schlumberger Well Services, Houston, TX (March 1976).

Schlumberger Well Services: *The Essentials of Perforating*, Schlumberger Well Services, Houston, TX.

Schmoe, W. P.: "Bottom-hole gas Separation increase Production," *Drill. and Prod. Prac.* API, (1958) **42**, 42–47.

Schwartz, D. H.: "Successful Sand Control Design for High-Rate Oil and Water Wells," *J. Pet. Tech.* (Sept. 1969).

Shaughnessy, C. M. and Kline, W. E.: "EDTA Removes Formation Damage at Prudhoe Bay," *J. Pet. Tech.* (Oct. 1983) 1783–92.

Shaughnessy, C. M. and Kunze, K. R.: "Understanding Sandstone Acidizing Leads to Improved Field Practices," *J. Pet. Tech.* (July 1981) 1196–1202.

Simmons, W. E.: "Optimizing Contiuous Flow Gas-Lift Wells," *Pet. Eng. Intl.* (Aug. 1972) 46–48, (Sept. 1972) 68–72.

Skinner, D. R.: "Efficient Use of Electric Power in Production Operations," *J. Pet. Tech.* (Aug. 1984) 1326–1334.

Slator, D. T. and Hanson, W. E. Jr.: "Continuous-String Light Workover Unit," *J. Pet. Tech.* (Jan. 1965) 39–44.

Sparlin, D. D.: "Fight Sand with Sand—A Realistic Approach to Gravel Packing," paper SPE 2649 presented at the SPE 44th Annual Meeting, Denver, Sept. 28–Oct. 1, 1969.

Sparlin, D. D.: "Sand and Gravel—A Study of Their Permeabilities," paper SPE 4772 presented at the SPE symposium on Formation Damage Control, New Orleans, Feb. 7–3, 1974.

Standing, M. B.: "Concerning the Calculation of Inflow Performance of Wells Producing from Solution-Gas Drive Reservoirs," *J. Pet. Tech.* (1971) 1141–1142.

Standing, M. B.: "A Pressure–Volume–Temperature Correlation For Mixtures of California Oils and Gases," *Drill. and Prod. Prac.*, API (1947) 275–287.

Standing, M. B.: *Reservoirs*, Course Manual in Reservoir Engineering Continental Shelf Development, Petroleum Industry Courses, NTH Trondheim (1980).

Standing, M. B.: *Volumetric and Phase Behavior of Oilfield Hydrocarbon Systems*, 9th printing, Society of Petroleum Engineers of AIME, Dallas, TX (1981).

Standing, M. B. and Katz, D. L.: "Density of Natural Gases," *Trans.*, AIME (1942) **146**, 140–149.

Stearns, G. M.: "An Experimental Investigation of the Volumetric Efficiency of Sucker Rod Pumps," *Drill. and Prod. Prac.*, API (1943) 108.

Stein, N.: "Designing Gravel Packs for Changing Well Conditions," *World Oil* (Feb. 1, 1983) 41–47.

Stein, N.: "Mechanical Properties of Friable Sands from Conventional Log Data," *J. Pet. Tech.* (July 1976) 757–763.

Stein, N., Odeh, Y., and Jones, Z.: "Estimating Maximum Sand-Free Production Rates From Friable Sands for Different Well Completion Geometries," *J. Pet. Tech.* (Oct. 1974) 1156–1158; *Trans.*, AIME, **257**.

Streltsova-Adams, T. D.: "Pressure Drawdown in a Well with Limited Flow Entry," *Soc. Pet. Eng. J.* (Nov. 1979) 1469–1476.

Streltsova-Adams, T. D. and McKinley, R. M.: "Effect of Partial Completion on the Duration of Afterflow and Beginning of the Formation Straight Line on Horner Plot," *J. Pet. Tech.* (March 1981) 550–552.

Strohm, P. J., Mantooth, M. A., and DePriester, C. L.: "Controlled Injection of Sand Consolidation Plastic," *J. Pet. Tech.* (April 1967) 487–494.

Suman, G. O. Jr., Ellis, R. C., and Synder, R. E.: *Sand Control Handbook*, second edition, Gulf Publishing Co., Houston, TX (1983).

Swetnam, J. K. and Sackash, M. L.: "Performance Review of Tapered Submersible Pumps in the Three-Bar Field," *J. Pet. Tech.* (Dec. 1978) 1781–1787.

Tait, H. C. and Hamilton, R. M.: "A Rod Pumping System to Reduce Lifting Cost," *J. Pet. Tech.* (Nov. 1984) 1971–1978.

Tarner, J.: "How Different-Size Gas Caps and Pressure Maintenance Affect Amount of

Recoverable Oil," *Oil Weekly* (June 12, 1944) 32.

Tausch, G. H. and Corley, C. B.: "Sand Exclusion in Oil and Gas Wells". *Drill. and Prod. Prac.*, API (1958) 66–82.

Tek, M. R., Grove, M. L. and Poettman, F. H.: "Method for Predicting the Back Pressure Behavior of Low-Permeability Natural Gas Wells," *Trans.*, AIME (1957) **210**, 302–309.

Tek, M. R., Coats, K. H., and Katz, D. L.: "The Effect of Turbulence on Flow of Natural Gas through Porous Reservoirs," *J. Pet. Tech.* (July 1962) 799–806; *Trans.*, AIME, **225.**

Tessem, R.: "High-Velocity Coefficient's Dependence of Rock Properties: A Laboratory Study". Thesis, Pet. Inst., NTH, Norway (Dec. 1980) 26.

Thompson, G. D.: "Effects of Formation Compressive Strength on Perforator Performance," *Drill. and Prod. Prac.*, API (1962).

Thompson, J. K.: "Use of Constant Pressure, Finite Capacity Type Curve for Performance Prediction of Fractured Wells in Low-Permeability Reservoirs," paper SPE/DOE presented at the SPE/DOE Low-Permeability Symposium, Denver, May 27–29, 1981.

Tinsley, J. M., Williams, J. R., Tiner, R. L., and Malone, W. T.: "Vertical Fracture Height—Its Effect on Steady-State Production Increase," *J. Pet. Tech.* (May 1969) 633–638.

Tracy, G. W.: "Simplified Form of the Material Balance Equation," *Trans.*, AIME (1955) **204**, 243.

Tsarevich, K. A. and Kuranov, I. F.: "Calculation of the Flow Rates for the Center Well in a Circular Reservoir under Elastic Conditions," *Problems of Reservoir Hydrodynamics*, Part I, Leningrad (1966) 9–34.

Turner, R. G., Hubbard, M. G., and Dukler, A. E.: "Analysis and Predictions on Minimum Flow Rate for the Continuous Removal of Liquids from Gas Wells," *J. Pet. Tech.* (Nov. 1969) 1475–1482.

Tyler, T. N., Metzger, Q. Q., and Twyford, L. Q.: "Analaysis and Treatment of Formation Damage at Prudhoe Bay, Alaska," *J. Pet. Tech.* (June 1985), 1010–1018.

van Everdingen, A. F.: "The Skin Effect and Its Influence on the Productive Capacity of a Well", *Trans.*, AIME (1953) **198**, 171–176.

van Everdingen, A. F. and Hurst, W.: "The Application of the Laplace Transformation to Flow Problems in Reservoirs," *Trans.*, AIME (1949) **186**, 305–324.

Vazquez, M. and Beggs, H. D.: "Correlations for Fluid Physical Property Prediction," *J. Pet. Tech.* (June 1980) 968–970.

Veatch, R. W. Jr.: "Overview of Current Hydraulic Fracturing Design and Treatment Technology," *J. Pet. Tech.*, Part 1 (April 1983) 677–687; Part 2 (May 1983) 853–864.

Veley, C. D.: "How Hydrolyzable Metal Ions React with Clays to Control Formation Water Sensitivity," *J. Pet. Tech.* (Sept. 1969) 1111–1118.

Vetter, O. J.: "Oilfield Scale—Can We Handle It!" *J. Pet. Tech.* (Dec. 1976) 1402–1408.

Vogel, J. V.: "Inflow Performance Relationships for Solution-Gas Drive Wells," *J. Pet. Tech.* (Jan. 1968) 83–92; *Trans.*, AIME, **243**.

Walker, T.: "A Full-Wave Display of Acoustic Signal in Cased Holes," *J. Pet. Tech.* (Aug. 1968) 811–824.

Warren, J. E. and Price, H. S.: "Flow in Heterogeneous Porous Media," *Trans.*, AIME, **222** (1961) II, 153.

Wattenberger, Robert A. and Ramey, H. J. Jr.: "Gas Well Testing with Turbulence, Damage, and Wellbore Storage," *J. Pet. Tech.* (Aug. 1968) 877–887; *Trans.*, AIME, **243**.

Westerman, G. W.: "Successful Application of Pump-off Controllers", paper SPE 6853 presented at the SPE 57th Annual Technical Conference and Exhibition, Oct. 9–12, 1977.

Whitson, C. H.: "Reservoir Well Performance and Predicting Deliverability", paper SPE 12518 (Nov. 1983).

Williams, B. B., Elliot, L. S., and Weaver, R. H.: "Productivity of Inside Casing Grave-Pack Completions," *J. Pet. Tech.* (April 1972) 419–425.

621

Williams, B. B., Gidley, J. L., and Schechter, R. S.: *Acidizing Fundamentals*, Monograph Senes, SPE, Dallas (1979) **6**.

Williamson, D. R.: "A Case Study of Electrical Submersible Pumps in the Q-1 Block, Dutch Sector", paper SPE 12970 presented at the 1984 European Petroleum Conference, London, England, October 25–28, 1984.

"Willis General Catalogue", Willis, Division of Smith International, Inc. Long Beach, CA (1979).

Winestock, A. G. and Colpitts, G. P.: "Advances in Estimating Gas Well Deliverability," *J. Can. Pet. Tech.* (July–Sept. 1965) 111–119.

Woelfline, W.: "Viscosity of Crude-Oil Emulsions," *Drill. and Prod. Prac.* API (1942) 148–153.

Wycoff, R. D., Botset, H. G., Muskat, M., and Meres, M. W.: "Flow of Gas–Liquid Mixtures through Sand," *Physics* (1936) **7**, 325–345, 346–363; *Trans.*, AIME (1937) **123**, 69–96.

SELECTED EXERCISES

CHAPTER 1

1.1 Design production manifold for the recently discovered Alma oil field. The field is planned for development with six production wells. The separation station will consist of two parallel, single-stage, two-phase production separators (A and B) and one three-phase test separator (T).

1.2 The existing production manifold in the Betula land field gathers the production of nine high-rate oil wells. Six of the wells are producing from the main pay zone, Betula A, and three from the secondary pay zone, Betula B.

Presently, the separation station consists of one two-stage, two-phase production train and one single-stage, three-phase test separator. The oil from the production train is transferred directly to a wash-tank and then to a storage tank. The separator gas is transferred to a low-pressure gas line through a gas metering station.

After seven years of production, three of the Betula A wells which drain the flank of the reservoir are showing a significant increase in water cut. At the same time, the wells producing the Betula B are showing a severe pressure decline (due to volumetric depletion).

Task: Propose modifications to the separation station to account for the changes in the production characteristics. Design for two optional modifications:

1. modification of the piping system only, without modifying the existing separators;
2. adding separators and/or changing two-phase to three-phase separators.

Present your solution in the form of a simple piping and instrumentation diagram (PID).

1.3 An important criterion in sizing a production tubing for high-rate oil wells is to maintain flow velocity below a certain critical value called *erosional velocity*. A widely accepted formula to calculate the critical erosional velocity, v_e, is given in the API RP 14-E:

$$v_e = c/(\rho_m)^{0.5}$$

where c is an empirical constant ranging between 125 for noncontinuous service to 100 for continuous service, and ρ_m is the average density of the oil and gas mixture prevailing in a cross section along the tubing.

Show that ρ_m can be expressed in terms of reservoir parameters as

$$\rho_m = \frac{m_o + m_g}{V_o + V_g} = \frac{12367\,\gamma_o p + 2.7\,R_p \gamma_g}{198.7p + R_p T}$$

where

m_o, m_g = free oil and gas masses
V_o, V_g = oil and gas volumes
γ_o = stock-tank oil gravity (water = 1.0)
γ_g = gas gravity (air = 1.0)
R_p = production gas/oil ratio, scf/STB
T = absolute temperature, °R
p = prevailing pressure in a tubing cross section
Z = gas compressibility (assume Z = 1.0)
ρ_m = average mixture density

1.4 Express the equation for the erosional velocity in problem 1.3 as q_o versus p relationship where p is the average flowing pressure in a given pipe cross section. Plot the relationship for the following well conditions:

pipe internal diameter .... 3.922 in.
flowing oil temperature (isothermal flow) .... 140°F
stock-tank oil gravity... °API 32
gas gravity.. 0.75 (air = 1.0)
production gas/oil ratio....................................... 600 scf/STB

1.5 Reservoir oil in the OK No. 1 oil well enters the perforations at approximately the bubble-point pressure.
    Calculate the density of the oil entering the wellbore given the following reservoir data:

bubble-point pressure, p_R..................................... 2426 psia
formation volume factor (at bubble point), B_o................. 1.21 Resbbl/STB
solution gas/oil ratio, at bubble point R_s .... 350 scf/STB
gas gravity, γ_g (air = 1.0)................................... 0.7
stock-tank oil gravity, γ_{API} .... 30°API

1.6 Oil well No. FB-32 (Fortune field, Central North Sea) has a productivity index of 35 STB/D/psi. The reservoir pressure is 2671 psia at mid-perforation depth of 6900 ft. The water fraction is 0.6.
    Tasks:

1. Draw the IPR curve in two versions:
   a. for total liquid production
   b. for oil production only

   Assume linear IPR curve down to atmospheric pressure.

2. Determine the required draw-down to produce a total liquid rate of 10,000 bbl/ D. Verify that the considered rate maintains a flowing bottomhole pressure above the bubble point (1900 psia).

3. To select and size a high-rate pump to be installed at a 5188-ft depth, it is necessary to plot the pump suction pressure versus liquid flow rate. Plot the rate versus pressure at 5188 ft assuming a 0.364 psi/ft constant average gradient of the well fluid flowing in the casing below the pump.

1.7 To verify a suspicion that increasing water cut in oil well San-Mateus 2 is due to water channeling behind the casing, the well has been tested by a multirate test. Test results are reported in table P-1.7 below. Determine the IPR of the oil zone from test data assuming it does not produce any water. Assess the recommendation to shut-in the well until the well will be worked over to repair the cement. The reservoir is undersaturated with low GLR oil.

Table P-1.7 San-Mateus Test Results

p_{wf} (psia)	q_{Total} (STB/D)	water cut (%)
4000	50	100
3750	130	55
3500	212	32
3000	335	25
2000	500	25
1000	612	26

Note:

$q_{Total} = q_o + q_w$
water cut $= q_w/q_{Total}$

1.8 The results of a multirate test of the Elk City No. 3 gas well are given in table P-1.8 below.
   Tasks:

1. Plot the backpressure curve and determine the coefficient C, and the exponent n, of the backpressure equation.
2. Express the backpressure equation in a normalized form:

$$q_g/q_{max} = [1 - (p_{wf}/p_R)^2]^n.$$

Table P-1.8 Multirate Test of the Elk City No. 3

Test point	p_{wf} (psia)	q_g (MMscf/D)
Shut-in	3355	0.000
1	3314	1.012
2	3208	2.248
3	2992	3.832
4	2651	5.486

1.9 The Vogel equation can be modified empirically to fit both non-darcy flow conditions and changes in reservoir conditions occurring with depletion or progressing water flood. The modified equation is

$$q_o/q_{max} = [1 - v(p_{wf}/p_R) - (1 - v)(p_{wf}/p_R)^2]^n$$

where

n = backpressure coefficient
v = reservoir fitting factor (depends on the depletion state and the water fraction in water-flooded reservoir)

Task: Rearrange the equation and write it as

$$p_{wf} = f(q_o)$$

1.10 The Haskell No. 3 oil well is producing from a solution-gas drive reservoir. Draw the IPR curve as determined by the following equations:

1. Vogel IPR equation
2. Modified Vogel equation with $V = 0.3$ and $n = 1.0$ (problem 1.9)
3. Backpressure equation with $n = 1$
4. Backpressure equation with $n = 0.8$

Well and single-rate test data:

Reservoir pressure.. 4000 psia
Bubble-point pressure .... 4200 psia
Test oil rate... 200 STB/D
Test bottomhole pressure .... 3220 psia

1.11 The oil well Ekofisk No. B-11 is producing from an undersaturated oil reservoir. Well data and single-rate test data are listed below. Draw the IPR of the well above and below the bubble point and determine the Absolute Open Flow (AOF).

Reservoir pressure.. 7200 psia
Bubble-point pressure .... 5200 psia
Test rate .... 4500 STB/D
Test bottomhole pressure .... 5600 psia

Table P-1.12 Multirate Test Data of C-5 Gas Well

p_{wf} (psia)	q_g (MMscf/D)
440	0.00
439.9	0.57
438.5	2.23
435	4.84
426	8.38
412	12.5

1.12 Plot the multirate test data of the C-5 gas well on a Cartesian graph paper and identify the coefficients A and B of the quadratic equation.

1.13 Compare the natural flow conditions of oil well Aroma No. 3 with the two alternative tubing configurations illustrated in figure P-1.13.

Additional well data:

Wellhead pressure .... 200 psia
Gas/liquid ratio .... 600 scf/STB
Flow gradient in the 5.5-in. liner................................ 0.31 psi/ft

IPR at 8000 ft is

$$q/480 = [1 - (p_{wf}/4000)^2]^{0.8}$$

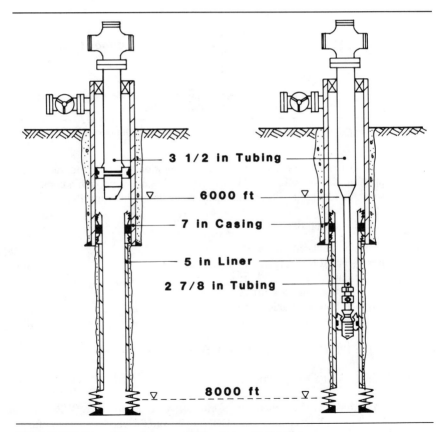

Figure P-1.13 Two options for recompleting Aroma-3 oil well.

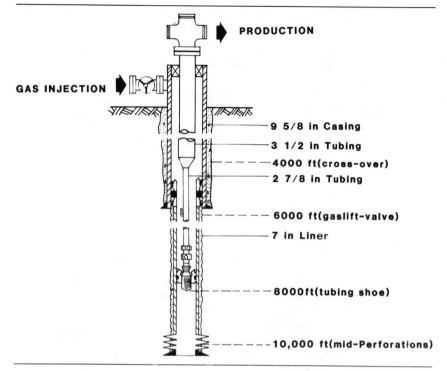

Figure P-1.14 The production string of the NTH-45 gas-lifted well.

1.14 Determine the equilibrium flow conditions (production rate and downhole pressure) in oil well No. NTH 45. The well is designed with a complex production string including gas-lift arrangement as illustrated in figure P-1.14.

Additional well data:

Constant wellhead pressure .... 200 psia
Reservoir GLR .... 600 scf/STB
Water cut 0%
Gas injection rate (gas lift)................................. 1200 scf/STB
Average flowing gradient in the liner.......................... 0.35 psi/ft
Reservoir pressure .... 5600 psia

The IPR of the well (at 10,000 ft) can be presented by

$$q_o/680 = [1 - (p_{wf}/4800)^2]^{0.8}$$

1.15 Construct the wellhead performance relationship curve (WPR) for the Aroma No. 3 oil well (problem 1.13). Determine from the curve the natural flow rates with wellhead pressures 100, 200, 300, 400, and 800 psia.

1.16 Construct the choke performance curve (CPR) for a 10/64 choke in oil well No. NTH 45 (problem 1.14) for two cases:

1. natural flow;
2. gas lift with gas injection rate of 1200 scf/STB at the bottom of the tubing.

The downstream choke pressure is constantly maintained at 50 psia.

1.17 Determine the natural flow conditions in the No. NTH 45 oil well (problems 1.14 and 1.16) when operating with a 10/64 choke. Investigate two production cases, natural flow, and gas lift with injection rate 1200 scf/STB. In addition, determine the choke size that will control a flow rate of 480 STB/D.

1.18 Construct the tubing intake performance curve (TPR) for oil well Aroma No. 3 (problems 1.13 and 1.15) with a fixed choke. Use the plot to investigate the stability of the natural flow conditions.

Well and choke data:

Tubing size .... $2\frac{7}{8}$ in.
Tubing depth .... 8000 ft
GLR .... 600 scf/STB
Choke opening.. $\frac{10}{64}$ in.
Separator (downstream choke) pressure .... 50 psia

IPR at 8000 ft is

$$q/480 = [1 - (p_{wf}/4000)^2]^{0.8}$$

CHAPTER 2

2.1 According to the reservoir development plan, well Ronia No. 27 will drain a circular-shaped reservoir with data specified below.
Tasks:

1. Draw the pressure distribution diagram, given

$$q_o = 1324 \text{ STB/D}$$

$$p_{wf} = 1600 \text{ psia}$$

2. Estimate the productivity index and plot the IPR of the well.

Well data:

Reservoir pressure	2370 psia
Permeability-thickness product	3640 md-ft
Oil formation volume factor	1.24 bbl/STB
Oil viscosity	1.62 cp
Wellbore radius	0.29 ft
Drainage area (no-flow outer boundaries)	80 acres
Skin factor	0
Bubble-point pressure	1400 psia

2.2 A skin factor of $+12$ was calculated from transient test data of the Ronia No. 27 oil well (problem 2.1). Determine the effect of the skin factor on the production rate when the well is producing with a draw-down of 400 psi (compare the production rate with and without skin factor).

2.3 Data on oil well No. B-29 is given in the table below. The well is completed in a carbonate reservoir and has been stimulated upon completion by injecting HCl acid.
   Tasks:

1. Calculate the pre- and post-stimulation production rates if the draw-down is limited to 450 psi.
2. Calculate the pre- and post-stimulation flow efficiencies.
3. Calculate the pre- and post-stimulation apparent wellbore radius.
4. Draw the pre- and post-stimulation IPR.

Well data:

Well spacing	80 acres
Wellbore radius, r_w	0.29 ft
Pay-zone thickness, h	80 ft
Formation volume factor, B_o	1.5 bbl/STB
Reservoir pressure, p_R	7055 psia
Bubble-point pressure, p_b	4800 psia
Permeability, k	24 md
Oil viscosity, μ_o	0.31 cp
Pre-stimulation skin factor, s	$+18.5$
Post-stimulation skin factor, s	-4.2

2.4 Determine the productivity index and the IPR of oil well Linn No. 3 at the present and at a future time. The well is producing from an undersaturated oil reservoir with a very low bubble-point pressure. Repeat the calculations for a situation where the well spacing in the field is to be reduced from 80 acres to 40 acres.

Well data:

$$r_w = 0.29 \text{ ft}$$
$$\text{well spacing} = 80 \text{ acres } (r_e = 1053 \text{ ft})$$

$$h = 40 \text{ ft}$$
$$k = 24 \text{ md}$$
$$s = +6$$

	p_R (psia)	B_o (bbl/STB)	μ_o (cp)
present	3000	1.23	0.76
future	2700	1.3	0.71

2.5 Calculate the pseudopressure function for the gas properties shown in table P-2.5.

Table P-2.5 Gas Properties

p (psia)	μ (cp)	Z
0		
15	0.0127	0.998
400	0.0130	0.960
800	0.0135	0.925

2.6 Determine the initial IPR of gas well Bingo No. 2 using the low-pressure (pressure-squared) approach and the real gas potential approach. The well is located in the center of a circular drainage area. Gas properties are listed in table P-2.6. Other well and reservoir data are:

Reservoir temperature, T_R .... 680°R
Reservoir pressure, p_R .... 4400 psia

Table P-2.6 Gas Properties

p (psia)	μ (cp)	Z
400	0.01286	0.937
800	0.01390	0.882
1200	0.01530	0.832
1600	0.01680	0.794
2000	0.01840	0.770
2400	0.02010	0.763
2800	0.02170	0.775
3200	0.02340	0.797
3600	0.02500	0.827
4000	0.02660	0.880
4400	0.02831	0.896

Permeability thickness product, kh .... 338 md-ft
Initial gas viscosity, μ_{gi} .... 0.0283 cp
Gas compressibility factor, Z_i 0.896
Skin factor, s .... $+3$
Rate-dependent skin coefficient, D .... $1.5 \times 10^{-6} \ (scf/D)^{-1}$
Wellbore radius, r_w .... 8.5 in.
Drainage area .... 160 acres

2.7 Develop an equation expression explicitly q_g versus $m(p)$ in the presence of a high-rate skin factor Dq_g.

2.8 Develop an analytical expression for the IPR of wells in saturated oil reservoirs using the approximation that $[k_{ro}/(\mu_o B_o)]$ versus p relationship is a straight line.

2.9 Predict the deterioration of the IPR of a well in an undersaturated reservoir where reservoir conditions are expected to change according to table P-2.9.

Table P-2.9 Depletion Characteristics

N_p (bbl)	P_R (psia)	$(\mu_o B_o)$ (cp)
5×10^6	4200	1.2
10×10^6	4100	1.1
15×10^6	4000	1.0

Additional well data:

$$k = 78 \text{ md}$$

$$h = 50 \text{ ft}$$

$$ln(r_e/r_w) = 7$$

$$s = +7$$

2.10 Predict the deterioration of the IPR in Campina wells and draw the respective IPR curves. Campina has a saturated oil reservoir producing by solution-gas drive and gas cap expansion. The predicted reservoir behavior is given in table P-2.10. A test of a key appraisal well, Campina No. 3, concluded that the initial IPR can be expressed by the backpressure equation where the initial q_{max} is 480 STB/D and the backpressure exponent is 0.8.

Table P-2.10 Campina Oil Field-Calculated Reservoir Behavior

N_p (bbl)	p_R (psia)	$k_{ro}/\mu_o B_o$ (1/cp)	R (scf/STB)
0	4000	0.2234	600
10×10^6	3520	0.1470	1000
20×10^6	3100	0.1117	1600
30×10^6	2800	0.0714	2500
40×10^6	2500	0.0446	5000
50×10^6	2300	0.0440	4800

2.11 Investigate the effect of reservoir depletion on the parameters in the saturated oil IPR equation.

$$q_o = \frac{(2\pi kh)}{ln(r_e/r_w) - 3/4 + s + s_A + Dq_o} \frac{(k_{ro}/\mu_o B_o)}{2p_R} (p_R^2 - p_{wf}^2)$$

and derive an expression for the ratio

$$\frac{(q_{omax})_{present}}{(q_{omax})_{future}}$$

Note: In the derivation, assume that the rate-dependent skin factor Dq is related to the exponent "n" in the backpressure equation. Furthermore, Dq can be eliminated by applying the exponent n to the following term in the radial flow equation:

$$\left\{ \frac{k_{ro}/\mu_o B_o}{2p_R} (p_R^2 - P_{wf}^2) \right\}^n$$

Similarly, express the backpressure constant "C" in terms of reservoir parameters and derive an expression for the ratio

$$\frac{C_{present}}{C_{future}}$$

2.12 Suggest an appropriate expression for parameters A and B in the quadratic equation that will fit the equations derived for gas wells from the radial flow model.

a. low-pressure gas:

$$q_g = \frac{0.703kh(p_R^2 - p_{wf}^2)}{\mu zT[ln(r_e/r_w) - 3/4 + s + Dq_g]}$$

b. high-pressure gas:

$$q_g = \frac{1.406 \, (p/\mu Z) \, (p_R - p_{wf})}{T[ln(r_e/r_w) - 3/4 + s + Dq_g]}$$

c. general gas solution:

$$q_g = \frac{0.703 \, kh \, [m(p_R) - m(p_{wf})]}{T[ln(r_e/r_w) - 3/4 + s + Dq_g]}$$

In addition, suggest the changes that will occur in the parameters of the quadratic equation during depletion.

Note: Consider that an ideal volumetric depletion follows the following expression:

$$p_R/Z = (p_R/Z)_i(1 - G_p/G)$$

where G is the volume of the initial gas in place and G_p is the cumulative gas production.

CHAPTER 3

3.1 A service company proposed to stimulate oil well Davis No. 3 using acid wash. The company estimates that the existing skin factor of $s = +7$ can be removed, and expects that the post-stimulation skin will be $s = -2$.

Task: Draw the IPR before and after stimulation.

Well data:

$$q_o/q_{max} = [1 - (p_{wf}/p_R)^2]^n$$

where

$$q_{max} = 480 \, \text{STB/D}$$

$$p_R = 4000 \, \text{psia}$$

$$n = 0.8$$

$$s = +7$$

$$ln(r_e/r_w) = 7$$

3.2 Well testing analysis in an oil well determined a skin factor of $+5.6$ due to formation damage. Using the radial damage model, plot the corresponding k_a versus r_a relationship.

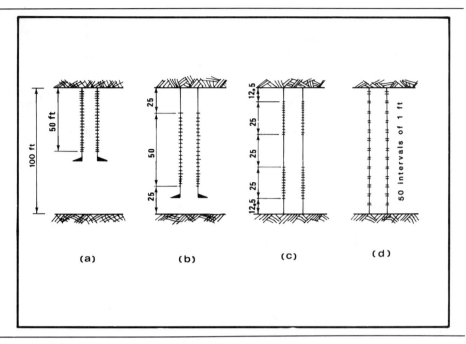

Figure P-3.3 Configurations of pay-zone penetration.

3.3 Compare the skin factor and the flow efficiency of the four perforation configurations illustrated in figure P-3.3

Additional well data:

$$k_H/k_v = 10$$

$$ln(r_e/r_w) - 0.75 = 7.0$$

$$r_w = 0.29 \text{ ft}$$

3.4 Equation 3.18, which determines the onset of the high-velocity flow effect, has been derived from the condition

$$\frac{\Delta p_{\text{non-darcy}}}{\Delta p_{\text{darcy}} + \Delta p_{\text{non-darcy}}} = 0.05$$

by using the following approximations:

$$1/r_a = 1/r_w$$

$$\beta_a = (2.73 \times 10^{10})k_a^{-1}$$

$$(1/r_a - 1/r_e)\beta_R = 0$$

Repeat the derivation of equation 3.18 and comment on the assumptions used.

3.5 Assess the need for a multirate test (versus single rate) given the following well data:

h	$= 100$ ft
h_p	$= 40$ ft
r_w	$= 0.33$ ft
B_o	$= 1.388$ STB/Resbbl
μ_o	$= 0.586$ cp
k	$= 500$ md
k_a	$= 125$ md
s	$= +6$ (geometric constant skin)
R_s	$= 725$ scf/STB
γ_{STO}	$= 0.825$ (water $= 1.0$)
γ_g	$= 0.7$ (air $= 1.0$)

Note: Oil density at reservor conditions is calculated using equation 1.27 in section 1.2.

3.6 Data for typical Eureka oil field wells are given in the list as follows.

1. Calculate the constants "A" and "B" to be used with the quadratic IPR equation.
2. Compare the effect of the high-velocity flow component with Darcy's model component given a flow rate of 4200 STB/D. Express your comparison as a ratio:

$$Bq_o^2/(Aq_o + Bq_o^2)$$

Well data:

Permeability	500 md
Pay-zone thickness	100 ft
Perforation interval (top penetration), hp	40 ft
Wellbore radius	0.33 ft
Drainage radius (radial no-flow boundaries)	527 ft
Constant (geometric skin factor)	$+6.22$
Reservoir pressure	2628 psia
Bubble point of reservoir fluid	2600 psia
Initial formation volume factor	1.388 bbl/STB

Initial oil relative permeability 1.0
Initial solution gas .... 72 scf/STB
Gas gravity 0.7
Oil-specific gravity (standard conditions) 0.825
Initial oil viscosity .... 0.586 cp
Formation damage permeability (assumed) .... 125 md
Damage thickness (assumed) .... 2 in

3.7 A model of the NTH No. 17 oil well pay zone upon completion is illustrated in figure P-3.7

The well is scheduled for treatment with acid to restore the original permeability near the wellbore.

Calculate the total skin factor for the illustrated model (both the constant and the rate-dependent skin) before and after the stimulation.

Well data:

Bit size .... $12\frac{1}{4}$ in.
Production casing .... $8\frac{5}{8}$ in.
Perforation density .... 4 shot/ft
Perforation phasing .... 180°

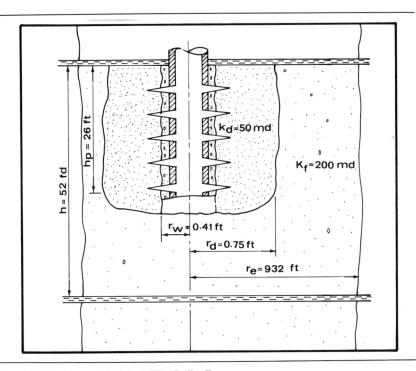

Figure P-3.7 Skin model of the NTH 17 oilwell.

Charge size (diameter)	0.5 in.
Charge type..	Welex Super Dyna Jet
API Berea penetration (TTP)	6.5 in.
Formation compressive strength	8000 psi
Berea compressive strength............................	6500 psi
Pay-zone depth..	9000 ft
Average overburden pressure	1.0 psi/ft
Pay-zone pore pressure................................	5000 psia
Formation permeability................................	200 md
Initial formation damage	50 md
Perforation crashed zone permeability..................	20 md
Perforation crashed zone thickness.....................	0.5 in.
Perforation interval...................................	26 in.

Note: Recent studies concluded that the crashed zone is less detrimental to productivity than the "weak" zone surrounding it. Assume, therefore, that the crush zone model accounts for the permeability impairment around the perforation tunnel, both in the crushed and weak zone.

3.8 A multirate test on the Jaffina No. 2 oil well indicates a total constant skin factor of $+22$. Estimate the combined effect of formation damage and partial penetration considering that they are the two most important contributors to the existing skin factor (all other contributors are negligible).

Well data:

Wellbore radius	0.29 ft
Pay-zone thickness	313 ft
Perforation interval (top pay = zone penetration), h_p	70 ft
Horizontal permeability...	978 md
Horizontal-to-vertical permeability ratio	10

3.9 Suggest a correction to equation 3.47,

$$s_T = s_c + s_a(h/h_p),$$

to account for the anomaly in the results. For negative s_a, the equation calculates a decreasing total skin factor with decreasing pay-zone penetration.

3.10 Well testing analysis of the Ronia No. 7L oil well concluded a total skin factor of $+58$ with negligible rate-dependent skin. As part of a diagnostic work conducted to determine the causes of the high skin, the components $s_c = +3$ and $s_p = +2$ were calculated from correlations. To assess the magnitude of possible formation damage and the effect of perforation flow efficiency, perform the following tasks:

1. Plot s_{dp} versus s_a relationship for the given s_T, s_c, s_p, and (h/h_p).
2. Plot k_{dp} versus k_a relationship as calculated from s_p and s_{dp} models.

3. Indicate on the above plots points corresponding to core flow efficiency (CFE in API RP 43) of 0.2, 0.6, 0.8, and 1.0.
4. Assess the ambiguity in determining the extent of formation damage in this well and comment on the assumptions regarding r_w, r_a, r_p, r_{dp}, L_p, k_a, and k_{dp}.

Well data:

Wellbore radius, r_w.. 0.37 ft
Formation permeability, k .... 42 md
Pay-zone thickness, h .... 100 ft
Perforated interval, h_p .... 62 ft
Perforation shot density.. 4 SPF
Perforation entry hole (diameter)....................................... 0.5 in.
Perforation penetration (corrected from L_{pB}), L_p .... 4.5 in.

Design assumptions:

Radius of damage, r_a.. 1 ft
Crushed zone radius, r_{dp}... 0.75 in.

3.11 Derive equation 3.40 for condensate blockage skin. Start the derivation with the condensate material balance expressed as

$$dS_o = (dv_o/v_{\text{pore}})$$

where

$$dv_o = q(\text{dt})(\text{dC})$$

3.12 Results of sieve analysis for a Gulf Coast well are given in table P-3.12. Determine the formation sand-size distribution and the corresponding gravel and screen sizes to be used with gravel pack.

Table P-3.12 Sieve Analysis

U.S. Sieve Number	Retained weight (gm)
30	2.5
50	7.9
100	28.1
140	32.5
200	41.1
325	45.2
pan	25.2

3.13 The oil well No. PPT-1 has been gravel-packed. The well is producing a single-phase oil from an undersaturated reservoir.
    Tasks:

1. Determine s_G.
2. Determine D_G.
3. Determine pressure drop due to the gravel pack alone at a production rate of 2500 STB/D.
4. Determine the pressure drop due to the gravel pack in a case when the well would be perforated with 4 shoot/ft instead of 8 shoot/ft considered originally.

Well data:

Reservoir permeability	400 md
Pay-zone thickness...	50 ft
Reservoir pressure	6200 psia
Formation volume factor (oil)	1.636 bbl/STB
Producing gas/oil ratio	1100 scf/STB
Oil-specific density	0.85
Gas gravity...	0.75
Bubble-point pressure..	5620 psia
Oil viscosity (initial)..	0.310 cp
Bubble-point oil viscosity	0.301 cp
Wellbore radius...	0.31 ft
Drainage radius...	1039 ft
Perforated interval (top pay zone)	30 ft
Perforation density...	8 shoot/ft
Perforation penetration (API RP 43), L_p	6 in.
Perforation diameter	0.5 in.
Gravel size (US MESH)	20/40

3.14 Calculate the average permeability of a contributing pay zone which measured core permeabilities as listed in table P-3.14.

Table P-3.14 Core Analysis Report

Sample	Depth (ft)	Permeability (md)	Rock Type
1	6831	0.0	shale
2	6832	0.0	shale
3	6833	631	sandstone
4	6834	982	sandstone
5	6835	1030	sandstone
6	6836	1700	sandstone
7	6837	900	sandstone
8	6838	740	sandstone
9	6839	0.0	shale
10	6840	0.0	shale
11	6841	0.0	shale
12	6842	1600	sandstone
13	6843	3010	sandstone

Table P-3.14 (continued)

Sample	Depth (ft)	Permeability (md)	Rock Type
14	6844	950	sandstone
15	6845	0.0	shale
16	6846	0.0	shale
17	6847	0.0	shale
18	6848	550	sandstone
19	6849	970	
20	6850	1900	sandstone
21	6851	1100	
22	6852	90	sandstone
23	6853	0.0	shale
24	6854	0.0	shale

CHAPTER 4

4.1 Reservoir characteristics of the Campina oil field are listed in table P-2.10. The corresponding IPRs were determined and plotted in problem 2.10.

Twenty wells are planned for developing the field. A typical well will be completed with $2\frac{7}{8}$-in. $\times$ 8000-ft production tubing. Mid-perforation depth (IPR reference depth) is 8000 ft. The initial q_{max} is 480 STB/D and the backpressure exponent is 0.8.

To assess the time that the field can be produced by natural flow before it will be necessary to introduce artificial lift, perform a production study that will include the following tasks:

1. Determine the decline of the wellhead pressure if a typical well in the field will produce at a constant rate of 100 STB/D.
2. Determine the cumulative production (per well and for the entire field) to the end of the plateau if the minimum allowable wellhead pressure is 300 psia.
3. Determine the time length of the above plateau rate (number of production days). Consider that all 20 wells are producing throughout the entire plateau period.
4. Explain the effect of well stimulation on the plateau level and the plateau length in tasks 2 and 3.
5. What will be the level and the length of the plateau rate (for the entire field) if the number of wells is increased to 30?
6. Determine the rate decline of an individual well (total number of wells is 20) if the wells will produce at a constant wellhead pressure of 200 psia.
7. Determine the production time elapsed from start-up until an individual well will reach a minimum economical rate of 150 STB/D.

4.2 Estimate the end of the infinite acting period and the start of the pseudosteady state production of Lima No. 2 gas well. The well is producing from a low-

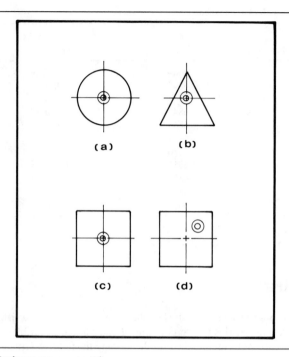

Figure P-4.2 Drainage area geometries.

permeability reservoir. As the shape of the drainage boundaries is not yet fully established, perform the calculation assuming the four drainage area shapes illustrated in figure P-4.2

Well and reservoir data:

Permeability... 2.2 md
Porosity.. 0.28
Total compressibility (initial) .... 0.00032 psi^{-1}
Well drainage area .... 160 acres
Initial gas viscosity... 0.021 cp

4.3 The transient behavior of the Labuan No. 12 oil well will be tested by producing the well at a constant production rate of 500 STB/D during the transient period. A constant rate will be maintained by a positive displacement pump.
   Tasks:

1. Determine the time to reach steady state.
2. Plot the pressure decline for the first 96 hours.

Reservoir and well data for the Labuan No. 12 oil well:

Net pay-zone thickness	45 ft
Average reservoir pressure	3500 psia
Oil viscosity	0.73 cp
Oil formation volume factor	1.45 bbl/STB
Total compressibility	$11.4 \times 10^6 \text{ psi}^{-1}$
Wellbore radius	0.29 ft
Skin factor	0.0
Drainage shape	radial
Drainage area	160 acres

4.4 Determine the rate decline of the Labuan No. 12 oil well (problem 4.3) during the transient period should it produce at a constant pressure of $pwf = 2800$ psia.

4.5 Typical well and reservoir data for wells in the Angora oil field are given below.

Permeability	0.75 md
Initial reservoir pressure	3000 psia
Initial oil viscosity	0.2 cp
Oil formation volume factor	1.642 bbl/STB
Pay-zone thickness	66 ft
Wellbore radius	0.33 ft
Total compressibility	$30 \times 10^6 \text{ psi}^{-1}$
Porosity	0.117
Water saturation	0.32
Well spacing	40 acres

Tasks:

1. Calculate the time to the end of the transient production.
2. Plot the transient wellbore pressure from start-up until the end of the transient period given that the well will produce (by sucker rod pump) at a constant rate of 80 STB/D.
3. Investigate the effect of
   (a) higher rate
   (b) larger skin factor
   (c) higher reservoir pressure
   (d) lower permeability
   on the period of transient production.
4. Investigate the effect of larger skin factor on the pressure decline at a constant production rate.

4.6 The oil well Abu-Jilda No. 13 is producing at a constant pressure. Its declining rate is recorded in table P-4.6
   Tasks:

1. Identify the decline exponent, b, the coefficient D, and the initial depletion rate, q_{oi}, to be used with Arps depletion equations.
2. Assess the drive mechanism in the reservoir.

Table P-4.6 Rate Decline in the Abu-Jilda Oil Well

t (month)	q_o (STB/month)
0.5	30000
14	9000
19	6532
25	4621
31	3541
39	2861
45	2252
50	1869
56	1593
67	1157
75	1040

4.7 Backpressure plots of isochronal test data of the Free No. 4 gas well exhibits a decrease of the backpressure coefficient, C. The decreasing coefficients are listed in table P-4.7.

Determine the steady-state value of C to be used with the steady-state IPR.

Table P-4.7 Backpressure Coefficients

Time (hr)	C
0.1	1.396
0.2	1.242
0.5	0.873
1.0	0.783
3.0	0.630
24	0.539

Well data:

Radius of drainage	3000 ft
Wellbore radius	0.29 ft
Backpressure exponent, n	0.867
Pay-zone thickness	120 ft
Permeability	30 md
Porosity	0.13
Formation temperature	90°F
Initial gas viscosity	0.012 cp
Gas compressibility factor	0.925
Total compressibility	0.0016 psi^{-1}

4.8 The Alma No. 13 gas well which produces from a tight carbonate reservoir, was tested by a true isochronal test. Test results are listed in table P-4.8
   Tasks:

1. Plot the results as backpressure curves and determine the backpressure exponent, n.
2. Use the type-curve match technique to predict the stabilized backpressure coefficient, C,
3. Explain why a simple flow-after-flow multirate test is impractical in this well.
4. Discuss the effect of test rates on the stabilization time of the well.

Well data:

Reservoir pressure .... 1898 psia
Porosity 0.13
Gas saturation 0.48
Gas viscosity .... 0.0155 cp
Effective gas permeability...................................... 9 md
Drainage boundaries radius .... 2980 ft

   Gas compressibility can be calculated by

$$c_g = 1/p$$

where p is in psia.
   Total compressibility can be calculated by

$$c_t = S_g/p.$$

Table P-4.8 Isochronal Test Data of Alma No. 13

Flow Time (hr)	q_g (MMscf/D)	p_{wf} (psia)
1	6.208	1682
2	"	1664
4	"	1646
Shut-in overnight		
1	5.291	1707
2	"	1693
4	"	1671
Shut-in overnight		
1	3.041	1754
2	3.041	1747
4	"	1742
Shut-in overnight		
1	1.822	1768
2	"	1767

4.9 The production rate of oil well No. A-08 in the Timor field has been declining rapidly during the first three production years. Simultaneously, the wellhead pressure has been declining also.

Verify that the rate decline is normal and that it is due to normal reservoir depletion rather than due to abnormal decrease in productivity. Perform the task using depletion type-curve analysis.

Production data recorded during the first 38 months and the corresponding flowing bottomhole pressure calculated from the recorded wellhead pressure are given in table P-4.9.

Additional well data:

Initial reservoir pressure .... 2590 psia
Wellbore radius .... 0.318 ft
Porosity... 0.25
Initial viscosity... 0.4 cp
Total initial compressibility .... 0.000148 psi^{-1}
Formation volume factor...................................... 1.3 bbl/STB
Net pay-zone thickness .... 54 ft

Table P-4.9 Production Characteristics of Well No. A-08

Month	q_o (STB/D)	GOR (scf/STB)	p_{wh} (psia)	p_{wf} (psia)
1	3522	1573	798	1944
2	3145	2022	764	1858
3	3145	1854	755	1818
4	3019	1910	755	1792
5	3019	2022	755	1796
6	2893	2022	726	1733
7	2767	1966	682	1653
8	2767	2022	653	1621
9	2717	2022	653	1609
10	2642	2022	624	1559
11	2755	1910	624	1582
12	2673	2022	581	1516
13	2516	2416	568	1477
14	2453	2472	552	1445
15	2390	2472	552	1439
16	2201	2697	508	1389
17	2107	3147	508	1332
18	2013	3034	479	1302
19	1950	2921	435	1199
20	1918	2921	435	1190
21	1887	2921	421	1166
22	1824	2865	421	1149
23	1736	2809	406	1108
24	1698	2921	406	1085
25	1667	2921	392	1078
29	1509	2472	363	1003
38	1132	2697	261	800

CHAPTER 5

5.1 Construct the pumping diagram and determine the maximum rate that can be produced from the Ras-Hafif No. 113–78 oil well (Zone V Ras-Hafif reservoir). Indicate on the diagram the suction and the discharge pressures.

Well data:

IPR (at 8000 ft):

$$q_o/q_{max} = [1 - (p_{wf}/p_R)^2]^n$$

where

q_{omax} = 600 STB/D

p_R = 2800 psia

n = 0.8

Mid-perforations	8000 ft
Tubing	$3\frac{1}{2}$ in.
Casing	7 in.
Pump installation depth	6000 ft
Minimum required pump submergence	100 ft (oil)
Wellhead pressure	200 psia
Casing-head (annulus) pressure	200 psia

Design assumptions:

a.	Average pressure gradient of gas in the annulus	0.05 psi/ft
b.	Average flowing gradient in the casing	0.387 psi/ft
c.	Average hydrostatic gradient or aerated annulus liquid	0.384 psi/ft
d.	Average pressure loss in the tubing (hydrostatic + friction)	0.42 psi/ft

PVT data at 250 psia:

Formation volume factor, B_o	1.072 bbl/STB
Solution gas, R_s	38 scf/STB

Note: In reality, all the listed pressure gradients depend, to varying degree, on the production rate. Assuming constant gradients is acceptable for preliminary design calculations.

5.2 Construct a pumping diagram for the Balluza No. 3 oil well. The well is producing with 50 psia bottomhole pressure. The pump is installed in the rat hole below the perforations.

Well data:

IPR at mid-perforations (5500 ft):

$qo = 0.32(1500 - pwf)$

Tubing...	3.5 in.
Casing	7 in.
Wellhead pressure...	200 psia
Pump installation depth......................................	6200 ft
Casing head (annulus) pressure	20 psia

Design assumptions:

Tubing flowing gradient	0.39 psi/ft
Rat-hole gradient (from perforations to pump)..................	0.385 psi/ft

5.3 The Balluza No. 4 oil well is producing with a 30 psia bottomhole pressure. Construct the pumping diagram and determine the suction and discharge pressures.

Well data:

Reservoir pressure (at mid-perforations 5500 ft)..............	1500 psia
Productivity index...	0.32 STB/D/psi
Tubing...	$2\frac{7}{8}$ (2.44 in. ID)
Pump installation depth......................................	4000 ft
Wellhead pressure...	2000 psia
Water cut..	0%
Stock-tank oil gravity	22 oAPI
Gas gravity	0.75 (air = 1.0)
Tubing roughness	0.00015 in.

PVT properties of the oil at 38 psia:

$B_o = 1.0$ STB/Resbbl

$R_s = 12$ scf/STB

Flowing gradient in the casing below the pump....................	0.39 psi/ft
Average oil viscosity in the well.................................	0.35 cp

To calculate pressure loss of single-phase incompressible fluid flow in horizontal pipes, use the following equation:

$$\Delta p_{\text{friction}} = f_m \frac{Lv^2\rho}{2g_c d}$$

where

$$f_m = 64/Re \qquad \text{for } Re < 2200$$
$$f_m = \{-1.8 \log[(6.9/Re) + \epsilon/3.7d]^{1.11}\}^{-2} \qquad \text{for } Re > 2200$$

and

$Re = \rho dv/\mu$
d = internal diameter, ft
v = average flow velocity, ft/sec
ρ = fluid density, lb_m/ft^3
μ = viscosity, lb/ft-sec
p = pressure, lb/ft^2
g_c = 32.2 $(lb_m \, ft/sec^2)/lb_f$
L = pipe length, ft

Useful conversions to oil-field units:

1. V ft/sec = $0.012q/d_i^2$
   where q is in bbl/D and d_i is in inches.
2. 1 cp = 0.000672 lb/(ft-sec)

5.4 Reservoir and production studies concluded that the IPR of the Ras-Hafif No. 113–78 oil well (exercise 5.1) will deteriorate according to the conditions in table P-5.4.

Table P-5.4 Production Conditions of Ras-Hafif No. 113–78 Oil Well

N_p (bbl)	p_R (psia)	q_{omax} (STB/D)	n
0	2800	600	0.8
5×10^6	2700	560	0.8
10×10^6	2500	500	0.8
15×10^6	2300	380	0.8

Ras Hafif development plans call for drilling and completing 25 to 30 wells to produce annually 2.5×10^6 bbl/year from zone V.
   Tasks:

1. Determine the pump-setting depth that will allow the production of 300 STB/D from each well for a period of six years without changing pump setting.
2. Investigate the alternative where the pump will be set initially as shallow as possible to allow production of 493 STB/D at initial stage (as calculated in exercise 5.1). Subsequently, determine the rate adjustments necessary to maintain the minimum pump submergence as long as possible without lowering the pump in the well. Recompletion and pump lowering will take place only when the rate will reach the minimum economical limit of 100 STB/D.

5.5 The characteristics of a jet pump when pumping a single phase liquid are expressed by a function relating the dimensionless pumping pressures to the dimensionless pumping rate. The relationship can be written as

$$p_D = \frac{N(m_D)}{1 + k_n - N(m_D)}$$

where

$$N(m_D) = 2A_D + [1 - (2A_D)]\frac{m_D^2 A_D^2}{(1 - A_D)^2}\frac{\rho_n}{\rho_f} - (1 + k_{td})(m_D + 1)^2 A_D^2 \frac{\rho_n}{\rho_m}$$

and

$$p_D = \frac{\Delta p_{\text{pump}}}{\Delta p_{\text{motor}}} = \frac{\Delta p_{\text{gained}}}{\Delta p_{\text{supplied}}} = \frac{p_d - p_f}{p_n - p_d} = \text{Dimensionless pumping pressure}$$

$$m_D = \frac{m_{\text{well-fluid}}}{m_{\text{power-fluid}}} = \frac{q_f \rho_f}{q_n \rho_n} = \text{Dimensionless pumping mass flow rate}$$

$$A_D = \frac{A_n}{A_t} = \text{Dimensionless pump size (cross section)}$$

In addition, pump efficiency is expressed as

$$E = \frac{(\text{power})_{\text{output}}}{(\text{power})_{\text{input}}} = \frac{(q\Delta p)_{\text{out}}}{(q\Delta p)_{\text{in}}} = \frac{(p_d - p_f)q_f}{(p_n - p_d)q_n} = m_D\, p_D(\rho_n/\rho_f)$$

The above expressions use the following nomenclature:

Flow areas, A, in.^{2}:

a_n, nozzle
a_t, throat
$a_e = (a_t - a_n)$, throat entrance

Pressures, p, psia:

p_n, nozzle upstream
p_d, discharge
p_f, pump suction
p_e, throat entrance (start mixing point)

Volumetric flow rate, q, B/D:

q_n, nozzle power fluid
q_f, well fluid (total)
q_o, well oil
q_m, discharged mixture

Density, , lb_m/ft^3:

ρ_n, power fluid
ρ_r, well fluid
ρ_m, discharged mixture

Pressure loss coefficients, k, dimensionless:

k_n, nozzle
k_t, throat
k_d, diffuser
$k_{td} = k_t + k_d$

Task: Investigate and plot the behavior of the dimensionless pumping pressure versus the dimensionless pumping rate assuming all other parameters remain constant.

5.6 Construct the gas lift diagram for the Carina No. 2 oil well. The well is "gas-lifted" by circulating gas from the casing-to-tubing annulus into the tubing by "U"-flowing around the tubing shoe. Determine from the diagram the continuous oil production rate and the corresponding gas injection rate. Determine also the surface injection pressure required to kick-off the well.

Well data:

Tubing... 3.5 in. × 8000 ft
Wellhead pressure... 200 psia
Formation GOR... 600 scf/STB
Water cut... 0.0
Surface gas injection pressure .... 900 psia

Well IPR:

$q_o = 0.2(2650 - p_{wf})$

Note: Average gas gradient in the annulus can be approximated by (assuming gradient of a static column):

$$\frac{p_{\text{downhole}}}{p_{\text{surface}}} = 1 + H/40000$$

where H is the height of the gas column expressed in feet and the pressures are expressed in psia.

5.7 Construct the gas-lift diagram for the Carina No. 1 oil well, which produces 200 STB/D by gas lift. The tubing-to-casing annulus is sealed by production packer and the gas is injected into the tubing through a downhole orifice. The pressure drop across the orifice is 100 psi.

Tasks:

1. Determine from the diagram the injection point.
2. Determine from the diagram the gas injection rate.
3. Determine the size of the compressor (compressor horsepower).
4. Determine the size of the downhole orifice.

Well data:

Tubing	3.5 in. × 8000 ft
Wellhead pressure	200 psia
Formation GOR	600 scf/STB
Water cut	0.0
Average pressure gradient below injection point	0.39 psi/ft
Casing injection pressure...................................	900 psia
Compressor suction pressure	56 psia
Compressor discharge pressure............................	1100 psia
Compressor discharge temperature	80°F
Injection gas gravity.......................................	0.65 (air = 1.0)
Specific heat ratio, $k = c_p/c_v$..............................	1.27
Orifice discharge coefficient................................	0.865
Computed temperature gradient of injection gas-in-the-tubing/casing annulus	1.2°F/100 ft
Gas compressibility factor (at orifice), Z.....................	0.93

Well IPR (at 8000 ft):

$$q_o = 0.2(2650 - p_{wf})$$

Useful design equations:

1. Approximate compressor power

$$P = 0.23q_g \, [(p_2/p_1)^{0.2} - 1]$$

where

q_g, gas compression rate, mscf/D
p_1, compressor suction pressure, psia
p_2, compressor discharge pressure, psia
P, compression power, HP

2. Orifice pressure loss equation

$$q_g = 155.5(CAp_{vc}) \left\{ \frac{2gk}{\gamma_g TZ(k-1)} [(p_{vt}/p_{vc})^{2/k} - (p_{vt}/p_{vc})^{(k+1)/k}] \right\}^{0.5}$$

where

q_g, gas flow rate, mscf/D
A, orifice area, in.$_2$
C, orifice discharge coefficient
γ_g, gas gravity (air = 1.0)
T, orifice upstream temperature, °R (460 + °F)
Z, gas compressibility factor
g, gravitational acceleration (32.3 ft/sec²)
k, specific heat ratio
p_{vc}, upstream orifice pressure, psia
p_{vt}, downstream orifice pressure, psia

5.8 Investigate the maximum production possible by gas lift and the corresponding gas injection rate for the Campina No. 3 oil well. The reservoir characteristics of the well are listed in table P-2.10, and the corresponding IPRs were determined and plotted in problem 2.10.
Consider two cases in your investigation:

a. unlimited supply of compressed gas for injection;
b. limited gas supply at a rate of q_{ig} = 0.4 MMscf/D.

Plot the maximum possible production and the corresponding injection gas required versus field's commutative production.

Additional well data:

Tubing .... 3.5 in. × 8000 ft
Mid-perforation depth (IPR reference) .... 8000 ft
Wellhead pressure .... 200 psia

5.9 Construct the LPR and the GPR of the Campina No. 3 oil well (problem 5.8) for field commutative production of N_p = 0, 10 × 10⁶, 20 × 10⁶, and 30 × 10⁶ bbl. Consider the case where the gas is injected at the bottom of the well (assume gas injection depth of 8000 ft).

5.10 Determine the economically optimal gas injection rate for the Campina No. 3 (problems 5.8 and 5.9) in a case where there is no restriction on the quantity of gas injection. Address the vaious depletion stages considered in problem 5.9.
The optimization function, z, is

$$z = D_o q_o + D_g q_o \text{GOR} - D_{ig} q_{ig}$$

where

z = daily revenue USD
D_o = wellhead oil sales revenue = 13 USD/STB
D_g = wellhead gas sales revenue = 2 USD/mscf
D_{ig} = cost of injection gas   = 1 USD/mscf

By derivation, the function exhibits an optimum (with unlimited gas injection) where

$$dq_o/dq_g = \frac{D_{ig}}{D_o + (GOR)D_g}$$

5.11 Investigate the optimum operating conditions of the Carina No. 1 oil well at initial stage (problem 5.7). In addition to well data given in problem 5.7, note that the gas injection depth is 6125 ft.

The investigation should follow the following tasks:

1. Determine the optimum operating point with unrestricted gas injection rate at initial stage.
2. Construct the gas-lift diagram for the optimal operating conditions at the initial production stage. Consider a downhole orifice that maintains 100 psi injection pressure drop.
3. Determine the surface injection pressure and the size of the orifice that will maintain 100 psi pressure drop at the injection point.
4. Draw the DPR with the calculated orifice and injection pressure established in tasks 2 and 3 and comment on the stability of the optimal point.
5. Increase the compressor injection pressure by 500 psi (compared to that calculated in task 2), select an orifice that will maintain the optimal operating conditions, draw the respective DPR, and observe for stability.

5.12 Investigate change trends of dependent variables in response to changes of the independent variables on the gas-lift diagram. To facilitate the investigation, table P-5.12 suggests to investigate four cases. For each case it lists four fixed independent variables, one independent variable to be changed, and three dependent variables that change spontaneously. Present your conclusions in a table and free-hand sketch.

Table P-5.12 Changes on the Phase Diagram

Fixed independent variables	Changed independent variable	Dependent variables
p_{ch} p_{wh} IPR $\Delta p_{orifice}$	q_o	D_{ov} q_{gi} $d_{orifice}$
p_{wh} D_{ov} IPR $\Delta p_{orifice}$	q_o	p_{ch} q_{gi} $d_{orifice}$
p_{ch} p_{wh} q_o $\Delta p_{orifice}$	IPR(N_p)	D_{ov} q_{gi} $d_{orifice}$
p_{wh} D_{ov} p_{ch} $\Delta p_{orifice}$	IPR(N_p)	q_o q_{gi} $d_{orifice}$

Table P-5.13 Future Operating Conditions of Carina No. 1 Oil Well

N_p (STB)	p_R (psia)	J (STB/D/psi)	p_{wh} (psia)	p_{ch} (psia)	D_{ov} (ft)
0	2650	0.2	200	900	6125
3 × 10⁶	2400	0.2	200	900	6125
6 × 10⁶	2200	0.2	200	900	6125
9 × 10⁶	2100	0.2	200	900	6125

Gas-Lift Operation Mode 1

N_p (STB)	$\Delta p_{orifice}$ (psi)	p_{vc} (psia)	p_{vt} (psia)	q_o (STB/D)	GLR$_{tubing}$ (scf/STB)	q_{gi} (scf/D)	$d_{orifice}$ (in.)
0	100	1050	950	200			
3 × 10⁶	100						
6 × 10⁶	100						
9 × 10⁶	100						

Gas-Lift Operation Mode 2

N_p (STB)	$d_{orifice}$ (in.)	p_{vc} (psia)	p_{vt} (psia)	q_o (STB/D)	GLR$_{tubing}$ (scf/STB)	q_{gi} (scf/D)	$p_{orifice}$ (psi)
0	0.125	1050	950	200			
3 × 10⁶	0.125						
6 × 10⁶	0.125						
9 × 10⁶	0.125						

Note that the pressure drop across the orifice is maintained constant in all the cases in spite of other induced and spontaneous changes in flow conditions. This can be achieved only by induced changes of orifice size.

Comment on the possibility of predicting spontaneous changes if the orifice is maintained constant and, thus, the pressure drop across it varies spontaneously.

Indicate the dependent variables that change spontaneously and the variables that need an induced change.

5.13 Future operating conditions of the Carina No. 1 oil well (problem 5.7) are given in table P-5.13. Determine the changes in injection and production conditions considering the two following modes:

Mode 1. Constant pressure drop across orifice.
Mode 2. Constant orifice size.

5.14 Construct the equilibrium curve for the Estourgie No. 74 oil well produced by gas lift with 100 mscf/D as injection rate.

Well data:

Tubing	$2\frac{7}{8}$ in. × 8000 ft
Formation GOR..	875 scf/STB
Wellhead pressure	50 psia
Productivity index	0.256 STB/D/psi
Reservoir pressure	1990 psia

Note: In graphical solution, consider depths of 8000, 6000, 4000, 2000, and 0, and interpolate between the data points.

5.15 Using the equilibrium curve of Estourgie No. 74 (problem 5.14), determine the injection depth and the surface injection pressure to produce oil at a rate of 200, 300, and 400 STB/D. Neglect the pressure drop across the downhole orifice.

INDEX

A

Abrupt backpressure change, 438–41
  rate decline following, 440–41
Absolute open flow (AOF), 30, 31, 33, 180
Absolute permeability, classifying reservoir
    type by, 111
Acid etching, along fracture wall, 408
Acid fracturing, 408
  limited conductivity, 413
Acidizing, matrix, 399, 400–407
Adiabatic flow, 91
Adjustable choke, 86
Afterflush stage, sandstone acidizing, 402
Allowables:
  definition/enforcement of, 125
  regulation by, 125
Altered permeability, near-wellbore, 241–50,
    271
Annulus access valve, 5
Annulus heading, 555
API Gas Lift Book (API), 556
API gravity, 15–16, 22
Apparent mixture density, 12
Apparent wellbore radius, 129, 131, 399
Aquifer wells, 184
Area, 598
Arps equations, 384–95
  exponential decline, 384–91
  hyperbolic decline, 389–95
Artificial lift, 459–62, 469–566
  methods of, 469–70
    features, 562–65
    gas lift, 528–66
    oilwell pumping, 469–528
    selecting, 560–65

performance of well producing with, 560–61
  See also Gas lift; Oilwell pumping
Available pressure, 100
Average compressibility factor, 49
Average ''gas-condensate'' correlation, 21
Average gas gravity, 17, 20, 22
Average grain diameter, 269
Average mixture density, 25, 27–28
Average permeability, calculation of for com-
    plex reservoir, 356–59
Average temperature, 49

B

Backpressure:
  analysis, 224–26
  curve, 29, 35
  equation, 33, 132, 157–58, 171, 274
    origin of, 133
  IPR, depletion effect on, 178–79
Backpressure plot, log-log, 43
Bailed samples, 327, 328
Biological incompatibility, 249
Blast joints, 4
Blockage skin factor, 238, 329–31
Bottomhole flowing pressure, 18, 29
  See also Wellbore flowing pressure
Bottomhole pressure, 180, 271, 441
  measure of, 6
Bridging, 246–49
Brons and Marting skin equation, 254–58
Bubble point, 14
Bubble-point correlation, 22
Bubble-point curve, 13
Bubble-point pressure, 17, 22, 24, 45